A961

51   Maths

ELEMENTARY
TECHNICAL
MATHEMATICS

MATHEMATICS FOR APPLIED ENGINEERING
Cairns

BASIC MATHEMATICS FOR ELECTRONICS
Juszli, Mahler, & Reid

ELEMENTARY TECHNICAL MATHEMATICS, 2nd ed.
Juszli & Rodgers

CONTEMPORARY TECHNICAL MATHEMATICS WITH CALCULUS
Paul & Shaevel

TECHNICAL MATHEMATICS WITH CALCULUS
Placek

APPLIED MATHEMATICS FOR ENGINEERING AND SCIENCE
Shere & Love

APPLIED MATHEMATICS FOR ELECTRONICS
Westlake & Noden

**PRENTICE-HALL SERIES
IN TECHNICAL MATHEMATICS**

Frank L. Juszli, Editor

PRENTICE-HALL, INC.
Englewood Cliffs, New Jersey

FRANK L. JUSZLI

President
Norwalk State Technical College

CHARLES A. RODGERS

Chairman, Mechanical Technology Department
Hartford State Technical College

ELEMENTARY

TECHNICAL

MATHEMATICS

SECOND EDITION

510

PRENTICE-HALL INTERNATIONAL, INC., London
PRENTICE-HALL OF AUSTRALIA, PTY. LTD., Sydney
PRENTICE-HALL OF CANADA, LTD., Toronto
PRENTICE-HALL OF INDIA PRIVATE LTD., New Delhi
PRENTICE-HALL OF JAPAN, INC., Tokyo

Current printing (last digit):
10 9 8 7

This revision of *Elementary Technical Mathematics* is an integrated presentation of algebra, geometry, and trigonometry designed for use in technical programs offered in community colleges, technical institutes, and industry.

The nature of the original textbook is retained as a student-oriented treatment which is careful but without extensive rigor. Abundant applications are provided; formulation is stressed; problem-solving methods for elementary functions are emphasized; and a careful, graphical approach is sustained.

Materials offered in the text are consistent with those required by quality engineering technology programs, as shown in careful studies of accredited curricula and a nationwide publishers' survey of the content needs of mathematics curricula in technical programs.

A summary shows that this text provides nearly 3000 exercises (with answers provided for about one-half of them), 275 illustrations and graphs which assist both the student and instructor in picturing mathematical and technical situations, and about 300 solved problems focusing on methods of solution.

The revision contains all of the material in the original text and adds treatments of:

1. fundamental laws of algebra,
2. synthetic division,
3. determinants,
4. conics,
5. polar equations.

The authors combine 35 years of experience in technical education in Connecticut. Frank L. Juszli, President of Norwalk State Technical College, has also written *Analytic Geometry and Calculus*, Prentice-Hall, Inc. (1961) and co-authored *Basic Mathematics for Electronics*, Juszli, Mahler, and Reid, Prentice-Hall, Inc. (1967). He is the technical mathematics series editor for Prentice-Hall. Charles A. Rodgers is chairman of the mechanical technology department at Hartford State Technical College.

The authors are grateful to the staffs of Connecticut's technical colleges and to readers of the first edition for offering suggestions valuable to this revision.

FRANK L. JUSZLI / CHARLES A. RODGERS

PREFACE

CONTENTS

ELEMENTARY
TECHNICAL
MATHEMATICS

This chapter is primarily devoted to the basic scales on a standard slide rule. Certain introductory remarks regarding numbers are made in preparation for the slide rule; these remarks embrace standard notation. Also included is a discussion of proportions and their properties.

STANDARD NOTATION AND THE SLIDE RULE 1

1-1   Standard Notation

In technical work it is necessary to refer to a large variety of measurements. Some of these measures require numbers that indicate great magnitudes— for example, the mean distance to the sun, which is approximately 93 million miles, or Avogadro's constant, which is a 24-digit number with leading digits 6025. Other measurements require numbers that indicate magnitudes very close to zero; the mass of an electron is 90-billionths of one-billionth of one-billionth of one gram.

Two of the numbers just mentioned are difficult to represent in ordinary notation because of the great number of zeroes necessary; the mass of the electron would require a number with a decimal point followed by a string of 28 zeroes before a nonzero digit arises. This difficulty suggests the need for a compact method of representing numbers that are near zero or are very large. The compact method used here introduces *standard notation*.

Proper use of standard notation relies in part upon the knowledge and use of the definition of a *power*, particularly powers of the number 10. We define the nth power of 10 by the expression

$$10^n = 10 \times 10 \times 10 \times \cdots \times 10 \qquad (n \text{ a positive integer}), \qquad (1)$$

where the number 10 occurs n times as a factor in the right member of (1). Thus,

$$10^2 = 10 \times 10 = 100, \qquad (2)$$
$$10^5 = 10 \times 10 \times 10 \times 10 \times 10 = 100,000 \qquad (3)$$

In (2), 100 is called the *second power* of 10 and the superscript, 2, is called the *exponent*; the number 10 is called the *base*. Thus, in (3), the base is 10, the exponent is 5, and 100,000 is the fifth power of 10.

It is convenient to recognize that the number of zeroes following the leading unity in a power of 10 agrees with the exponent when the exponent is a positive integer. Thus, in (2), the exponent is 2 and the power has two zeroes following the leading unity; in (3), the exponent is 5 and the power has five zeroes following the leading unity.

A number greater than 10 may be expressed as the product of a number between 1 and 10, multiplied by a positive integral power of 10. We have, as examples,

$$358 = 3.58 \times 100 = 3.58 \times 10^2, \qquad (4)$$
$$680,000 = 6.8 \times 100,000 = 6.8 \times 10^5. \qquad (5)$$

Expressions (4) and (5) are examples of *standard notation*, where standard notation involves expressing a number as the product of a number between 1 and 10, multiplied by the proper power of 10.

We also have negative integral powers of 10, all of which have values between 0 and 1. Thus,

$$10^{-1} = \frac{1}{10} = 0.1,$$

$$10^{-4} = \frac{1}{10} \times \frac{1}{10} \times \frac{1}{10} \times \frac{1}{10} = 0.0001,$$

$$10^{-n} = \left(\frac{1}{10}\right)^n.$$

In the standard notation of numbers between 1 and 10, we have

$$0.0056 = 5.6 \times 0.001 = 5.6 \times 10^{-3}, \tag{6}$$

$$0.0000082 = 8.2 \times 0.000001 = 8.2 \times 10^{-6}. \tag{7}$$

The selection of the proper exponent to use in standard notation is readily made. In (5) we start with the number 680,000; first, we wish to re-express this as a number between 1 and 10, namely 6.8. This requires moving the decimal point five places to the left, which is a multiplication by 10^{-5}. We must compensate for this multiplication by multiplying by 10^5, hence the final expression. In (7), the decimal point is moved six places to the right, or a multiplication by 10^6; compensation requires introduction of the factor 10^{-6} and we have the expression shown.

Some laws of exponents are shown below. The laws will be discussed in much greater detail in Chap. 6.

Law 1.

$$10^m \times 10^n = 10^{m+n}.$$

Law 2.

$$10^m \div 10^n = 10^{m-n}.$$

Law 3.

$$(10^m)^n = 10^{mn}.$$

Examples of uses of the laws of exponents are:

Law 1.

$$10^2 \times 10^3 = (10 \times 10) \times (10 \times 10 \times 10) = 10^5,$$

$$10^4 \times 10^{-1} = (10 \times 10 \times 10 \times 10) \times \frac{1}{10} = 10^3.$$

Law 2.

$$10^4 \div 10^3 = (10 \times 10 \times 10 \times 10) \div (10 \times 10 \times 10) = 10.$$

Law 3.

$$(10^2)^3 = 10^2 \times 10^2 \times 10^2 = 10^6.$$

Let us show two examples that combine the use of standard notation and the laws of exponents.

EXAMPLE 1. Estimate the value of the expression

$$\frac{42,000 \times 0.0078}{(1980)^2}. \tag{8}$$

Solution. First we convert all parts of (8) to standard notation, obtaining

$$\frac{4.2 \times 10^4 \times 7.8 \times 10^{-3}}{(1.98 \times 10^3)^2}.$$

By the laws of exponents, we now have

$$\frac{4.2 \times 7.8 \times 10^1}{(1.98)^2 \times 10^6} = \frac{4.2 \times 7.8}{(1.98)^2} \times 10^{-5}. \tag{9}$$

Since we wish only to estimate the value of (8), we estimate in (9) that $(1.98)^2$ is approximately 4; dividing this into 4.2 gives a quotient slightly greater than unity; multiplying this quotient by 7.8 gives an approximate product of 8. Thus, (9) becomes approximately 8×10^{-5}. A more correct answer is 8.89×10^{-5}.

EXAMPLE 2. Approximately how many seconds are in 12 years?

Solution. There are 60 seconds in one minute, 60×60 seconds in one hour, $60 \times 60 \times 24$ seconds in one day, approximately $60 \times 60 \times 24 \times 365$ seconds in one year, and $60 \times 60 \times 24 \times 365 \times 12$ seconds in 12 years. Reverting to standard notation, we have

$$6 \times 10^1 \times 6 \times 10^1 \times 2.4 \times 10^1 \times 3.65 \times 10^2 \times 1.2 \times 10^1$$

or $$6 \times 6 \times 2.4 \times 3.65 \times 1.2 \times 10^6 \approx 400 \times 10^6 = 4 \times 10^8.$$

A more correct answer is 3.78×10^8.

Exercises

In Exercises 1–15, express the given number in standard notation.

1. 0.00625.   *Ans.* 6.25×10^{-3}.

2. 386,000.

3. 216,000.   *Ans.* 2.16×10^{5}.

4. 0.000004.

5. 0.4963.   *Ans.* 4.963×10^{-1}.

6. Thirty-six billion.

7. Eight-tenths of one-millionth.   *Ans.* 8×10^{-7}.

8. Forty-thousandths.

9. 316-thousandths of one-thousandth.   *Ans.* 3.16×10^{-4}.

10. 37.5 billion.

11. 0.09 thousandths.   *Ans.* 9×10^{-5}.

12. 365 millionths.

13. Three thousandths of one million.   *Ans.* 3×10^{3}.

14. Three millionths of one thousand.

15. 365 thousandths.   *Ans.* 3.65×10^{-1}

In Exercises 16–25, perform the indicated operations and express the answer in standard notation.

16. $\dfrac{200 \times 400}{0.016}$.   *Ans.* 5×10^{6}.

17. $\dfrac{0.005 \times 30 \times 10^{5}}{0.00006}$.

18. $\dfrac{6.6 \times 20 \times 1000}{33,000} + \dfrac{40}{(20)^{2}}$.   *Ans.* 4.1.

19. $\dfrac{93,000,000}{186,000}$.

20. $\dfrac{40 \times 10^{3} \times 200 \times 10^{-6}}{(0.008)^{2}}$.   *Ans.* 1.25×10^{5}.

21. $\dfrac{0.005 \times 20}{(0.0005)^{2}}$.   *Ans.* 4×10^{5}.

22. $\dfrac{450 \times 2,000 \times 0.04}{12,000,000}$.

23. $\dfrac{3 \times 10^{12}}{4,000 \times 1,500,000}$. *Ans.* 5×10^2.

24. $\dfrac{0.024}{2 \times 10^{-6}}$.

25. $\dfrac{4 \times 10^3}{2 \times 10^{-3}}$. *Ans.* 2×10^6.

1-2   More on Notation; Significant Figures

Certain standards will be discussed here regarding notation and significant figures. The first is a convention regarding the use of a zero before the decimal point. We may say that a bolt, as measured by a micrometer, is 252-thousandths of an inch in diameter. It would be proper to write the diameter as .252 in.; however, the use of a leading decimal point can sometimes be confusing; therefore, we will adopt a convention designed to minimize the possibility of confusion. We will say that the bolt is of diameter 0.252 in., where the introduction of a zero before the decimal point makes the decimal point less likely to escape observation.

We will frequently refer to *significant figures* as we progress. In measurements significant figures (or *significant digits*) are those believed to be closer to the true value than any other digits would be. Thus, for a given dimension 3.250 ± 0.002, we have four significant figures, whereas for 3.25 ± 0.01 we have three significant figures. Significant figures may include trailing zeroes. Thus, if a given dimension is exactly 3 inches, a scale calibrated in tenths may measure it as 3.0 in., a scale calibrated in hundredths may measure it as 3.00 in., and a scale calibrated in thousandths may measure it as 3.000 in. The dimensions given as 5.6 and 5.600 differ in the number of significant figures. For 5.6, accuracy only to tenths may be presumed; for 5.600, accuracy to thousandths is presumed.

1-3   Nomenclature of the Slide Rule

The *slide rule* is a computational device capable of performing many arithmetic, exponential, and trigonometric operations, depending upon the number and the nature of the scales present. It may be used to perform such operations as multiplication, division, reciprocation, squares, cubes, square roots, cube roots, powers of any base (within certain limits), proportion, trigonometric operations, combined operations, certain numerical conversions, and more. Let us begin the discussion of the standard slide rule with some nomenclature.

The slide rule consists of three main parts: the *body*, the *sliding bar*, and the *cursor*. The body consists of an upper and a lower bar, each of which contains certain specially constructed scales. The sliding bar, which also contains several scales on one or both sides, is movable, making horizontal transfer operations possible. The cursor is used as the carrier of a hairline which makes possible vertical transfers and transfers to the reverse side of the rule.

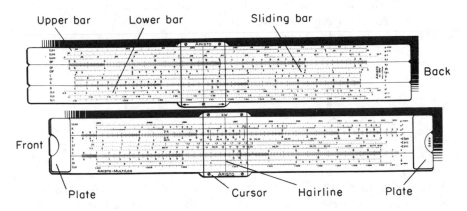

Courtesy of Charvos-Roos Corp.

FIGURE 1–1

Figure 1-1 shows a typical slide rule and indicates the names of the parts. Legends are provided at the right-hand end of the scales of the slide rule shown. These legends, to be discussed later, make transfer operations clear. Scales are given names at the left end; these names are letters of the alphabet.

1-4   Reading the Slide Rule

Except for the LL, S, T, and ST scales of most slide rules, no provision is made for decimal points in numbers; that is, the slide rule does not distinguish among the numbers 327, 3.27, 0.00327, and 3,270,000, or any other numbers whose significant figures are 327. We will refer initially to the D-scale, from which the majority of operations are oriented.

We note that the D-scale starts and ends with the number 1. These 1's, as stated above, could be 100, 10,000, 0.0001, or any other number whose only significant figure is 1. We note further that the D-scale is subdivided into ten intervals by calibration lines indicated by the boldest engravings 1, 2, 3, $\cdots$, 8, 9, 1. These calibrations are indicated by the arrows in Fig. 1-2. We will call these calibration lines *primary lines*, and the numbers identified by the primary lines will be called *primary numbers*.

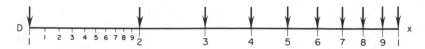

FIGURE 1-2

If the hairline rests on a primary line, the number read there has one and only one significant digit in it; that is, if the hairline rests on the primary 3 near the center of the D-scale, as shown in Fig. 1-3, the number to be read

FIGURE 1-3

there is a number containing the digit 3 preceded or succeeded by any number of zeroes. Representative examples are 0.003, 3, and 300,000.

EXAMPLE 3. Find the number 0.0002 on the D-scale.

Solution. Place the hairline over the primary 2 indicated by the arrow and 0.0002 in Fig. 1-3.

EXAMPLE 4. Find the number 200,000 on the D-scale.

Solution. Place the hairline over the primary 2 exactly as in Example 3.

EXAMPLE 5. Find the number 700 on the D-scale.

Solution. Place the hairline over the primary 7 as shown in Fig. 1-3.

Between any two primary numbers are ten subdivisions, indicated by calibration lines that are slightly shorter than those at the primary positions. These are called *secondary* lines. We note that some of the secondary lines are given numerical designations etched on the rule, whereas others are not; this is a matter of available space. An inspection of the D-scale will show 100 secondary subdivisions. If the hairline rests on a secondary line,

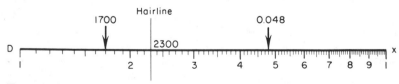

FIGURE 1-4

the number read there contains two and only two significant figures. An example is the number 2300, which lies on the third secondary division to the right of the primary 2. This is shown in Fig. 1-4.

EXAMPLE 6. Find the number 1700 on the D-scale.

Solution. Place the hairline over the secondary 7 between primary 1 and primary 2 as shown in Fig. 1-4.

EXAMPLE 7. Find the number 0.048 on the D-scale.

Solution. Place the hairline over the eighth secondary line to the right of primary 4 as shown in Fig. 1-4.

Further inspection of the D-scale shows that all secondary intervals are subdivided—some into ten subdivisions, others into five subdivisions, and others into only two. Once again, this irregularity is due to available space. These subdivisions are called *tertiary* subdivisions. Tertiary numbers are more difficult to read than primary or secondary numbers because of the inconsistency in the number of tertiary lines subdividing the secondary intervals. Referring to the D-scale, we note that the first tertiary line to the right of secondary 15 represents the number 151. The first tertiary line to the right of secondary 35 represents the number 352. The first tertiary line to the right of secondary 85 represents the number 855.

EXAMPLE 8. Find the number 665 on the D-scale.

Solution. Figure 1-5 shows an enlargement of the D-scale between primary 6 and primary 7. Also indicated are the secondary 66 and secondary 67 which, for tertiary convenience, may be called 660 and 670. Now 665 is at the single tertiary line straddled by 660 and 670.

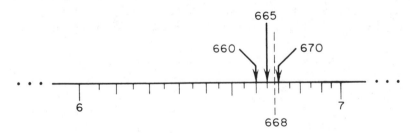

FIGURE 1-5

EXAMPLE 9. Find the number 668 on the D-scale.

Solution. In view of Example 8 and Fig. 1-5, we can see that there is no line on the D-scale which can be identified by the number 668. We can only approximate the location of 668 by estimating that it is 3/5 of the way through the 665–670 interval as shown in Fig. 1-5.

EXAMPLE 10. Find the number 1132 on the D-scale.

Solution. Figure 1-6 shows the interval between secondary 11 and secondary 12 on the D-scale. The third line to the right of 11 can be designated by the tertiary number 113 (or by the four-figure number 1130). Likewise, the fourth line to the right of 11 can be called 1140. Now, 1132 is about 2/10 of the way through the indicated 1130–1140 interval and is shown by the dotted line in Fig. 1-6.

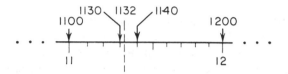

FIGURE 1–6

EXAMPLE 11. Find the number 1005 on the D-scale.

Solution. The leftmost primary 1 on the D-scale may be called 1000. The line immediately to the right of 1000 is tertiary and may take on the description 1010. Now 1005 is midway between 1000 and 1010, or midway between the first and second lines on the left end of the D-scale.

1-5   Multiplication

Before discussing multiplication on the slide rule, some comments about the theory of the rule seem to be in order. Some of these comments may be made with reference to Fig. 1-7, which shows two ordinary 12-in. rules laid

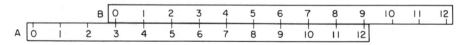

FIGURE 1–7

adjacent to each other. (Note here that the calibrations on the rules in Fig. 1-7 are equally spaced as opposed to the nonuniformly spaced calibrations on all but the L-scale of the slide rule.) The zero (index) of Rule B is placed opposite the 3 of Rule A. Note now that every number on Rule A is 3 greater than the opposing number on Rule B. The simple illustration in Fig. 1-7 shows that two ordinary foot rules may serve as instruments to add two numbers. The steps are simple. To add 3 + 2, place the zero (index) of Rule B opposite 3 on Rule A. Now move down Rule B to the number 2. Opposite the 2 on B, the sum 5 is found on A.

The method described above is precisely that used in multiplication on the slide rule. It must be recognized from Fig. 1-7 that two identical scales were used and, since the calibrations were equally spaced, the operation performed was addition. On the slide rule, the calibrations are not spaced as ordinary numbers would be, but instead are spaced as the logarithms of the numbers are spaced. Now, a law of logarithms states that the addition of the logarithms of two numbers obtains the logarithm of their *product*, so that operations similar to the one shown in Fig. 1-7 perform multiplications on the slide rule. *Multiplication can be performed using any two identical scales on the standard slide rule.* It is convenient if one of the two identical scales is on the sliding bar and the other is on the body. Examination of the slide rule indicates several scale pairs which meet these requirements, namely the C-D, A-B, CF-DF and Cl-Dl pairs.

EXAMPLE 12. Multiply 3 by 2 on the C and D scales.

Solution. Using the requested scales and the procedure discussed with reference to Fig. 1-7, the following steps as illustrated in Fig. 1-8 are appropriate.

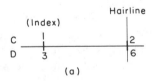

FIGURE 1–8

Step. 1. Place the C-index (left-hand primary 1 of the C-scale) opposite 3 on the D-scale.

Step 2. Place the hairline over the number 2 on the C-scale.

Step 3. Under the hairline, opposite the number 2 on the C-scale is the number 6 on the D-scale, which is the desired product. Note from the second portion of Fig. 1-8 that the multiplier and multiplicand were interchanged without significant change in the procedure.

EXAMPLE 13. Multiply 2 by 2.5 on the A and B scales.

Solution. Using the requested scales and the three-step procedure in Example 12, along with reference to Fig. 1-9, we have:

Step 1. Place the B-index opposite 2 on the A-scale. (Note from Fig. 1-9 that the B-index is shown twice, since the B-scale is a double scale.)

Step 2. Place the hairline over 25 on the B-scale. (Note that 25 is available twice and either choice might serve.)

Step 3. Under the hairline from the B-scale read the product 5.0.

FIGURE 1–9

EXAMPLE 14. Multiply 4 by 5 on the C and D scales.

Solution. Referring to Fig. 1-10, we proceed.

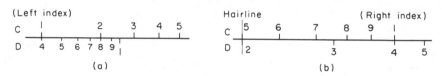

FIGURE 1–10

Step 1. Place the C-index opposite 4 on the D-scale. If we choose to use the C-index at the *left* end of the C-scale, we will encounter difficulty in Step 2, as demonstrated in Fig. 1-10(a), where it is seen that the number 5 on the C-scale lies well beyond the end of the D-scale and will be inaccessible for the hairline. It is therefore suggested that the *right* C-index be placed opposite the 4 as shown in Fig. 1-10(b).

Step 2. Place the hairline over 5 on the C-scale.

Step 3. Read the product, 20, under the hairline on the D-scale.

It is observed from Example 14 that either index may be used in a multiplication operation. Introduction of the CF-scale may serve as an escape device when improper indexing has occurred in a combined operations problem. This will be discussed more fully later.

EXAMPLE 15. Multiply 852 by 0.000355.

Solution. Following the steps suggested in Examples 12–14, we obtain a solution with the significant figures 302. This does not mean that the product is three hundred and two, because the decimal point is not yet properly located. Reverting to standard notation, the intended product can be written as

$$8.52 \times 10^2 \times 3.55 \times 10^{-4} = 30.2 \times 10^{-2} = 0.302.$$

Example 15 introduces two considerations. First, the number 852 must be located approximately since there is no tertiary line denoting it; second, standard notation is used to locate the decimal point.

A summary of multiplication may be stated thus:

> *To multiply two numbers, use two identical scales, one on a stationary bar, the other on the sliding bar. Place the index (primary 1) of the slide scale opposite the multiplicand on the stationary scale. Now place the hairline over the multiplier on the slide scale. Read the product from the stationary scale under the hairline.*

The folded scales, CF and DF, may be used as alternatives to the C and D scales in certain operations including multiplication. Careful inspection of the folded scales will reveal that they are exactly like the C and D scales except that the index is near the center of the scales. Actually, a direct transfer from the D-scale to the DF-scale accomplishes a multiplication by π. It may be seen that the folded scales, in being used as alternatives to re-indexing, can eliminate the need for moving the C-index past the center of the D-scale in multiplication operations. At any time that the C-scale may be used, the CF-scale may be used as an alternative, with the product being switched from the D-scale to the DF-scale.

EXAMPLE 16. Find the circumference of a circle of radius 3.

Solution. The circumference of a circle is given by the equation $C = 2\pi r$. Here, $r = 3$, so that $C = 2\pi(3) = 6\pi$. Now, place the hairline over 6 (the diameter) on the D-scale and read the circumference, 18.81, from the DF-scale under the hairline.

Exercises

Perform the indicated multiplications in each of the given exercises.

1. $1.5 \times 2.5 = 3.75$.

2. $1.1 \times 4.1 = 4.51$.

3. $1.05 \times 4.15 = 4.358$.

4. $1.03 \times 5.5 = 5.665$.

5. $1.08 \times 25.5 = 27.54$.

6. $11 \times 5.45 = 59.95$.

7. $121 \times 0.05 = 6.05$.

8. $0.0111 \times 44.4 = 0.4928$.

9. $2.64 \times 1.35 = 3.56$.

10. $2.64 \times 3.12 = 8.24$.

11. $2.64 \times 4.08 = 10.77$.

12. $2.64 \times 7.24 = 19.11$.

13. $2.64 \times 0.00825 = 0.0218$.

14. $0.806 \times 947 = 763$.

15. $43.2 \times 46500 = 2.01 \times 10^6$.　　　　**16.** $3.14 \times 0.0595 = 0.1868$.

17. $11.10 \times 3.75 = 41.6$.　　　　**18.** $11.02 \times 3.75 = 41.3$.

19. $10.80 \times 3.75 = 40.5$.　　　　**20.** $10.08 \times 3.75 = 37.8$.

21. $5280 \times 27.5 = 1.452 \times 10^5$.　　　　**22.** $365 \times 3600 = 1.314 \times 10^6$.

23. $33{,}000 \times 0.000082 = 2.71$.　　　　**24.** $16.5 \times 0.00174 = 0.0287$.

25. $28\pi = 88.0$.

1-6　Division

Division is recognized as the inverse of multiplication; that is, if two numbers are multiplied to obtain a product, division of the product by either of the two numbers will give the other number. A familiar example is the case of $2 \times 3 = 6$; in dividing 6 by 3, the quotient 2 is obtained; in dividing 6 by 2, the quotient 3 is obtained. Multiplication may be performed by the addition of logarithms; division is obtained by the subtraction of logarithms, where addition and subtraction may be regarded as inverse operations.

Figure 1-11 shows what may be considered to be the multiplication $2 \times 3 = 6$. It also shows the division $6 \div 3 = 2$. By careful inspection of Fig. 1-11, it may be seen that the steps of division are as follows:

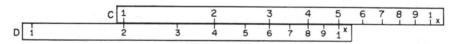

FIGURE 1–11

Step 1. To divide 6 by 3, we oppose 6 on the D-scale by 3 on the C-scale.

Step 2. The index of the C-scale lies opposite the quotient (in this case 2) on the D-scale.

We note from the preceding division example that we use two identical scales and that the division operation is seen as the inverse operation of multiplication.

EXAMPLE 17. Divide 2 by 8.

Solution. From Fig. 1-12 the following steps are evident:

Step 1. Place 8 on the C-scale opposite 2 on the D-scale.

Step 2. Place the hairline over the C-index.

Step 3. Read the quotient, 0.25, from the D-scale under the hairline.

It is worth noting here from Fig. 1-12 that two other number pairs whose quotient is 0.25 are opposed and readily apparent, namely the $1 \div 4$ and $1.5 \div 6$ pairs.

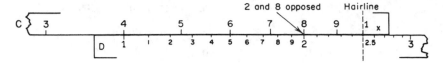

FIGURE 1–12

EXAMPLE 18. Divide 827 by 0.00373.

Solution. Following the steps for division previously established, we have:

Step 1. Oppose 827 on the D-scale by 373 on the C-scale.

Step 2. Place the hairline over the C-index.

Step 3. Read the significant figures of the quotient, 222, from the D-scale under the hairline.

Note that 222 is not the quotient, because recognition of the location of the decimal point was not made. To locate the decimal point, we resort to standard notation thus:

$$\frac{827}{0.00373} = \frac{8.27 \times 10^2}{3.73 \times 10^{-3}} = 2.22 \times 10^5 = 222,000.$$

EXAMPLE 19. Divide 0.00492 by 0.826.

Solution. Following the steps shown in Examples 17 and 18, we find the significant figures of the quotient to be 595. If we resort to standard notation,

$$\frac{0.00492}{0.826} = \frac{4.92 \times 10^{-3}}{8.26 \times 10^{-1}} = 0.595 \times 10^{-2} = 0.00595.$$

Examples 18 and 19 were introduced to show decimal point location combined with a division operation.

A summary of division on the slide rule may be stated thus:

> *To divide two numbers, any two identical scales may be used—one on the stationary bar, the other on the sliding bar. Place the divisor on the sliding scale opposite the dividend on the stationary scale. Read the quotient from the stationary scale opposite the index of the sliding scale.*

Exercises

Perform the indicated division operations.

1. $20.5 \div 4.1 = 5.$

2. $20.2 \div 8.6 = 2.35.$

3. $3.82 \div 18.2 = 0.209.$

4. $1030 \div 1.13 = 912.$

5. $1160 \div 95 = 12.2$.

6. $84.5 \div 4050 = 0.0209$.

7. $505 \div 3.33 = 151.6$.

8. $0.0018 \div 0.107 = 0.0168$.

9. $0.906 \div 0.116 = 7.81$.

10. $61.6 \div 1.97 = 31.27$.

11. $0.113 \div 0.00161 = 70.2$.

12. $12.7 \div 3.5 = 3.63$.

13. $43 \div 6.7 = 6.42$.

14. $88.4 \div 26.6 = 3.32$.

15. $808 \div 16.3 = 49.6$.

16. $746 \div 33{,}000 = 0.0226$.

17. $4.26 \div 4850 = 8.78 \times 10^{-4}$.

18. $\pi \div 180 = 0.01745$.

19. $180 \div \pi = 57.3$.

20. $344 \div 0.0172 = 20{,}000$.

21. $12 \div 13.12 = 0.916$.

22. $8500 \div 5280 = 1.610$.

23. $0.00287 \div 16.5 = 1.74 \times 10^{-4}$.

24. $1.314 \times 10^6 \div 365 = 3600$.

25. $763 \div 947 = 0.806$.

1-7 Combined Operations Involving Multiplication and Division

Operations combining multiplication and division are best performed (to minimize moves of the slide or cursor) by alternating division operations with multiplication operations, starting with division. The reason for this alternation is evident when we recall that a division operation terminates at an index and a multiplication operation initiates there.

EXAMPLE 20. Perform the operation

$$\frac{4.28 \times 37.6}{0.0785 \times 6590}.$$

Solution. Start with a division operation, $4.28 \div 0.0785$. In Fig. 1-13(a), we oppose 428 on the D-scale by 785 on the C-scale, obtaining the quotient $428 \div 785$ opposite the C-index. It is not necessary to know the numerical value of $428 \div 785$. Our next step is to multiply the quantity $428 \div 785$ by

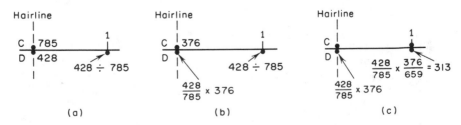

(a) (b) (c)

FIGURE 1-13

376. This requires placing the C-index opposite 428 ÷ 785, *which is already accomplished by the prior division.* Now place the hairline over 376 on the C-scale as shown in Fig. 1-13(b). At this point, under the hairline on the D-scale is the number $\frac{428}{785} \times 376$, which is to be divided by 659. Figure 1-13(c) shows the division by placing 659 of the C-scale under the hairline (which was already over (428 ÷ 785) × 376 on the D-scale) and reading the quotient, (428 ÷ 785) × (376 ÷ 659), from the D-scale opposite the C-index. To locate the decimal point, we have

$$\frac{4.28 \times 37.6}{0.0785 \times 6590} = \frac{4.28 \times 3.76 \times 10^1}{7.85 \times 10^{-2} \times 6.59 \times 10^3} = 0.313.$$

Example 20 was conveniently set up as the product of two numbers divided by the product of two other numbers. When we have the product of several numbers, a similar situation can be created. For example, in multiplying $a \times b \times c \times d$, this may be expressed as

$$\frac{a}{1/b} \times \frac{c}{1/d}.$$

Now division by $1/b$ and $1/d$ can initiate from a reciprocal scale, where the C1 and D1 scales are reciprocals of C and D respectively. This means that a division operation involving the C and D scales may be performed as a multiplication operation on the C1 and D1 scales.

EXAMPLE 21. Multiply $0.826 \times 42.5 \times 0.065 \times 1280$.

Solution. Rewrite the problem to read

$$\frac{0.826}{1/42.5} \times \frac{0.065}{1/1280}$$

and proceed as follows:

Step 1. Place the hairline over 826 on the D-scale.

Step 2. To divide 826 by $\frac{1}{425}$, place 425 of the C1-scale under the hairline. This obtains the quotient $826 \div \frac{1}{425}$ (or the product 826×425) on the D-scale opposite the C-index. (See Fig. 1-14(a).)

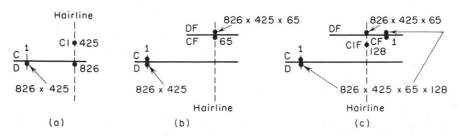

(a)   (b)   (c)

FIGURE 1–14

Step 3. Now multiply by 65. Since 65 on the C-scale is not accessible, place the hairline over 65 on the CF-scale and read the product $826 \times 425 \times 65$ from the DF-scale under the hairline. (See Fig. 1-14(b).)

Step 4. To divide $826 \times 425 \times 65$ by $\frac{1}{1280}$, place 128 of the D1F-scale under the hairline. Now the requested four-factor product is opposite either the CF-index on the DF-scale or opposite the C-index on the D-scale. This number is 292. (See Fig. 1-14(c).) Now locate the decimal point by standard notation, obtaining 2920.

It is important to comment here that the solution of Example 21 relies upon both folded scales, both of the folded reciprocal scales, and upon the reciprocal scales. Many of the more common slide rules do not possess these scales.

Exercises

1. $\dfrac{4.85 \times 26.4}{8.26} = 15.5.$

2. $335 \times 4.12 \times \pi = 4.34 \times 10^3.$

3. $\dfrac{6.14 \times 1.45 \times 0.043}{7.48 \times 0.036} = 1.42.$

4. $\dfrac{48\pi}{7} = 21.52.$

5. $16.5 \times 3.12 \times 0.052 \times 0.0046 = 0.01233.$

6. $\dfrac{6.54}{4.85 \times 22.6} = 0.0596.$

7. $8.3 \times 69 \times 425 \times 1.6 \times 7.2 = 2.81 \times 10^6.$

8. $\dfrac{4.26}{0.054 \times 375 \times 9.7} = 0.0217.$

9. $365 \times 24 \times 60 \times 60 = 3.15 \times 10^7.$

10. $\dfrac{5280 \times 12}{39.37} = 1611.$

11. $4.83 \times \dfrac{1}{12.7} = 0.380.$

12. $\dfrac{1}{63} \div 0.054 = 0.294.$

13. $\dfrac{1}{746} \div \dfrac{1}{855} = 1.146.$

14. $0.465 \div \dfrac{1}{27} = 12.57.$

15. $\dfrac{89.3 \times 21.6}{465} = 4.15.$

16. $\dfrac{412}{46.1 \times 318} = 0.0281.$

17. $\dfrac{0.0844 \times 962}{324} = 0.251.$

18. $\dfrac{989 \times 6460}{0.606} = 1.054 \times 10^7.$

19. $\dfrac{1}{0.05} \div 0.25 = 80.$

20. $9.3 \div \dfrac{1}{27} = 251.4.$

21. $\dfrac{1.2 \times 5280}{78.74} = 80.55.$

22. $\dfrac{0.072 \times 154}{\pi} = 3.53.$

23. $\dfrac{0.108 \times 424 \times 0.25}{10.6 \times 0.167} = 6.48.$

24. $\dfrac{766 \times 2.08 \times 111}{38.3} = 4.62 \times 10^3.$

25. $\dfrac{94.5 \times 254}{5.08 \times 1.505} = 3.14 \times 10^3.$

1-8   Proportions

The solution of problems involving proportions is particularly simple on the slide rule. All that is required is a pair of identical scales. Perhaps the easiest way to explain the solution of proportion problems is through the use of examples.

EXAMPLE 22. Solve for a and b in

$$\frac{62}{75} = \frac{24}{a} \quad \text{and} \quad \frac{62}{75} = \frac{b}{43}.$$

Solution. We may solve both of the given problems with a single setting of the slide rule.

Step 1. Place 62 of the C-scale opposite 75 of the D-scale as in Fig. 1-15.

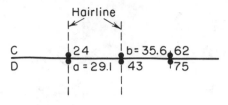

FIGURE 1-15

Step 2. Place the hairline over 24 on the C-scale and read $a = 29.1$ from the D-scale under the hairline. To solve for b, place the hairline over 43 of the D-scale and read the solution $b = 35.6$ from the C-scale under the hairline.

The operation here is conveniently symmetrical. For a proportion which is the equality of two ratios (fractions), both of the numerators (62 and 24 or 62 and b) are on one scale and both of the denominators (75 and a or 75 and 43) are on the companion scale.

We reassert that any two identical scales may be used in solving a proportion problem. To avoid the possibility of re-indexing or resorting to the folded scales, the A-B pair might be used with the sacrifice of some accuracy.

EXAMPLE 23. If 88 fps is 60 mph, what is the speed in miles per hour of a vehicle travelling 52 fps?

Solution. Here the suggested proportion is

$$\frac{88}{60} = \frac{52}{a}.$$

Place 88 on the C-scale opposite 60 on the D-scale. Place the hairline over 52 of the C-scale. Read the solution $a = 35.5$ mph from the D-scale under the hairline.

EXAMPLE 24. How many millimeters are in 3, 5, and 7 inches?

Solution. It is known that 1 in. $= 25.4$ mm. Therefore we have the ratios

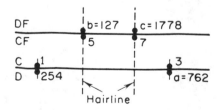

FIGURE 1-16

$$\frac{1}{25.4} = \frac{3}{a} = \frac{5}{b} = \frac{7}{c}.$$

Place the primary 1 of the C-scale opposite 25.4 of the D-scale. Now opposite 3, 5, and 7 of the C-scale or CF-scale, read $a = 76.2$ mm., $b = 127$ mm., and $c = 177.8$ mm., respectively. These solutions are shown in Fig. 1-16.

Exercises

1. How many gallons are contained in 3 cubic feet and 8 cubic feet? 1 cubic foot = 7.5 gallons. *Ans.* 22.5, 60.

2. How many pounds of concrete are there in 2.5, 17, and 31 cubic feet of concrete? Assume 1 cubic foot of concrete weighs 150 pounds.

3. How many ounces are in 1.8, 9.3, and 22 pounds? One pound = 16 ounces. *Ans.* 28.8, 148.8, 352.

4. What are the distances, in feet, of the quarter-mile, 2-mile, and 5-mile foot races? One mile = 5280 feet.

5. How many square inches are in 2.5, 7.3, and 11.1 square feet? One square foot = 144 square inches.

Solve for the literal quantities.

6. $\dfrac{x}{4} = \dfrac{3}{5.7} = \dfrac{7.3}{y}.$ *Ans.* $x - 2.104; y = 13.87.$

7. $\dfrac{88}{60} = \dfrac{x}{43} = \dfrac{110}{y}.$ *Ans.* $x = 63.1; y = 75.$

8. $\dfrac{x}{2000} = \dfrac{36}{39.37} = \dfrac{3000}{y}.$ *Ans.* $x = 1830; y = 3280.$

9. $\dfrac{746}{33,000} = \dfrac{x}{26,000} = \dfrac{2100}{y}.$ *Ans.* $x = 588; y = 93,300.$

10. $\dfrac{812}{x} = \dfrac{y}{29.5} = \dfrac{365}{12}.$ *Ans.* $x = 26.7; y = 898.$

11. $\dfrac{1}{25.4} = \dfrac{12}{x} = \dfrac{y}{75}.$ *Ans.* $x = 305; y = 2.95.$

1-9 Squares and Square Roots

Referring to Fig. 1-17, we see two specially constructed scales. Scale E is such that the length units laid off along it are half as long as those laid off along scale F. Said another way, there are twice as many units on the E-scale

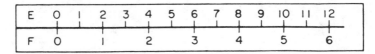

FIGURE 1–17

as there are on the F-scale for a given length. Direct transfer from the F-scale to the E-scale is a doubling operation; conversely, direct transfer from the E-scale to the F-scale is a halving operation.

If we now refer to the slide rule, inspection shows that the A (and B) scale is a double scale. Two full cycles are completed on the A-scale in the same space in which one cycle is completed on the D-scale. With both scales laid out in logarithmic units, the operator who is familiar with logarithms may realize that doubling the logarithm (by direct transfer from the single D-scale to the double A-scale) squares the number on the D-scale. Also, halving the logarithm by direct transfer from the A-scale to the D-scale takes the square root of the number on the A-scale.

The legends on the right end of the D-scale and A-scale of many slide rules are vividly clear. If x is hairlined on the D-scale, then x^2 is also hairlined on the A-scale.

EXAMPLE 25. Square (a) 4, (b) 0.00285, (c) 61,900.

Solution. The dotted lines in Fig. 1-18 indicate the position of the hairline where 4, 285, and 619 are on the D-scale, and the hairline is placed over them. The significant figures of the squares are found by direct transfer to the A-scale, and the only requirement now is to locate the decimal point.

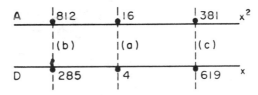

FIGURE 1–18

Here we use standard notation once again:

(a) $(4)^2 = 16$,

(b) $(0.00285)^2 = (2.85 \times 10^{-3})^2 = 8.12 \times 10^{-6}$,

(c) $(61,900)^2 = (6.19 \times 10^4)^2 = 38.3 \times 10^8 = 3.83 \times 10^9$.

The square root operation is somewhat more complicated, for the reason that the initial scale, namely the A-scale, is a double scale. In taking the square root of a number such as 365, we know that the hairline must be placed over 365 on the A-scale; however, since 365 is found twice on the A-scale, we are forced to make a decision as to which 365 we are to use. Some pertinent discussion follows.

Many operators recall the method of taking square roots by the arithmetic longhand method; the first step in the process leads to finding a trial divisor and calls for grouping the given number into groups of two integers, moving from the decimal point toward the first significant figure. We submit an alternate method here which accomplishes the same goal, but uses standard notation. Express the given number in modified standard notation such that the number will appear as a number between 1 and 100, multiplied by an *even* power of 10. Examples follow:

(*a*) $385 = 3.85 \times 10^2$ (left half),

(*b*) $0.0000265 = 26.5 \times 10^{-8}$ (right half),

(*c*) $12,870,000 = 12.87 \times 10^6$ (right half),

(*d*) $0.000523 = 5.23 \times 10^{-4}$ (half left).

we note in (*a*) and (*d*) that, in obtaining a modified standard notation with an even power of 10 multiplied by a number between 1 and 100, the leading number is between 1 and 10. In (*b*) and (*c*), the leading number is between 10 and 100. We note, too, from Fig. 1-19, that the square root operation for a one-digit square (1, 4, 9) originates from the left half of the A-scale and the square root of a two-digit number (16, 25, 36, 49, 64, 81) originates from the right half of the A-scale. These facts formulate a rule regarding the choice of halves of the A-scale in taking a square root.

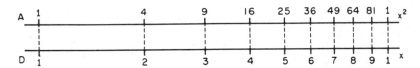

FIGURE 1-19

In taking the square root of a number, place the hairline over the number on the A-scale and read the square root from the D-scale under the hairline. First, express the number in modified standard notation with an even power of 10, multiplied by a leading number between 1 and 100. If the leading number is between 1 and 10, use the left half of the A-scale. If the leading number is between 10 and 100, use the right half of the A-scale.

EXAMPLE 26. Find the square root of (*a*) 0.00265, (*b*) 38,700, (*c*) 0.00000665, (*d*) 828,000.

Solution. Refer to Fig. 1-20 to see the settings of the hairline on the A-scale

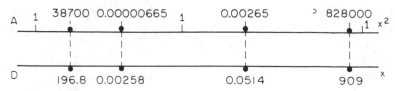

FIGURE 1-20

for each of the four solutions requested. In (a) we have $0.00265 = 26.5 \times 10^{-4}$, suggesting that we use the right half of the A-scale. Now, by the law of exponents and the slide rule, we have

(a) $(0.00265)^{1/2} = (26.5 \times 10^{-4})^{1/2} = \sqrt{26.5} \times 10^{-2} = 5.14 \times 10^{-2}$,

(b) $(38,700)^{1/2} = (3.87 \times 10^4)^{1/2} = \sqrt{3.87} \times 10^2 = 1.968 \times 10^2$,

(c) $(0.00000665)^{1/2} = (6.65 \times 10^{-6})^{1/2} = \sqrt{6.65} \times 10^{-3} = 2.58 \times 10^{-3}$,

(d) $(828,000)^{1/2} = (82.8 \times 10^4)^{1/2} = \sqrt{82.8} \times 10^2 = 9.09 \times 10^2$.

Exercises

Find the indicated squares and square roots.

1. $(1.54)^2 = 2.37$

2. $(223)^2 = 4.97 \times 10^4$.

3. $(0.00674)^2 = 4.54 \times 10^{-5}$

4. $(1.17 \times 10^{-3})^2 = 1.369 \times 10^{-6}$.

5. $(3.39 \times 10^4)^2 = 1.149 \times 10^9$.

6. $(0.3)^2 = 0.09$.

7. $(8500)^2 = 7.225 \times 10^7$.

8. $(0.011)^2 = 1.21 \times 10^{-4}$.

9. $(106)^2 = 1.124 \times 10^4$.

10. $(674 \times 10^{-5})^2 = 4.54 \times 10^{-5}$.

11. $\sqrt{605} = 24.6$.

12. $\sqrt{4560} = 67.5$.

13. $\sqrt{0.00319} = 0.0565$.

14. $\sqrt{0.000733} = 0.0271$.

15. $\sqrt{8,050,000} = 2837$.

16. $\sqrt{9.49 \times 10^{14}} = 3.08 \times 10^7$.

17. $\sqrt{6.34 \times 10^{21}} = 7.96 \times 10^{10}$.

18. $\sqrt{0.16} = 0.4$.

19. $\sqrt{0.81} = 0.9$.

20. $\sqrt{1.6} = 1.263$.

21. $\sqrt{8.1} = 2.845$.

22. $\sqrt{160} = 12.63$.

1-10   Cubes and Cube Roots

In the preceding section we observed that a direct transfer from the single D-scale to the double A-scale performs a squaring operation and an A-to-D transfer performs a square root operation. Inspection of the slide rule reveals that the K-scale is a *triple* scale. A direct transfer from the D-scale to the K-scale triples a logarithm, and therefore it cubes the number. This fact may further be revealed by examination of the legends at the right end of some rules. If the hairline is placed over a number x on the D-scale, it is also over the number x^3 on the K-scale. Conversely, a direct transfer from the K-scale to the D-scale takes a cube root.

EXAMPLE 27. Evaluate (a) $(1.5)^3$, (b) $(0.00265)^3$, (c) $(42,800)^3$.

Solution. Referring to Fig. 1-21, we see that the hairline is placed over the numbers 15, 265, and 428 on the D-scale; it is also over the numbers 338, 187, and 788 on the K-scale, where the latter numbers are the significant figures of the cubes of the former numbers. Using standard notation we locate the decimal points:

(a) $(1.5)^3 = 3.38$,

(b) $(0.00265)^3 = (2.65 \times 10^{-3})^3 = 18.7 \times 10^{-9} = 1.87 \times 10^{-8}$,

(c) $(42,800)^3 = (4.28 \times 10^4)^3 = 78.8 \times 10^{12} = 7.88 \times 10^{13}$.

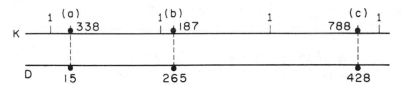

FIGURE 1–21

Taking the cube root of a number N requires direct transfer from the K-scale to the D-scale. A problem once again arises, as in the case of square roots, as to which portion of the K-scale we should use. The K-scale is a triple scale, and we must determine which third of the K-scale is appropriate for N. We submit the following rules which assist us in making the proper choice.

In taking the cube root of a number N, re-express the number in the form $N = R \times 10^p$, where p is a multiple of 3 and $1 < R < 1000$. Place the hairline over R on the K-scale, choosing the

(a) left third of the K-scale if $1 < R < 10$,

(b) center third of the K-scale if $10 < R < 100$,

(c) right third of the K-scale if $100 < R < 1000$.

EXAMPLE 28. Evaluate (a) $\sqrt[3]{2650}$, (b) $\sqrt[3]{0.0000485}$, (c) $\sqrt[3]{0.827}$.

Solution. We revert to the type of notation suggested in the previously stated rule for cube roots:

(a) $\sqrt[3]{2650} = (2.65 \times 10^3)^{1/3}$ (left third),

(b) $\sqrt[3]{0.0000485} = (48.5 \times 10^{-6})^{1/3}$ (center third),

(c) $\sqrt[3]{0.827} = (827 \times 10^{-3})^{1/3}$ (right third).

The choices of thirds of the K-scale to be used are listed above. Figure 1-22 shows the choices made with the hairline over the appropriate numbers on the K-scale and over the significant figures of the cube roots on the D-scale.

FIGURE 1–22

Completing the solutions by standard notation, we have:

(a) $(2.65 \times 10^3)^{1/3} = \sqrt[3]{2.65} \times 10^1 = 1.382 \times 10$,

(b) $(48.5 \times 10^{-6})^{1/3} = \sqrt[3]{48.5} \times 10^{-2} = 3.64 \times 10^{-2}$,

(c) $(827 \times 10^{-3})^{1/3} = \sqrt[3]{827} \times 10^{-1} = 9.36 \times 10^{-1}$.

Numbers raised to the $\frac{3}{2}$ or $\frac{2}{3}$ power can be evaluated by joint use of the D, A, and K scales. Consider the following two problems.

EXAMPLE 29. Evaluate (a) $(0.0346)^{3/2}$, (b) $(62,800)^{2/3}$.

Solution. In (a), $(0.0346)^{3/2}$ is really a square root and a cube problem; that is, we can cube 0.0346 and then take the square root of the result or we may find the square root of 0.0346, then cube the result. The latter method is usually preferable. Referring to Fig. 1-23, we see that if we start by placing

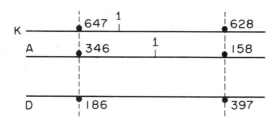

FIGURE 1–23

the hairline over 0.0346 on the A-scale (left half), then the number $(0.0346)^{1/2}$ is under the hairline on the D-scale, and the number $(0.0346)^{3/2}$ is under the hairline on the K-scale. Using standard notation we have

$$(0.0346)^{3/2} = (\sqrt{3.46 \times 10^{-2}})^3 = (1.86 \times 10^{-1})^3 = 6.47 \times 10^{-3}.$$

In (b), $(62,800)^{2/3}$] can be found by finding the square of the cube root of 62,800. Place the hairline over 628 on the center third of the K-scale. Now the cube root (significant figures, 397) is one the D-scale under the hairline as shown in Fig. 1-23. The square of 397 (158) is on the A-scale, also under the hairline. Hence,

$$(62,800)^{2/3} = (\sqrt[3]{62.8 \times 10^3})^2 = (3.97 \times 10)^2 = 15.8 \times 10^2.$$

Exercises

Perform the indicated operations.

1. $(6.2)^3 = 238.3.$

2. $(0.0819)^3 = 5.49 \times 10^{-4}.$

3. $(1.54 \times 10^3)^3 = 3.65 \times 10^9.$

4. $(2.21 \times 10^{-2})^3 = 1.079 \times 10^{-5}.$

5. $\sqrt[3]{1.5} = 1.148.$

6. $\sqrt[3]{15} = 2.466.$

7. $\sqrt[3]{150} = 5.31.$

8. $\sqrt[3]{0.00724} = 0.1935.$

9. $\sqrt[3]{0.0000442} = 0.0354.$

10. $\sqrt[3]{3.55 \times 10^5} = 70.8.$

11. $\sqrt[3]{4.27 \times 10^{-14}} = 3.495 \times 10^{-5}.$

12. $(525)^{2/3} = 65.0.$

13. $(0.000616)^{3/2} = 1.52 \times 10^{-5}.$

14. $(4.76 \times 10^4)^{2/3} = 1312.$

15. $(3.82 \times 10^{-5})^{3/2} = 2.36 \times 10^{-7}.$

16. $(3.04 \times 6.85)^3 = 9020.$

17. $\left(\dfrac{5.25 \times 8.46}{65.4}\right)^3 = 0.314.$

18. $\left(\dfrac{16.6}{12.5}\right)^3 = 2.35.$

19. $\sqrt[3]{6} \times \sqrt[2]{5} = 4.06.$

20. $\dfrac{\sqrt[3]{85.4}}{\sqrt[2]{116.5}} = 0.408.$

21. $\dfrac{(5.31)^3}{(1.148)^3} = 100.$

22. $\left(\dfrac{5.31}{1.148}\right)^3 = 100.$

23. $(0.5)^{2/3} = 0.63.$

24. $(0.63)^{3/2} = 0.5.$

25. $\dfrac{\sqrt[3]{750}}{\sqrt[3]{75}} = 2.16.$

26. $\dfrac{\sqrt[3]{640}}{\sqrt[2]{64}} = 1.074.$

27. $\dfrac{\sqrt[3]{0.081}}{\sqrt[2]{0.081}} = 1.52.$

28. $(0.0043)^3 \times \sqrt[2]{0.64} = 6.32 \times 10^{-8}.$

29. $\dfrac{\sqrt[2]{48,500}}{(0.85)^3} = 358.$

30. $\sqrt[3]{125} \times \sqrt[2]{1050} = 162.$

In arithmetic the magnitude or size of a quantity is usually expressed by a number. In our early school years, all the numbers we studied were integers. As our arithmetic progressed, the numbers we studied were the ratio of two integers, or fractions; eventually these fractions were expressed in decimal form. We also learned fundamental operations (addition, subtraction, multiplication, and division) of these different number types.

Algebra introduces additional types of numbers. One is the signed number, another is the literal number, and another is the number in the power form. In this chapter we will discuss these algebraic numbers, provide exercises in manipulating them by the fundamental operations, and provide formulation exercises to demonstrate how they arise.

2 ALGEBRAIC EXPRESSIONS AND OPERATIONS

2-1   Signed Numbers

Finances are often referred to in terms of gain or loss, time is referred to as future or past, and temperature is denoted as above or below some preassigned zero. All these references suggest the introduction of signs on the quantities involved to indicate gain or loss, future or past, above or below.

Let us start by creating some sign conventions and using our creations to demonstrate certain rules regarding the use of signed numbers. Referring to Fig. 2-1(a), we will orient all time around today, calling today zero; two days ago is −2 days, three days from now is +3 days, From Fig. 2-1(b), we will

(a)

(b)

FIGURE 2-1

orient money holdings around a zero amount; a loss of $3 is −3 and a gain of $1 is +1. From the scales shown in Fig. 2-1 and the notions pictured there, we will provide examples of sums, differences, products, and quotients of signed numbers.

EXAMPLE 1. A man has $4 and earns $8 more. What are his new assets?

Solution. This is a case of the addition of signed numbers. The 4 which he has is a +4, the 8 which he earns is +8. His new assets are

$$+4 + (+8) = +12.$$

This is interpreted as two moves to the right in Fig. 2-1(b); the first is of magnitude 4 starting from zero, and the second is of magnitude 8, starting from the point where the first move terminated.

EXAMPLE 2. A man has $52 in assets but receives a bill for $85. What are his new assets.

Solution. Once again, this is the addition of two signed numbers. The $52 which he has is +52; the $85 which he "gains" is −85. His new assets are

$$+52 + (-85) = -33.$$

This is interpreted from Fig. 2-1(b) as a move of 52 to the right from zero, followed by a move of 85 to the left, with the second move starting from the point where the first move stopped.

EXAMPLE 3. A man has assets of \$150. He is told that a debt of \$35 has been cancelled. What are his new assets?

Solution. This is the subtraction of two signed numbers, since he "loses" a debt. The 150 which he has is $+150$; the 35 is a loss of -35, giving

$$150 - (-35) = 185.$$

EXAMPLE 4. A man acquires a debt of \$5 per day for each of seven days. What is his change in assets?

Solution. This is a product of two signed numbers. The debt of 5 is -5. The time is $+7$. The change in assets is

$$(-5) \times (+7) = -35,$$

indicating that, in seven days, he acquires a debt of \$35.

EXAMPLE 5. Ten days ago a man had \$50 more in assets than he has today. If his change in assets is the same each day, what is his daily change?

Solution. This is a case of the division of two signed numbers. Ten days ago is -10, \$50 more is $+50$. The change is

$$\frac{50}{-10} = -5,$$

or a \$5 loss each day

Absolute value

It is sometimes convenient to ignore direction as assigned in Fig. 2-1 and refer to the magnitude of a quantity without reference to sign. When we do so with a number, we call the value of that number its *absolute value*. Thus, $+7$ and -7 have the same absolute value, symbolized $|7|$.

We may use Examples 1–5 and the definition of absolute value to form some rules about the fundamental operations of signed numbers:

> **Rule 1.** *To add two numbers of like sign, add their absolute values and prefix the sum with the common sign.*

> **Rule 2.** *To add two numbers of different signs, subtract their absolute values and prefix the difference with the sign of the number of greater absolute value.*

> **Rule 3.** *To subtract two signed numbers, change the sign of the subtrahend and proceed as in addition.*

Rule 4. *The product or quotient of two numbers of the same sign is positive.*

Rule 5. *The product or quotient of two numbers of different sign is negative.*

Exercises

Perform the indicated operations in Exercises 1–20.

1. $6 + 5$.   *Ans.* 11.   **2.** $6 + (-5)$.

3. $6 - (+5)$.   *Ans.* 1.   **4.** $6 - (-5)$.

5. $-7 + 4$.   *Ans.* -3.   **6.** $-7 + (-4)$.

7. $-7 - (+4)$.   *Ans.* -11.   **8.** $-7 - (-4)$.

9. $13 \times (-2)$.   *Ans.* -26.   **10.** $(-12)(-5)$.

11. $(-144) \div 12$.   *Ans.* -12.   **12.** $(-72) \div (-8)$.

13. $\dfrac{6 - (-5)}{4 + (-3)}$.   *Ans.* 11.   **14.** $5 - \dfrac{6 + 3}{6 - (-3)}$.

15. $\dfrac{-3 - (-12)}{4 + (-7)}$.   *Ans.* -3.   **16.** $\dfrac{3 + (-12)}{-4 - (-7)}$.

17. $(-8)(-3 + 5)$.   *Ans.* -16.   **18.** $-10 + \dfrac{4 + (-8)}{-2}$.

19. $\dfrac{-8 - (-4)}{-2}$.   *Ans.* 2.   **20.** $\dfrac{-3 + (-7)}{2} - 5$.

A ball rolling up an inclined plane slows at the rate of 5 ft./sec. each second. It started (initial velocity) at 60 ft./sec. In Exercises 21–24:

21. What is its rate at the end of 5 sec.? 20 sec.?

Ans. 35 ft./sec., -40 ft./sec.

22. Is the ball moving up or down the plane at the end of 15 sec.? How fast?

23. How many seconds have elapsed when the ball is momentarily at rest?

Ans. 12 sec.

24. At the end of 3 sec., the ball is travelling up the plane at 45 ft./sec.; at the end of how many seconds is the ball travelling down the plane at 45 ft./sec.?

25. In a tug-of-war game, forces of 80, 60, and 75 lb. are exerted to the right and forces of 65, 85, and 70 lb. are exerted to the left. What is the net (resultant) force and in which direction does it act?   *Ans.* 5 lb. left.

26. A water tank is fed by two pipes at the rate of 3.5 ft.³/min. and 4.2 ft.³/min. Water is being removed by three users at 0.6 ft.³/min., 4.2 ft.³/min., and 3.2 ft.³/min.

Is the tank filling or emptying? At what rate? If the 0.6 ft.³/min. user were eliminated, would the tank be filling or emptying? At what rate?

27. A student obtains marks of 68, 73, 95, and 70 on quizzes. Without actually computing his average mark, determine whether his average is over or under 74; over or under 80; over or under 78.

28. A man has assets of $1000. He takes on a debt of $200 and "loses" a debt of $400. He then divides his assets equally among his three sons. How much does each son get? *Ans.* $400.

29. Assume that time zones on the face of the earth are each 1000 miles wide and that a clock must be set back 1 hour for each time zone traversed by a westbound traveller. A pilot starts flying westward from point A at 12:00 noon. He flies westward for 6 hours to point B, rests there for 1 hour, then flies eastward for 4 hours. If he travels at a uniform rate of 500 mph while he is in flight, what time did his clock read when he arrived at point B? What time should his clock have read to be correct for that time zone when he is at point B? What time should his clock read at the end of his journey? *Ans.* 6:00, 3:00, 10:00.

Laws of Addition and Multiplication

Five laws applicable to real numbers and algebraic quantities in this text are stated here.

1. Commutative Law of Addition. *This law asserts that the order of addition is unimportant; i.e., numbers can be added in any order without affecting the result.*

thus, $a + b = b + a$

or, $3 + 5 = 5 + 3 = 8.$

This law permits additions of a column upward or downward.

2. Commutative Law of Multiplication. *This law asserts that the order of multiplication does not affect the product.*

thus, $a \times b = b \times a.$

or, $5 \times 3 = 3 \times 5 = 15.$

Through this law we are permitted to express factors in any order or perform multiplication in any order.

3. Associative Law of Addition. *The terms of a sum may be grouped in any order.*

thus, $\quad a + b + c = (a + b) + c = a + (b + c)$

or $\quad 2 + 3 + 4 = (2 + 3) + 4 = 2 + (3 + 4)$

$$= 5 + 4 = 2 + 7 = 9.$$

This law permits us to group added terms at will. It is useful in special techniques of adding columns.

4. Associative Law of Multiplication. *The terms of a product may be grouped in any order.*

thus, $\qquad abc = (ab)c = a(bc)$

or $\quad 2 \times 3 \times 4 = (2 \times 3)4 = 2(3 \times 4)$

$$= 6 \times 4 = 2 \times 12 = 24.$$

This law permits flexibility in factoring and enables special groupings which simplify multiplication operations.

5. Distributive Law of Multiplications. *The product of a number a and the sum b + c equals the sum of the separate products ab and bc.*

thus, $\quad a(b + c) = ab + ac.$

or $\quad 3(4 + 5) = 3 \times 4 + 3 \times 5 = 12 + 15 = 27.$

This law permits removal of grouping symbols and, in many cases, allows simplification.

Variations and extensions of these laws to more than two or three members are allowable. That is, an extension of the Associative Law of Addition might read

$$a + b + c + d = (a + b) + (c + d) = a + (b + c) + d$$
$$= a + (b + c + d) = (a + b + c) + d, \text{ etc.}$$

2-2 Literal Quantities

Literal quantities are used when an effort is being made to remain general. For instance, the familiar expression for the circumference of a circle, $2\pi r$, is appropriate to any circle in a plane. The radius of the circle is expressed as r, the general radius. It will be the goal of this section to show the origin of some literal quantities and to provide some formulation and manipulation exercises.

EXAMPLE 6. Give an expression for the perimeter of a rectangle whose length is twice its width.

Solution. Here, since no specific magnitude is assigned to either the width or the length, a general dimension may be assigned. We cannot say with exactness that the length is 10 and the width is 5, with the perimeter $10 + 5 + 10 + 5 = 30$, although this is an example of *one* rectangle which satisfies the conditions of the problem. Another could be of width 3.5 and length 7; another is of length $2\sqrt{2}$ and width $\sqrt{2}$. To list all of the numerical possibilities is impossible, so we resort to literal expressions. Referring to Fig. 2-2, we see two literal possibilities. Choosing appropriate

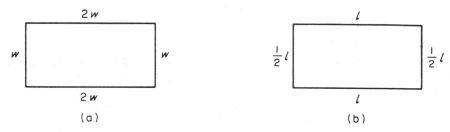

(a)   (b)

FIGURE 2–2

letters (*w* for width and *l* for length), the perimeter from Fig. 2-2(a) is

$$2w + w + 2w + w = 6w,$$

and the perimeter from Fig. 2-2(b) is

$$l + \tfrac{1}{2}l + l + \tfrac{1}{2}l = 3l.$$

It is worth noting from Fig. 2-2 that any literal quantities could have been chosen for the length and width, as long as the $2:1$ ratio was satisfied.

EXAMPLE 7. Give an expression for the area of a rectangle whose length is twice its width.

Solution. Referring to Fig. 2-2(a), the area is the product of $2w$ by w, or $2w^2$. In Fig. 2-2(b), the area is the product of $\tfrac{1}{2}l$ by l, or $\tfrac{1}{2}l^2$.

A discussion of some notation seems in order here. One goal of notation is often compactness, to reduce lengthy expressions or indicated operations to simple expressions. For example, if x is added to itself so that we have x involved seven times, we may express this as

$$x + x + x + x + x + x + x.$$

This lengthy expression is abbreviated by the simple expression $7x$, read "seven x." In general, if we have n x's added together,

$$x + x + x + \cdots + x = nx \qquad (n\ x\text{'s added}),$$

where n is called the *coefficient* of x.

Similarly, the product of $7x$'s could be

$$x \cdot x \cdot x \cdot x \cdot x \cdot x \cdot x,$$

but it is more compactly written as x^7, read "x to the seventh power." In general,

$$x \cdot x \cdot x \cdots x = x^n \qquad (n\ x\text{'s multiplied}).$$

The expressions x^7 and $7x$ are called *terms*, or *monomials*, where monomials are defined as algebraic expressions which are not joined by addition or subtraction signs. Other examples of monomials are 25, $32x^2/5$, x^2y^3, $4I^2R$, and $4\pi r^3/3$. Algebraic expressions involving sums are called *polynomials;* they are *binomials* if two terms are summed, *trinomials* if three terms are summed. Examples of polynomials are $x + y$, $1/r_1 + 1/r_2$, $x^2 + 2x + 3$, and $hb/2 + hb'/2$.

Terms are alike if they contain the same literal quantities raised to the same powers (with coefficients not necessarily the same). As examples of *like* terms, we have $4R$ and $0.3R$, $6\pi r^2$ and $2\pi r^2$ and $2\pi r^2$, $r_1 r_2/(r_1 + r_2)$, and $0.12 r_1 r_2/(r_1 + r_2)$. Examples of *unlike* terms are $2\pi r$ and πr^2, I^2R and IR^2, $6(x + y)$ and $6(x - y)$.

The exercises that follow provide for the creation of algebraic expressions; the creation of such expressions is called *formulation*—a process that will demand much of our attention in this and later chapters.

Exercises

Give algebraic expressions for the word statements given in 1–20.

1. The product of velocity v and time t. *Ans. vt.*

2. The sum of the horizontal and vertical components F_{1x} and F_{2x}.

3. The sum of the squares of x and y. *Ans. $x^2 + y^2$*

4. The square root of the sum of the squares of a and b.

5. The product of r_1 and r_2 divided by their sum. *Ans. $r_1 r_2/(r_1 + r_2)$.*

6. Four-thirds of the cube of the radius r, all multiplied by π.

7. The difference, x less y, divided by the sum of x and y.

Ans. $(x - y)/(x + y)$.

8. The square of the sum of u and v.

9. The square root of the quotient of the power p divided by the resistance r.

Ans. $\sqrt{p/r}$.

10. One-half of the product of the graviational constant g multiplied by the square of the time t.

11. The cube of the difference x less y.

Ans. $(x - y)^3$

12. The difference of the cube of x less the cube of y.

13. The product of π and the fourth power of diameter D, all divided by 32.

Ans. $\pi D^4/32$.

14. The fourth power of the product of $\pi/32$ and diameter D.

15. The sum of the diameter and one-half the circumference of a circle of radius r.

Ans. $2r + \pi r$.

16. The surface area of a cube, each edge of which has the length x.

17. The surface area of a cube, each edge of which has the length $x + a$.

Ans. $6(x + a)^2$.

18. The square of one-half the sum of x and y.

19. One-half of the sum of the square of x and y.

Ans. $\frac{1}{2}(x^2 + y^2)$

20. The square root of the product of x and y, all divided by the cube of their sum.

21. Give expressions for the perimeters and areas of the polygons shown in Fig. 2-3.

Ans. (a) $6s + 6r$, (c) $6r + 10s$; $9rs$.

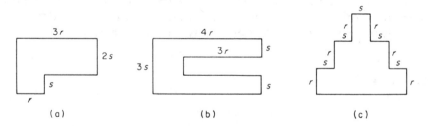

FIGURE 2–3

22. How much money is taken in at a theater if m adult tickets are sold at d dollars each and n children's tickets are sold at c cents each?

23. Three boxes of dimensions W, L, and H are stacked. Box A lies on the floor on its W by L side; box B stands on its L by H side atop box A; box C stands on its W by H side atop box B. How tall is the stack?

Ans. $H + W + L$.

24. The turning moment of a lever is the product of the mass and the moment arm. A clockwise moment is called positive, and a counterclockwise moment is called negative. If the mass is represented by m and the moment arm by d, give the expression for the total moment in Fig. 2-4.

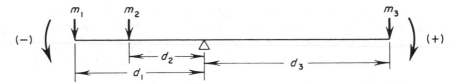

FIGURE 2–4

25. A metal bar of length L_0 when the temperature t is zero is heated. Heat expands the bar by an amount which is the product of L_0 by the change in temperature Δt by the coefficient of linear expansion c. Give a general expression for the length of the bar when t is not zero.   *Ans.* $L_0 + L_0 c \, \Delta t$.

26. The area of a trapezoid is one-half of the altitude, h, multiplied by the sum of the bases b and b'. If b equals h and b' is twice h, give an expression for the area in terms of h alone.

27. A boat travels in still water at h mph. A river has a current of c mph. The boat is to make a one-way trip of m miles in the river. Give expressions for the length of time required for the trip if the trip is upstream; downstream.
                Ans. $m/(h - c)$; $m/(h + c)$.

28. The weight of an object may be described as the product of the volume and density of the object. Assuming a density d, give an expression for the weight of each of the solid figures shown in Fig. 2-5.   *Ans.* (a) $abcd$, (b) $\pi r^2 hd$.

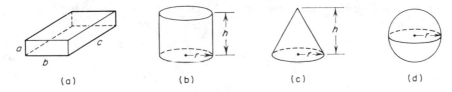

FIGURE 2–5

29. Give an expression for the surface area of the solid figures in Figs. 2-5(a) and 2-5(b).

30. A fancy box is built in the form of Fig. 2-5(a). The bottom costs r cents per area unit, the sides cost s cents per area unit, and the top costs t cents per area unit. Give an expression for the total cost of the box.
                Ans. $rbc + 2sac + 2sab + tbc$

2-3   Grouping Symbols

We frequently refer to a group of persons or items as a unit. A man's financial standing, which is singular, is usually the sum of a number of positive and negative amounts. The separate amounts can be shown in implied addition and the sum regarded as a unit. Thus, $x + y - 2z$ may be regarded as a unit; the key which tells the reader to regard it as such is the use of grouping symbols surrounding it. Thus, using *parentheses* ( ), *brackets* [ ], or *braces* { }, we have our group as $(x \times y - 2z)$, $[x + y - 2z]$, or $\{x + y - 2z\}$.

It may be useful to refer to the sum of eight of the above groups; we do this by introducing the coefficient 8 thus: $8(x + y - 2z)$. It is important to recognize that the grouping symbol may be removed by multiplying each term in the group by the coefficient of the group. Thus,

$$8(x + y - 2z) = 8x + 8y - 16z.$$

When no coefficient is written in front of the group, the coefficient is assumed to be $+1$.

When one set of grouping symbols encloses another, the usual procedure for the removal of the symbols is to remove the innermost set first. Let us consider some examples.

EXAMPLE 8. Remove all of the grouping symbols and collect like terms for the expression

$$2(3b - 5) - 2\{b - [3b + 4(b - 1)] + 2\}.$$

Solution. Inspection shows that the parentheses grouping $b - 1$ are innermost. These may be removed by multiplying $b - 1$ by 4. At the same time we may remove the parentheses from the left term by multiplying $3b - 5$ by 2. The revised expression is now

$$6b - 10 - 2\{b - [3b + 4b - 4] + 2\}.$$

Now we remove the brackets by multiplying by -1:

$$6b - 10 - 2\{b - 3b - 4b + 4 + 2\}.$$

Removing the braces by multiplying by -2, we have

$$6b - 10 - 2b + 6b + 8b - 8 - 4.$$

All of these terms containing b here are alike, so they can be collected as

$$6b - 2b + 6b + 8b = 18b.$$

The nonliteral terms are collected as

$$-10 - 8 - 4 = -22.$$

The original expression, therefore, reduces to

$$18b - 22.$$

EXAMPLE 9. Remove grouping symbols and collect like terms for the expression

$$3\{[a - 2(a - b)] - 2(a + b)\} + 6(b + 2a).$$

Solution. Proceeding as in Example 8, we have the following steps:
Step 1:
$$3\{[a - 2a + 2b] - 2a - 2b\} + 6b + 12a$$
Step 2:
$$= 3\{a - 2a + 2b - 2a - 2b\} + 6b + 12a$$
Step 3:
$$= 3a - 6a + 6b - 6a - 6b + 6b + 12a = +3a + 6b.$$

We point out here that, in the removal of grouping symbols, if like terms occur within a given set of symbols, these like terms may be collected before the symbols are removed. Thus, examining Step 2 of Example 9, we can collect the terms inside the braces as:

$$3\{-3a\} + 6b + 12a = -9a + 6b + 12a = +3a + 6b.$$

Exercises

In Exercises 1–20 remove all of the grouping symbols and collect like terms.

1. $3 + (4 - 5)$ *Ans.* 2.

2. $(8 - 2) + 2(5 - 7)$

3. $3 - (4 + 5)$ *Ans.* −6.

4. $(6 - 3) + 2(5 - 2)$

5. $7(9 - 5) + 3(6 - 9)$ *Ans.* 19.

6. $8 - 3 - 4(4 - 6) - 5$

7. $4(5 - 3) - 3(5 - 3)$ *Ans.* 2.

8. $3 + 2 - 3(4 + 2) - 1 + 2$

9. $9 - (-6 + 1)$ *Ans.* 14.

10. $a - b - (c - b)$

11. $3 - (-2 - 3)$ *Ans.* 8.

12. $a + b - (c + b)$

13. $-a - (b - a)$ *Ans.* $-b$.

14. $7x - [4x + 3(x - 2)]$

15. $a - (-b + a)$ *Ans.* b.

16. $4x - 5\{x - 2[(4 - 2y) + 3(y - x)]\}$

17. $7x - 3\{x + 4[(x - y) - 2(3y - 2)]\}$ *Ans.* $84y - 8x - 48$.

18. $3\{8 - [2(5 - x) - x]\}$

19. $4[4(4 - 1) - 1] - 1$ *Ans.* 43.

20. $6\{4 - [3 - (2 - x) + x] - 2x\}$

21. $-2\{-2[-2(-x + 1) + 1] + 1\} + 1.$ *Ans.* $8x - 5$.

In Exercises 22–25, we are given a triangle with sides a, b, *and* c, *where* c *is the largest side and* a *is the smallest side. Formulate the expressions requested using grouping symbols, then simplify where possible.*

22. The perimeter less twice the sum of the largest and smallest sides.

23. The perimeter tripled, less the difference $c - 2b$.   *Ans.* $3a + 5b + 2c$.

24. The sum of the three quantities, where the three quantities are all of the possible arrangements formed by subtracting twice the sum of two sides from the third side.

25. The sum of the squares of the three sides, diminished by $3d$, where d is the sum of the products of the sides taken two at a time. (*Note:* there are three such products.)   *Ans.* $a^2 + b^2 + c^2 - 3ab - 3ac - 3bc$.

In Exercises 26–29, we are given the expression

$$y_{av} = \frac{y_1 + y_2 + y_3}{3}.$$

26. $y_1 = a, y_2 = 2a, y_3 = 3a$.

27. $y_1 = a + b, y_2 = a - b, y_3 = a$.   *Ans.* a.

28. $y_1 = 2b - 3c, y_2 = 2(a - b), y_3 = c - b$.

29. $y_1 = 2(a + b + c), y_2 = b - 3c, y_3 = a - (2b - c)$.   *Ans.* $(3a + b)/3$.

2-4 Operations with Zeroes

Elementary operations with zeroes are readily summarized by the following statements:

1. $a + 0 = a$; $0 + a = a$.
2. $a - 0 = a$; $0 - a = -a$.
3. $a \cdot 0 = 0$; $0 \cdot a = 0$.
4. $0 \div a = 0 \ (a \neq 0)$.
5. Division by zero is impossible. That is, $a \div 0$ and $0 \div 0$ are impossible operations.

As an illustration of (5), we can begin with the statement that multiplication and division are inverse operations. That is, if $a \cdot b = c$, then $c/b = a$ and $c/a = b$. Now, by (3) above, *any* number multiplied by zero equals zero; therefore; $0 \div 0$ yields no certain result. If we attempt the operation $a \div 0 = b$, where we wish b to be either zero or nonzero, then $a = b \cdot 0$, which requires a to be zero; now b will be any number, so that no single result occurs again.

Two examples of division by zero follow. They involve batting averages where a batter's average is determined by dividing his hits by his trips to the plate.

EXAMPLE 10. What is a batter's average if he has no hits in four times at bat?

Solution. This is an example of (4) above where

$$0 \div 4 = 0.$$

EXAMPLE 11. What is a batter's average if he has no hits in no times at bat?

Solution. It is best that we avoid attempting to describe his average. Any attempt to describe it would be a violation of (5) above since we have the case of $0 \div 0$.

EXAMPLE 12. What is a batter's average if he has three hits in no times at bat?

Solution. This situation is not possible. He could have no hits if he was never at bat. Once again (5) is involved.

2-5 Laws of Exponents

In Sec. 2-2 we mentioned a fact which we will now call a definition, namely:

$$a \cdot a \cdot a \cdot a \cdots \quad (n \text{ factors}) = a^n,$$

where a^n is the nth power of a; n is called the *exponent* or *index* and a is called the *base*.

Certain laws of exponents with which the student must become familiar are listed here, where m and n are integers and $a \neq 0$.

$$a^m \times a^n = a^{m+n}, \tag{1}$$

$$a^m \div a^n = a^{m-n}, \tag{2}$$

$$(a^n)^m = (a^m)^n = a^{mn}, \tag{3}$$

$$(ab)^m = a^m b^m, \tag{4}$$

$$\left(\frac{a}{b}\right)^m = \frac{a^m}{b^m} \tag{5}$$

Rendering laws (1)–(5) into verbal form, we have:

1. To multiply powers of like bases, add the exponents over the common base.
2. To divide powers of like bases, subtract the exponent of the divisor from the exponent of the dividend. This difference of exponents will be the exponent of the quotient.
3. To raise a power to a power, multiply exponents.
4. The power of the product of two factors is the product of the powers of the two factors.
5. The power of the quotient of two factors is the quotient of the powers of the two factors.

EXAMPLE 13. Simplify $b^2 \cdot b^5$.

Solution. By (1),

$$b^2 \cdot b^5 = b^{2+5} = b^7.$$

The reason for adding exponents is illustrated by reverting to definitions:

$$b^2 = b \cdot b \quad \text{and} \quad b^5 = b \cdot b \cdot b \cdot b \cdot b$$

so $\qquad b^2 \cdot b^5 = (b \cdot b) \cdot (b \cdot b \cdot b \cdot b \cdot b) = b^7.$

EXAMPLE 14. Simplify $b^5 \div b^3$.

Solution. By (2), we have

$$b^5 \div b^3 = b^{5-3} = b^2.$$

By the definition of a power, we have

$$\frac{b^5}{b^3} = \frac{b \cdot b \cdot b \cdot b \cdot b}{b \cdot b \cdot b} = b \cdot b = b^2.$$

EXAMPLE 15. Simplify the expression $(b^2)^3$.

Solution. By (3), $(b^2)^3 = b^{2 \cdot 3} = b^6$. By definition,

$$(b^2)^3 = b^2 \cdot b^2 \cdot b^2 = b \cdot b \cdot b \cdot b \cdot b \cdot b = b^6.$$

EXAMPLE 16. Simplify the expression

$$\frac{(a^2b^3)^2}{(ab^2)^3}.$$

Solution. Using (3) and (4), we have

$$\frac{(a^2b^3)^2}{(ab^2)^3} = \frac{a^4b^6}{a^3b^6}.$$

Applying (2),

$$\frac{a^4b^6}{a^3b^6} = a^{4-3}b^{6-6} = a.$$

A few corollaries follow from the previously listed laws of exponents. Let us list two of them. First,

$$a^0 = 1 \qquad (a \neq 0). \tag{6}$$

Law (6) can be established by a few simple steps:

$$\frac{a^m}{a^m} = a^{m-m} = a^0 = 1.$$

Verbally, law (6) states that any nonzero base raised to the zero power is unity.

Another corollary asserts that

$$a^{-m} = \frac{1}{a^m} \qquad (a \neq 0). \tag{7}$$

Law (7) may be shown as

$$a^{-m} = a^{0-m} = \frac{a^0}{a^m} = \frac{1}{a^m}.$$

Verbally, law (7) says that we may reciprocate a power by changing the sign of the exponent.

The seven laws shown above also apply to fractional exponents. When exponents are expressed as fractions, radicals are introduced. It is not our intention to explore radicals here, but merely to identify radicals with exponents. We accept the definition

$$\sqrt[n]{a} = a^{1/n}. \tag{8}$$

Expression (8) enables us to switch from radical notation to exponent notation, thereby enabling us to apply laws (1)–(7) to radical quantities.

EXAMPLE 17. Express $\sqrt[3]{a^2}$ in exponent notation.

Solution. By (8) and (3),

$$\sqrt[3]{a^2} = (a^2)^{1/3} = a^{2/3}.$$

EXAMPLE 18. Simplify the expression $(27)^{4/3}$.

Solution. The base, 27, may be rewritten as (3^3); therefore,

$$(27)^{4/3} = (3^3)^{4/3}.$$

Now, by (3),

$$(3^3)^{4/3} = 3^4 = 81.$$

EXAMPLE 19. Simplify the expression $3(x^0 + 1)$.

Solution. By (6), $x^0 = 1$; therefore we have

$$3(x^0 + 1) = 3(1 + 1) = 3(2) = 6.$$

Exercises

Simplify the expressions in Exercises 1–20. Show the results in terms of positive or zero exponents only.

1. $x^2 \cdot x^4$.   *Ans.* x^6.   **2.** $x^a \cdot x^b$.

3. $x^3 \cdot x^2 \cdot x^{-3}$.   *Ans.* x^2.   **4.** $x^a \cdot x^b \cdot x^{u-o}$.

5. $(x^2 y^3)(x^3)(xy)$.   *Ans.* $x^6 y^4$.   **6.** $(x^0 + 1)(x^0 - 1)$.

7. $3(x + y)^0(x)$.   *Ans.* $3x$.   **8.** $\dfrac{a^{x+y}b^{x-y}}{a^{x-y}b^{x+y}}$.

9. $\dfrac{I^2 R}{IR}$.   *Ans.* I.   **10.** $\dfrac{\pi r^2 h}{2\pi r}$.

11. $\dfrac{a^2 b^3}{ab^2}$.   *Ans.* ab.   **12.** $\sqrt[2]{a} \cdot \sqrt[3]{a}$.

13. $\sqrt[2]{a} \div \sqrt[4]{a}$.   *Ans.* $a^{1/4}$.   **14.** $\dfrac{5x^0 + 1}{5x^0 - 1}$.

15. $\dfrac{5(x^0 - 1)}{10}$ *Ans.* 0. **16.** $\dfrac{5(x + 1)^0}{10}$.

17. $(x^2)^3 \div (x^3)^2$. *Ans.* 1. **18.** $\dfrac{gt^2 \cdot t}{t^3}$.

19. $\dfrac{a^{2/3}\, b^{1/3}}{a^{-3/2}\, b^{-1/2}}$ *Ans.* $a^{13/6}\, b^{5/6}$. **20.** $\dfrac{(24)^2(4)^3}{(6)^3(4)^5}$.

In Exercises 21–26, formulate the given expressions. Simplify wherever possible.

21. The quotient of the area of a circle of radius r divided by the circumference of the circle. *Ans.* $r/2$.

22. The quotient of the hypotenuse (use the Pythagorean theorem) of a right triangle of legs a and b, divided by twice the area of the triangle.

23. The quotient of the area of a square of side s, divided by the perimeter of the square. *Ans.* $s/4$.

24. The quotient of the volume of a cube of side s, divided by the total area of the cube.

25. The average of the five quantities a, b, c, d, e.

26. The square root of the average of the squares of the quantities in Exercise 25.

27. Give expressions for the area divided by the perimeter of each of the figures in Fig. 2-3.

28. P_1 has an ordinate y_1 and an abscissa x_1; P_2 has an ordinate y_2 and an abscissa x_2. Give an expression for the difference of the ordinates at P_2 and P_1 divided by the difference of the abscissas at P_2 and P_1. *Ans.* $(y_2 - y_1)/(x_2 - x_1)$.

29. The geometric mean of n positive numbers is defined as the nth root of the product of the n numbers. Give an expression for the geometric mean of the numbers a, b, c, d. What is the numerical value of the geometric mean of the numbers 1, 2, 8? *Ans.* $\sqrt[4]{abcd}$, $\sqrt[3]{16}$.

2-6 Algebraic Products

The expression $3xy$ indicates a multiplication operation of three factors, the factors 3, x, and y. The numerical coefficient, 3, indicates that three quantities described by the product xy are under consideration. For instance, if a group of rectangles are each of length x and width y, then $3xy$ could represent the combined areas of three such rectangles.

The expression $3xy$ is a monomial, as opposed to $3x + y$, which is a binomial (two terms), and $3 + x - y$, which is a trinomial (three terms). The more inclusive term "polynomial" describes an algebraic expression of two or more terms. We will discuss here the products of two monomials, of monomials and polynomials, and of two polynomials. Note the following rule:

> To multiply two monomials, combine the literal terms according to the laws of exponents, and then multiply this literal product by the product of the coefficients.

EXAMPLE 20. Multiply $5x^2y^3z$ by $-3xyz$.

Solution. Multiply the literal quantities,

$$(x^2y^3z)\cdot(xyz) = x^3y^4z^2.$$

The product of the coefficients is $(5)\cdot(-3) = -15$. The desired result is therefore $-15x^3y^4z^2$.

EXAMPLE 21. Simplify $\dfrac{3x^2y}{5z}\cdot\dfrac{10yz}{x}$.

Solution. Following the procedures shown in Example 20, we have

$$\frac{3x^2y}{5z}\cdot\frac{10yz}{x} = \frac{30x^2y^2z}{5xz} = 6xy^2.$$

> To multiply a monomial by a polynomial, multiply each term of the polynomial by the monomial and combine the resulting products by the proper signs.

EXAMPLE 22. Perform the operation $x^2(x + y - z)$.

Solution. Multiply each term of the polynomial by the monomial and combine the resulting terms:

$$x^2(x + y - z) = x^3 + x^2y - x^2z.$$

Note that each term of the product now contains the common monomial factor x^2. Recognition of the presence of such common factors is useful in factoring operations (which will be discussed later).

EXAMPLE 23. Remove parentheses from the expression

$$\frac{2y}{x^2}(3xy - 5x^2z + w).$$

Solution. Multiplying each term of the trinomial by the monomial, we have the product

$$\frac{2y}{x^2}(3xy - 5x^2z + w) = \frac{6y^2}{x} - 10yz + \frac{2wy}{x^2}.$$

To multiply two polynomials, multiply each term of the first by each term of the second and collect like terms.

EXAMPLE 24. Multiply $(x - 5)$ by $(2x + 3)$.

Solution. Multiplying each term of $x - 5$ by each term of $2x + 3$, we have

$$x \cdot 2x = 2x^2,$$
$$-5 \cdot 2x = -10x,$$
$$3 \cdot x = 3x,$$
$$-5 \cdot 3 = -15.$$

Collecting like terms from these four products, we obtain the desired product

$$(x - 5)(2x + 3) = 2x^2 - 7x - 15.$$

EXAMPLE 25. Multiply $(x^2 - 3x + 5)(x^2 + x - 1)$.

Solution. Establishing an array which will show all of the nine products and will columnize descending powers of x, we have

$$
\begin{array}{l}
x^2 - 3x + 5 \\
x^2 + \ x - 1 \\
\hline
x^4 - 3x^3 + 5x^2 \\
\quad\quad\ \ x^3 - 3x^2 + 5x \\
\quad\quad\quad\quad\ -\ x^2 + 3x - 5 \\
\hline
x^4 - 2x^3 + \ x^2 + 8x - 5.
\end{array}
$$

Some special products appropriate to factoring merit attention here:

$$a(x + y + z) = ax + ay + az, \tag{9}$$
$$(x + a)(x - a) = x^2 - a^2, \tag{10}$$
$$(x + a)(x + b) = x^2 + (b \mid a)x + ab, \tag{11}$$
$$(ax + b)(cx + d) = acx^2 + (bc + ad)x + bd, \tag{12}$$
$$(x + y)(x^2 - xy + y^2) = x^3 + y^3, \tag{13}$$
$$(x - y)(x^2 + xy + y^2) = x^3 - y^3, \tag{14}$$
$$(x + y)^2 = x^2 + 2xy + y^2, \tag{15}$$
$$(x - y)^2 = x^2 - 2xy + y^2, \tag{16}$$
$$(x + y)^3 = x^3 + 3x^2y + 3xy^2 + y^3, \tag{17}$$
$$(x - y)^3 = x^3 - 3x^2y + 3xy^2 - y^3. \tag{18}$$

EXAMPLE 26. Perform the operation $(2a - b^2)^3$.

Solution. Referring to (18), which is the cube of a difference, we see the solution with $2a = x$ and $b^2 = y$; substituting into (18), we have

$$(2a - b^2)^3 = (2a)^3 - 3(2a)^2(b^2) + 3(2a)(b^2)^2 - (b^2)^3$$
$$= 8a^3 - 12a^2b^2 + 6ab^4 - b^6.$$

EXAMPLE 27. Perform the operation $(3x + w^2)(3x - w^2)$.

Solution. This is the product of the sum of two quantities multiplied by the difference of the two same quantities, and it exactly fits form (10), which shows the product to be the difference of the squares of the two quantities. We have, therefore,

$$(3x + w^2)(3x - w^2) = (3x)^2 - (w^2)^2 = 9x^2 - w^4.$$

Exercises

Obtain the indicated products in Exercises 1–20. Simplify each of the products.

1. $3(2x - 5y)$.   *Ans.* $6x - 15y$.

2. $3x(5ax - 7by)$.

3. $(2x - 3)(x + 1)$.   *Ans.* $2x^2 - x - 3$.

4. $(4t - 3s)(4t + 3s)$.

5. $(4t - 3s)^2$.   *Ans.* $16t^2 - 24ts + 9s^2$.

6. $(3t + 4s)^3$.

7. $(a + 2)(a - 3)$.   *Ans.* $a^2 - a - 6$.

8. $(a + 2)(a + 6)$.

9. $(3a + 2)(2a - 3)$.   *Ans.* $6a^2 - 5a - 6$.

10. $5(x^2 - 3)(x + 1)$.

11. $abc^2(a + bc - 2ac)$.   *Ans.* $a^2bc^2 + ab^2c^3 - 2a^2bc^3$.

12. $(x - y + 5)(x - y - 5)$.

13. $(2ab)(-3a^2bc)(-4ab^2c^2)$.   *Ans.* $24a^4b^4c^3$.

14. $(x^2 - 9y^2)^2$.

15. $(4a - 3b + 2)(a - 2b)$.   *Ans.* $4a^2 - 11ab + 6b^2 + 2a - 4b$.

16. $\dfrac{x^2y^2}{ab}\left(ac + ab + \dfrac{a}{x}\right)$.

17. $(1 - 9x + 4x^3)(3x + 2 - x^2)$.

$$Ans.\ 2 - 15x - 28x^2 + 17x^3 + 12x^4 - 4x^5.$$

18. $2a - (x - y)2a + (x - y)$.

19. $(9s^2 - 6st^2 + 4t^4)(3s + 2t^2)$. $\qquad Ans.\ 27s^3 + 8t^6$.

20. $(x + y)(x - 2y)(x + 3y)$.

In Exercises 21–26, show literal quantities for the given expressions. Simplify wherever possible.

21. The product of three successive integers if the least is x.

$$Ans.\ x^3 + 3x^2 + 2x.$$

22. The product of three successive odd integers if the least is x.

23. The volume of a block whose length is twice its width and whose height exceeds its width by 3. Call the width w. $\qquad Ans.\ 2w^3 + 6w^2$.

24. The volume of the pan formed from the sheet-metal rectangle shown in Fig. 2-6(a) if the four equal shaded squares are removed from the corners and the remaining sheet is folded along the dotted lines into the shape of a shallow pan.

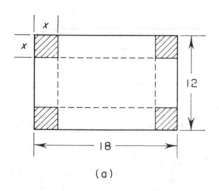 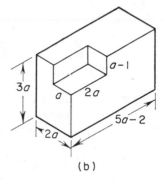

(a) (b)

FIGURE 2–6

25. The volume of the block shown in Fig. 2-6(b). $\qquad Ans.\ 28a^3 - 10a^2$.

26. The total surface area (for the nine planes) of the block in Fig. 2-6(b).

27. The volume of the frustum of a cone is given as the product of two quantities. The first quantity is 1/3 of the product of π and the altitude; the second quantity is the sum of the squares of the radii of the bases, increased by the product of the radii of the bases. If the smaller radius is 3 units smaller than the larger radius R and the altitude is 2 units greater than R, give an expression for the volume in terms of R. $\qquad Ans.\ \pi(R^3 - R^2 - 3R + 6)$.

28. A group of people purchase tickets at a theater. The number of adult tickets purchased exceeds the number of children's tickets by 18. The adult price exceeds the children's price by 55 cents per ticket. Given an expression for the total cost of the tickets if m tickets are purchased and the cost of the adult tickets is c cents each.

29. Give an expression for the area of the hook shown in Fig. 2-7(a).

Ans. $40a^2 + 12\pi a^2$.

30. Give an expression for the area of the cross shown in Fig. 2-7(b).

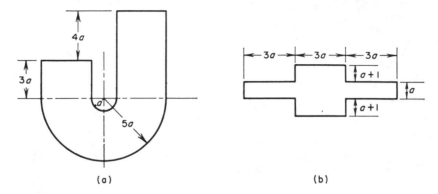

(a)   (b)

FIGURE 2-7

2-7   Division

The process of division of one polynomial by another is similar to arithmetic long division. Example 28 shows a sample division problem; following the sample is a set of simple rules to follow in division.

EXAMPLE 28. Divide $26x - 31x^2 + 6x^4 - 6$ by $1 + 2x^2 - 4x$.

Solution. Rearranging the terms of the divisor and dividend in descending order of exponents, we proceed as follows:

$$
\begin{array}{r}
3x^2 + 6x - 5 \\
2x^2 - 4x + 1 \overline{\smash{\big)}\ 6x^4 - 31x^2 + 26x - 6} \\
\underline{6x^4 - 12x^3 + 3x^2} \\
12x^3 - 34x^2 + 26x \\
\underline{12x^3 - 24x^2 + 6x} \\
-10x^2 + 20x - 6 \\
\underline{-10x^2 + 20x - 5} \\
-1.
\end{array}
$$

The preceding division example shows a quotient of $3x^2 + 6x - 5$ and a remainder of -1. Frequently the division process is considered complete if the greatest exponent of the remainder is less than the greatest exponent of the divisor.

A suggested set of steps for division follows:

Step 1. Arrange the terms of the divisor and dividend in the same (ascending or descending) order of exponents.

Step 2. Divide the first term of the divisor into the first term of the dividend; this result will be the first term of the quotient.

Step 3. Multiply the divisor by the first term of the quotient, placing the products under similar terms of the dividend.

Step 4. Subtract the product from the dividend, then repeat Steps 2 and 3 using the difference obtained as the new dividend.

Step 5. Continue the process until a zero remainder is found, or until the greatest exponent of the remainder is less than the greatest exponent of the divisor.

EXAMPLE 29. Divide $a^2 - b^2 - c^2 + 2bc$ by $a + b - c$.

Solution. We will use the five-step procedure shown, except for arranging the terms in descending or ascending order of the exponents. Also, since ac and bc terms may arise in the division process, we will provide room for them.

$$
\begin{array}{r}
a - \quad b + c \\
a + b - c \,\overline{\big)\, a^2 \qquad - b^2 + 2bc - c^2} \\
a^2 + ab \qquad\qquad -ac \\
\overline{\quad - ab - b^2 + 2bc} \\
- ab - b^2 + \ bc \\
\overline{\qquad\qquad + \ bc - c^2 + ac} \\
+ \ bc - c^2 + ac \\
\overline{\qquad\qquad\qquad 0.}
\end{array}
$$

The operation in Example 29 is not as orderly as that in Example 28 because three literal quantities are present and the orderly arrangement of the terms in the dividend is not possible. One more example will be provided here, showing an unusual quotient.

EXAMPLE 30. Divide 1 by $x - 1$.

Solution. Following the steps suggested, we have

$$
x - 1 \overline{\smash{\big)}\ 1} \quad \frac{1}{x} + \frac{1}{x^2} + \frac{1}{x^3} + \cdots
$$

$$
\begin{array}{r}
\dfrac{1}{x} + \dfrac{1}{x^2} + \dfrac{1}{x^3} + \cdots \\[2mm]
x - 1 \,\overline{\smash{\big)}\ 1} \\[2mm]
1 - \dfrac{1}{x} \\[2mm]
\hline
\dfrac{1}{x} \\[2mm]
\dfrac{1}{x} - \dfrac{1}{x^2} \\[2mm]
\hline
\dfrac{1}{x^2} \\[2mm]
\dfrac{1}{x^2} - \dfrac{1}{x^3} \\[2mm]
\hline
\text{etc.}
\end{array}
$$

Note that the quotient in Example 30 appears to be endless, that each new term of the quotient is $1/x$ times the previous term. This is similar to the division $1 \div 3 = 0.3333\cdots$, where each new term of the quotient is $1/10$ of the value of the previous term.

Division of a monomial by a monomial is accomplished by dividing the coefficients, then dividing the literal quantities by the laws of exponents and multiplying the two results. An example follows:

$$
33x^2y^3 \div 11xy = \frac{33}{11} \cdot \frac{x^2y^3}{xy} = 3xy^2.
$$

Exercises

Perform the divisions in Exercises 1–24.

1. $12x^3y^2 \div 3x^2y.$ *Ans. 4xy.*

2. $(16x - 12y) \div 4.$

3. $(ax + ay - az) \div a.$ *Ans. $x + y - z$.*

4. $(x^2 - 4y^2) \div (x - 2y).$

5. $(x^2 - 4y^2) \div (x + 2y).$ *Ans. $x - 2y$.*

6. $(x^2 + 6xy + 9y^2) \div (x + 3y).$

7. $(x^2 - 4xy + 4y^2) \div (x - 2y).$ *Ans. $x - 2y$.*

8. $(x^5 - 1) \div (x - 1).$

9. $(x^3 - 1) \div (x - 1)$.   *Ans.* $x^2 + x + 1$.

10. $(x^3 + 1) \div (x + 1)$.

11. $(x^5 + 1) \div (x + 1)$.   *Ans.* $\bar{x}^4 - x^3 + x^2 - x + 1$.

12. $(\pi R r + \pi r^2) \div \pi r$.

13. $(a^2 b^3 c - 4ab^2 c^2) \div abc$.   *Ans.* $ab^2 - 4bc$.

14. $(x^2 + x - 2)(x - 3) \div (x + 2)$.

15. $(x - 1)(x + 2)(x - 3) \div (x - 1)$.   *Ans.* $x^2 - x - 6$.

16. $(625s^4 - 81) \div (5s - 3)$.

17. $(T_2^4 - T_1^4) = (T_2 - T_1)$.   *Ans.* $T_2^3 + T_2^2 T_1 + T_2 T_1^2 + T_1^3$.

18. $(16x^4 - 1) \div (2x + 1)$.

19. $(625s^4 - 81) \div (5s + 3)$.   *Ans.* $125s^3 - 75s^2 + 45s - 27$.

20. $(a^2 + 5ab - ac + 6b^2 - 5bc - 6c^2) \div (a + 2b - 3c)$.

21. $(x^2 - 4y^2 + 12yz - 9z^2) \div (x - 2y + 3z)$.   *Ans.* $x + 2y - 3z$.

22. $(4x^4 - 12x^3 + 15x^2 - 17x + 12) \div (2x - 3)$.

23. $(x - 3x^2 + 4x^4 - 12) \div (2x + 3)$.   *Ans.* $2x^3 - 3x^2 + 3x - 4$.

24. $(3 + 4x - 5x^2 + 3x^3) \div (3 + x - x^2)$.

25. Given are four consecutive integers with the least integer N. If the three smaller numbers are multiplied by each other and this product is divided by the largest integer, show that a remainder of -6 will be obtained.

26. In Exercise 25, find the remainder if the least integer is $N - 1$.

The following represent expressions where a binomial variable is carried as a unit. A monomial could be substituted for the binomial to simplify the division indicated.

27. $[(a + b)^2 - (c - d)^2] \div [(a + b) - (c - d)]$.   *Ans.* $a + b + c - d$.

28. $[(x + 2y)^2 + 3(x + 2y) - 4] \div (x + 2y + 4)$.

29. $[x^2(a - 2b)^2 + 4x(a - 2b) + 4] \div x(a - 2b) + 2$.

                                                                      Ans. $x(a - 2b) + 2$.

30. $[(a + b)^3 - (c + d)^3] \div (a + b - c - d)$.

2-8   Factoring

Factoring is, in effect, a division process and can therefore be considered as inverse multiplication. We have, for example, the multiplication

$$(xy) \cdot (a + 2b) = axy + 2bxy.$$

Here the two factors, xy and $a + 2b$, are multiplied to obtain the product $axy + 2bxy$. Frequently it is useful to find the separate factors which are multiplied to obtain a given product; this process is called *factoring*.

Finding the factors of a product successfully depends largely upon the examination of the product. Expressions (9)–(18) in Sec. 2-6 show several different products obtained from special combinations of factors. Expression (9) shows

$$a(x + y + z) = ax + ay + az,$$

or, as a factoring example,

$$ax + ay + az = a(x + y + z). \tag{19}$$

It should be clear here that the product shown in (9) is the product of a monomial and a binomial, and each term of the product $ax + ay + az$ contains a common monomial factor, namely a. Now, from (19), with the recognition of the presence of the monomial factor, we remove that factor by what is, in effect, dividing each term by a.

In any factoring problem involving polynomials, it is prudent to examine the problem first for the presence of a factor common to each term.

EXAMPLE 31. Factor (a) $4x^2 \times 4x$, (b) $a^4b^2x - a^3bx^2$,

and (c) $6(a - 2b)^3x - 3(a - 2b)^2x^2$.

Solution. (a) $4x^2 + 4x = 4x(x + 1)$,

(b) $a^4b^2x - a^3bx^2 = a^3bx(ab - x)$,

(c) $6(a - 2b)^3x - 3(a - 2b)^2x^2 = 3x(a - 2b)^2[2(a - 2b) - x]$.

In the solutions above, it is seen that in (a) the factor common to each term is $4x$, in (b) the common factor is a^3bx, and in (c) the common factor is $3x(a - 2b)^2$.

Another common factoring problem involves a product such as that in (10). Reversing (10), we see

$$x^2 - a^2 = (x - a)(x + a), \tag{20}$$

where a word statement for (20) is: "The factors of the difference of the squares of two numbers are the difference of the numbers and the sum of the numbers."

EXAMPLE 32. Factor: (a) $4x^2 - y^2$, (b) $a^2b^2 - 81c^2$, and (c) $(x - 2)^2 - 4(x + 2)^2$.

Solution. In each case we recognize that the given expression involves the difference of two squares, therefore (20) is appropriate. The solutions are:

(a) $4x^2 - y^2 = (2x + y)(2x - y)$,

(b) $a^2b^2 - 81c^2 = (ab + 9c)(ab - 9c)$,

(c) $(x - 2)^2 - 4(x + 2)^2 = [x - 2 - 2(x + 2)][x - 2 + 2(x + 2)]$
$$= (-x - 6)(3x + 2).$$

The product of two binomials is a common expression in factoring. This product is illustrated by expressions (10), (11), and (12). From (11) we have

$$x^2 + (a + b)x + ab \overset{.}{=} (x + a)(x + b), \tag{21}$$

from (12),

$$acx^2 + (bc + ad)x + bd = (ax + b)(cx + d), \tag{22}$$

and, from (15) and (16),

$$x^2 \pm 2xy + y^2 = (x \pm y)^2. \tag{23}$$

Actually, (22) is the general expression embracing both (21) and (23). Let us examine here a problem of type (22). First, we will show a multiplication with comments.

EXAMPLE 33. Multiply $(3x - 2)(2x + 5)$.

Solution. Treating the operation as an exercise in long multiplication, we have

$$
\begin{array}{r}
3x - 2 \\
2x + 5 \\
\hline
6x^2 - 4x \\
15x - 10 \\
\hline
6x^2 + 11x - 10.
\end{array} \tag{24}
$$

Examining the product (24) and the factors which were multiplied to obtain it, we observe the following facts: the first term of the product is the product of the first terms of the two factors, the last term of the product is the product of the last terms of the factors, and the center term of (24) is the sum of two products, each of which is the product of the first term of one of the factors by the second term of the other. Note that the same examination applies to (21) and (23).

EXAMPLE 34. Factor $2x^2 - x - 10$.

Solution. Following the examination process discussed in Example 33, we come to a few conclusions. First, the factors are binomials of the form $ax + b$ and $cx + d$. Second, since the first term of the product is $2x^2$ and no fractions are present, the first terms of the two factors are $2x$ and x. Third, since the last term of the product is -10, the last terms of the factors are either ± 10 with ∓ 1 or ± 5 with ∓ 2. This analysis leaves us with the possibilities

$$(2x + 10)(x - 1), \qquad (2x + 5)(x - 2),$$
$$(2x - 10)(x + 1), \qquad (2x - 5)(x + 2),$$
$$(2x + 1)(x - 10), \qquad (2x + 2)(x - 5),$$
$$(2x - 1)(x + 10), \qquad (2x - 2)(x + .5),$$

of which all give us a trinomial product with first term $2x^2$ and last term -10, but only one of the eight provides a trinomial with center term $-x$; this one is $(2x - 5)(x + 2)$.

The method of factoring displayed in Example 34 may appear to contain certain elements of guesswork. For trinomials whose first and last terms contain several factors, the method is lengthy. However, at this point it is the only useful method available; later a more direct method will evolve in the discussion of quadratics.

EXAMPLE 35. Factor: (a) $x^2 - 4x + 4$, (b) $36a^4 + 60a^2b + 25b^2$, (c) $(a + b)^2 - 3(a + b) - 4$, (d) $12m^2 - m - 6$, (e) $a^2x^4 - 16a^2$.

Solution.

(a) $x^2 - 4x + 4 = (x - 2)(x - 2)$,
(b) $36a^4 + 60a^2b + 25b^2 = (6a^2 + 5b)(6a^2 + 5b)$,
(c) $(a + b)^2 - 3(a + b) - 4 = (a + b - 4)(a + b + 1)$,
(d) $12m^2 - m - 6 = (3m + 2)(4m - 3)$,
(e) $a^2x^4 - 16a^2 = a^2(x^4 - 16) = a^2(x^2 - 4)(x^2 + 4)$
$$= a^2(x - 2)(x + 2)(x^2 + 4).$$

The preceding example provides five problems which may be considered as being products of binomials. Parts (a) and (b) show squares of binomials. Part (c) uses a binomial unknown in an otherwise trinomial factoring problem. Part (e) shows successive steps of factoring. After removal of the common monomial factor a^2, the remaining factor, $x^4 - 16$, is seen as the difference of two squares. Now,

$$x^4 - 16 = (x^2 - 4)(x^2 + 4)$$

but the facctor $x^2 - 4$ is also the difference of two squares, so

$$x^2 - 4 = (x - 2)(x + 2)$$

and the complete solution is as shown in (e).

EXAMPLE 36. Factor $27x^3 - (a + b)^3$.

Solution. This expression is the difference of two cubes and may be written in the form

$$(3x)^3 - (a + b)^3,$$

which matches form (14). The solution is

$$(3x)^3 - (a + b)^3 = [3x - (a + b)][(3x)^2 + (3x)(a + b) + (a + b)^2]$$
$$= [3x - a - b][9x^2 + 3ax + 3bx + a^2 + 2ab + b^2].$$

Exercises

Factor the given expressions in Exercises 1–50. Obtain the simplest factors in each case.

1. $\pi r^2 + 2\pi r$.   *Ans.* $\pi r(r + 2)$.

2. $a^2 b^2 - 2abc$.

3. $-a^2 x^2 + a^2$.   *Ans.* $a^2(1 - x)(1 + x)$.

4. $Bh + 4Mh + bh$.

5. $nx + x - fnx$.   *Ans.* $x(n + 1 - fn)$.

6. $12x^2 + 6xy - 18x$.

7. $(a + b)x - (a + b)y$.   *Ans.* $(a + b)(x - y)$.

8. $a^2 - b^2$.

9. $a^2 - 16b^2$.   *Ans.* $(a - 4b)(a + 4b)$.

10. $64b^2 - 81y^2$.

11. $(x + y)^2 - x^2$.   *Ans.* $y(2x + y)$.

12. $16z^8 - 1$.

13. $x^2 + 5x + 6$.   *Ans.* $(x + 3)(x + 2)$.

14. $x^2 + 7x + 6$.

15. $x^2 - x - 6$.   *Ans.* $(x - 3)(x + 2)$.

16. $x^2 + x - 6$.

17. $x^2 - 5x - 6$.   *Ans.* $(x - 6)(x + 1)$.

18. $x^2 + 5x - 6$.

19. $m^2 - 10m + 25$.   *Ans.* $(m - 5)(m - 5)$.

20. $s^2 - 12s + 36$.

21. $a^3 - b^3$.   *Ans.* $(a - b)(a^2 + ab + b^2)$.

22. $8x^3 + 27y^3$.

23. $(a + b)^3 - (a - b)^3$.   *Ans.* $2b(3a^2 + b^2)$.

24. $0.001m^6 - 64n^{12}$.

25. $m^6n^3 - m^3n^6$.   *Ans.* $m^3n^3(m - n)(m^2 + mn + n^2)$.

26. $(a + b)^2 - 5(a + b) - 24$.

27. $12x^2 + x - 20$.   *Ans.* $(4x - 5)(3x + 4)$.

28. $12x^2 - 239x - 20$.

29. $12x^2 + 14x - 20$.   *Ans.* $2(6x - 5)(x + 2)$.

30. $81m^2 - 90mn + 25n^2$.

31. $5s^2 - 20s + 20$.   *Ans.* $5(s - 2)(s - 2)$

32. $64x^4 - 16$.

33. $x^3 - x$.   *Ans.* $x(x + 1)(x - 1)$.

34. $x^3 + 2x^2 + x$.

35. $4m^2 - 100$.   *Ans.* $4(m + 5)(m - 5)$.

36. $(30)^2 - (29)^2$.

37. $(\frac{5}{6})^2 - (\frac{1}{6})^2$.   *Ans.* $\frac{2}{3}$.

38. $121y^2 - 88y + 16$.

39. $12a^2b^2 - 24a^2b - 36a^2$.   *Ans.* $12a^2(b - 3)(b + 1)$.

40. $(a + b)^2 - (a - b)^2$.

41. $(r + s)(a + b) - t(a + b)$.   *Ans.* $(a + b)(r + s - t)$.

42. $4a^2 + a + 2a^3$.

43. $n + n(n - 1) + n(n - 1)(n - 2)$.   *Ans.* $n(n^2 - 2n + 2)$.

44. $(r + s)^2 - 2a(r + s) - 3a^2$.

45. $s^2z^2 - 6sz(s + z) + 9(s + z)^2$.   *Ans.* $(sz - 3s - 3z)(sz - 3s - 3z)$.

46. $3r^4 - 2r^2 - 40$.

47. $3m^4 - 10m^2n^2 + 3n^4$.   *Ans.* $(3m^2 - n^2)(m^2 - 3n^2)$.

48. $4a^2 - 8 + 6a - 3a^2 - 8a$.

49. $-20a - 4 - 16a^2$.   *Ans.* $-4(a + 1)(4a + 1)$.

50. $m - mn$.

It is recognized in squaring a binomial that the result is a trinomial whose first and last terms are squares of the first and last terms, respectively, of the binomial and whose middle term is twice the product of the two terms of the binomial. Using this information, provide the missing terms of the following expressions which are given as perfect squares.

51. $x^2 - 2x + (\ \ )$. *Ans.* 1.

52. $m^2 - (\ \ ) + 16$.

53. $s^2 + (\ \ ) + 49t^2$. *Ans.* 14st.

54. $a^2 + 16ab + (\ \ )$.

55. $4k^2 + (\ \ ) + 9h^2$. *Ans.* 12hk.

56. $25m^2n^2 - (\ \ ) + 36b^4$.

57. $(s + t)^2 - (\ \ ) + 4y^2$. *Ans.* $4y(s + t)$.

58. $x^2 - 5x + (\ \ )$.

59. $4x^2 - 7x + (\ \ )$. *Ans.* $\frac{49}{16}$.

60. $r^2 - (\ \ ) + t^2/4$.

2-9   Addition and Subtraction of Fractions

From arithmetic we learned that a fraction is of the form a/b, where a is the numerator and b is the denominator. In the case of an ordinary algebraic monomial such as $5g$, the coefficient, 5, may be regarded as a numerator, stating (enumerating) how many of the g's are present. The g portion is the name or denomination of the quantity being considered.

With arithmetic fractions, such as $\frac{3}{4}$, there are 3 of the quantities called "fourths," hence the bottom portion of the fraction gives name to (denominates) the expression and the top portion of the fraction states (enumerates) how many of the fourths are present. We have previously learned that only *like* quantities may be combined by addition or subtraction; this truth applies to fractions as well. The criterion for judging "likeness" of fractions is to determine whether or not their "names" (denominators) are the same. Now $3a$ and $4b$ cannot be combined as $7a$ or $7b$ because a and b are different. Similarly, $\frac{3}{5}$ and $\frac{4}{9}$ cannot be combined as $\frac{7}{5}$ or $\frac{7}{9}$ because "ninths" and "fifths" are different.

In combining two fractions by addition or subtraction, either "name" (denominator) or both can be modified so that both fractions have a common name. This process is called "establishing a common denominator" and it is usually prudent to employ a *least* common denominator. Hence, to add $\frac{3}{5}$ and $\frac{4}{9}$, we may choose to convert each fraction to its equivalent in the common name "45ths." Now

$$\frac{3}{5} = \frac{27}{45} \quad \text{and} \quad \frac{4}{9} = \frac{20}{45},$$

and we have 27 and 20 of the quantities called "45ths" to be added as 47 "45ths," or

$$\frac{27}{45} + \frac{20}{45} = \frac{47}{45}.$$

We emphasize that numerators of fractions may be combined by addition only when the denominators are alike.

Certain properties of fractions must be recognized when manipulating their numerators and denominators:

> **Property 1.** *If both the numerator and denominator of a fraction are multiplied or divided by the same nonzero quantity, the value of the fraction is unchanged.*

> **Property 2.** *Multiplying the numerator, or dividing the denominator, of a fraction by a quantity multiplies the fraction by that quantity.*

> **Property 3.** *Multiplying the denominator, or dividing the numerator, of a fraction by a quantity divides the fraction by that quantity.*

Property 1 is especially appropriate in reducing a fraction to its lowest terms or in establishing a new denominator. Examples follow.

EXAMPLE 37. Reduce to lowest terms the fractions (a) $\frac{6}{9}$, (b) a^2/ab, and (c) $(x^2 - 1)/(x^2 - 2x + 1)$.

Solution. (a) To reduce $\frac{6}{9}$ to lowest terms, we factor the numerator and denominator and cancel common factors. This is shown as

$$\frac{6}{9} = \frac{\cancel{3} \cdot 2}{\cancel{3} \cdot 3} = \frac{2}{3}.$$

This cancellation of common factors is an exercise of property 1, which states that the numerator and denominator can be divided by the same nonzero quantity (in this case, 3) without changing the value of the fraction.

(b) Using the procedure as shown in (a), first factor, then divide by the factor common to the numerator and denominator, thus:

$$\frac{a^2}{ab} = \frac{\cancel{a} \cdot a}{\cancel{a} \cdot b} = \frac{a}{b}.$$

(c) Using the steps of factoring, then cancelling, we have

$$\frac{x^2 - 1}{x^2 - 2x + 1} = \frac{(x-1)(x+1)}{(x-1)(x-1)} = \frac{x+1}{x-1}.$$

The preceding discussion and examples regarding fractions require the emphasis of a certain point. Only common *factors* of the numerator and denominator can be cancelled in the exercise of property 1. Example 38 serves to point out the reason for this emphasis.

EXAMPLE 38. Simplify the fraction $x/(x^2 + x)$.

Solution. The erratic student may be tempted to cancel the x *terms* of the numerator and denominator and obtain an equally erratic result. If we *factor* the numerator and denominator, then divide by the common *factor*, we have

$$\frac{x}{x^2 + x} = \frac{1 \cdot x}{(x+1) \cdot x} = \frac{1}{x+1}.$$

Property 1 also enables us to modify denominators in preparation for addition and subtraction, as was indicated in the addition of $\frac{3}{5}$ and $\frac{4}{9}$ previously discussed in this section. Consider some examples.

EXAMPLE 39. Add $(3x/5) + (x/4)$.

Solution. Addition in this form cannot be accomplished since the denominators are different. If the denominator of $3x/5$ is multiplied by 4 and the denominator of $x/4$ is multiplied by 5, the fractions will have the same denominators, namely 20. By property 1, however, if we are to retain an *unchanged* value of the fraction, both the numerator and the denominator must be multiplied by the same quantity; hence

$$\frac{3x}{5} = \frac{3x(4)}{5(4)} = \frac{12x}{20}$$

and

$$\frac{x}{4} = \frac{x(5)}{4(5)} = \frac{5x}{20}.$$

Now,

$$\frac{3x}{5} + \frac{x}{4} = \frac{12x}{20} + \frac{5x}{20} = \frac{12x + 5x}{20} = \frac{17x}{20}.$$

EXAMPLE 40. Combine terms as indicated:

$$\frac{x}{x+1} - \frac{3}{x} + \frac{2x}{x-1}.$$

Solution. Here the least common denominator is the product of the three denominators. This will call for multiplying the first, second, and third terms respectively by $x(x-1)/x(x-1)$, $(x+1)(x-1)/(x+1)(x-1)$, and $x(x+1)/x(x+1)$. This presents the result

$$\frac{x(x)(x-1) - 3(x+1)(x-1) + 2x(x)(x+1)}{x(x+1)(x-1)} = \frac{3x^3 - 2x^2 + 3}{x^3 - x}.$$

EXAMPLE 41. Add the fractions

$$\frac{x-1}{x^3 + x^2} + \frac{x-2}{x^2 + 2x + 1}.$$

Solution. To determine what new factors might be inserted into the denominators to obtain a least common denominator, we write the given expression with the denominators factored as

$$\frac{x-1}{(x)(x)(x+1)} + \frac{x-2}{(x+1)(x+1)}.$$

By inspection, we can make the denominators alike by multiplying the first fraction by $(x+1)/(x+1)$ and the second fraction by x^2/x^2, producing the new expression

$$\frac{(x-1)(x+1) + (x^2)(x-2)}{x^2(x+1)^2} = \frac{x^3 - x^2 - 1}{x^2(x+1)^2}.$$

EXAMPLE 42. Combine the expression

$$\frac{2x}{1-x} + \frac{5x}{-x-1} - \frac{3}{x^2-1}.$$

Solution. Multiplying the first and second terms by $-1/-1$ and factoring the third denominator, we have

$$\frac{-2x}{x-1} + \frac{-5x}{x+1} - \frac{3}{(x-1)(x+1)}.$$

Now, establishing a least common denominator, we have

$$\frac{-2x(x+1) - 5x(x-1) - 3}{(x-1)(x+1)} = \frac{-7x^2 + 3x - 3}{x^2 - 1} = \frac{7x^2 - 3x + 3}{1 - x^2}.$$

Inspection of Examples 39–42 readily reveals that the least common denominator is the least number into which all of the given numbers will divide evenly. This least number, called the *least common multiple* (LCM) contains all of the factors involved in the separate given numbers, with the exponent of a factor in the LCM equal to the greatest exponent of that factor in any of the given numbers. That is, the LCM of a^4b^2c, $a^3b^3c^2$, and abc^5 is $a^4b^3c^5$.

Exercises

Find the least quantity into which the given quantities in Exercises 1–5 will divide evenly; that is, find the least common multiple of the given numbers.

1. a^2b, ab^2, a^3b.   *Ans.* a^3b^2.

2. 2, 4, 8, 18.

3. $x + y$, $x^2 - y^2$, $x^2 + 2xy + y^2$.   *Ans.* $(x + y)^2(x - y)$.

4. $x^4 - x^2$, $x^3 - x$, $x^2 - 2x + 1$, x^3.

5. $a^2 - b^2$, $b - a$, $2a + 2b$, ab.   *Ans.* $-2ab(a^2 - b^2)$.

In Exercises 6–17, reduce the given expressions to lowest terms.

6. $\dfrac{12xy}{16x^2y^3}$.

7. $\dfrac{2x + 2y}{4x^2 - 4y^2}$.   *Ans.* $\dfrac{1}{2(x - y)}$.

8. $\dfrac{2x + 2y}{4x^2 - 16y^2}$.

9. $\dfrac{a^2 - 4ab + 4b^2}{a^2 - 4b^2}$.   *Ans.* $\dfrac{a - 2b}{a + 2b}$.

10. $\dfrac{m^2 - 3m - 4}{m^2 - 2m - 8}$.

11. $\dfrac{3 + 2r - r^2}{r^2 + r - 12}$.   *Ans.* $-\dfrac{r + 1}{r + 4}$.

12. $\dfrac{r^3 - s^3}{r^2 - s^2}$.

13. $\dfrac{m^3 + m^2n - 6mn^2}{m^2n - 2n^2m}$.   *Ans.* $\dfrac{m + 3n}{n}$.

14. $\dfrac{(m^2 + mn + n^2)(x + y)}{m^3 - n^3}$.

15. $\dfrac{(a - 2b)^3}{a^2b - 4ab^2 + 4b^3}$.   *Ans.* $\dfrac{a - 2b}{b}$.

16. $\dfrac{a - a^2}{a - 1}$.

17. $\dfrac{(m+n)^2 - 5(m+n) + 6}{(m+n)^2 + 3(m+n) - 10}.$ *Ans.* $\dfrac{m+n-3}{m+n+5}.$

In Exercises 18–40, simplify the given expressions to single fractions.

18. $\dfrac{a}{4} - \dfrac{3a}{8} + \dfrac{5a}{2}.$

19. $\dfrac{3}{2a} - \dfrac{4}{5a}.$ *Ans.* $\dfrac{7}{10a}.$

20. $\dfrac{x}{2b} - \dfrac{3x}{4b}.$

21. $\dfrac{\pi r^2}{4} - \dfrac{4\pi r^3}{3}.$ *Ans.* $\dfrac{\pi r^2(3 - 16r)}{12}.$

22. $\dfrac{2x^2 + 1}{3x^2} + \dfrac{x - 4}{6x} - \dfrac{5}{12}.$

23. $\dfrac{x - 4y}{3} - \dfrac{2x + 3y}{5}.$ *Ans.* $\dfrac{-x - 29y}{15}.$

24. $\dfrac{1}{r_1 + r_2} - \dfrac{1}{r_1 - r_2}.$

25. $3 - \dfrac{4}{a^2}.$ *Ans.* $\dfrac{3a^2 - 4}{a^2}.$

26. $x + y - \dfrac{x}{4y}.$

27. $\dfrac{x + y}{x - y} - \dfrac{x - y}{x + y}.$ *Ans.* $\dfrac{4xy}{x^2 - y^2}.$

28. $\dfrac{5}{a^2 - b^2} - \dfrac{4}{a - b}.$

29. $\dfrac{a + b}{x - y} - \dfrac{a - b}{x + y}.$ *Ans.* $\dfrac{2(bx + ay)}{x^2 - y^2}.$

30. $\dfrac{x + 4y}{x^2 - 16y^2} - \dfrac{5}{4y - x}.$

31. $r - 2 + \dfrac{1}{r}.$ *Ans.* $\dfrac{(r - 1)^2}{r}.$

32. $2m^2 + 6m + 6 + \dfrac{2}{m - 1}.$

33. $\dfrac{x + 1}{x^2 - 2x + 1} + \dfrac{x - 2}{x^2 - x} - \dfrac{2 - x}{x^2 - 5x + 6}.$ *Ans.* $\dfrac{3x^3 - 10x^2 + 9x - 6}{x(x - 1)^2(x - 3)}.$

34. $\dfrac{m + p}{(m - n)(m - p)} - \dfrac{p}{(n - m)(m - p)} + \dfrac{m}{(p - m)(m - n)}.$

35. $\dfrac{1}{a + b} - \dfrac{2a}{(a + b)^2} - \dfrac{a - b}{(a + b)^2}.$ *Ans.* $\dfrac{2(b - a)}{(a + b)^2}.$

36. $\dfrac{x+4}{x+3} + \dfrac{x-3}{x-4} - \dfrac{4}{3}.$

37. $\dfrac{c(t_1 - t_2)}{t_3 - t_2} - 1.$ *Ans.* $\dfrac{ct_1 - ct_2 - t_3 + t_2}{t_3 - t_2}.$

38. $\dfrac{x-b}{b} - \dfrac{1+x-a}{a}.$

39. $\dfrac{m+n}{m-n} - \dfrac{n-m}{m+n} + \dfrac{3n}{n-m}.$ *Ans.* $\dfrac{2m^2 - 3mn - n^2}{m^2 - n^2}.$

40. $\dfrac{m+3n}{(2m-n)(m-2n)} + \dfrac{n+2m}{(n-2m)(m+2n)} + \dfrac{n-3m}{(2n-m)(2m-n)}.$

2-10   Multiplication and Division of Fractions

In arithmetic the product of two or more fractions is computed by placing the product of the numerators over the product of the denominators and cancelling factors common to the numerator and denominator for purposes of simplification. In algebra the process is the same.

EXAMPLE 43. Simplify the product

$$\frac{2x + 2y}{x - 2y} \cdot \frac{x^2 - 4xy + 4y^2}{2x^2 - 2y^2}.$$

Solution. Factoring the numerators and placing their implied product over the factored product of the denominators, we have

$$\frac{2(x + y)(x - 2y)(x - 2y)}{(x - 2y)(2)(x + y)(x - y)} = \frac{x - 2y}{x - y}.$$

Division of two fractions is accomplished by inverting the divisor and proceeding as in multiplication.

EXAMPLE 44. Simplify the given expression:

$$\frac{x + 2y}{3ab} \div \frac{x^2 - 4y^2}{6a^2b}.$$

Solution. Inverting the divisor and proceeding as in multiplication, we have

$$\frac{x + 2y}{3ab} \cdot \frac{6a^2b}{x^2 - 4y^2} = \frac{(x + 2y)(3)(2)(a)(a)(b)}{3(a)(b)(x - 2y)(x + 2y)} = \frac{2a}{x - 2y}.$$

EXAMPLE 45. Simplify the given expression:

$$\left(3 + \frac{2x}{5}\right) \div \left(5 + \frac{2x}{3}\right).$$

Solution. First, the divisor and dividend are both converted to single fractions, then the division process is carried through as in Example 44. Proceeding, we have

$$\frac{15+2x}{5} \div \frac{15+2x}{3} = \frac{15+2x}{5} \cdot \frac{3}{15+2x} = \frac{3}{5}.$$

Exercises

Perform the indicated operations, reducing the solutions to the simplest form.

1. $\dfrac{4a}{x^3} \cdot \dfrac{12bx^2}{16a^2}.$ *Ans.* $\dfrac{3b}{ax}.$

2. $\dfrac{x^3}{4ay^2} \cdot \dfrac{20a^2y}{5xy^2}.$

3. $\dfrac{m-n}{mn} \cdot \dfrac{m^2n}{m-n}.$ *Ans. m.*

4. $\dfrac{m^2-n^2}{m} \cdot \dfrac{m^2}{m^2-mn}.$

5. $\dfrac{6R-18}{5} \cdot \dfrac{10R}{2R-6}.$ *Ans. 6R.*

6. $\dfrac{2x+y}{4x^2-y^2} \cdot (8x^3-y^3).$

7. $\dfrac{a^2-b^2}{a+b} \cdot \dfrac{a^2+ab+b^2}{a^3-b^3}.$ *Ans.* 1.

8. $\dfrac{a^2-2a-3}{a^2-9} \cdot \dfrac{a^2+6a+9}{a^2-a}.$

9. $\dfrac{a^3-ax^2}{a^2+ax} \cdot \dfrac{ax^2-x^3}{x^2}.$ *Ans.* $(a-x)^2.$

10. $\dfrac{R^2+3R-10}{R^2-6R-7} \cdot \dfrac{R-7}{R+5}.$

11. $\dfrac{x^2-5x-6}{x^2-6x} \cdot \dfrac{x^2+3x-10}{x^2-x-2}.$ *Ans.* $\dfrac{x+5}{x}.$

12. $\dfrac{2x^2-x-1}{3x^2+7x+2} \cdot \dfrac{x^2+7x+10}{2x^2+5x+2} \cdot \dfrac{3x^2+x}{x^2+4x-5}.$

13. $\dfrac{x^2+7x+12}{x^2+2x-15} \cdot \dfrac{x+5}{x+4}.$ *Ans.* $\dfrac{x+3}{x-3}.$

14. $\dfrac{8-2x-x^2}{x^2+5x+4} \cdot \dfrac{2x^3+2x^2}{2x-x^2}.$

15. $\dfrac{3+2x-x^2}{x^2+x-2} \cdot \dfrac{1-x^2}{x^2-3x}.$ *Ans.* $\dfrac{x^2+2x+1}{x^2+2x}.$

16. $\left(1 + \dfrac{a}{b}\right) \cdot \left(\dfrac{a}{b + a}\right).$

17. $\dfrac{h^2 - k^2}{h^2 k} \cdot \dfrac{hk^2}{h + k}.$ *Ans.* $\dfrac{k(h - k)}{h}.$

18. $\dfrac{ax + bx^2}{(c + x)^2} \cdot \dfrac{c + x}{x^3} \cdot \dfrac{cx + x^2}{a + bx}.$

19. $\left(2 - \dfrac{m}{n}\right)\left(\dfrac{m - 1}{m^2 - 4mn + 4n^2}\right)\left(\dfrac{m}{n} - 2\right).$ *Ans.* $\dfrac{1 - m}{n^2}.$

20. $\dfrac{3abc}{5d} \div \dfrac{2d}{15a^2b^2}.$

21. $\dfrac{8xy^2}{6z} \div \dfrac{2x^3y^3}{3x^2z^2}.$ *Ans.* $\dfrac{2z}{y}.$

22. $\dfrac{x^2 - y^2}{2x + 3y} \div \dfrac{x - y}{4x + 6y}.$

23. $\left(\dfrac{4Rt^2}{9mp} \cdot \dfrac{18m^2}{7R^2}\right) \div \left(\dfrac{Rt^2}{14m^2p^2}\right).$ *Ans.* $\dfrac{16m^3p^2}{R^2}.$

24. $\left(\dfrac{a^2}{b^2} - \dfrac{2a}{b} - 3\right) \div \left(\dfrac{a^2}{b} - 9b\right).$

25. $\dfrac{15 - 2h - h^2}{6h^2 - h - 1} \div \dfrac{3h^2 + 16h + 5}{4h^2 - 1}.$ *Ans.* $\dfrac{3 + 5h - 2h^2}{9h^2 + 6h + 1}.$

26. $\dfrac{k^4 - kh^3}{4h^2 - k^2} \div \dfrac{k^4 - k^2h^2}{k + 2h}.$

27. $\dfrac{2a^2 - 6a}{10a^2 - a - 2} \div \left(\dfrac{-a^2 + 6a - 9}{5a^2 + 2a} \cdot \dfrac{2a^3 + a^2}{5a^4 - 2a^3}\right).$

Ans. $\dfrac{2a^3(5a - 2)}{-4a^3 + 12a^2 + a - 3}.$

28. $\left(\dfrac{m}{n} - \dfrac{n}{m}\right) \div \left(\dfrac{m^2}{n} - \dfrac{n^2}{m}\right).$

29. $\dfrac{a^3b^3}{a^3 + b^3} \cdot \dfrac{a^2 - b^2}{(a - b)^2} \cdot \left(\dfrac{1}{a^2} - \dfrac{1}{ab} + \dfrac{1}{b^2}\right).$ *Ans.* $\dfrac{ab}{a - b}.$

30. $\left[(c^4 - 16d^4) \div \dfrac{c^2 - d^2}{cd}\right] \div c^2(c^2 + d^2).$

2-11   Complex Fractions

A *complex fraction* is defined here as a fraction in which either the numerator or denominator (or both) is (are) fractional in form. We will discuss here two methods of simplifying complex fractions.

The first method involves reducing the numerator and/or denominator into proper fractions and then simplifying by standard division of fractional quantities as shown in the preceding section.

EXAMPLE 46. Simplify the complex fraction

$$\frac{1/a}{1/a - 1/b}. \tag{25}$$

Solution. Expression (25) is a complex fraction according to our definition and it can be written as the division

$$\frac{1}{a} \div \left(\frac{1}{a} - \frac{1}{b} \right). \tag{26}$$

The divisor in (26) can now be reduced to a single fraction, giving us

$$\frac{1}{a} - \frac{1}{b} = \frac{b-a}{ab}$$

and (26) becomes

$$\frac{1}{a} \div \frac{b-a}{ab}. \tag{27}$$

Inverting the divisor in (27) and proceeding as in multiplication, we have

$$\frac{1}{a} \div \frac{b-a}{ab} = \frac{1}{a} \cdot \frac{ab}{b-a} = \frac{b}{b-a}.$$

The second method of simplification of a complex fraction is often more direct than the method shown in Example 46. We may regard (25) as a fraction whose primary numerator is $1/a$ and whose primary denominator is $1/a - 1/b$. Now the primary numerator has a secondary denominator a, and the primary denominator has two secondary denominators a and b. The least common multiple of these secondary denominators is ab. If we multiply both the primary numerator and primary denominator by the least common multiple of the secondary denominators, we have

$$\frac{(1/a) \cdot ab}{(1/a - 1/b) \cdot ab} = \frac{b}{b-a},$$

which agrees with the first solution. In this case, the second method is much more direct than the first method shown.

EXAMPLE 47. Simplify the expression

$$a - \frac{b}{a - \dfrac{a}{b+a}}. \tag{28}$$

Solution. Using methods applied to Example 46, we may proceed in repeated operations. Simplify the lowest-order mixed number of (28), giving

$$a - \frac{a}{b+a} = \frac{ab + a^2 - a}{b+a}.$$

Now, (28) may be written as

$$a - \frac{b}{\dfrac{ab + a^2 - a}{a+b}} = a - \frac{b(a+b)}{ab + a^2 - a} = \frac{a^2 b + a^3 - a^2 - ab - b^2}{ab + a^2 - a}.$$

Exercises

Simplify the given complex fractions.

1. $\dfrac{\dfrac{a}{b}}{a}.$ *Ans.* $\dfrac{1}{b}.$ **2.** $\dfrac{a}{\dfrac{b}{a}}.$

3. $\dfrac{a}{\dfrac{1}{b}}.$ *Ans. ab.*   **4.** $\dfrac{\dfrac{a}{b}}{\dfrac{1}{b}}.$

5. $\dfrac{-\dfrac{1}{a}}{\dfrac{1}{ab}}.$ *Ans.* $-b.$ **6.** $\dfrac{\dfrac{1}{x}}{\dfrac{1}{x-y}}.$

7. $\dfrac{\dfrac{1}{x} - \dfrac{1}{y}}{\dfrac{1}{xy}}.$ *Ans.* $y - x.$ **8.** $\dfrac{\dfrac{1}{x} - \dfrac{1}{y}}{\dfrac{1}{x^2} - \dfrac{1}{y^2}}.$

9. $\dfrac{\dfrac{1}{x} - \dfrac{1}{y}}{\dfrac{1}{x^2 y^2}}.$ *Ans.* $xy(y - x).$ **10.** $\dfrac{\dfrac{m}{m-n}}{\dfrac{m+n}{n}}.$

11. $\dfrac{\dfrac{m}{m+n}}{\dfrac{n}{m-n}}.$ *Ans.* $\dfrac{m^2 - mn}{n^2 + mn}.$ **12.** $\dfrac{\dfrac{a^2}{b^2} - 2\dfrac{a}{b} - 3}{\dfrac{a - 3b}{ab}}.$

13. $\dfrac{\dfrac{x^2}{y^2} - 3\dfrac{x}{y} - 4}{\dfrac{x+y}{y}}.$ *Ans.* $\dfrac{x - 4y}{y}.$ **14.** $\dfrac{3(x^2 + 2x - 15)}{\dfrac{x-3}{2}}.$

15. $\dfrac{r_1}{\dfrac{r_1}{r_2 + 1}}.$ *Ans.* $r_2 + 1.$ **16.** $1 - \dfrac{1}{1 - \dfrac{1}{1 - \frac{1}{4}}}.$

17. $\dfrac{1 + \dfrac{3}{x} - \dfrac{1}{x^2} - \dfrac{3}{x^3}}{x^2 + 2x - 3}$. *Ans.* $\dfrac{x+1}{x^3}$.

18. $\dfrac{1 - \frac{3}{2}}{-1 - \dfrac{1}{2 - \frac{5}{2}}}$.

19. $2 - \dfrac{2}{2 - \dfrac{2}{2 - \frac{1}{2}}}$ *Ans.* -1.

20. $\dfrac{1 + \dfrac{3}{x} + \dfrac{3}{x^2} + \dfrac{1}{x^3}}{1 + \dfrac{2}{x} + \dfrac{1}{x^2}}$.

An important part of the solution of a physical problem is the selection of compatible dimensional units for the various physical quantities represented in the equation to be solved.

The technician and engineer should be well acquainted with dimensional units, their conversion, and the procedure of inspecting equations for compatibility of units.

DIMENSIONAL
ANALYSIS 3

3-1　Introduction

The application of mathematics to a physical problem requires more than the correct manipulation of numbers and equations. Physical problems involve quantities expressed in terms of numbers and units, such as 10 ft., 6 kw-hr, and 10^{-5} dyne sec./cm². A correct numerical procedure will be in vain if an incorrect combination of units is used in an equation relating physical quantities.

Although the basic dimensions consist only of length, mass, and time, there are several different units that may be used for each of these dimensions. It is usually necessary that the two sides of an equation have a dimensional equality, such as 5 sec + 2 sec. = 7 sec. However, it is obviously incorrect to state that 5 sec. + 2 min. = 7 sec., even though both sides have the dimension of time. An equality, or balance, of units is necessary, which often requires that some of the known quantities in a physical relation be converted to other units.

The purpose of this chapter is to present a study of units and procedures that emphasize and assist the following:

1. Converting units.
2. Checking equations for balance of units.
3. Creating unit equations to help solve problems.

3-2　Converting Simple Quantities

The ability to convert a quantity of given units to an equivalent value in terms of other related units is very often required, especially in technical and scientific work. Although various books contain tables of conversion factors for some of the more common units, it would require an enormous set of tables to include all possible conversions. However, numerous conversions may be made quite conveniently with the aid of only a relatively few basic unit relations.

Simple quantities expressed in terms of one unit are easily converted to an equivalent value in terms of another unit if the relation between the two units is known. A length of 3 ft. is readily converted to the equivalent value of 36 in. if it is known that there are 12 inches per foot. However, many quantities are expressed in terms of complex combinations of units, and errors are more likely to occur when converting the units of such a quantity.

In order to avoid error, a methodical procedure for converting units is not only desirable but almost a necessity because there are many units and several systems of units in common technical use; the basic units of these systems are presented later in this chapter. In addition, within a given system of units there are various combinations of units that may be used for the same concept, or type of quantity. Energy units commonly used in the English system, for example, include the foot-pound, British thermal unit, and horsepower-minute.

The purpose of the examples that follow is to build a methodical procedure for converting units. Although they are quite elementary, they serve as steppingstones to more complex problems in which the same simple procedure may be used. Familiarity with the methodical procedure is emphasized.

In each of the examples below the problem is to convert a quantity of given units to its equivalent value in terms of some other related units. The procedure involves multiplying the original number and units by various ratios of related units until the desired value is obtained. The units are treated as algebraic quantities and are cancelled out until the desired units are obtained.

EXAMPLE 1. Convert a length of 3 ft. to its equivalent in inches.

Solution:

$$(3 \text{ ft.})\left(12\frac{\text{in.}}{\text{ft.}}\right) = 36 \text{ in.}$$

If the units in the equation are treated as algebraic quantities, the foot units cancel each other.

$$(\cancel{\text{ft.}})\left(\frac{\text{in.}}{\cancel{\text{ft.}}}\right) = \text{in.}$$

A balanced equation of units is obtained, and the original unit has been cancelled out.

In each example a unit in the second bracket serves to cancel a unit in the first bracket. Some conversions require a sequence of several brackets, but the units of each are selected so that at least one preceding unit is cancelled. It is suggested that a line be drawn through each unit that may be cancelled. The ratio of units used in a bracket will depend upon what ratios are conveniently remembered or available. We may often use different sequences and ratios to achieve the same conversion.

EXAMPLE 2. Convert a force of 0.25 ton to its equivalent in ounces.

Solution:

$$(0.25 \text{ ton})\left(2000 \frac{\text{lb.}}{\text{ton}}\right)\left(16\frac{\text{oz.}}{\text{lb.}}\right) = 8000 \text{ oz.,}$$

$$(\cancel{\text{tons}})\left(\frac{\cancel{\text{lb.}}}{\cancel{\text{ton}}}\right)\left(\frac{\text{oz.}}{\cancel{\text{lb.}}}\right) = \text{oz.}$$

The reciprocal of a known ratio of units may be used. If there are 60 sec./min., then it may be stated that there is $\frac{1}{60}$ minute per second, or 1 min./60 sec.

EXAMPLE 3. Convert a speed of 15 miles/hr. to its equivalent in ft/sec.

Solution.

$$\left(15\,\frac{\text{miles}}{\text{hr.}}\right)\left(5280\,\frac{\text{ft.}}{\text{mile}}\right)\left(\frac{1}{3600}\,\frac{\text{hr.}}{\text{sec.}}\right) = 22\,\frac{\text{ft.}}{\text{sec.}},$$

$$\left(\frac{\cancel{\text{miles}}}{\cancel{\text{hr.}}}\right)\left(\frac{\text{ft.}}{\cancel{\text{mile}}}\right)\left(\frac{\cancel{\text{hr.}}}{\text{sec.}}\right) = \frac{\text{ft.}}{\text{sec.}}$$

EXAMPLE 4. An engine consumes fuel at the rate of 0.5 gal./min. Convert this rate to tons/day. The fuel weighs 6.5 lb./gal. and the engine runs 8 hr./day.

Solution.

$$\left(\frac{\cancel{\text{gal.}}}{\cancel{\text{min.}}}\right)\left(\frac{\cancel{\text{lb.}}}{\cancel{\text{gal.}}}\right)\left(\frac{\text{tons}}{\cancel{\text{lb.}}}\right)\left(\frac{\cancel{\text{min.}}}{\cancel{\text{hr.}}}\right)\left(\frac{\cancel{\text{hr.}}}{\text{day}}\right) = \frac{\text{tons}}{\text{day}},$$

$$(0.5)(6.5)\left(\frac{1}{2000}\right)(60)(8) = 0.78.$$

Exercises

For each of the conversions indicated, write a sequence of numbers and units as in the preceding examples.

1. A machine processes a material at the rate of 5 oz./sec. Convert to tons/hr.
Ans. 0.56 ton/hr

2. A section of pipe weighs 12 oz. per inch of length. Convert to tons/mile.

3. An electric current of 3.2 amperes may be expressed as 3.2 coulombs/sec. Convert to electrons/sec. There is $1.6(10)^{-19}$ coulomb of electric charge per electron.
Ans. $2(10)^{19}$ electrons/sec.

4. Find the equivalent of 10,000 Btu/hr. in horsepower. Use the relations 778 ft-lb./Btu and 33,000 ft-lb./min. $= 1$ hp.

5. A pumping station consumes 200 kilowatt-hours of energy each day, working 8 hr./day. Find the rate of energy consumption (power) in ft-lb./min. There are 778 ft-lb./Btu and 3413 Btu/kw-hr. *Ans.* $1.1(10)^6$ ft-lb./min.

6. Avogadro's number, $6.02(10)^{23}$, gives the number of atoms per gram-atomic weight of any element. Convert this information to atoms/cm.^{3} for aluminum, which has a density of 2.7 gm./cm.^{3} and a value of 27 gm./gm.-atomic wt.

7. An airplane travelling at 600 miles/hr. consumes fuel at the rate of 30 gal./min. Using this information, find the consumption of fuel in pounds per mile travelled. Assume the fuel weighs 7 lb. per gal. *Ans.* 21 lb./mile.

8. There is one curie of radioactivity in an object when its atoms are disintegrating at the rate of $3.7(10)^{10}$ disintegrations per second. The probability that an atom of I^{131} (iodine isotope) will disintegrate at any time is about $9.9(10)^{-7}$ disintegrations/sec. atom. How many atoms of I^{131} are present in a one-curie specimen?

9. A cable drum is rotating at 90 rev./min. The drum surface turns through a distance of 4 ft./rev. How fast is the cable being wound onto the drum, in in./sec.?

Ans. 72 in./sec.

10. A furnace consumes 500 lb. coal/hr. Assume there is 0.9 lb. carbon/lb. coal, and the carbon requires 3 lb. oxygen/lb. carbon. There is about 0.2 lb. oxygen/lb. air, and 0.076 lb. air/ft.^{3} of air. Arrange this information to find the combustion air required in ft.^{3}/min.

3-3 Systems of Units

There are three systems of units commonly used in technical work: the English, MKS, and CGS systems. The English units are used by some English-speaking nations, and include the familiar foot and pound units. Most widely used around the world are the metric units which make up the MKS and CGS systems. MKS is the abreviation for meter-kilogram-second; CGS represents centimeter-gram-second. Metric units are used universally in scientific work.

Table 3-1 gives the units for some of the various physical concepts in the English, MKS, and CGS systems. The English system is often called the *foot-pound-second* system, specifying a unit of force (the pound) instead of a mass unit. All three systems use the second for the basic unit of time. We shall adopt the abbreviations gm. for gram, kg. for kilogram, M. for meter, cm. for centimeter, and mm. for millimeter.

It may seem strange that two different systems of units, MKS and CGS, have been developed from metric units. The reason is that various definitions and relations of physical concepts, formed many years ago, were in some instances expressed in terms of grams and centimeters, while in other cases were more convenient in terms of kilograms and meters. This brought about different derived units for each of such quantities as force (dyne and newton), energy (erg and joule), electric charge (statcoulomb and coulomb), and others not considered here.

When numerical values are to be inserted for the various quantities of a scientific law or relation, it is usually necessary to avoid mixing units of the different systems. Certain laws may contain special constants, depend-

Table 3-1

A BRIEF COMPARISON OF UNIT SYSTEMS

	English	MKS	CGS
Length:	foot	meter	centimeter
Mass:	slug	kilogram	gram
Force:	pound	newton	dyne
Energy:	ft-lb.	newton-M.	dyne-cm.
		= joule	= erg
		= wattsecond	
		= volt-coulomb	
Power:	$\dfrac{\text{ft-lb.}}{\text{sec.}}$	watt	$\dfrac{\text{erg}}{\text{sec.}}$
Density:	$\dfrac{\text{slug}}{\text{ft.}^3}$	$\dfrac{\text{kg.}}{\text{M.}^3}$	$\dfrac{\text{gm.}}{\text{cm.}^3}$
Charge:		coulomb	statcoulomb*
Electric current:		ampere	statampere*

*CGS electrostatic units.

ing on whether MKS or CGS units are to be employed. Coulomb's law for electrostatic force is typical, requiring a special factor if MKS units are used. Some laws are expressed in such a way that mixed units are allowed, an example being the gas law $P_1V_1/T_1 = P_2V_2/T_2$ In this case pressure P might be in lb./in.^{2} while volume V might be in cubic meters or any other unit of volume. The units on the left side, however, must be the same as those on the right.

A more complete study of units would reveal variations of both the MKS and CGS systems. Since the variations concern electric and magnetic concepts, their study is more appropriate in physics and electricity.

Exercises

1. The English units for moment of inertia are slug-ft^2. What are the corresponding MKS and CGS units?

2. Coulomb's force law contains a special constant K if MKS units are to be used. If Q, R, and F have units of charge, length, and force, respectively, what are the units of K?

$$F = \frac{KQ_1Q_2}{R^2}.$$

3. Newton's gravitational constant may have the units newton-M.^{2}/kg.^{2} Give the units for the CGS and English systems.

4. A certain quantity is expressed in erg/sec. cm.^{2} What units would be used in the English and MKS systems?

5. In the equation for horsepower, F, S, and T have units of force, length, and time, respectively. The constant K must have units which cause the right side of the equation to be in net units of horsepower. What are the units of K in the English system?

$$\text{hp.} = \frac{FS}{TK}.$$

6. If viscosity may be measured in terms of lb. sec./ft.^{2}, what are the corresponding MKS and CGS units?

3-4   Relations for Converting Units

Table 3-2 contains unit relations that may be useful in the remaining exercises of this chapter. Although many more might be listed, a few relations committed to memory can greatly reduce dependence upon tables.

Table 3-2

SOME USEFUL UNIT RELATIONS

Length	*Mass*
1 M. = 100 cm. = 1000 mm.	1 kg. = 1000 gm.
1 mile = 5280 ft.	1 slug = 14.6 kg.
1 in. = 2.54 cm	
	Force
Energy	1 newton = 10^5 dynes
1 joule = 10^7 ergs	1 lb. = $4.45(10^5)$ dynes
1 ft-lb. = 1.36 joules	1 ton = 2000 lb.
1 Btu = 778 ft-lb.	
1 calorie = 4.18 joules	*Power*
1 kilowatt-hour = 3413 Btu	1 hp. = 550 ft-lb./sec.
1 Btu = 252 calories	1 hp. = 0.75 kilowatt
	1 kilowatt = 3413 Btu/hr.

The prefixes in the following list are used quite frequently with a wide variety of units to modify the quantitative meaning. Each prefix in the list is followed by the numerical information it carries.

micro-　$\dfrac{1}{1,000,000}$

milli-　$\dfrac{1}{1000}$

centi-　$\dfrac{1}{100}$

kilo-　1000

mega-　1,000,000

An electric current of 0.006 amperes may be stated as 6 milliamperes, while 50,000 volts may be expressed as 50 kilovolts.

EXAMPLE 5. Convert $2(10)^7$ ft-lb. of energy to kilowatt-hours.

Solution A.

$$(\text{ft-lb.})\left(\frac{\text{sec. hp.}}{\text{ft-lb.}}\right)\left(\frac{\text{kw.}}{\text{hp.}}\right)\left(\frac{\text{hr.}}{\text{sec.}}\right) = \text{kw-hr.,}$$

$$(2(10)^7)\left(\frac{1}{550}\right)(0.75)\left(\frac{1}{3600}\right) = 7.5.$$

Solution B.

$$(\text{ft-lb.})\left(\frac{\text{Btu}}{\text{ft-lb.}}\right)\left(\frac{\text{kw-hr.}}{\text{Btu}}\right) = \text{kw-hr.,}$$

$$(2(10)^7)\left(\frac{1}{778}\right)\left(\frac{1}{3413}\right) = 7.5.$$

A quantity known as the gm-mole is often encountered in chemistry and physics. A gm-mole of a substance is that mass which, if measured in grams, is equal to the molecular weight of the substance. Oxygen, for example, has a molecular weight of 32 and requires 32 grams to constitute a gm-mole. A kg-mole of oxygen is 32 kg. Consequently, a kg-mole equals 1000 gm-moles for any given substance.

The importance of the gm-mole is due to the fact that for all substances a gm-mole always contains the same number of molecules, known as Avogadro's number $(6.02(10)^{23})$. The number of atoms in a gm-atomic weight is the same as the number of molecules in a gm-mole (gm-molecular weight), being Avogadro's number in both cases. A gm-atomic weight of oxygen is 16 grams, corresponding to the atomic weight of oxygen.

Two temperature scales, centigrade (Celsius) and Kelvin, are associated with metric units. The zero of the centigrade scale is at the freezing point of water, while the Kelvin scale starts at absolute zero, the lowest temperature theoretically possible. However, a degree of change on the centigrade scale equals a degree of change on the Kelvin scale.

The Fahrenheit and Rankine temperature scales are associated with English units. The Fahrenheit scale reads 32° at the freezing point of water, while the Rankine scale starts at absolute zero. A degree of temperature change on the Fahrenheit scale equals a degree of change on the Rankine scale.

The following relations may be used for converting temperatures. The symbol T_c, for example, represents a temperature on the centigrade scale.

$$T_c = \tfrac{5}{9}(T_f - 32), \qquad T_k = T_c + 273,$$
$$T_k = \tfrac{5}{9} T_r, \qquad T_r = T_f + 460.$$

It is necessary to distinguish the concept of temperature from that of temperature change. For indicating temperature, the degree mark is placed before the scale symbol, such as 25°C. A temperature change is often indicated by placing the degree mark after the scale symbol, appearing, for example, as 25 C°. The units of temperature change are related as follows:

$$1\ C° = 1\ K°, \qquad 1\ F° = 1\ R°, \qquad 5\ C° = 9\ F°.$$

EXAMPLE 6. The temperature of an object is increased from 28°C to 78°C. Calculate the temperature change in K°, F°, and R°.

Solution.

$$78°C - 28°C = 50\ C° = 50\ K°,$$

$$(50\ C°)\left(\frac{9F°}{5C°}\right) = 90F° = 90R°.$$

It may be helpful to remember that the C° represents a greater change of temperature than does the F°.

EXAMPLE 7. The specific heat of aluminum is about 0.21 cal./gm. C°, which means that 0.21 calories of heat are required to raise the temperature of a gram of aluminum 1 C°. What is the equivalent value expressed as joules/kg. K°?

Solution.

$$\left(\frac{cal.}{gm.\ C°}\right)\left(\frac{joules}{cal.}\right)\left(\frac{gm.}{kg.}\right)\left(\frac{C°}{K°}\right) = \frac{joules}{kg.K°},$$

$$(0.21)(4.18)(1000)(1) = 878.$$

EXAMPLE 8. Convert the value obtained in Example 7 to the equivalent in Btu/slug R°.

Solution.

$$\left(\frac{joules}{kg.K°}\right)\left(\frac{ft\text{-}lb.}{joule}\right)\left(\frac{Btu}{ft\text{-}lb.}\right)\left(\frac{kg.}{slug}\right)\left(\frac{K°}{R°}\right) = \frac{Btu}{slug\ R°},$$

$$(878)\left(\frac{1}{1.36}\right)\left(\frac{1}{778}\right)(14.6)\left(\frac{5}{9}\right) = 6.7.$$

Exercises

For each of the conversions indicated, write a sequence of numbers and units as in the preceding examples. Table 3-2 should be a sufficient reference.

1. How many Btu/hr. are equivalent to 5 megawatts of power?

2. The ideal gas constant has the value $8.32(10)^7$ ergs/gm-mole K°. Convert to joules/kg-mole K°. *Ans.* $8.32(10)^3$ joules/kg-mole K°.

3. The temperature coefficient of electrical resistance is about 0.004 ohms/ohm C° for pure metals. This may be thought of as a change in resistance of 0.4%/C°. Convert to %/F° and %/K°. *Ans.* 0.22%/F°, 0.4%/K°.

4. Find the equivalent of 1 horsepower in Btu/min.

5. It is estimated to require $4(10)^7$ ft-lb. of energy, supplied to a motor, in order to pump a certain quantity of water to a higher elevation. Convert this information to cost in cents. The electric company charges 3 cents/kw-hr. *Ans.* 45¢

6. A battery discharge of 5 ampere-hours is to be expressed in terms of statampere-seconds. One ampere equals $3(10)^9$ statamperes.

7. Avogadro's number, $6.02(10)^{23}$, is the number of molecules/gm-mole of a substance. Convert Avogadro's number to find the number of molecules/cm.³ for a gas at standard temperature and pressure, a condition under which it is known that gases occupy a volume of 22.4 liters per gm-mole of gas. There are 1000 cm.³ per liter. *Ans.* $2.68(10)^{19}$ molecules/cm.³

8. Momentum is the product of mass times velocity. Convert a momentum of 50 kg-M./sec. to its equivalent in slug-ft./min.

9. A magnetic force is distributed along a conductor so as to exert a force of 80 newtons per meter of length. Convert to dynes/cm. and lb./in. *Ans.* $8(10)^4$ dynes/cm., 0.46 lb./in.

10. The thermal conductivity of steel is about 320 Btu in./ft.² hr. F°. What is the equivalent value in cal.cm./cm.²sec. C°.? (It may simplify this problem at the present time to know that there are about 930 cm.² per ft.².)

11. Each foot of length along a new road requires 20 ft.³ of concrete, which a machine pours at the rate of 24 tons/hr. Find the length of road poured in an 8-hr. day. Assume the concrete weighs 150 lb./ft.³. *Ans.* 128 ft./day.

12. A certain refrigeration machine requires 220 ft-lb. of compressor work per Btu of heat removal. Convert this information to kilowatts of power required per ton of refrigeration. It is defined that there is heat removal at the rate of 200 Btu/min. per ton of refrigeration.

3-5   Units and Exponents

Many quantities are expressed in terms of several units, some of which may be squared, cubed, or raised to higher powers. The procedure of the previous examples may be used to convert the units of such a quantity. As indicated previously, the units of products or quotients of physical quantities are obtained by treating the units of the original quantities algebraically.

For example, the expression involving pressure, volume, and temperature from the ideal gas law may have units obtained as follows:

$$\frac{PV}{T} \qquad \frac{\left(\frac{lb.}{ft.^2}\right)(ft.^3)}{^\circ R} = \frac{lb.\ ft.}{^\circ R}$$

When a ratio of units is raised to some power, the units are also raised to the power.

$$\left(12\,\frac{in.}{ft.}\right)^2 = (12)^2\left(\frac{in.}{ft.}\right)^2 = 144\,\frac{in.^2}{ft.^2}.$$

The preceding example indicates a useful procedure. To illustrate, the number of cubic centimeters per cubic inch is obtained by cubing the number of centimeters per inch.

$$\left(2.54\,\frac{cm.}{in.}\right)^3 = (2.54)^3\left(\frac{cm.}{in.}\right)^3 = 16.4\,\frac{cm.^3}{in.^3}.$$

This is the same as the product of the three edges of a one-inch cube, with each edge taken in centimeters.

EXAMPLE 9. Convert a specific weight of 0.50 lb./in.^{3} to its equivalent in tons/ft.^{3}

Solution.

$$\left(\frac{lb.}{in.^3}\right)\left(\frac{in.^3}{ft.^3}\right)\left(\frac{tons}{lb.}\right) = \frac{tons}{ft.^3},$$

$$(0.50)(12)^3\left(\frac{1}{2000}\right) = 0.43.$$

EXAMPLE 10. If a substance contains $(10)^{18}$ atoms/in.^{3}, what is the number of atoms/cm.^{3}?

Solution.

$$\left(\frac{atoms}{in.^3}\right)\left(\frac{in.^3}{cm.^3}\right) = \frac{atoms}{cm.^3}$$

$$((10)^{18})\left(\frac{1}{2.54}\right)^3 = 6.1(10)^{16}.$$

EXAMPLE 11. The Stefan-Boltzmann constant, used in the equation for rate of heat transfer by radiation, has the value $5.7(10)^{-12}$ watts/cm.^{2} $^\circ K^4$. Convert the constant to its value in Btu/hr. ft.^{2} $^\circ R^4$.

Solution.

$$\left(\frac{\text{watts}}{\text{cm.}^2\,{}^\circ\text{K}^4}\right)\left(\frac{\text{kw.}}{\text{watt}}\right)\left(\frac{\text{Btu}}{\text{kw-hr.}}\right)\left(\frac{\text{cm.}^2}{\text{in.}^2}\right)\left(\frac{\text{in.}^2}{\text{ft.}^2}\right)\left(\frac{{}^\circ\text{K}^4}{{}^\circ\text{R}^4}\right) = \frac{\text{Btu}}{\text{hr. ft.}^2\,{}^\circ\text{R}^4}$$

$$(5.7(10)^{-12})\left(\frac{1}{1000}\right)(3413)(2.54)^2(12)^2\left(\frac{5}{9}\right)^4 = 1.73(10)^{-9}.$$

We have made use of the fact that the ratio of any Kelvin temperature to its corresponding Rankine temperature is five to nine, or $\frac{5}{9}$.

The radiation constant of Example 11 requires an absolute temperature unit, either $^\circ$K or $^\circ$R. The centigrade and Fahrenheit scales should not be used because their zero points do not represent true zero temperature. Scientific laws that involve temperature will usually require the use of an absolute temperature scale. If the difference of two temperatures (temperature change) is involved, the requirement becomes meaningless, since 1 F$^\circ$ equals 1 R$^\circ$, and 1 C$^\circ$ equals 1 K$^\circ$.

It is important to distinguish a power of a temperature difference from a difference of powers of temperature. $(T_2 - T_1)^4$ is not the same as $(T_2^4 - T_1^4)$. The former does not require units of an absolute temperature scale because it is a temperature difference raised to a power.

Exercises

Write a sequence of numbers and units for each conversion, crossing out units which cancel until the desired units are obtained.

1. The speed of a rocket increases by 300 ft./sec. each second. We may say it has an acceleration of 300 ft./sec. sec. or 300 ft./sec.^{2} Convert to miles/hr. min.

Ans. 12,300 miles/hr. min.

2. How many lb./ft.^{2} are equivalent to a pressure of 20,000 dynes/cm.^{2}?

3. When the sun is directly overhead, a square centimeter of the earth's surface receives energy at the rate of about 2 calories/min. Convert this information to hp./mile^2. *Ans.* 4.9(10)^6 hp./mile^2.

4. If T_2 is 310°K and T_1 is 300°K, what is the difference between $(T_2 - T_1)^4$ and $(T_2^4 - T_1^4)$? If the Kelvin temperatures were converted to centigrade, which expression would be unchanged in value?

5. A painter in a housing development finds that he uses 5 gallons of paint per house. The painted area is 1200 ft.^{2} per house. Find the cubic centimeters of paint used per square foot of painted area. There are 231 in.^{3}/gal.

Ans. 16 cm.^{3}/ft.^{2}

6. The viscosity of a certain fluid is given as 0.50 dyne sec./cm.^{2}. Find the viscosity in English units, lb. sec./ft.^{2}.

7. Reynolds number is the name for a dimensionless quantity used in the study of fluid flow, as in pipes. If Reynolds number is $\rho VD/\mu$, show that it is dimensionless using CGS units. V is the fluid velocity in cm./sec., ρ (rho) is its density, μ (mu) is its viscosity in gm./cm. sec., and D is the pipe diameter.

8. Show that Reynolds number, described in Exercise 7, is dimensionless using English units. The units of viscosity are slug/ft. sec.

9. The velocity of a freely falling object, dropped from a height h, may be obtained from $V = (2gh)^{1/2}$. Using English and MKS units, show that this expression has units of velocity. The letter g represents acceleration due to gravity.

10. When an electric current of I amperes flows through a resistance R for t seconds, the amount of heat produced may be calculated from I^2Rt. If R has the units volts/ampere, and an ampere is a coulomb/sec., show that I^2Rt may be in joules.

11. For a uniformly loaded simple beam, the maximum deflection is $D = 5WL^4/384EI$. If L is the length in inches, E is the modulus of elasticity for the beam in lb./in.^{2}, and I is the moment of inertia of the beam cross section in inches^4, what units are required for the load W in order that D may be in inches?

Ans. W lb./in.

12. The maximum shearing stress due to torsion in a drive shaft is often calculated from $S = TR/J$. If S, T, and R have respectively the units lb./in.^{2}, in-lb., and in., what are the units of the polar moment of inertia J?

3-6   Mass, Weight, and Force

It should be noted that *mass* and *weight* are different concepts. Weight is force, the force of gravity exerted by two objects upon each other. If an object is said to weigh 16 lb., it means that there are 16 lb. of gravity force acting on both the object and the earth, which tends to bring them together. The gravity force, or weight, is not a property of the object alone. It depends upon the mass of both the object and the earth, and the distance between them.

Mass may be considered as the amount of matter in an object and is a property of the object: If the mass of an object is 10 kg., the gravity force (weight) acting upon the object at the surface of the earth is 98 newtons. If the object were on the moon its mass would still be 10 kg., but its weight would be reduced considerably.

Units of force have been defined in terms of mass and acceleration units in Newton's second law of motion, $F = Ma$. One dyne, for example, is defined as the amount of unbalanced force which will cause a mass of 1 gm. to have an acceleration of 1 cm./sec.^{2} How many dynes should be required to give the gram an acceleration of 980 cm./sec.^{2}? Since the force is proportional to acceleration ($F = Ma$), the required force is 980 dynes. It happens that the acceleration of a falling object, caused by gravity at the surface of the earth, is 980 cm./sec.² Therefore the gravity force acting on 1 gm. at the surface of the earth is 980 dynes. Table 3-3 gives the gravity forces acting on various masses at the surface of the earth.

If we use the letter g to represent the acceleration due to gravity, and refer to the gravity force as weight W, Newton's law becomes $W = Mg$.

Table 3-3

GRAVITY FORCES ACTING ON UNITS
OF MASS AT THE EARTH'S SURFACE

System	Mass	Gravity force	Acceleration (g)
MKS	1 kg.	9.8 newtons	9.8 M./sec.²
CGS	1 gm.	980 dynes	980 cm./sec.²
English	1 slug	32.2 lb.	32.2 ft./sec.²
	1 kg.	2.2 lb.	
	454 gm.	1 lb.	

The units of weight, mass, and g must be from the same system of units. This relation will give the weight of a mass if the value of g is known for the location of the mass.

EXAMPLE 12. What is the weight of a 5-kg. mass: (a) at the surface of the earth? (b) on a planet where g is 12 M./sec.²?

Solution.

(a) $W = Mg = (5 \text{ kg.})\left(9.8 \dfrac{\text{M.}}{\text{sec.}^2}\right) = 49$ newtons.

(b) $W = Mg = (5 \text{ kg.})\left(12 \dfrac{\text{M.}}{\text{sec.}^2}\right) = 60$ newtons.

At first inspection the units of Example 12 do not appear to form an equality or balance of units. We have noted, however, that force units are defined in terms of mass and acceleration units in such a way ($F = Ma$) that:

1 newton = 1 kg-M./sec.²

1 dyne = 1 gm-cm./sec.²

1 lb.   = 1 slug-ft./sec.²

These equivalencies may be used when converting units and checking equations for balance of units.

EXAMPLE 13. The gravity force on a satellite is 200 lb. at an altitude where g is 25 ft./sec.^{2} (a) What is its mass? (b) What would it weigh at the earth's surface?

Solution.

(a) $W = Mg$,

        lb. $= $ (slug)(ft./sec.^{2}),

        $200 = (M)(25)$,

        $M = 8$ slugs.

b) $W = Mg = (8)(32.2)$,

        $W = 258$ lb. ($= 258$ slug-ft./sec.^{2}).

Many balances used for weighing objects give readings in grams. The gram is not a unit of weight or force but is a mass unit. Although it is common practice to speak of an object as "weighing" so many grams, it is really the mass that has been determined.

3-7 Equations and Equality of Units

The physical quantities represented on one side of an equation usually must have units arranged so as to be identical or equivalent to the arrangement of units on the other side. Only quantities having identical or equivalent units may be added, subtracted, or set equal. Consequently, the units of an equation must form an equality, such as Btu + Btu = Btu. For convenience we shall refer to this condition of dimensional equality as a *balance of units*.

As a routine but important step in the solution of a physical problem, the equations used should always be checked for balance of units at the time of inserting known values. If two or more equations are to be solved simultaneously, it is necessary that the same units be used for like quantities in all equations. For example, if time and displacement are the unknowns in two equations, the units of time and displacement involved in known quantities must be the same for both equations.

Certain equations are based on definitions of special or arbitrary concepts and may not have a balance of units. The expression for intensity level, or decibels, is an example: $L = \log (I_1/I_2)$. Although L is in bels, the right side of the equation is dimensionless.

EXAMPLE 14. Using the CGS system, show a balance of units for the equation of motion $S = \frac{1}{2}at^2$. The letters S, a, and t represent quantities of length, acceleration, and time, respectively.

Solution.

$$S = \tfrac{1}{2}(a)(t)^2,$$

$$\text{cm.} = \left(\frac{\text{cm.}}{\text{sec.}^2}\right)(\text{sec.}^2),$$

$$\text{cm.} = \text{cm.}$$

The constant $\tfrac{1}{2}$ has no units.

When both mass and force units appear in an equation it should be remembered that they are related by the expresssion $F = Ma$, or $W = Mg$, as indicated in Sec. 3-6.

EXAMPLE 15. Show a balance of units for the kinetic energy equation, $E = \tfrac{1}{2}mv^2$, using the English system. E, m, and v represent energy, mass, and velocity respectively.

Solution.

$$E = \tfrac{1}{2}(m)(v)^2,$$

$$\text{ft-lb.} = (\text{slug})\left(\frac{\text{ft.}^2}{\text{sec.}^2}\right).$$

Using the relation $F = Ma$ from Sec. 3-6, we may state that 1 lb. $=$ 1 slug-ft./ sec.^{2} or, by transposing, 1 slug $=$ 1 lb. sec.^{2}/ft. Either the lb. or slug may be replaced in order to form an obvious balance of units. Replacing the slug with its equivalent gives

$$\text{ft-lb.} = \left(\frac{\text{lb. sec.}^2}{\text{ft.}}\right)\left(\frac{\text{ft.}^2}{\text{sec.}^2}\right),$$

$$\text{ft-lb.} = \text{ft-lb.}$$

Exercises

1. Show a balance of MKS units for the energy-mass relation $E = Mc^2$. The letter c represents the speed of light.

2. Do Exercise 1 using CGS and English units.

3. An expression for estimating the power of a nuclear reactor is $P = FEk$, where P is the power in watts and E is the energy released from each fission. If E has the units Mev/fission, and k is the conversion factor joules/Mev, what are the units of F? The Mev (million electron volts) is an energy unit.

Ans. fissions/sec.

4. Show that the units of E/B, an electric field strength divided by a magnetic field strength, are those of velocity in the MKS system. E may have the units volts/meter, and B may be in newtons/ampere meter. An ampere is a coulomb/sec.

5. Impulse is equated to change of momentum in the equation $Ft = M(V_2 - V_1)$. F, t, and M are force, time, and mass, respectively. Show a balance of CGS units. The quantity $(V_2 - V_1)$ represents velocity change and has the units cm./sec. It is not necessary to write (cm./sec. $-$ cm./sec.) for the units of $(V_2 - V_1)$.

6. Do Exercise 5 using MKS and English units.

7. The useful output power of a pump may be expressed as $P = WQ$, where W is the useful work done on each lb. of fluid, or ft-lb./lb. If power P is in ft-lb./sec. what are the units of Q? *Ans.* lb./sec.

8. Show a balance of English units for the equation of motion $S = V_1 t + \frac{1}{2}at^2$. S, V_1, t, and a have units of length, velocity, time, and acceleration (ft./sec.^{2}), respectively.

9. In certain cases the pressure drop due to fluid flow in a horizontal pipe is given by $(P_1 - P_2) = 32uLV/D^2$. V and u are the fluid velocity and viscosity, while L and D are the length and diameter of pipe. If $(P_1 - P_2)$ is in dynes/cm.^{2} (CGS units), what are the units of viscosity? *Ans.* dyne sec./cm.^{2}

10. Do Exercise 8 in MKS and CGS units.

11. Convert the answer of Exercise 9 to an alternate form involving a mass unit. *Ans.* gm./cm. sec.

12. From kinetic theory, the average gas molecule kinetic energy is a function of absolute temperature, or $\frac{1}{2}mV^2 = 3kT/2$. Show a balance of CGS units. V, m, and T have units of velocity, mass, and absolute temperature. The Boltzmann constant k has the units erg/°K.

13. The expression $LI^2/2$ represents the magnetic field energy of an inductor. I is in amperes, and the inductance L may have the units volts/ampere per sec. (volt sec./ampere). Show that the units of the expression are equivalent to joules. An ampere is a coulomb/sec.

14. In the equation $wh - Fs = wV^2/2g$ each term represents energy. Show a balance of MKS units. F and w have units of force while h and s have units of length. V has units of velocity, and g is the acceleration of gravity (meters/sec.^{2}).

15. Do Exercise 14 in CGS and English units.

16. The speed of sound through a material may be calculated from $V = (E/d)^{1/2}$. Show that V will be in ft./sec. if E is in lb./ft.^{2} and the material density d is in slugs/ft.^{3}

3-8   Formulation of Units

It is often possible to construct an equation of units that may expedite the solution of a physical problem. This procedure is of considerable value in a problem where there is no recourse to a specific physical law or relation.

The units of the known pieces of information are assembled, along with the units of the unknown, to form an equation of units. The known numerical values are then placed in position as indicated by the units.

It is important to note that a balanced equation of units may be formed that does not correspond to a correct relation of physical quantities. For example, the lb-ft. of torque in a drive shaft might erroneously be set equal to the ft-lb. of energy transmitted by the shaft during some period of time. Torque and energy are not like quantities and should not be equated. Also, a process that takes place at a variable rate may incorrectly be treated as operating at a constant rate. Consequently, the physical quantities involved must be well understood when formulating units, and the proposed unit equation should be checked for physical sense.

EXAMPLE 16. Pump A can fill a tank in 4.20 hr. Pump B can fill a tank in 9.70 hr. How many hours will it take to fill the tank if both A and B are pumping? The pumps have constant delivery rates.

Solution. A pumps at the rate of one tank/4.2 hr., or 0.238 tanks/hr. B pumps at the rate of 1 tank/9.7 hr., or 0.103 tanks/hr. An equation of units may be set up based on the central idea that the amount pumped by A plus the amount pumped by B equals 1 tank volume.

$$\left(\frac{\text{tanks}}{\text{hr.}}\right)(\text{hr.}) + \left(\frac{\text{tanks}}{\text{hr.}}\right)(\text{hr.}) = \text{tanks},$$

$$(0.238)(T) + (0.103)(T) = \text{one},$$

$$T = \frac{1}{0.341} = 2.93 \text{ hr.}$$

This procedure is correct only if the pumps have constant delivery rates.

EXAMPLE 17. Find the amount contributed to the tank by each pump in Example 16 and check the solution.

Solution.

Pump A:

$$\left(\frac{\text{tanks}}{\text{hr.}}\right)(\text{hr.}) = \text{tanks},$$

$$(0.238)(2.93) = 0.7.$$

Pump B:

$$(0.103)(2.93) = 0.3.$$

Check: The sum of 0.7 tanks and 0.3 tanks (slide rule accuracy) is 1 tank, the specified total.

We may use formulation of units as an aid in remembering the laws and relations of science. Assume that one has temporarily forgotten the correct expression for centripetal acceleration and is considering $a = v^2r$ and $a = v^2/r$, where v represents velocity and r has units of length. The English units for v^2r would be (ft.^{2}/sec.^{2})(ft.), or ft.^{3}/sec.^{2} The units for v^2/r would be ft.^{2}/sec.^{2} ft., or ft./sec.^{2}, the correct units for acceleration.

We have indicated previously that the basic dimensions usually are taken to be length (L), mass (M), and time (T). The dimensions of most quantities may be expressed by the dimensional symbols in the form $L^aM^bT^c$, where a, b, and c are positive or negative exponents.

Consider the dimensions for force. Force has been defined in terms of mass and acceleration $(F = Ma)$. Therefore we may write the symbols for Ma, giving $(M)(L/T^2)$ or MLT^{-2}, as the dimensions for force. Table 3-4 gives the dimensions of some physical quantities. There are some quantities, such as temperature and angle, which are considered dimensionless in the MLT system.

Table 3-4

MLT DIMENSIONS OF PHYSICAL QUANTITIES

Quantity	Dimensions	Quantity	Dimensions
Length	L	Velocity	LT^{-1}
Mass	M	Acceleration	LT^{-2}
Time	T	Force	MLT^{-2}
Area	L^2	Pressure	$ML^{-1}T^{-2}$
Volume	L^3	Energy	ML^2T^{-2}
Density	ML^{-3}	Specific weight	$ML^{-2}T^{-2}$

Dimensional analysis has been used extensively as an aid in clarifying the relations of fluid flow, heat transfer, electricity, mechanics, and other fields of study. Assume we have made the observation that the magnitude of centripetal acceleration depends only on the magnitude of velocity and radius of circular path. We may write that the acceleration is a function of v and r:

accel. $= f(v, r)$

or

accel. $= k(v)^a(r)^b$,

where a and b are exponents to be determined, and k is a constant without units. Since acceleration has the dimensions LT^{-2} (such as ft./sec.²), and velocity v has the dimensions LT^{-1}, we may write

$$LT^{-2} = (LT^{-1})^a(L)^b$$
$$= (L^aT^{-a})(L)^b$$
$$= (L^{a+b})(T^{-a}).$$

By equating the exponents of like dimensions, $a = 2$, $a + b = 1$, and $b = -1$. Inserting the values of a and b into the original relation gives

accel. $= kv^2r^{-1}$.

Since $k = 1$ (determined experimentally), we may write

accel. $= v^2/r$.

EXAMPLE 18. From the observation that the kinetic energy of an object is a function of its mass and velocity, develop the form of the expression for kinetic energy.

Solution.

$$\text{K.E.} = f(m, v) = k(m)^a(v)^b,$$
$$(L)(MLT^{-2}) = (M)^a(LT^{-1})^b,$$
$$ML^2T^{-2} = M^aL^bT^{-b};$$
$$a = 1, \qquad b = 2;$$
$$\text{K.E.} = kmv^2 \qquad (\tfrac{1}{2}mv^2).$$

Exercises

1. A large batch of metal parts can be processed by machine A in 3.0 days. Machine B would take 4.0 days, and machine C would take 5.0 days. How many days will it take if all three machines operate? *Ans.* 1.3 days.

2. If the batch of the preceding problem consists of 10,000 parts, how many are handled by each machine?

3. A beam of electrons has a speed of $2.0(10)^6$ meters/sec., and is measured as 0.0010 amperes. For every ampere there is a flow of $6.28(10)^{18}$ electrons/sec. Find the number of electrons per cm. length of the beam (electrons/cm.). *Ans.* $3.1(10)^7$ electrons/cm.

4. The equation $H = CAT^4$ is used in calculating the rate at which energy (heat) is radiated from an object. If A is the surface area in ft.², T the temperature in °R, and H the rate of radiation in Btu/hr., what are the units of the constant C?

5. If peanuts cost 28¢ a lb. and cashews cost 75¢ a lb., how many lb. (W) of cashews should be mixed with 25 lb. of peanuts to sell at 59¢ a lb.? (*Note:* Write an expression for the total cost in cents, and divide by the expression for total lb.)

Ans. 48 lb.

6. It is found that 2 drops of a certain fluid will form a thin film which covers 2400 cm.² of a water surface. If the volume of a drop is 0.001 cm.³, what is the film thickness?

7. A jet plane consumed 2400 gal. of fuel at the rate of 120 lb./min. while on a flight of 1200 miles. What was its speed in miles/hr.? Assume the fuel weighs 6 lb./gal.

Ans. 600 miles/hr.

8. From the observation that the velocity of a freely falling object is a function of g (acceleration of gravity), and h (height from which it has dropped), develop the equation for its velocity. The proportionality constant k is $(2)^{1/2}$.

9. If for copper there are 63.6 gm./gm-atomic wt., and 8.89 gm./cm.³, what is the number of atoms per cubic cm. of copper? Using Avogadro's number, there are $6.02(10)^{23}$ atoms/gm-atomic wt.

Ans. $8.4(10)^{22}$ atoms/cm.³

10. The following ratios are associated with events which take place in a nuclear reactor.

N = neutrons produced by thermal fission/neutron absorbed in fuel.
P = total neutrons produced/thermal neutron absorbed in anything.
f = neutrons absorbed in fuel/thermal neutron absorbed in anything.
E = total neutrons produced/neutron produced by thermal fission.

Write an equation giving f in terms of N, E, and P.

11. The period T of a vibratory motion is the time required for a complete oscillation, such as that of a mass suspended from a spring. Which of the following equations is correct if T is in sec., m is in gm., and K is a spring constant in dynes/cm.?

(*a*) $T = C(mK)^{1/2}$.   (*b*) $T = C(m/K)^{1/2}$.   (*c*) $T = C(K/m)^{1/2}$.

C is a constant without dimensions.

12. Let H represent the Btu/hr. of heat energy conducted through a solid wall of thickness L and area A, due to a temperature difference ΔT across the wall thickness. The conductivity of the wall material is k, a quantity with the units Btu in./ft.² F° hr. By formulating units, obtain the equation giving H in terms of L, A, k, and ΔT.

In Chap. 2 we were concerned with the manipulation of algebraic quantities, usually in the form of addition, subtraction, multiplication, and division of those quantities. These operations involved primary collection and simplification of quantities. Little mention was made of equalities and the solutions of equations.

The simplest of the algebraic equations are linear equations in one unknown, and in this chapter we will discuss such equations and their solutions. Linear equations are very important to students of technical studies because they occur so frequently in such topics as heat, electricity, chemistry, mechanics, light, and finance, to mention a few.

4 LINEAR EQUATIONS IN ONE UNKNOWN

4-1   Definitions

A statement that asserts that two algebraic expressions are equal to each other is called an *equality*. The two expressions are called *members* or *sides* of the equality. Equalities are of two kinds, *identities* and *equations*.

Identities are true for all values of the literal quantities present. The identity symbol is a triple bar $\equiv$. Thus,

$$(x + 1)^3 \equiv x^3 + 3x^2 + 3x + 1$$

is an identity because it is true for any value assigned to x. The equality

$$2x - 5 = 3 \tag{1}$$

is true only if $x = 4$ and is called an *equation* as opposed to an identity.

In (1) the value $x = 4$ is said to satisfy the equation and is called a *root* or *solution* of the equation. More than one value can satisfy an equation; accordingly, an equation may have more than one root. As an example.

$$x^3 - 2x^2 - x + 2 = 0 \tag{2}$$

has the solutions $x = -1, 1, 2$. Equations can have any number of solutions, depending upon the nature of the equation.

In this early approach to equations, our discussions will be limited to those equations that have only one solution. Further, we shall restrict ourselves to equations in one variable, with certain exceptions. The use of the term *variable* suggests the need of defining variables and their antonyms, which are called *constants*.

In the equation showing the area of a circle,

$$A = \pi r^2, \tag{3}$$

the area A and the radius r are regarded as variables. Accordingly, (3) can be used to find the area of a circle from any given radius. Thus, r can vary according to the dimension of the circle under consideration. The area A obtains its value from the value assigned to r and is therefore variable along with r. The quantity π is a fixed number $3.14159 \cdots$ and can assume no other value; accordingly, it is called a *constant*. It is common practice in algebra to select, as symbols for variables, letters near the end of the alphabet. Letters from the beginning of the alphabet are commonly chosen as symbols for constants. This practice is often abandoned in applications, however, for in applications the symbols chosen are frequently suggestive of the quantities which they represent, such as A for area, r for resistance, i for intensity, f for focal length, and so forth.

Equations possess certain properties which will be mentioned here and are useful in later work. These properties we will accept without proof; certain of them are familiar from axioms studied in plane geometry. Four properties include:

Property 1. *If equals are added to equals, the sums are equal.*

Property 2. *If equals are subtracted from equals, the differences are equal.*

Property 3. *If equals are multiplied by equals, the products are equal.*

Property 4. *If equals are divided by equals, the quotients are equal. (The zero divisor is excepted here.)*

The use of the above properties in the solution of a problem is demonstrated in Example 1.

EXAMPLE 1. Determine the value of y which satisfies the equation

$$\frac{y}{2} + 5 = 7. \tag{4}$$

Solution. Here we have the assertion that the number $y/2 + 5$ is equal to 7. By property 3 we can multiply both members of (4) by 2; giving

$$y + 10 = 14. \tag{5}$$

By property 2, 10 can be subtracted from both members of (5), giving the solution $y = 4$.

Through successive applications of properties 1–4, the solutions of problems in succeeding sections may be obtained. This will be discussed more fully later.

4-2   Linear Equations in One Unknown

A linear equation in one unknown, y, may be written in the form

$$Ay + B = 0. \tag{6}$$

where $A \neq 0$. It is identified by the presence of one and only one unknown and by the fact that the unknown is present only in the first degree. In (6), y is the unknown and A and B are constants.

The solution of (6) is readily obtained by using properties 2 and 4 successively. Subtracting B from both sides of (6), we have

$$Ay = -B,$$

and, dividing both sides by A, we obtain the solution

$$y = -\frac{B}{A}.$$

The linear equation in one unknown may be given or it may be derived from data. It may, in its original form, appear to be considerably different from (6), but is reducible to the form of (6). Consider two examples.

EXAMPLE 2. Solve for k if

$$2k + 4 = 3k - 5 + k. \tag{7}$$

Solution. Collecting like terms in the right member of (7), we have

$$2k + 4 = 4k - 5. \tag{8}$$

Subtracting $2k + 4$ from each member of (8), we have

$$0 = 2k - 9. \tag{9}$$

where (9) is now in the form of (6) with comparable parts $A = 2$, $B = -9$, and k is the unknown, The solution of (9) is now $k = \frac{9}{2}$.

We may check the solution. Since the solution is defined as a number which satisfies the original equation, we substitute $k = \frac{9}{2}$ into (7), obtaining

$$2(\tfrac{9}{2}) + 4 \overset{?}{=} 3(\tfrac{9}{2}) - 5 + \tfrac{9}{2}, \tag{10}$$

where we question whether or not this is an equality. If (10) is truly an equality, then $k = \frac{9}{2}$ is a solution of (7). Clearing parentheses in (10), we have

$$9 + 4 \overset{?}{=} \tfrac{27}{2} - 5 + \tfrac{9}{2}$$

and

$$13 = 13.$$

Having arrived at the equality $13 = 13$, we are at least fairly confident that $k = \frac{9}{2}$ is a solution of (7).

EXAMPLE 3. A certain rectangular field has a perimeter of 60 yards. Find its dimensions if its length is 4 yards greater than its width.

Solution. Call the width w; this necessitates that the length is $w + 4$ (see Fig. 4-1(a)). The perimeter is the sum of the four sides, or

$$(w) + (w + 4) + w + (w + 4) = 60,$$

from which

$$4w + 8 = 60$$

and

$$w = 13.$$

The statement $w = 13$ asserts that the rectangle is of width 13 yards. It was given that the length exceeds the width by 4 yards; therefore, the length is 17 yards.

(a)   (b)

FIGURE 4–1

Solution 2. Call the length l as shown in Fig. 4-1(b). Now the width is 4 yards less than the length, or $l - 4$, and the perimeter is

$$(l) + (l - 4) + (l) + (l - 4) = 60,$$

from which

$$4l = 68$$

and

$$l = 17,$$
$$l - 4 = 13.$$

We have obtained the dimensions by using either the length or the width as the unknown. In each case a linear equation in one unknown was involved.

Exercises

In Exercises 1–24 find the solution of the given equation. Check the solution obtained by substitution into the given equation.

1. $5a - 7 = 13$.   *Ans.* $a = 4$

2. $2a + 7 = 13$.

3. $3m + 5 = 14$.   *Ans.* $m = 3$.

4. $4k - 2 = 26$.

5. $7x - 8 = 3x$ *Ans.* $x = 2$.

6. $5y - 8 = 13 - 2y$.

7. $4m + 2 = 2m - 9$.   *Ans.* $m = -\frac{11}{2}$.

8. $3p + 2p = 4p + 12$.

9. $4(m - 3) = 6m$.   *Ans.* $m = -6$.

10. $9y = 3(8 + 2y)$

11. $6(k + 4) = 3k + 27$.   *Ans.* $k = 1$.

12. $2(x - 5) = 32 - x$.

13. $6(4 - m) + 8m = 36$.   *Ans.* $m = 6$.

14. $9y = 36 - 3(4 - y)$.

15. $4(x - 3) + 3(x + 8) = 5x$.   *Ans.* $x = -6$.

16. $12(z - 9) - 14z = 100$.

17. $5.5(k + 3) = 2.5(40 - k)$ *Ans.* $k = 10.44$

18. $0.3(T - 40) = 5(0.4T) - 15$.

19. $45.6(R + 12) - 109.2 = 16.5(R - 3)$ *Ans.* $R = -16.75$

20. $0.05(M + 5) = 6(0.09M) - 4.1$.

21. $6(1.05T - 4) - 0.2(3 - 7T) = 0$.   *Ans.* $T = 3.195$.

22. $3(k - \frac{1}{2}) - 5(k - \frac{3}{2}) = 1$.

23. $9(1.08y + 2) - 0.4(6y + 2) = 7$.   *Ans.* $y = -\dfrac{10.2}{7.32}$.

24. $2(y + \frac{3}{2}) - 6(y - \frac{2}{3}) = 4$.

25. The sum of what two consecutive odd integers is 76?   *Ans.* 37, 39.

26. The sum of what three consecutive integers equals 120?

27. The dimensions of a circle are such that the circumference exceeds the radius by 8 in. Find the radius.   *Ans.* 1.53 in.

28. The length of a rectangle is 3 in. less than twice the width. Its perimeter is 24 in. Find the dimensions.

29. The length of a metallic bar increases by 0.008 per cent of its original length for each centigrade degree increase in temperature. After a 132°C increase in temperature, the length of the bar is 24.7873 in. What was the original length? *Ans.* 24.5283 in.

30. The perimeter of the object sketched in Fig. 4-2 is 40 in. Find the height of the object.

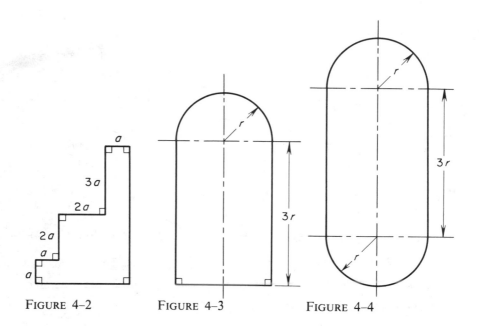

FIGURE 4–2   FIGURE 4–3   FIGURE 4–4

31. The perimeter of the Norman window shown in Fig. 4-3 is 22 ft. Find the radius. *Ans.* 1.975 ft.

32. The perimeter of the racetrack shown in Fig. 4-4 is one mile. Find the radius of the circular ends.

33. The Fahrenheit temperature reading always exceeds 9/5 of the centigrade reading by 32. Find the centigrade reading when the Fahrenheit reading is 197°. *Ans.* $91\frac{2}{3}°$.

34. In Fig. 4-5 the distance $AD = 36$ ft. Find BC and CD.

35. In simple interest computations, the amount equals the principal plus the interest. The interest accumulates at the rate of 6 per cent of the original principal per year. The amount at the end of 8 years is $512. Find the principal.

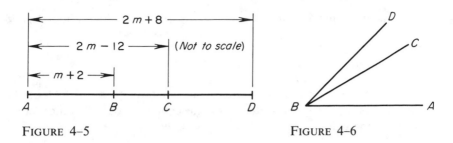

FIGURE 4–5   FIGURE 4–6

36. A triangle is such that side b is 2/3 of side a and side c is 2/3 of side b. The perimeter is 50 in. Find side c.

37. In Fig. 4-6 the angle ABC is 2.5 times the size of angle CBD. If angle ABD is 56°, find angle ABC.   *Ans.* 40°.

4-3   Equations Involving Fractions

Many fractional equations in one unknown can be reduced to the form

$$Ax + B = 0$$

by clearing fractions. Fractions can be cleared by multiplying each term of the given equation by the least common multiple of the denominators involved. We mentioned the least common multiple briefly in Sec. 2-9, and now we will elaborate on it. The *LCM* of a group of numbers is the smallest number which is divisible without remainder by each of the numbers. Thus, the *LCM* of the numbers 2, 3, 12, 16, and 48 is 48 because 48 is the smallest number into which each of the given numbers will divide exactly.

EXAMPLE 4. Find the LCM of 15, 20, 12, and 18.

Solution. Let us list the prime factors of each of the given numbers:

$$15 = 3 \cdot 5,$$
$$20 = 2 \cdot 2 \cdot 5,$$
$$12 = 2 \cdot 2 \cdot 3,$$
$$18 = 2 \cdot 3 \cdot 3.$$

Note that the factor 2 occurs at most twice in any set of factors; this is in $20 = 2 \cdot 2 \cdot 5$ and in $12 = 2 \cdot 2 \cdot 3$. The factor 3 occurs at most twice; this is in $18 = 2 \cdot 3 \cdot 3$. The factor 5 occurs at most once. The smallest number into which 15, 20, 12, and 18 each will divide evenly contains as its factors the sets of factors cited in the preceding three sentences. Thus, the desired LCM is

$$2 \cdot 2 \cdot 3 \cdot 3 \cdot 5 = 180.$$

If we multiply each term of a fractional equation by the LCM of the denominators of the separate terms of the equation, we will immediately clear all of the denominators. Refer to Example 5.

EXAMPLE 5. Find the solution of

$$\frac{x}{2} + \frac{3x + 1}{8} = \frac{2(x - 4)}{5} - \frac{x + 18}{20}. \tag{11}$$

Solution. Using methods shown in Example 4, we find that the LCM of 2, 8, 5, and 20 is 40. Now we will multiply each term of (11) by 40, giving us

$$\frac{(40)(x)}{2} + \frac{(40)(3x + 1)}{8} = \frac{(40)(2)(x - 4)}{5} - \frac{(40)(x + 18)}{20}. \tag{12}$$

Now each denominator of (12) divides exactly into 40, which is the numerator factor just inserted. The result is an equation without denominators, namely

$$20x + 5(3x + 1) = (8)(2)(x - 4) - 2(x + 18). \tag{13}$$

We solve (13) using methods shown in the preceding section, obtaining the solution $x = -5$.

Check: It is well to mention the method of checking the solution $x = -5$. We properly check $x = -5$ against the *original* equation (11), as opposed to any of the other expressions that we have obtained. If we choose to check the solution against (12) or (13) or any other equation that is the result of our manipulation of (11), we may be misled by our conclusion. Thus, if (13) were wrong (contained an error which we introduced) and all manipulations between (13) and the final answer were done properly, the final wrong answer would check against (13), but would not check against the original expression (11).

In Example 5 none of the denominators contained a literal quantity. In cases of reciprocals and inverse variation, an unknown may appear in the denominator. This occurrence does not alter the method of solution.

EXAMPLE 6. Find the solution of

$$\frac{3}{2x} + \frac{2x - 3}{x^2 - 1} = \frac{7}{2(x - 1)}. \tag{14}$$

Solution. First we find the LCM of the denominators of (14). Examining the factors we have

$$2x = (2)(x),$$
$$x^2 - 1 = (x - 1)(x + 1), \tag{15}$$
$$2(x - 1) = (2)(x - 1),$$

where, from (15), the smallest number into which all of the denominators will divide without remainder is the quantity $2(x)(x - 1)(x + 1)$; this is the LCM by which we will multiply all terms of (14). After multiplying and cancelling, we have

$$3(x^2 - 1) + 2x(2x - 3) = 7x(x + 1)$$

or

$$3x^2 - 3 + 4x^2 - 6x = 7x^2 + 7x. \tag{16}$$

The second-degree terms of (16) cancel additively (if they did not cancel, we would require different methods of solution), giving

$$13x = -3$$

and the desired solution

$$x = -\tfrac{3}{13}.$$

Exercises

In Exercises 1–20, find the value of the unknown which satisfies the given equation. Check all of the answers by substituting the solution back into the original equation.

1. $\dfrac{a}{10} = \dfrac{3}{5}.$ *Ans.* $a = 6.$

2. $\dfrac{4}{b} = \dfrac{32}{12}.$

3. $\dfrac{7}{91} = \dfrac{12}{w}.$ *Ans.* $w = 156.$

4. $\dfrac{8}{15} = \dfrac{m + 2}{9}.$

5. $\dfrac{11}{2y} = \dfrac{5}{18}.$ *Ans.* $y = 19.8.$

6. $\dfrac{9}{2(x+1)} = \dfrac{3}{8}.$

7. $\dfrac{2k-4}{6} = \dfrac{14-k}{9}.$ *Ans. k = 5.*

8. $\dfrac{4}{a+1} = \dfrac{5}{a-1}.$

9. $\dfrac{m+5}{4} + \dfrac{1}{2} = \dfrac{2m-3}{6}.$ *Ans. m = 27.*

10. $\dfrac{r-3}{6} - \dfrac{2}{3} = \dfrac{2r-9}{4}.$

11. $\dfrac{b-2}{6} - \dfrac{12}{21} = \dfrac{b-4}{7}.$ *Ans. b = 14.*

12. $\dfrac{m+10}{3} - \dfrac{3}{9} = \dfrac{m+5}{2}.$

13. $\dfrac{3}{x} - \dfrac{3}{x^2-x} = \dfrac{4}{3x}.$ *Ans. $x = \dfrac{14}{5}.$*

14. $(m-1)^2 - 3(m^2+2m) - m(1-2m) = 0.$

15. $\dfrac{6}{x-1} - \dfrac{4}{x+4} = \dfrac{2}{x}.$ *Ans. $x = -\dfrac{4}{11}.$*

16. $\dfrac{b}{3} - \dfrac{b-3}{4} = \dfrac{b+4}{8}.$

17. $\dfrac{6}{s+2} = \dfrac{8}{s-3} - \dfrac{2}{s-1}.$ *Ans. $s = \dfrac{11}{17}.$*

18. $\dfrac{2x+5}{x^2+3x+2} + \dfrac{3x-2}{x^2-1} = \dfrac{5x}{x^2+x-2} + \dfrac{2}{x^2+5x+6}.$

19. $\dfrac{7-m}{m^2-1} - \dfrac{m+1}{m^2+5m+4} = \dfrac{-2m+1}{m^2+3m-4}.$ *Ans. m = −7.*

20. $\dfrac{4}{a+2} + \dfrac{1}{a-2} = \dfrac{12}{4(a-2)}.$

21. The total resistance R of a circuit with resistances r_1 and r_2 in parallel is given as

$$\frac{1}{R} = \frac{1}{r_1} + \frac{1}{r_2}.$$

Find the value of r_1 if $R = (r_1 + 3)/2$ and $r_2 = r_1 - 3$.   *Ans. $r_1 = 1.$*

22. The angle ϕ between two intersecting lines may be found by the equation

$$\tan \phi = \frac{m_2 - m_1}{1 + m_1 m_2},$$

where m_1 and m_2 are the slopes of the lines. Find m_1 if $\tan \phi = 3.22$ and $m_2 = 1.04$.

Ans. −0.497.

23. The sum S of n terms of a geometric progression is given by the equation

$$S = \frac{a - rl}{1 - r},$$

where a is the value of the first term, r is the common ratio, and l is the value of the nth term. Find the ratio if $a = 27$, $l = \frac{16}{3}$ and $S = \frac{211}{3}$. *Ans. $r = 2/3$.*

24. The length of a certain rectangle exceeds its width by 4 ft. If the width is increased by 4 ft. and the length decreased by 3 ft., the area is increased by 5 sq. ft. Find the dimensions of the original rectangle.

25. In Fig. 4-7, EC is parallel to AB and AB exceeds EC by 5 in. The area of triangle ABD is three times the area of triangle ECD. Find AB.

Ans. $AB = \frac{120}{11}$.

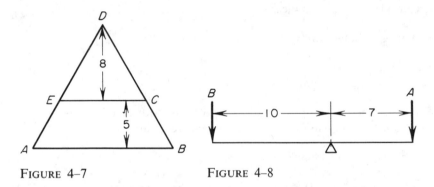

FIGURE 4–7   FIGURE 4–8

26. In Fig. 4-8, forces A and B are applied to a lever as shown. If A is 3 greater than B, find both forces.

4-4   Literal Equations and Formulas

In the exercises and examples given in the preceding sections of this chapter we confined ourselves to equations that involved one or more unknown terms, but each unknown term was described in terms of the same literal quantity. However, most formulas taken from the sciences involve more than one literal quantity. It will be our goal to solve, for one of the literal quantities, an equation involving two or more literal quantities. This will still be an equation in one unknown, and the method of solution will remain unaltered.

We will list here a suggested set of operations that are useful in obtaining the solution of an equation in one unknown. There are other ways of reaching a solution; the steps listed are intended only as a guide.

Step. 1. Clear fractions by multiplying each term by the least common multiple of the denominators.

Step. 2 Clear parentheses.

Step 3. Add quantities to each side (or subtract them) so that all terms involving the unknown will collect in one member of the equation and all others in the other member.

Step 4. Factor out the unknown as a common factor of the one or more terms involving the unknown.

Step 5. Divide both members by the coefficient of the unknown.

Consider some examples.

EXAMPLE 7. Solve for m_1 if

$$\tan \phi = \frac{m_2 - m_1}{1 + m_1 m_2}. \tag{17}$$

Solution. Applying step 1 to (17), we multiply both members by $1 + m_1 m_2$ to obtain an expression with the fraction cleared, namely

$$(1 + m_1 m_2) \tan \phi = m_2 - m_1. \tag{18}$$

Applying step 2 to (18), we remove parentheses to obtain

$$\tan \phi + m_1 m_2 \tan \phi = m_2 - m_1.$$

Now we apply step 3. The goal here is to isolate the unknown m_1; that is, we wish to transpose all terms containing m_1 to one side of the equal sign and all others to the other side. We can accomplish this by adding m_1 to each side and subtracting $\tan \phi$ from each side:

$$m_1 m_2 \tan \phi + m_1 = m_2 - \tan \phi. \tag{19}$$

Factoring the left side of (19) in compliance with step 4, we obtain

$$m_1(m_2 \tan \phi + 1) = m_2 - \tan \phi. \tag{20}$$

Following step 5, we divide each member of (20) by the coefficient of m_1, namely $m_2 \tan \phi + 1$, obtaining the desired result

$$m_1 = \frac{m_2 - \tan \phi}{1 + m_2 \tan \phi}. \tag{21}$$

Check: To check our solution, we substitute (21) into (17) to see if the latter satisfies the former. This is similar to the method described in preceding sections, but the algebra here is much more difficult:

$$\tan \phi \overset{?}{=} \frac{m_2 - \dfrac{m_2 - \tan \phi}{1 + m_2 \tan \phi}}{1 + \left(\dfrac{m_2 - \tan \phi}{1 + m_2 \tan \phi}\right) m_2}. \tag{22}$$

Multiplying the numerator and denominator of the right member of (22) by $1 + m_2 \tan \phi$, we have

$$\tan \phi \overset{?}{=} \frac{m_2 + m_2^2 \tan \phi - m_2 + \tan \phi}{1 + m_2 \tan \phi + m_2^2 - m_2 \tan \phi}. \tag{23}$$

Collecting terms, factoring, and cancelling in (23), we have

$$\tan \phi = \tan \phi.$$

In Example 7 we solved an example which required the use of all five of the steps mentioned earlier in this section. Many equations require fewer steps; note Example 8.

EXAMPLE 8. Solve for r if

$$F = \frac{Wv^2}{gr}.$$

Solution. First we clear fractions, obtaining

$$Fgr = Wv^2.$$

There are no parentheses to clear; no transposition is necessary, and no factoring is necessary. We divide now by the coefficient of r to obtain the solution

$$r = \frac{Wv^2}{Fg}.$$

EXAMPLE 9. A metallic bar is originally of length L_0. The length changes c times the original length for each degree centigrade change in the temperature. Find the new length L after a temperature change of Δt and solve the resulting equation for L_0.

Solution. Formulating the given information, we have

$$L = L_0 + L_0 c \, \Delta t.$$

Factoring the right side, we have

$$L = L_0(1 + c\Delta t).$$

Dividing by $1 + c\Delta t$,

$$L_0 = \frac{L}{1 + c\Delta t}.$$

EXAMPLE 10. A uniformly accelerating body increases its velocity from v_0 to v_t over a given time period. Its average velocity $\bar{v}$ during that time period equals 1/2 of the sum of the initial and final velocities. Obtain an expression for v_0 in terms of $\bar{v}$ and v_t.

Solution. From the given information,

$$\bar{v} = \frac{v_0 + v_t}{2}. \tag{24}$$

Clearing fractions and transposing in (24), we have

$$v_0 = 2\bar{v} - v_t.$$

Exercises

In Exercises 1–30 solve the given equation for the literal quantity indicated in parentheses. Each of the equations may be encountered in either mathematics or science.

1. $E = IR$, (I). *Ans.* $I = E/R$.

2. $I = \dfrac{E}{R + r}$, (R).

3. $I = \dfrac{2E}{R + 2r}$, (r). *Ans.* $r = \dfrac{E}{I} - \dfrac{R}{2}$.

4. $I = \dfrac{E}{R + r/2}$, (r).

5. $w = 2\pi f$, (f). *Ans.* $f = w/2\pi$.

6. $x = 2\pi f L - \dfrac{1}{2\pi f C}$, ($C$).

7. $\dfrac{P_1}{P_2} = \dfrac{V_2}{V_1}$, (V_1). $\qquad$ *Ans.* $V_1 = \dfrac{P_2 V_2}{P_1}$.

8. $P_t V_t = P_0 V_0 \left(1 + \dfrac{t}{273}\right)$, (t).

9. $W = RI^2 t$, (t). $\qquad$ *Ans.* $t = W/RI^2$.

10. $\dfrac{v_1^2}{2g} + \dfrac{p_1}{\gamma} + x_1 = \dfrac{v_2^2}{2g} + \dfrac{p_2}{\gamma} + x_2 + h_L$, (p_1).

11. $V_s = \pi[(r + h)^2 - r^2]$, (r). $\qquad$ *Ans.* $r = V_s/2\pi h - h/2$.

12. $R = \dfrac{r_1 r_2}{r_1 + r_2}$, (r_2).

13. $k = 0.4\left(1 - \dfrac{A_1}{A_2}\right)$, (A_2). $\qquad$ *Ans.* $A_2 = \dfrac{A_1}{1 - 2.5k}$.

14. $a^2 = b^2 + c^2 - 2bc \cos A$, $(\cos A)$.

15. $\dfrac{1}{R} = \dfrac{1}{r_1} + \dfrac{1}{r_2} + \dfrac{1}{r_3}$, (R). $\qquad$ *Ans.* $R = \dfrac{r_1 r_2 r_3}{r_1 r_2 + r_2 r_3 + r_1 r_3}$.

16. $s = \dfrac{gt^2}{2} + v_0 t + s_0$, (g).

17. $A = \dfrac{h}{2}(b_1 + b_2)$, (b_1). $\qquad$ *Ans.* $b_1 = \dfrac{2A}{h} - b_2$.

18. $k = \dfrac{a - b}{a + b}$, (b).

19. $A = 2(xy + xz + yz)$, (z). $\qquad$ *Ans.* $z = (A - 2xy)/2(x + y)$.

20. $A = 2\pi r^2 + 2\pi rh$, (h).

21. $V = \pi h^2 \left(r - \dfrac{h}{3}\right)$, (r). $\qquad$ *Ans.* $r = \dfrac{3V + \pi h^3}{3\pi h^2}$.

22. $R = \dfrac{P}{L}(L - b + a)$, (L).

23. $h = x - \dfrac{y'[1 + (y')^2]}{y''}$, (y''). $\qquad$ *Ans.* $y'' = \dfrac{y'[1 + (y')^2]}{x - h}$.

24. $r^2 = \dfrac{(s - a)(s - b)(s - c)}{s}$, (a).

25. $\delta = \dfrac{Px^2}{48EI}(3l - 4x)$, (l). $\qquad$ *Ans.* $l = \dfrac{48EI\delta + 4Px^3}{3Px^2}$.

26. $E = k(T_1^4 - T_2^4)$, (T_1^4).

27. $\bar{e} = L \cdot \dfrac{i_2 - i_1}{t_2 - t_1}$, (t_2). $\qquad$ *Ans.* $t_2 = t_1 + \dfrac{L(i_2 - i_1)}{\bar{e}}$.

28. $S = \dfrac{a - rl}{1 - r}$, (r).

29. $l = a + (n - 1)d$, $\ (n)$. $\hspace{2.5cm}$ *Ans.* $n = (l - a + d)/d$.

30. $S = \dfrac{n}{2}(a + l)$, $\ (a)$.

31. In Fig. 4-9, two concentric circles differ in radius by an amount h. Find r in terms of both h and the area A of the ring. $\hspace{1cm}$ *Ans.* $r = (A - \pi h^2)/2\pi h$.

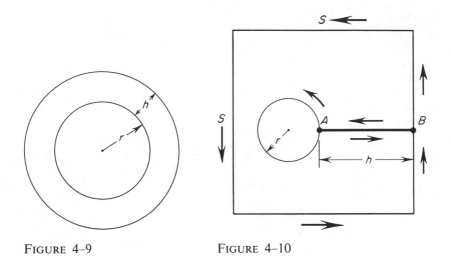

FIGURE 4–9 $\hspace{3cm}$ FIGURE 4–10

32. In Fig. 4-10 a tracer starts at A, traces once around the circle of radius r, proceeds to B, then once around the square of side s, back to B and then returns to A. Give an expression for r in terms of s, h, and D, where D is the total distance traversed by the tracer.

33. In Fig. 4-11, a trapezoid with bases a and b is mounted on a rectangle of sides b and c. Give an expression for c in terms of a, b, h, and A, where A, is the area of the combined figures. $\hspace{1cm}$ *Ans.* $c = [h(a + b) - 2A]/(a - b)$.

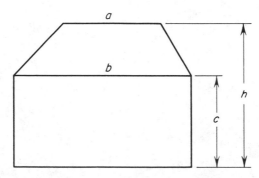

FIGURE 4–11

34. In a circuit, the total resistance R is given by the expression

$$\frac{1}{R} = \frac{1}{r_1} + \frac{1}{r_2},$$

where r_1 and r_2 are resistances in parallel. If $r_1 = k$ and r_2 exceeds r_1 by 3, find R in terms of k alone.

35. A boat cruises at a uniform rate of R mph in still water. It makes a round trip of m miles up and m miles down a river. The river's current flows at a uniform rate of r mph. The time required to make the round trip is T hours. From this information obtain the equation

$$m = \frac{T}{2R}(R^2 - r^2).$$

36. A square metallic plate of side s is heated, causing each side to increase in length by an amount Δs, changing the area of the plate by an amount ΔA. Show that

$$\frac{\Delta A}{\Delta s} = 2s + \Delta s.$$

37. A vehicle travels h miles in t_1 hours, then k miles in t_2 hours, resulting in an average speed $\bar{v}$ for the total trip. Formulate the equation

$$h = \bar{v}(t_1 + t_2) - k.$$

38. In Fig. 4-12 a seesaw arrangement is shown. Forces A, B, and C are applied in the positions shown. The turning effect (moment) provided by a force equals the product of the force times the distance of that force from the fulcrum F. To have equilibrium, the sum of the clockwise moments equals the sum of the counterclockwise moments. From this information obtain an expression for x in terms of $A, B, C, h,$ and k. *Ans.* $x = (Ch - Bk)/(A + B)$.

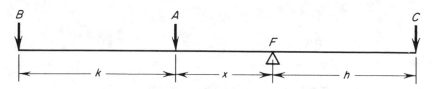

FIGURE 4-12

The more common types of variation that occur in technical applications are classified as algebraic, logarithmic, exponential, *and* trigonometric. *Perhaps the simplest algebraic variation is the so-called* linear *type. A common instance is temperature measurement, in which two different scales are popularly used: the Fahrenheit and the centigrade. A change in temperature changes both the Fahrenheit and centigrade temperature readings. Therefore it is most useful to be able to (a) produce a relationship between Fahrenheit and centigrade for any temperature, (b) find a centigrade reading mathematically if we know the Fahrenheit reading, and vice versa, (c) construct a graph or picture of the variation involved to assist in making further interpretations easily, and (d) manipulate the Fahrenheit-centigrade relationship in broadening its use.*

In this chapter we will be concerned with deriving and plotting linear forms and with applying those forms to certain useful applications.

5 LINEAR EQUATIONS

5-1   The Cartesian Coordinate Plane

Let us assume that a person has instructions to drive a nail into a wall for purposes of hanging a picture. The proper house, the proper room in the house, and the proper wall in the room have been identified and he must now be told where on that wall he must drive the nail. For our purposes we will choose the west wall of the living room. There are an infinite number of positions available to him. Most of us, in identifying the proper place to drive the nail, automatically use a reference point, often unknowingly. A description such as "two feet from the ceiling" uses the ceiling as a reference, but does not locate a single point; instead, it locates a horizontal line parallel to the ceiling and two feet below it; hence this description is inadequate to locate a point. Equally inadequate would be a single description such as "four feet from the south wall," for this locates a vertical line four feet from the south wall. If, however, we use the dual description "two feet from the ceiling and four feet from the south wall," we locate a single point where the vertical and horizontal lines intersect. More important, we have used a reference point from which measurements were made. This reference point is the point where two lines meet; the first line is the line formed by the intersection of the ceiling with the west wall and the second line is the line formed by the intersection of the south wall with the west wall. These two lines are perpendicular, and the point at which they intersect is the reference point from which the two-foot and four-foot measurements originate.

The concept just described is used in locating points in a plane in mathematics. The plane is called a *Cartesian coordinate plane* and is pictured in Fig. 5-1. All points in the plane are located with reference to the intersection of a horizontal and a vertical axis; this intersection is called the *origin,*

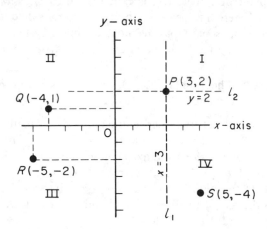

FIGURE 5–1

O. The axes are named; the horizontal axis is the *axis of abscissas* and the vertical axis is the *axis of ordinates*. In Fig. 5-1 the axis of abscissas is called the *x-axis* and the axis of ordinates is called the *y-axis*.

Note in Fig. 5-1 that points *P*, *Q*, *R*, and *S* are shown with numbers in accompanying parentheses. These numbers locate the point relative to the origin. Point *P* is 3 units to the right of the *y*-axis, or along the line $x = 3$. Note that any point on the line $x = 3$ is 3 units to the right of the *y*-axis; hence, the description $x = 3$ is sufficient to describe the line through *P*. Referring again to *P*, the abscissa there is 3. Now, *P* is also on the line $y = 2$; accordingly, the ordinate of *P* is 2. We might describe *P* as "the point 3 units to the right of the origin and 2 units above it" or "the point with abscissa 3 and ordinate 2." We shorten the terminology involved by saying that the coordinates of *P* are (3, 2). Note that the number pair used to describe *P* has the abscissa listed first and the ordinate last.

Another standard shown in Fig. 5-1 refers to direction. Note that point *Q* has a negative abscissa −4 and a positive ordinate +1. In general, if a point is to the right of the *y*-axis, its abscissa is positive; if it is to the left of the *y*-axis, its abscissa is negative. Similarly, positive ordinates are above the *x*-axis and negative ordinates are below it. Thus, the point *R* has a negative abscissa −5 and a negative ordinate −2. Also, *S* has a positive abscissa 5 and a negative ordinate −4.

One more standard shown in Fig. 5-1 is represented by the roman numerals. The axes divide the coordinate plane into four parts called *quadrants*. It is standard to number them by calling the (+, +) region Quadrant I and then proceeding in a counterclockwise direction to Quadrants II, III, and IV.

The abscissa-ordinate pair is referred to as the *coordinates* of the point in question; hence, the plane designed is called a plane of coordinates and the particular plane described here is called the Cartesian coordinate plane. The system used here in locating points is often called the *rectangular coordinate system;* it is perhaps the most common system, but is not the only one since others, notably the polar coordinate system, are also available.

EXAMPLE 1. Locate the points *P*(3, 7), *Q*(−2, −5) and *R*(5, −2) on a Cartesian coordinate plane.

Solution. First, construct two perpendicular lines, labelling the vertical line the *y*-axis and the horizontal line the *x*-axis, as in Fig. 5-2. Next, lay off equal units of length along the axes (these units of length are arbitrarily chosen). Now, to plot *P*(3, 7), we know from standards previously established that *P* is 3 units to the right of the *y*-axis and 7 units above the *x*-axis. Point *Q* is 2 units to the left of the origin and 5 units below it. Point *R* is 5 units to the right of *O* and 2 units below it.

The plotting of points is not always an exact procedure. If, in using the

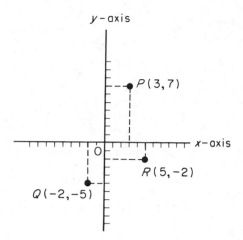

FIGURE 5–2

coordinate plane displayed in Fig. 5-2, we were asked to plot the point (−3.45, 5.14), we would be obliged to admit that we could only approximate the location of the point in view of the decimals involved. Graphing is most useful, despite its limitations, in pictorially representing a variation, enabling us to study a variation more easily.

Exercises

In which quadrants are the points:

1. $(3, -5)$. *Ans.* IV.

2. $(-2, -4)$.

3. $(-3.5, 4.2)$. *Ans.* II.

4. $(9.8, \pi)$.

5. $(\frac{33}{5}, -\frac{19}{8})$. *Ans.* IV.

6. If a point lies on the *x*-axis, what is its ordinate?

7. If a point lies on the *y*-axis, what is its abscissa?

8. If a point lies on both the *x*-axis and the *y*-axis, what are its coordinates?

9. What is the sign of the ordinate of a point if it lies in either Quadrant III or IV?

Given the points P(3, k) and Q(3, k + 1), in Exercises 10–12,

10. Are *P* and *Q* on the same vertical line?

11. Are *P* and *Q* on the same horizontal line?

12. Does P lie above or below Q?

13. Plot a triangle ABC with vertices $A(-3, -6)$, $B(-4, 7)$, and $C(5, 0)$.

14. Three vertices of a square are at $(-1, 3)$, $(4, 3)$, and $(4, -2)$. What are the coordinates of the fourth vertex?

15. The line segment AB terminates at $A(-3, -8)$ and $B(-3, 4)$. What are the the coordinates of the midpoint of AB?

16. A particle starts at $A(8, -10)$ and moves in such a way that each move covers three units to the left and one unit upward. What are the coordinates of the point after six such moves?   *Ans.* $(-10, -4)$.

17. The coordinates of the vertices of a square $ABCD$ are $A(3, 0)$, $B(0, 3)$, $C(3, 6)$, and $D(6, 3)$. What are the coordinates of the point of intersection of its diagonals?

18. A circle of radius 5 units is constructed on a Cartesian coordinate plane. How many intersections does it have with the x-axis if its center is at (a) $(3, 4)$, (b) $(-3, 5)$, (c) $(-9, 6)$, (d) $(6, 0)$?   *Ans.* (a) 2, (b) 1, (c) 0, (d) 2.

5-2   Distance Between Two Points; Slope

Given any two points P_1 and P_2 along a horizontal line, we can readily find the distance between them. In Fig. 5-3, the distance from P_1 to P_2 is $+7$

FIGURE 5-3

units of length; this can be determined by counting the units from P_1 to P_2. The choice of $+7$ units, as opposed to the choice of -7 units, is made because we are proceeding to the right (a positive direction). This $+7$ can also be shown as

$$P_1P_2 = 4 - (-3) = +7,$$

where the value of the initial point (-3) is subtracted from the value of the terminal point $(+4)$. Reversing directions in Fig. 5-3, the distance P_2P_1 can be shown as

$$P_2P_1 = -3 - (+4) = -7.$$

Distances along horizontal and vertical lines in a Cartesian coordinate plane are found as shown in Fig. 5-3.

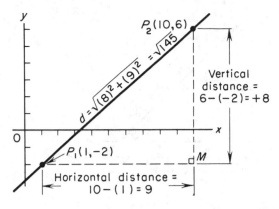

FIGURE 5-4

Let us assume that the two points under consideration do not lie on a vertical or horizontal line, but lie instead on a slanting line. Refer to Fig. 5-4. Here we are asked to find the distance from P_1 to P_2. The *horizontal* distance P_1M is the x-value at P_2 ($x_2 = 10$) less the x-value at P_1 ($x_1 = 1$), or

$$P_1M = 10 - (1) = 9.$$

Similarly, the *vertical* distance from P_1 to P_2 is the y-value at P_2 ($y_2 = 6$) less the y-value at P_1 ($y_1 = -2$), or

$$MP_2 = 6 - (-2) = 8.$$

Now, by the Pythagorean theorem, the distance is

$$d = \sqrt{(\text{horizontal distance})^2 + (\text{vertical distance})^2} \tag{1}$$

or

$$d = \sqrt{(8)^2 + (9)^2} = \sqrt{145}.$$

In the generalized sense, the distance between two points is shown in Fig. 5-5. There the given points are $P_1(x_1, y_1)$ and $P_2(x_2, y_2)$. The *horizontal* distance from P_1 to P_2 is

$$MP_2 = x_2 - x_1 \tag{2}$$

and the vertical distance between P_1 and P_2 is

$$P_1M = y_2 - y_1. \tag{3}$$

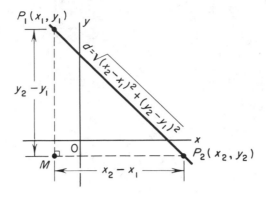

FIGURE 5-5

By the Pythagorean theorem and (1), (2), and (3),

$$d = \sqrt{(x_2 - x_1)^2 + (y_2 - y_1)^2},\qquad(4)$$

where (4) is called the *distance equation* and is useful in finding the distance between any two points $P_1(x_1, y_1)$ and $P_2(x_2, y_2)$.

EXAMPLE 2. Find the distance between $(-6, -2)$ and $(-1, 12)$.

Solution. Call either point P_1. Let us choose $P_1(x_1, y_1) = (-6, -2)$ and $P_2(x_2, y_2) = (-1, 12)$. Now we have the assignments $x_1 = -6$, $y_1 = -2$, $x_2 = -1$, and $y_2 = 12$. Substituting this into (4), we have

$$d = \sqrt{[-1 - (-6)]^2 + [12 - (-2)]^2} = \sqrt{(5)^2 + (14)^2} = \sqrt{221}.$$

We may find the distance mentally. Consider simply that the x-value changes from -6 to -1, or 5 units, and the y-value changes from -2 to $+12$, or 14 units. Now,

$$d = \sqrt{5^2 + 14^2} = \sqrt{221}.$$

EXAMPLE 3. Find the distance from $(-2, 9)$ to $(-2, -7)$.

Solution. Note that the x-value of both points is the same; therefore, the line joining the two points is vertical. Now the change in y is the distance. This change in y is

$$-7 - (+9) = -16,$$

which is the distance requested.

The *slope* of a line is defined with reference to Fig. 5-6. There $P_1(x_1, y_1)$ and

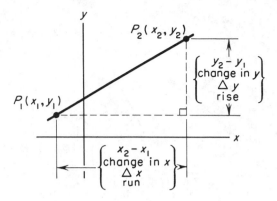

FIGURE 5–6

$P_2(x_2, y_2)$ are any two given points on a line. The slope m of the line is defined by the relationships taken from Fig. 5-6:

$$m = \frac{y_2 - y_1}{x_2 - x_1} = \frac{\text{change in } y}{\text{change in } x} = \frac{\Delta y}{\Delta x} = \frac{\text{rise}}{\text{run}}. \tag{5}$$

EXAMPLE 4. Find the slope of the straight line passing through $P_1(4, -3)$ and $P_2(-5, 9)$.

Solution. Using P_1 as the initial point and P_2 as the terminal point,

$$y_2 - y_1 = \Delta y = \text{rise} = \text{change in } y = 9 - (-3) = +12,$$
$$x_2 - x_1 = \Delta x = \text{run} = \text{change in } x = -5 - (4) = -9.$$

Applying (5), we have

$$m = \frac{y_2 - y_1}{x_2 - x_1} = \frac{+12}{-9} = -\frac{4}{3}.$$

Discussion: If we had chosen P_2 as the initial point and P_1 as the terminal point, we would have had

$$m = \frac{y_1 - y_2}{x_1 - x_2} = \frac{-12}{+9} = -\frac{4}{3}.$$

This asserts that the slope between two points is unchanged if we reverse the assignments of the initial and terminal points.

EXAMPLE 5. A vehicle is accelerating uniformly; that is, during equal time intervals, its velocity changes by equal amounts. If velocity $v = 4$ fps when time $t = 3$ sec. and $v = 14$ fps when $t = 8$ secs., find the rate of change of velocity per unit of time.

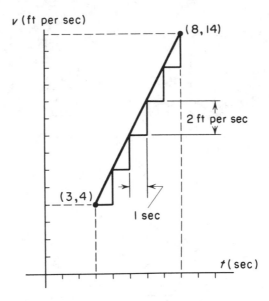

FIGURE 5–7

Solution: In Fig. 5-7 we have shown a graphical solution. In $8 - 3 = 5$ secs., the velocity has changed $14 - 4 = 10$ fps. This means that a 5-sec. change in t is accompanied by a 10-fps change in v, or

$$\frac{\Delta v}{\Delta t} = \frac{10 \text{ fps}}{5 \text{ sec.}} = 2 \text{ ft./sec.}^2 \tag{6}$$

The solution (6) is shown in Fig. 5-7 where we see a 2-fps change in the velocity for each 1-sec. change in time. We also observe from the units in (6) that $\Delta v/\Delta t$ is acceleration.

Discussion: Using the definition of slope,

$$m = \frac{v_2 - v_1}{t_2 - t_1} = \frac{14 - 4}{8 - 3} = 2,$$

where m may be interpreted as acceleration. Actually, the slope of a line may take on a variety of interpretations, depending upon the quantities assigned to the abscissa and ordinate axes.

Exercises

In Exercises 1–13, find the distance between the given points. Also find the slope of the straight line joining the points.

1. $(0, 0)$, $(3, 4)$.   *Ans.* $d = 5$, $m = \frac{4}{3}$.

2. (0, 0), (4, 3).

3. (−5, 12), (0, 0).   *Ans. $d = 13, m = -\frac{12}{5}$.*

4. (−5, −12), (0, 0).

5. (6, −14), (−3, 4).   *Ans. $d = 9\sqrt{5}, m = -2$.*

6. (4, 5), (6, −7).

7. (−6, 4), (3, −9).   *Ans. $d = 5\sqrt{10}, m = -\frac{13}{9}$.*

8. (7, −9), (−4, −6).

9. (12, −3), (15, −3).   *Ans. $d = 3, m = 0$.*

10. (5.2, 4), (4.2, −3.6).

11. (6, −3), (6, 7).   *Ans. $d = 10$, m is not defined.*

12. (a, b), (b, a).

13. (a + b, b), (a, a + b).   *Ans. $d = \sqrt{a^2 + b^2}, m = -a/b$.*

In Exercises 14–20, what are the units of the slope of a line if the abscissa and ordinate units are as given?

14. Abscissa, time; ordinate, distance.

15. Abscissa, number of tickets; ordinate, total cost.   *Ans.* Cost per ticket.

16. Ordinate, force; abscissa, area.

17. Abscissa, time; ordinate, number of electrons passing a point.
                                                    Ans. Electric current.

18. Abscissa and ordinate units the same.

19. Ordinate, interest accumulated; abscissa, time.   *Ans.* Interest rate.

20. Ordinate, cubic feet; abscissa, square feet.   *Ans.* Feet.

21. Show by use of the definition of slope that the points (−2, −5), (1, −4), (4, −3) lie on the same straight line.

22. Using the distance formula, show that the points (−2, −5), (1, −4) and (0, −1) are the vertices of a right triangle. Without sketching the triangle, identify the right angle.

23. A vehicle travels at a uniform velocity. The distance d travelled is 24 ft. when time t is 4 secs. Also, $d = 52$ ft. when $t = 11$ secs. What is the velocity of the vehicle? Using the velocity determined, find d when $t = 10$ secs. What was d when t was zero?

24. Two vehicles, A and B, travel the same route with the same velocity. For A, $d = 120$ ft. when $t = 2$ secs. and $d = 300$ ft. when $t = 6$ secs. For B, $d = 80$ ft. when $t = 2$ secs. Find d for vehicle B when $t = 6$ secs. At any instant, by how many feet does A lead B?

25. A straight line passes through $(3, 0)$ with a slope of $-\frac{1}{2}$. A point P on the line has an abscissa of 9. What is the ordinate of P? *Ans.* -3.

26. A straight line passes through $(8, 6)$ with a slope of -4. How many units from the origin is the point where the line crosses the y-axis?

Ans. 38 units above.

27. If a line passes through $(6, 4)$ and $(-3, -7)$, at what point does it intercept the y-axis? *Ans.* Where $y = -\frac{10}{3}$.

5-3   Division of a Line Segment

A line segment may be divided into any number of equal parts. Let us discuss the division of a line segment by referring to the method of division used in plane geometry; this is considered in Example 6.

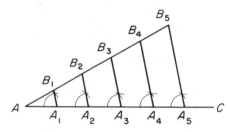

FIGURE 5–8

EXAMPLE 6. Divide the line segment AB_5 shown in Fig. 5-8 into 5 equal parts.

Solution. Using a plane geometry method, we construct any line AC forming an angle with AB_5. Along AC mark off 5 equal units of length of any convenient size; these equal lengths are AA_1, A_1A_2, A_2A_3, etc. in Fig. 5-8. Draw the line A_5B_5. Now construct A_4B_4, A_3B_3, etc. parallel to A_5B_5. Now B_1, B_2, B_3, and B_4 divide AB_5 into 5 equal parts. This method employs the theorem which asserts that "if parallel lines intercept equal line segments on one transversal, they will intercept equal line segments on any other transversal."

The method shown in Fig. 5-8 can be used, slightly modified, in determining the coordinates of the points of division of a line segment if the coordinates of the end points are known. Before presenting a general case, let us discuss a specific case in Example 7.

EXAMPLE 7. Given the line segment AB with end points $A(-6, 2)$ and $B(4, 7)$, divide the line segment into 5 equal parts and give the coordinates of each of the points of division.

Solution. Refer to Fig. 5-9, where we have plotted A and B. The horizontal distance from A to B is

$$4 - (-6) = +10$$

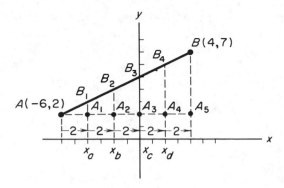

FIGURE 5-9

units. These 10 units may be divided into 5 equal parts of 2 units each. A horizontal line AA_5 is divided into 5 equal parts. Vertical lines A_1B_1, A_2B_2, etc. are drawn, dividing AB into 5 equal parts according to the geometric method shown in Example 6. The x-coordinates of B_1, B_2, etc. are

$$x_a = -6 + \tfrac{1}{5}(10) = -4,$$
$$x_b = -6 + \tfrac{2}{5}(10) = -2,$$
$$x_c = -6 + \tfrac{3}{5}(10) = 0,$$
$$x_d = -6 + \tfrac{4}{5}(10) = 2.$$

The y-coordinates of the points of division may be found analogously. Coordinates of the points of division are $(-4, 3)$, $(-2, 4)$, $(0, 5)$ and $(2, 6)$.

Let us now consider a general expression for division of a line segment. Given segment P_1P_2, where $P_1(x_1,y_1)$ and $P_2(x_2,y_2)$ are the end points, we wish to find the coordinates of the rth point of division removed from P_1 if P_1P_2 is divided into k equal parts. To find x_r (the x-coordinate of the rth point of division removed from P_1), we proceed as follows:

First, the horizontal distance from P_1 to P_2 is $x_2 - x_1$. Now we are dividing P_1P_2 into k equal parts, so that each horizontal part is of width $(x_2 - x_1)/k$ and r of these parts accumulate to $r(x_2 - x_1)/k$ units. The rth point removed from P_1 has the x-coordinate

$$x_r = x_1 + \frac{r}{k}(x_2 - x_1). \tag{7}$$

By similar reasoning,

$$y_r = y_1 + \frac{r}{k}(y_2 - y_1), \tag{8}$$

where (7) and (8) give the coordinates of the rth point of division removed from P_1 if the line segment P_1P_2 is divided into k equal parts.

The midpoint of a line segment. If we wish to find the midpoint (x_m, y_m) of a line segment P_1P_2, then, from (7) and (8), $k = 2$ and $r = 1$, so that

$$x_m = x_1 + \frac{1}{2}(x_2 - x_1) = \frac{x_1 + x_2}{2}, \tag{9}$$

$$y_m = y_1 + \frac{1}{2}(y_2 - y_1) = \frac{y_1 + y_2}{2}, \tag{10}$$

where (9) and (10) give the coordinates requested. The conclusion in (9) and (10) is not surprising because a midcoordinate is an *average* coordinate. To find the average of two quantities, we add them together and divide them by 2, as shown in (9) and (10).

Applications of equations (7) and (8) are called *interpolation*, and are particularly useful when values are desired which lie between two values listed in a table of logarithms, trigonometric functions, and others. Interpolation will be considered more fully in a later chapter.

Exercises

1. Sketch on graph paper the straight line connecting the points $A(2, 1)$ and $B(11, 6)$. Find the midpoint of AB. *Ans.* (6.5, 3.5).

2. Sketch on graph paper the straight line connecting the points $A(-3, 2)$ and $B(5, 5)$. Find the midpoint of AB.

3. For the line segment AB of Exercise 1, find the coordinates of the second point of division removed from A if AB is divided into 3 equal parts. *Ans.* $(8, 4\frac{1}{3})$.

4. For the line segment AB of Exercise 2, find the coordinates of the second point of division removed from A if AB is divided into 3 equal parts.

5. Sketch on graph paper the straight line connecting the points $A(6, -2)$ and $B(-4, 3)$. Find the coordinates of the third point of division removed from A if AB is divided into 5 equal parts. *Ans.* (0, 1).

6. Sketch on graph paper the straight line connecting the points $A(7, -1)$ and $B(-3, -6)$. Find the coordinates of the third point of division removed from A if AB is divided into 5 equal parts.

7. A line segment AB has its midpoint at $(2, 4)$ and point A at $(-3, 7)$. Find the coordinates of point B. *Ans.* (7, 1).

8. A line segment AB has its midpoint at $(-2, -3)$ and point A at $(-8, -7)$. Find the coordinates of point B.

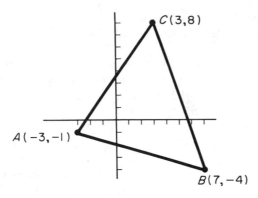

FIGURE 5-10

9. In Fig. 5-10, find the midpoints of AB, BC, and AC.

Ans. $(2, -\frac{5}{2})$, $(5, 2)$, $(0, \frac{7}{2})$.

10. In Fig. 5-10, find the coordinates of the second point of division removed from A if AB is divided into 6 equal parts.

11. A certain investment P grows by the same amount each year. At the end of year 4 its value is $1200; at the end of year 9 its value is $1550. What is its value at the end of year 7; year 13; year 2?   Ans. $1410, $1830, $1060.

12. In Fig. 5-11 a small portion of the curve $y = \log x$ is shown. From it we read $\log 15.03 = 1.17696$ and $\log 15.04 = 1.17725$. Assuming for the brief interval shown that AB is a straight line, use the division of a line segment to find the approximate value of $\log 15.036$.   Ans. $\log 15.036 = 1.17713$.

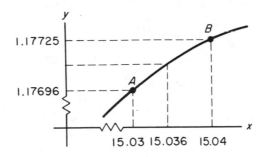

FIGURE 5-11

13. From trigonometry we are given ctn $16°45'00'' = 3.3226$ and ctn $16°45'60'' = 3.3191$. Using division of a line segment, find the approximate value of ctn $16°45'28''$, assuming that, for the brief interval under consideration, we have a straight line.   Ans. ctn $16°45'28'' = 3.3210$.

14. Modify equations (7) and (8) to locate the $(k - r)$th point of division from P_2. Show that the resulting expressions are equivalent algebraically to (7) and (8).

5-4   Determining Linear Equations
from Given Conditions

Let us suppose that we have two quantities x and y which are related by the fact that y is always 3 units greater than x. This means that when $x = 2$, $y = 5$; when $x = 7.2$, $y = 10.2$; when $x = -3$, $y = 0$; etc. Actually, any (x, y) pair which satisfies the equation

$$y = x + 3 \qquad\qquad (11)$$

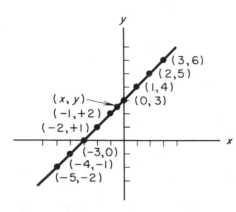

FIGURE   5-12

is a suitable number pair. There are indefinitely many such pairs. If all of these pairs were plotted on a Cartesian coordinate plane, they would lie in a straight line as shown in Fig. 5-12 where only certain of the number pairs are shown. Any point along the line can be designated as (x, y) where the x and y of (x, y) are the same x and y used in (11).

We note, too, from Fig. 5-12, that the slope of the line is unity, as can be determined by the selection of any two points and application of (5). Let us create a special description of the slope, using the general point (x, y) and any point shown in Fig. 5-12, say the point $(3, 6)$. Now we have

$$\frac{y - 6}{x - 3} = \text{slope}.$$

But the slope is $m = 1$, so that

$$\frac{y - 6}{x - 3} = 1. \qquad\qquad (12)$$

Simplifying (12), we obtain the equation

$$y = x + 3,$$

which agrees with (11). What was demonstrated here is the fact that, given the slope of a line ($m = 1$) and a point $(3, 6)$ on the line, we can obtain the equation of the line. The slope, incidentally, was obtained from knowledge of the coordinates of any two points on the line.

We may obtain the equation of a straight line knowing *one* point on the line and the slope of the line. The equation of the line may be written in a variety of forms. A demonstration of some of these forms follows.

Two-Point Form

Given any two points $P_1(x_1, y_1)$ and $P_2(x_2, y_2)$ on a straight line, let us derive the equation of the line. We do this by equating two expressions for the slope. Refer to Fig. 5-13. Using the given points,

$$m = \frac{y_2 - y_1}{x_2 - x_1}. \tag{13}$$

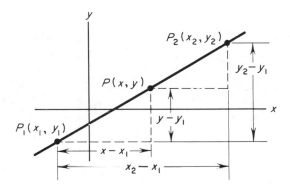

FIGURE 5–13

Using the general point $P(x, y)$ and either of the given points (we chose P_1 in Fig. 5-13),

$$m = \frac{y - y_1}{x - x_1}. \tag{14}$$

Equating (13) and (14), we have

$$\frac{y - y_1}{x - x_1} = \frac{y_2 - y_1}{x_2 - x_1}, \tag{15}$$

where (15) is the *two-point form* of a straight line.

EXAMPLE 8. Find the equation of the line passing through $(-4, 3)$ and $(2, -5)$.

Solution. We choose to designate $(-4, 3)$ as P_1 so that $x_1 = -4$ and $y_1 = 3$, and (2, −5) as P_2 so that $x_2 = 2$ and $y_2 = -5$. Substituting into (15), we have

$$\frac{y - (3)}{x - (-4)} = \frac{-5 - (3)}{2 - (-4)}$$

or

$$\frac{y - 3}{x + 4} = -\frac{8}{6}$$

from which

$$3y + 4x = -7$$

is the equation of the line in question.

Point-Slope Form

Let us suppose that we know the slope m of a straight line and a point $P_1(x_1, y_1)$ through which it passes. We can obtain the equation of the line readily by referring to (15). There the right member is an expression for the slope; but we are given the slope as m. Replacing the right member of (15) by m, we have

$$\frac{y - y_1}{x - x_1} = m, \tag{16}$$

where (16) is the equation of a line known to pass through $P_1(x_1, y_1)$ with slope m and is called the *point-slope form*.

EXAMPLE 9. Find the equation of the line passing through (−4, 3) with a slope of −1.

Solution. Call (−4, 3) the point $P_1(x_1, y_1)$ so that $x_1 = -4$ and $y_1 = 3$. The slope is $m = -1$. Substituting into (16), we have

$$\frac{y - (+3)}{x - (-4)} = -1.$$

Simplifying, we have

$$y = -x - 1.$$

Slope-Intercept Form

Let us suppose again that we are given the slope of a line and a point on the line, as in the point-slope case. This time, however, the given point will be the *y-intercept*, that is, the distance from the origin to the point where the line crosses the *y*-axis. Call the coordinates of the *y*-intercept $(0, b)$. The *y*-intercept is therefore called b and the slope is once again m. Now, referring to (16), we have $x_1 = 0$ and $y_1 = b$. Substituting into (16),

$$\frac{y - b}{x - 0} = m$$

from which

$$y = mx + b, \tag{17}$$

where (17) is the *slope-intercept form* of a straight line.

EXAMPLE 10. Find the equation of a straight line with slope -3 and *y*-intercept $+5$.

Solution. Referring to (17) we have $m = -3$ and $b = +5$. Substituting, we have

$$y = -3x + 5.$$

Intercept Form

Let us suppose that we are given the intercepts of a straight line. The line crosses the *x*-axis at $x = a$ and the *y*-axis at $y = b$, where a is the *x*-intercept and b is the *y*-intercept. The coordinates of the *x*-intercept are $(a, 0)$ and the coordinates of the *y*-intercept are $(0, b)$. Now we have the two-point form with $x_1 = a$, $y_1 = 0$, $x_2 = 0$, and $y_2 = b$. Substituting into the two-point form (15),

$$\frac{y - 0}{x - a} = \frac{b - 0}{0 - a},$$

which can be simplified to read

$$\frac{x}{a} + \frac{y}{b} = 1, \tag{18}$$

where (18) is the *intercept form* of a straight line.

EXAMPLE 11. Find the equation of the straight line with *x*-intercept 12 and *y*-intercept -6.

Solution. Referring to (18), we have $a = 12$ and $b = -6$. Substituting we have

$$\frac{x}{12} + \frac{y}{-6} = 1,$$

from which

$$x - 2y = 12.$$

EXAMPLE 12. Find the slope of the line

$$3x - 4y = 12. \tag{19}$$

Solution. If we solve (19) for y, we will have the slope-intercept form. Solving,

$$y = \tfrac{3}{4}x - 3. \tag{20}$$

Comparing (20) to (17), the coefficient of x is $\tfrac{3}{4}$ and is also the requested slope.

EXAMPLE 13. What is the y-intercept of the line passing through $(-3, -6)$ and $(-2, -3)$?

Solution. If we use the two-point form to obtain the equation of the line, then manipulate the equation into the slope-intercept form, we will be able to recognize the y-intercept. Now, substituting into (15),

$$\frac{y + 3}{x + 2} = \frac{-3 - (-6)}{-2 - (-3)},$$

from which

$$\frac{y + 3}{x + 2} = 3$$

and

$$y = 3x + 3. \tag{21}$$

Comparing (21) to (17), we recognize the y-intercept as $b = +3$.

Exercises

In Exercises 1–12, find the equation of the straight line satisfying the given conditions.

1. Passes through $(0, 0)$ and $(3, 2)$. *Ans.* $y = 2x/3.$

2. Passes through $(0, 0)$ and $(-3, 2)$.

3. Passes through $(3, -5)$ and $(-4, 6)$.   *Ans.* $7y + 11x + 2 = 0$.

4. Passes through $(2, -9)$ with slope $\frac{1}{2}$.

5. Passes through $(5, 0)$ with slope $\frac{1}{5}$.   *Ans.* $x - 5y = 5$.

6. Passes through $(-7, 2)$ with slope $\frac{3}{4}$.

7. Has slope $-\frac{1}{2}$ and y-intercept 4.   *Ans.* $y = -x/2 + 4$.

8. Has slope $m = -\frac{3}{5}$ and y-intercept -5.

9. Has slope $-\frac{5}{3}$ and x-intercept $\frac{10}{3}$.   *Ans.* $y = -5x/3 + \frac{50}{9}$.

10. Has x-intercept 5 and y-intercept -2.

11. Has x-intercept $\frac{1}{2}$ and y-intercept -4.   *Ans.* $8x - y = 4$.

12. The x-intercept is twice the y-intercept and the line passes through $(-9, 6)$.

In Exercises 13–18, given the equation

$$Ax + By = C, \tag{22}$$

provide answers for the questions asked.

13. What is the slope of (22)?   *Ans.* $-A/B$.

14. What is the y-intercept of (22)?

15. What is the x-intercept of (22)?   *Ans.* C/A.

16. What is the relationship between A and B if the slope of (22) is $-\frac{3}{2}$?

17. What is the relationship between A and B if the slope of (22) is $+1$?

18. Which constant must be zero if (22)
(*a*) passes through the origin?
(*b*) is vertical?
(*c*) is horizontal?

19. Show that all of the lines passing through $P(3, 2)$ in Fig. 5-14 can be represented by the equation

$$y = m(x - 3) + 2.$$

20. Show that the equations of all of the parallel lines shown in Fig. 5-15 can be represented by the equation

$$y = -\tfrac{3}{4}x + b,$$

where b is a y-intercept.

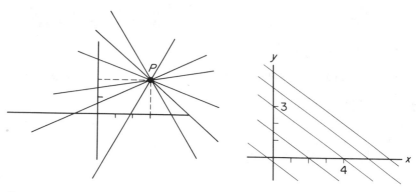

FIGURE 5–14   FIGURE 5–15

21. Jones and Smith design the temperature scales shown in Fig. 5-16. Draw up an equation relating degrees Smith (S) to degrees Jones (J). What equation relates Smith to Fahrenheit? Jones to centigrade?

Ans. $J = 2S/5 + 50$; $F = 18S/25 + 32$; $J = C + 50$.

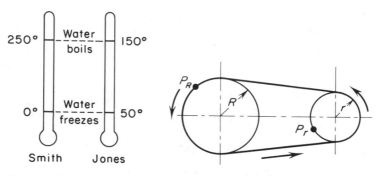

FIGURE 5–16   FIGURE 5–17

22. In Fig. 5-17 a belt system is pictured. Wheels of radii R and r rotate, giving motion to a nonslipping belt. Show that the distances travelled by P_R and P_r in a given amount of time are equal; show also that the number of circumferences completed by P_R and P_r are in the ratio $r : R$.

5-5   Graphing Linear Equations

Each of the forms of the straight line derived in Sec. 5-4 may be reduced to the form

$$Ax + By = C. \tag{23.0}$$

Certain observations of (23.0) are in order. First, A, B, and C are constants.

Second, A and B cannot both be zero. Third, x and y are variables and they are present in the first degree at the highest.

Graphing (23.0) can be a simple task. Since two points determine a straight line, the x-intercept and the y-intercept can be readily determined, plotted, and a straight line passed through them. To find the x-intercept, let $y = 0$, from which $x = C/A$; to find the y-intercept, let $x = 0$, from which $y = C/B$.

The intercepts of (23.0) may not be distinct, or they may be unfortunately close together. If this is the case, we may solve for y such that

$$y = -\frac{A}{B}x + \frac{C}{B} \qquad (23.1)$$

where (23.1) is in the slope-intercept form, $y = mx + b$, with slope $m = -A/B$ and y-intercept C/B. To plot (23.1), we may plot the y-intercept and proceed from that point in the direction required by m.

EXAMPLE 14. Graph the equation

$$3x + 2y = 6. \qquad (23.2)$$

Solution. To graph (23.2), determine the intercepts. If $x = 0$, $y = 3$ and if $y = 0$, $x = 2$. We plot the intercepts and pass a line through them as in Fig. 5-18. Note that we plotted a third point $(4, -3)$ which satisfies (23.2) and was arbitrarily chosen. This third point falls on the given line, giving us confidence that the line was properly graphed. If the three points are not collinear (that is, do not fall in a straight line), all three points bear checking.

EXAMPLE 15. Graph the equation

$$2y - x = 0. \qquad (23.3)$$

Solution. Solving (23.3) for y, we have

$$y = \tfrac{1}{2}x.$$

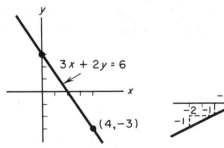

FIGURE 5–18

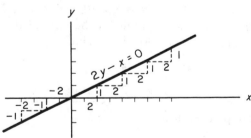

FIGURE 5–19

Now we observe that the line passes through the origin with a slope of $\frac{1}{2}$. We can start our graphing at the origin and move off at a slope of $\frac{1}{2}$; that is, run 2 and rise 1 or run -2 and rise -1 as shown in Fig. 5-19.

Examining (23.0), we observe more properties. First, if $A = 0$, then $By = C$ is a horizontal line C/B units removed from the x-axis. Second, if $B = 0$, then $Ax = C$ is a vertical line C/A units removed from the y-axis. Third, if $C = 0$, the intercepts are both zero and the line passes through the origin.

5-6   Parallel and Perpendicular Lines

If two lines are parallel, their slopes are equal; thus, for the equations

$$Ax + By = C \tag{23.40}$$

and

$$Dx + Ey = F, \tag{23.41}$$

we have parallelism if certain conditions are met. If we solve (23.40) and (23.41) for y, we have

$$y = -\frac{A}{B}x + \frac{C}{B}, \tag{23.50}$$

$$y = -\frac{D}{E}x + \frac{F}{E}. \tag{23.51}$$

The slopes of (23.50) and (23.51) are, respectively, $-A/B$ and $-D/E$; if the lines are parallel, these are equal, hence,

$$-\frac{A}{B} = -\frac{D}{E}, \tag{23.6}$$

where equation (23.6) provides a test for parallelism of two straight lines. Note that (23.6) involves neither C nor F. Note further that (23.6) asserts that two lines are parallel if the ratio of the x-coefficient to the y-coefficient is the same for both lines. Thus,

$$3x - 2y = 5$$
$$-6x + 4y = 25$$

are parallel since

$$\frac{3}{-2} = \frac{-6}{4}.$$

EXAMPLE 16. Give the equation of the line parallel to $2x + y = 9$ and passing through (5, 4).

Solution. Since the desired line parallels $2x + y = 9$, it is of the form

$$2x + y = k, \tag{23.7}$$

where the ratio of the coefficients of the x-term and the y-term is undisturbed. Now, (23.7) passes through the point where $x = 5$ and $y = 4$. Substituting,

$$2(5) + 4 = k,$$

from which $k = 14$. Substituting $k = 14$ into (23.7), the desired solution is

$$2x + y = 14.$$

Two lines are perpendicular if their slopes are negative reciprocals of each other. This is shown as follows:

Given line l_1 shown in Fig. 5-20, of the form $y = mx + b$. A point

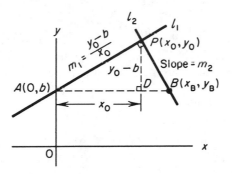

FIGURE 5–20

$P(x_0, y_0)$ is on l_1. A line perpendicular to l_1 is drawn through P; call this line l_2. Our goal is to show that the slope of l_2 is $m_2 = -1/m_1$, where m_1 is the slope of l_1 and m_2 is the slope of l_2. Let us proceed by first finding the coordinates of B.

From plane geometry, PD is the mean proportional between AD and DB. That is,

$$\overline{PD^2} = (AD)(DB)$$

from which

$$(y_0 - b)^2 = (x_0)DB \text{ and } DB = \frac{(y_0 - b)^2}{x_0}.$$

Now, the coordinates of B are

$$x_B = x_0 + DB = x_0 + \frac{(y_0 - b)^2}{x_0}, \quad y_B = b.$$

Finding the slope of PB by using the coordinates of P and B, we have

$$m_2 = \frac{y_0 - y_B}{x_0 - x_B} = \frac{y_0 - b}{x_0 - \left[x_0 + \dfrac{(y_0 - b)^2}{x_0} \right]} = \frac{y_0 - b}{-\dfrac{(y_0 - b)^2}{x_0}} = -\frac{x_0}{y_0 - b}.$$

Comparing m_1 to m_2, we have

$$m_2 = -\frac{1}{m_1} \quad \text{or} \quad m_1 m_2 = -1. \tag{23.8}$$

The conclusion reached in (23.8) is: *if two lines are perpendicular, their slopes are negative reciprocals.*

EXAMPLE 17. Give the equation of the lines perpendicular to

$$y = 2x + 5.$$

Solution. The slope of the given line is $m = +2$; therefore the slope of the perpendicular, by (23.8), is $-\frac{1}{2}$. Since we require *any* line perpendicular to $y = 2x + 5$, let the y-intercept be b, producing the solution

$$y = -\frac{1x}{2} + b$$

In Fig. 5-21, we see four of the family of lines perpendicular to $y = 2x + 5$.

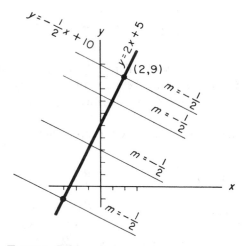

FIGURE 5–21

EXAMPLE 18. Give the equation of the line perpendicular to $y = 2x + 5$ and passing through (2, 9).

Solution. From Example 17, the equation of the line perpendicular to $y = 2x + 5$ is $y = -1x/2 + b$. Now the point (2, 9) is on $y = -1x/2 + b$, so that

$$9 = -\tfrac{1}{2}(2) + b,$$

from which $b = 10$ and the equation of the desired line is

$$y = -\tfrac{1}{2}x + 10,$$

which is shown in Fig. 5-21.

Exercises

1. Given the equation $ax + by = c$. Show that multiplying each term by a constant k does not affect either the slope or the y-intercept.

Given the equations $ax + by = c$, $dx + ey = f$, in Exercises 2–4:

2. What relationship involving the constants must exist if the lines are parallel? *Ans. $a/d = b/e$.*

3. What relationship involving the constants must exist if the lines are perpendicular? *Ans. $-d/e = b/a$.*

4. What relationship involving the constants must exist if the lines have the same y-intercept? *Ans. $c/b = f/e$.*

5. Find the equation of the line perpendicular to $2x - 3y = 6$ and passing through the origin.

6. Given l_1 as $Ax + By = C$. Show that the line l_2, obtained by interchanging A and B and changing the sign of either A or B, will be perpendicular to l_1.

Given the line l_1 as $2x - y = 6$, find the equation of the line in Exercises 7–10.

7. Parallel to l_1 and passing through (2, 2). *Ans. $2x - y = 2$.*

8. Perpendicular to l_1 and passing through (2, 2). *Ans. $x + 2y = 6$.*

9. Parallel to l_1, with y-intercept -8.

10. Perpendicular to l_1 at (6, 6).

11. Find the equation of the perpendicular bisector of the line segment terminating at $P(-1, 3)$ and $R(5, 5)$. *Ans. $y + 3x = 10$.*

12. Given the triangle with vertices $A(-3, -4)$, $B(0, 4)$ and $C(4, -2)$. Find the equation of the altitude drawn from B to AC. *Ans. $2y + 7x = 8$.*

13. It is known that the line $x + ky = 7$ is perpendicular to the line $3x - 5y = 6$. Find k. *Ans.* $k = \frac{3}{5}$.

14. Given l_1 as $4x + y = 9$ and l_2 as $8x + 2y = k$. What value of k will cause l_1, and l_2 to be graphed as the same line?

15. Given l_1 as $4y - 3x = 12$ and l_2 as $ax + by = c$. If l_1 is perpendicular to l_2, what is the ratio $a : b$? *Ans.* $+\frac{4}{3}$.

16. Given the line l_1 as $2y = x + 2$. Lines l_2 and l_3 are drawn perpendicular to l_1 at the points $(2, 2)$ and $(4, 3)$ respectively. What is the distance between the y-intercepts of l_2 and l_3?

5-7 Simultaneous Solutions

If two straight lines are graphed on a Cartesian coordinate plane, they will intersect in one point, provided they are not parallel. This point of intersection possesses a set of coordinates which simultaneously satisfies both of the equations and is called the *simultaneous solution* of the two lines. The simultaneous solution can be found both graphically and algebraically. We will discuss both methods here.

EXAMPLE 19. By graphical methods find the point of intersection of

$$x + y = 8, \tag{24}$$

$$x - y = 4. \tag{25}$$

Solution. Refer to Fig. 5-22 where the graphs of (24) and (25) are shown.

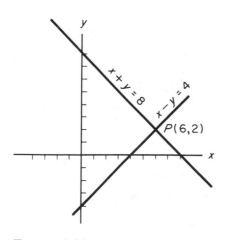

FIGURE 5–22

The lines intersect at $P(6, 2)$. Note that the coordinates $(6, 2)$ satisfy both (24) and (25) since $6 + 2 = 8$ and $6 - 2 = 4$. No other point on (24) is also on (25).

We may make an observation about the graphical method of solution shown in Example 19. The method may not be exact, owing to inaccuracies which develop in the graphing process. This would be more apparent if the points of intersection were represented by fractional or irrational coordinates. We will discuss here three algebraic methods of obtaining simultaneous solutions of linear equations. Our approach will be a general one, followed by example problems.

Solution by Substitution

Given two nonparallel lines

$$Ax + By = C, \tag{26}$$
$$Dx + Ey = F, \tag{27}$$

we may solve either equation for either unknown and substitute the result into the other equation. Proceeding, we solve (26) for y, such that

$$y = -\frac{Ax}{B} + \frac{C}{B}. \tag{28}$$

Substituting (28) into (27), we have

$$Dx + E\left(-\frac{Ax}{B} + \frac{C}{B}\right) = F,$$

from which, after several algebraic steps,

$$x = \frac{EC - FB}{AE - BD}. \tag{29}$$

If we substitute (29) into either (26) or (27), we obtain a value for y. Choosing (26), we have

$$A\left(\frac{EC - FB}{AE - BD}\right) + By = C,$$

from which we obtain the value

$$y = \frac{AF - CD}{AE - BD}. \tag{30}$$

Expressions (29) and (30) are the x-coordinate and y-coordinate, respectively, of the point of intersection of (26) and (27). Figure 5–23 shows all of the important expressions on a Cartesian coordinate plane. Observe that the intersection point

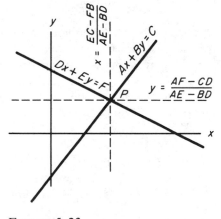

FIGURE 5–23

P is actually the intersection of lines (29) and (30). In our solution we at one point solved the horizontal line (29) against $Ax + By = C$ to obtain point P.

Solution by Comparison

We may find the point of intersection of (26) and (27) by solving both equations for the same unknown and then comparing results. Choosing to solve both for y, we have

$$y = -\frac{Ax}{B} + \frac{C}{B} \tag{31}$$

and

$$y = -\frac{Dx}{E} + \frac{F}{E}. \tag{32}$$

Comparing (31) and (32,)

$$-\frac{Ax}{B} + \frac{C}{B} = -\frac{Dx}{E} + \frac{F}{E}, \tag{33}$$

from which we may obtain

$$x = \frac{EC - FB}{AE - BD}, $$

which is identical with (29) obtained by the substitution method. From this point we complete the solution as in the substitution method.

Solution by Elimination

We may choose to eliminate one of the unknowns by the subtraction of one of the equations from the other. Elimination of an unknown by subtraction occurs only if that unknown has the same coefficient in both equations. If the coefficients are the same but opposite in sign, addition will eliminate the unknown. Let us proceed, choosing to eliminate the y term by multiplying (26) by E and (27) by B; thus

$$AEx + BEy = CE, \tag{34}$$
$$BDx + BEy = BF. \tag{35}$$

Subtracting (35) from (34), we have

$$AEx - BDx = CE - BF, \tag{36}$$

and, solving (36) for x, we have (29). To obtain y, we proceed as in previous methods.

We may ask which method we should use in solving a system. The answer depends largely upon the nature of the coefficients or the manner in which the equations are given. Thus, if both equations are already solved for one of the unknowns, that is, for the same unknown, comparison may be most useful. If one equation is readily solved for an unknown and the other equation may not easily be solved for that unknown, then substitution may be the easiest. If both equations are given in the same algebraic form, addition or subtraction may be the easiest.

EXAMPLE 20. Find the simultaneous solution of

$$3x - 5y = 23, \tag{37}$$

$$x + 4y = 2. \tag{38}$$

Solution. Let us multiply (38) by 3 and subtract.

$$\begin{array}{r} 3x - 5y = 23 \\ 3x + 12y = 6 \\ \hline - 17y = 17 \end{array}$$

from which $y = -1$. Substituting $y = -1$ into (38), we have

$$x + 4(-1) = 2,$$

from which $x = 6$ and the complete solution is the point $(6, -1)$.

Discussion: We chose here solution by subtraction which required multiplying all terms of (38) by 3. There may be some question about the validity of such a multiplication. The equations

$$Ax + By = C \quad \text{and} \quad kAx + kBy = kC$$

graph as the same equation and are called *equivalent equations;* this may be demonstrated by obtaining the slope-intercept form of both equations and comparing the slopes and y-intercepts.

EXAMPLE 21. Two vehicles A and B proceed along the same route. Vehicle A travels at a constant speed of 30 mph; vehicle B travels at a constant speed of 40 mph. How long does it take B to catch A if A had a 50-mile head start? Where is the point at which B catches A?

Solution. Upon formulating the distance-time relationships, we have, for A,

$$s = 30t + 50, \tag{39}$$

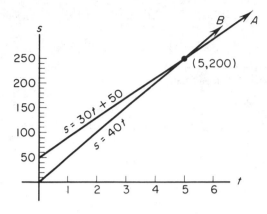

FIGURE 5–24

and, for B,

$$s = 40t, \tag{40}$$

where t is time in hours and s is distance travelled in miles. Figure 5-24 shows the graphical solution of (39) and (40). We may solve the system algebraically by comparison where

$$30t + 50 = 40t,$$

from which $t = 5$. Substituting $t = 5$ into (40), we obtain $s = 200$. The solution ($t = 5$ hr., $s = 200$ miles) means that B and A are simultaneously at the same point exactly 5 hours and 200 miles from the starting position which was taken as $t = 0$ and $s = 0$ for B and $t = 0$, $s = 50$ for A.

Exercises

In Exercises 1–20, solve the given systems algebraically. Choose any of the three methods discussed. It is suggested that graphical solutions also be shown to check for gross errors and to assist in interpretation.

1. $x + y = 7,$
$\quad x - y = 3.$
Ans. (5, 2).

2. $y - x = 9,$
$\quad x + y = 15.$

3. $y = 8 - x,$
$\quad y - 2 = x.$
Ans. (3, 5)

4. $11 - y = x,$
$\quad 7 + x = y.$

5. $2x + y = 7,$
    $x - 2y = 6.$
                                                     Ans. $(4, -1).$

6. $x + 4y = 7,$
    $3x - y = 8.$

7. $2x + 3y - 14 = 0,$
    $3x - 4y - 4 = 0.$
                                                     Ans. $(4, 2)$

8. $3x + 4y = 4,$
    $4x + 3y = 10.$

9. $3x + 5y = 9,$
    $4x - 6y = -7.$
                                                  Ans. $(\frac{1}{2}, \frac{3}{2}).$

10. $5m - 2n = \frac{7}{6},$
    $3m + 7n = -\frac{3}{4}.$

11. $8r - \frac{1}{2}P = 60,$
    $3r + 2P = 40.$
                                                  Ans. $(8, 8).$

12. $2t - \frac{1}{3}x = 9,$
    $7t - 2x = 19.$

13. $F = \frac{9}{5}C + 32,$
    $F = C.$
                                         Ans. $(-40, -40).$

14. $5(k - 1) + \frac{3}{2}(p + 2) = 9,$

$$\frac{k}{2} + \frac{2}{3}(p + 10) = \frac{17}{2}.$$

15. $3(x - 10) - \frac{1}{3}(y + 2) = 17,$
    $x + 2y = -1.$
                                       Ans. $(15, -8).$

16. $C = \frac{5}{9}(F - 32),$
    $F = 2C.$

17. $r = \frac{2}{3}t + 21,$
    $t = 4r - 3.$
                          Ans. $r = -\frac{57}{5}, t = -\frac{243}{5}.$

18. $14.2x - 1.3y = 14,$
    $3.7x + 11.5y = 23.$

19. $1.4x - 1.7y = 22,$
    $2.5x + 1.2y = 20.$
                                   Ans. $(10.19, -4.56).$

20. $2(x - 3y) + y = 19,$
    $\frac{1}{2}(x + 3y) = -9.$

21. The sum of two numbers is 24. Their difference is 12. What are the numbers?

22. The perimeter of a rectangle is 30 ft. The length is 4 ft. less than twice the width. What are the dimensions of the rectangle?

Two racers, A and B, leave a point P *travelling the same route. Racer A travels at a constant rate of 3.5 mph and departs from* P *at 12:00 noon. Racer B travels at 4 mph and departs from* P *at 2:00 P.M. on the same day. In Exercises 23–28:*

23. Draw up the distance-time equation for A.

24. Draw up the distance-time equation for B.

25. The two-hour head start by A is how large in terms of distance?
Ans. 7 miles.

26. At what time will B catch A? *Ans.* 4:00 A.M.

27. How far from *P* will B catch A? *Ans.* 56 miles.

28. Show the solution to Exercises 26 and 27 graphically.

Two racers A and B travel along the same route according to the equations

$$s = v_a t + s_a,$$
$$s = v_b t + s_b,$$

where s is distance, v is average speed (called constant here), and t is time. For $t \geqq$ *0, what conditions involving* $v_a, v_b, s_a,$ *and* s_b *must exist if:*

29. A remains a constant distance from B. *Ans.* $v_a = v_b$.

30. A is initially ahead of B, but B eventually passes A.
Ans. $s_a > s_b$; $v_b > v_a$.

31. A is always ahead of B. *Ans.* $s_a > s_b$; $v_a \geqq v_b$.

32. A starts ahead of B and continues to move further ahead of B.
Ans. $s_a > s_b$; $v_a > v_b$.

33. A and B travel in exactly opposite directions.
Ans. v_a and v_b are of opposite sign.

34. A fund grows by simple interest according to the equation

$$A = P + Pni,$$

where *i* is the yearly interest rate, *n* is the number of years of growth, *P* is the original principal, and *A* is the amount to which the principal grows. Two accounts are established. The first account, with principal $1000, grows at the rate of 3 per cent annually. The second account, with principal $850, grows at 5 per cent annually. What is the amount when the two accounts are equal, and how many years pass before the accounts become equal?

35. Three radios and four clocks cost a total of $128. Two of the same radios and seven of the same clocks cost a total of $133. What are the individual costs of the clocks and the radios? *Ans.* clocks, $11; radios, $28.

36. Two forces, A and B, are applied to a see-saw system as shown in Fig. 5–25. Force A is 6 lb. applied at an unknown distance from the fulcrum F; it is in equilibrium with an unknown force y at B which is 4 ft. from F. If A is increased by 3 lb., force y must be increased by 2.25 lb. to maintain equilibrium. Find x and y.

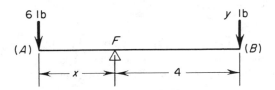

FIGURE 5–25

37. A boat travels at a constant rate in still water. It travels downstream 18 miles in two hours; the return trip requires 6 hours. Find the rate of the boat in still water and the rate of the current. *Ans.* Boat, 6 mph; current, 3 mph.

38. A certain alloy is 10 per cent zinc and 6 per cent tin; 25 lb. of the alloy have some pure zinc and pure tin added, producing another alloy which is 25 per cent zinc and 20 per cent tin. How much pure zinc and pure tin are added?
Ans. $\frac{465}{66}$ lb. zinc; $\frac{405}{66}$ lb. tin.

39. A man invests $\frac{1}{5}$ of his money at 5 per cent per year and the remainder of his money at 4 per cent. His yearly income from the investments is $240. How much did he invest at each rate?

40. Eleven coins consisting of quarters and dimes have a value of $2.15. How many dimes and quarters are involved? *Ans.* $7Q + 4D$.

5-8 Systems Involving More Than Two Unknowns

Systems involving three or more linear equations can be solved (if the solutions exist) by reducing the number of unknowns through methods shown in Sec. 5-7. The procedure is somewhat involved, but is very orderly. Let us consider an example to provide discussion of the method.

EXAMPLE 22. Find the solution of the system

$$x + y - z = 4, \tag{41}$$
$$2x - 3y + z = 1, \tag{42}$$
$$x - 4y - 2z = -7. \tag{43}$$

Solution. Here we are instructed to find an (x, y, z) set which simultaneously satisfies all of the equations (41), (42), and (43). We may proceed by successively eliminating unknowns until we are left with one equation in one unknown. Here we will choose to eliminate x from the system first. If we subtract (43) from (41), we have

$$\begin{array}{r} x + y - z = 4 \\ \underline{x - 4y - 2z = -7} \\ 5y + z = 11 \end{array} \qquad (44)$$

where (44) is an equation in y and z. If we choose to eliminate x from another pair of the given equations, we will obtain a second equation in y and z which may be solved against (44). Proceeding, let us double all terms in (43) and subtract the result from (42), giving

$$\begin{array}{r} 2x - 3y + z = 1 \\ \underline{2x - 8y - 4z = -14} \\ 5y + 5z = 15. \end{array} \qquad (45)$$

Now we observe that (44) and (45) constitute two equations in two unknowns and may be solved by methods discussed in the preceding section. Subtracting (45) from (44), we have

$$\begin{array}{r} 5y + z = 11 \\ \underline{5y + 5z = 15} \\ - 4z = -4 \end{array}$$

from which $z = 1$.

At this point we have found a value of z which, with the proper x and y companions, may constitute a solution. We may find the proper value of y by substituting $z = 1$ into either (44) or (45). Choosing (44),

$$5y + (1) = 11,$$

from which $y = 2$.

Now we substitute $y = 2$, $z = 1$ into any of the original equations to obtain x. Choosing (41),

$$x + 2 - 1 = 4,$$

from which

$$x = 3.$$

The desired (x, y, z) set is $(3, 2, 1)$. To check this set, we must show that it satisfies *all* of the given equations. We already know that it satisfies (41) because (41) was used in finding x from the derived y and z.

Substituting into (42),

$$2(3) - 3(2) + 1 \overset{?}{=} 1,$$

which checks as $\quad 1 = 1.$

Substituting into (43),

$$3 - 4(2) - 2(1) \overset{?}{=} -7,$$

which checks as $\quad -7 = -7.$

The method used in Example 22 proves very orderly. It is useful for n equations in n unknowns, where by subtracting equation pairs we may produce $n - 1$ equations in $n - 1$ unknowns. These $n - 1$ equations may also be subtracted in pairs to produce $n - 2$ equations in $n - 2$ unknowns. The process is repeated until we are left with one equation in one unknown.

Prudent selection of the original pairs to be subtracted can often shorten the labor involved. Consider Example 23.

EXAMPLE 23. Solve the system

$$a + b - 3c = 7, \tag{46}$$
$$a + b + 4c = 0, \tag{47}$$
$$5a \quad + 2c = 8. \tag{48}$$

Solution. Inspecting the system carefully, we note that subtracting (47) from (46) eliminates both a and b, producing the result $-7c = 7$, from which $c = -1$. Substituting $c = -1$ into (48) gives $a = 2$; substituting $a = 2$, $c = -1$ into either (46) or (47) produces $b = 2$, and the solution is $(a, b, c) = (2, 2, -1)$.

Simultaneous systems are frequently solved by use of determinants, which are discussed in Sections 5-9 and 5-10.

Exercises

In Exercises 1–8 determine the solution of the given system.

1. $x + y \quad\quad = 9,$ *Ans.* $x = 10,$
   $\quad x - y + 3z = 2,$ $y = -1,$
   $\quad\quad 4y - 3z = 5.$ $z = -3.$

2. $2x - 4y + 3z = 1,$
   $5x - 2y + 6z = 4,$
   $\quad\; y - z = \frac{1}{12}.$

3. $m - n \quad\;\; = -6,$
   $m \quad\;\; + p = -9,$
   $3n + p = 1.$

Ans. $m = -4,$
$n = 2,$
$p = -5.$

4. $3r + 2s + 3t = -7,$
   $5r - 3s + 2t = -4,$
   $7r + 4s + 5t = 2.$

5. $r + \quad s + \quad t = 2.7,$
   $6r + 7s - 5t = -8.8,$
   $10r + 16s - 3t = -6.4.$

Ans. $r = 1.3,$
$s = -0.8,$
$t = 2.2.$

6. $\quad 2x + 3y - 7z = 13,$
   $-5x + 2y + 2z = -5,$
   $\quad\; x - 4y - 3z = 16.$

7. $2r - 3s + 3t = 7,$
   $3r + \quad s - 2t = -11,$
   $5r - 2s + 4t = 11.$

Ans. $r = -1.$
$s = 2.$
$t = 5.$

8. $4x - 3y - 4z = -5,$
   $3x + 2y + 2z = 14.5,$
   $2x + 5y - 3z = -13.5.$

9. Let C, F, and W represent respectively the prices, in cents per lb., of cashews, filberts, and walnuts. The cost for a mixture containing 1 lb. of each is $2.40. The cost for a mixture containing 2 lb. of cashews, 2 lb. of filberts, and 1 lb. of walnuts is $4.00. A mixture containing 3 lb. of cashews, 1 lb. of filberts, and 2 lb. of walnuts cost $4.60. Find C, F, and W.   *Ans.* $C = 70$, $F = 90$, $W = 80$.

10. Let S, C, and W represent, respectively, the densities, in lb. per cubic ft., of steel, concrete, and wood. The total weight of 1 cu. ft. of each is 650 lb. The weight of 2 cu. ft. of steel, 3 cu. ft. of concrete, and 4 cu. ft. of wood is 1550 lb. The weight of 3 cu. ft. of steel, 4 of concrete, and 5 of wood is 2200 lb. Find S, C, and W. This exercise demonstrates a system of *inconsistent* equations which defies solution by ordinary means.

11. The standard equation of a circle is given as

$$x^2 + y^2 + ax + by + c = 0.$$

It is known that a certain circle passes through the points $P(-2, 3)$, $Q(5, 4)$, and $R(6, -3)$. If we substitute the coordinates of P, Q, and R into the standard equation, we will obtain three equations in a, b, and c from which numerical values of a, b, and c may be obtained. By substituting these derived values into the standard equation, we will obtain the equation of the circle passing through P, Q, and R. The method described here is the *method of undetermined coefficients* and is useful in determining equations from experimental data. Find the equation in question.

Ans. $x^2 + y^2 - 4x - 21 = 0.$

12. The standard form of a parabola with a vertical axis is given as

$$y = ax^2 + bx + c.$$

It is known that a certain parabola with a vertical axis passes through the points $(3, -3)$, $(1, -2)$ and $(5, -2)$. Find the equation of the parabola in question by using the method described in Exercise 6.   *Ans.* $y = x^2/4 - 3x/2 - \frac{3}{4}$.

13. In Fig. 5-26 a schematic is shown to illustrate Kirchhoff's law. From the schematic we can obtain the equations

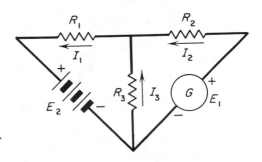

$$I_1 R_1 + I_3 R_3 = E_2,$$

$$I_2 R_2 - I_3 R_3 = E_1,$$

$$I_1 - I_2 - I_3 = 0.$$

Find numerical values of I_1, I_2, and I_3 if we are given the values $R_1 = 1.1$; $R_2 = 0.8$; $R_3 = 1.0$; $E_1 = 10.5$; and $E_2 = 7.4$.   FIGURE 5–26
Ans. $I_1 = 2.37$; $I_2 = 7.16$; $I_3 = -4.77$.

14. A man has coins consisting entirely of quarters, dimes, and nickels. He has 12 coins of value $1.45. If the number of quarters and nickels were interchanged, the value would be $1.65. How many coins of each denomination did he originally have?

15. An equation of the form $ax + by + cz = d$ graphs as a plane surface. Three planes can intersect in one point; this point is the solution of the system. Find the point of intersection of

$$2x - 3y + z = 0,$$

$$5x + 4y - 2z = 7,$$

$$x + 8y - 5z = 4.$$

5-9   Solutions of Systems by Use of Determinants

In Section 5-7 we showed that the solution of the system

$$Ax + By = C$$

$$Dx + Ey = F$$

has the (x, y) values

$$x = \frac{EC - FB}{AE - BD}, \qquad y = \frac{AF - CD}{AE - BD}. \tag{49}$$

In this discussion it is important to note that each of the numerators and denominators of (49) is the difference of two products; such expressions may be rearranged into arrays called *determinants*.

Switching our given equations into notation more commonly used in discussions involving determinants, solution of the system

$$a_1x + b_1y = c_1 \tag{50}$$
$$a_2x + b_2y = c_2$$

is readily found (by elimination methods) to be

$$x = \frac{c_1b_2 - c_2b_1}{a_1b_2 - a_2b_1}, \qquad y = \frac{a_1c_2 - a_2c_1}{a_1b_2 - a_2b_1}. \tag{51}$$

We introduce here the symbol

$$\begin{vmatrix} a_1 & b_1 \\ a_2 & b_2 \end{vmatrix} \tag{52}$$

which is called a *determinant*, or more specifically, a *determinant of second order*.

By definition, the determinant (52) is of value equal to the difference of the diagonal products, or

$$\begin{vmatrix} a_1 & b_1 \\ a_2 & b_2 \end{vmatrix} = a_1b_2 - a_2b_1. \tag{53}$$

We note here that the denominators of (51) are precisely of the value cited in (53) and may therefore be expressed as determinants exactly like (52). The numerators of (51), being the difference of products, are also readily expressed as determinants.

Nomenclature of each part of (52) follows. Each of the four numbers a_1, a_2, b_1, b_2 is called an *element; a_1* and a_2 constitute the *first column; b_1* and b_2 constitute the *second column*. Elements a_1 and b_1 are the *first row;* a_2 and b_2 are the *second row*. Elements a_1 and b_2 are along the *principal diagonal; a_2* and b_1 are along the *secondary diagonal*.

We note carefully that the value of the determinant in (53) is the product along the principal diagonal less the product along the secondary diagonal.

EXAMPLE 24. Using (53), evaluate the determinant which has $a_1 = 1$, $b_1 = -1$, $a_2 = -2$, and $b_2 = 3$.

Solution: Substituting the known elements into (53), we have

$$\begin{vmatrix} a_1 & b_1 \\ a_2 & b_2 \end{vmatrix} = \begin{vmatrix} 1 & -1 \\ -2 & 3 \end{vmatrix} = (1)(3) - (-2)(-1) = 3 - (2) = 1.$$

EXAMPLE 25. Evaluate the determinant

$$\begin{vmatrix} 3 & -4 \\ 1 & 0 \end{vmatrix}.$$

Solution: Using (53),

$$\begin{vmatrix} 3 & -4 \\ 1 & 0 \end{vmatrix} = (3)(0) - (1)(-4) = 0 + 4 = 4.$$

We now apply determinants to express the solution of the system (50) by structuring (51) in determinant form. Careful examination shows that (51) may be written as

$$x = \frac{\begin{vmatrix} c_1 & b_1 \\ c_2 & b_2 \end{vmatrix}}{\begin{vmatrix} a_1 & b_1 \\ a_2 & b_2 \end{vmatrix}}, \qquad y = \frac{\begin{vmatrix} a_1 & c_1 \\ a_2 & c_2 \end{vmatrix}}{\begin{vmatrix} a_1 & b_1 \\ a_2 & b_2 \end{vmatrix}}. \qquad (54)$$

Careful scrutiny shows how (54) can be expressed from (50) by inspection: First, the denominators in (54) are arrayed precisely as the coefficients of x and y are arrayed in (50). Second, the numerator of x in (54) is similar to the denominator with c's replacing a's. Third, the numerator of y in (54) is similar to the denominator with c's replacing b's.

EXAMPLE 25. Using determinants, find the solution of

$$y = \frac{3x}{2} - 8$$

$$y = \frac{x}{3} - \frac{10}{3}.$$

Solution: Revising the given equations to the form of (50), we have

$$3x - 2y = 16$$
$$-x + 3y = -10$$

and the solutions are:

$$x = \frac{\begin{vmatrix} 16 & -2 \\ -10 & 3 \end{vmatrix}}{\begin{vmatrix} 3 & -2 \\ -1 & 3 \end{vmatrix}} = \frac{(16)(3) - (-10)(-2)}{(3)(3) - (-1)(-2)} = \frac{48 - 20}{9 - 2} = \frac{28}{7} = 4,$$

$$y = \frac{\begin{vmatrix} 3 & 16 \\ -1 & -10 \end{vmatrix}}{\begin{vmatrix} 3 & -2 \\ -1 & 3 \end{vmatrix}} = \frac{(3)(-10) - (-1)(16)}{7} = \frac{-30 + 16}{7}$$

$$= \frac{-14}{7} = -2.$$

Special conditions are required of (50) to assure solutions. We recall that a solution exists if the graphs of the two straight lines intersect in one point. We recall, also, from Section 5-6, that the lines are parallel if the ratio of the x-coefficient to the y-coefficient is the same for both lines. This means that if $a_1/b_1 = a_2/b_2$, then equations (50) are parallel (or coincident). From this we may obtain

$$a_1b_2 - a_2b_1 = 0. \tag{55}$$

Comparing (55) with the denominator in (51), we see that a zero denominator yields a no-solution condition.

Exercises

In Exercises 1–10 find the coordinate pairs satisfying the given equations. Use determinants for the solutions. If no solution exists, explain why.

1. $x + y = 5,$
   $x + 2y = 7.$ *Ans.* (3, 2).

2. $a + b = 12,$
   $2a + b = 19.$

3. $x + y = 5,$
   $x - y = 1.$ *Ans.* (3, 2).

4. $a - b = 2,$
   $a + b = 12.$

5. $x - 3y = 7,$
   $2x + 5y = -8.$ *Ans.* (1, -2).

6. $m - 3n = -12,$
$2m + 3n = 21.$

7. $3a = 2b + 6,$
$b = a - 1.$ *Ans.* (4, 3).

8. $5F = 9C + 160,$
$F = C.$

9. $0.3m = 1.2n + 0.5,$
$n - 1.5m = 0.4.$ *Ans.* $(-0.653, -0.580)$.

10. $ax + by = c,$
$kax + kby = d.$

11. Using determinants to solve the systems

$x - y = 5$ and $x - y = 5$
$2x - 2y = 10$ $2x - 2y = 15$

results in two different confusions. Explain why, using their graphs as a basis of explanation.

12. For additional exercises, refer to Exercises 1–20 following Section 5-7. Use determinants for their solutions.

5-10   Determinants of Higher Order

Given three equations in three unknowns

$$a_1 x + b_1 y + c_1 z = d_1$$
$$a_2 x + b_2 y + c_2 z = d_2 \tag{56}$$
$$a_3 x + b_3 y + c_3 z = d_3,$$

a third order determinant of the coefficients of x, y, and z would appear as

$$\begin{vmatrix} a_1 & b_1 & c_1 \\ a_2 & b_2 & c_2 \\ a_3 & b_3 & c_3 \end{vmatrix} = \Delta. \tag{57}$$

Solution of (56) by elimination methods would yield similar denominators (Δ) for x, y, and z such that

$$\Delta = a_1 b_2 c_3 + b_1 c_2 a_3 + c_1 a_2 b_3 - a_3 b_2 c_1 - b_3 c_2 a_1 - c_3 a_2 b_1, \tag{58}$$

which may be seen as taking the three triple products along the solid diagonal lines in (59) as positive and the three along the dotted diagonals as negative.

$$\Delta = \begin{vmatrix} a_1 & b_1 & c_1 \\ a_2 & b_2 & c_2 \\ a_3 & b_3 & c_3 \end{vmatrix} \begin{matrix} a_1 & b_1 \\ a_2 & b_2 \\ a_3 & b_3 \end{matrix} \tag{59}$$

The actual solution of (56) can be shown to be

$$x = \frac{\begin{vmatrix} d_1 & b_1 & c_1 \\ d_2 & b_2 & c_2 \\ d_3 & b_3 & c_3 \end{vmatrix}}{\Delta}, \qquad y = \frac{\begin{vmatrix} a_1 & d_1 & c_1 \\ a_2 & d_2 & c_2 \\ a_3 & d_3 & c_3 \end{vmatrix}}{\Delta}, \qquad z = \frac{\begin{vmatrix} a_1 & b_1 & d_1 \\ a_2 & b_2 & d_2 \\ a_3 & b_3 & d_3 \end{vmatrix}}{\Delta}.$$

$$\tag{60}$$

Note from (60) that the x-numerator is the same as Δ with d's replacing a's; the y-numerator is the same as Δ with d's replacing b's; the z-numerator is the same as Δ with d's replaing c's.

EXAMPLE 26. Evaluate the third order determinant

$$\begin{vmatrix} 1 & 3 & 2 \\ 0 & 2 & -2 \\ 2 & -1 & 0 \end{vmatrix}.$$

Solution: Referring to (59), repeating the first and second columns for clarity, taking the "down-right" diagonal products as positive and the "up-right" diagonal products as negative, we have

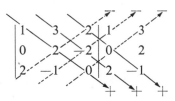

and the value is

$$(1)(2)(0) + (3)(-2)(2) + (2)(0)(-1) - (2)(2)(2) - (-1)(-2)(1)$$
$$- (0)(0)(3)$$

or

$$0 - 12 + 0 - 8 - 2 - 0 = -22.$$

EXAMPLE 27. Using determinants, solve the system

$$x + y - 2z = 1$$
$$2x - y \quad\quad = 4$$
$$x \quad\quad + 3z = -2.$$

Solution: Using (60) and (57), we have the solutions

$$x = \frac{\begin{vmatrix} 1 & 1 & -2 \\ 4 & -1 & 0 \\ -2 & 0 & 3 \end{vmatrix}}{\begin{vmatrix} 1 & 1 & -2 \\ 2 & -1 & 0 \\ 1 & 0 & 3 \end{vmatrix}} = \frac{(-3) + (0) + (0) - (-4) - (0) - (12)}{(-3) + (0) + (0) - (2) - (0) - (6)}$$

$$= \frac{-11}{-11} = 1,$$

$$y = \frac{\begin{vmatrix} 1 & 1 & -2 \\ 2 & 4 & 0 \\ 1 & -2 & 3 \end{vmatrix}}{\Delta} = \frac{(12) + (0) + (8) - (-8) - (0) - (6)}{-11}$$

$$= \frac{22}{-11} = -2,$$

$$z = \frac{\begin{vmatrix} 1 & 1 & 1 \\ 2 & -1 & 4 \\ 1 & 0 & -2 \end{vmatrix}}{\Delta} = \frac{(2) + (4) + (0) - (-1) - (0) - (-4)}{-11}$$

$$= \frac{11}{-11} = -1.$$

Substituting the triple $(1, -2, -1)$ into all three original equations will serve as a check of the solution.

Minors

A careful inspection of (57) and (58) reveals an interesting reduction of a third order determinant to the algebraic sum of three second order determinants. Referring to (58), we factor a_1 from two terms, $-a_2$ from two terms, and a_3 from two terms, obtaining

$$= \begin{vmatrix} a_1 & b_1 & c_1 \\ a_2 & b_2 & c_2 \\ a_3 & b_3 & c_3 \end{vmatrix} = a_1(b_2c_3 - b_3c_2) - a_2(b_1c_3 - b_3c_1)$$

$$+ a_3(b_1c_2 - b_2c_1). \tag{61}$$

Now the expanded portion of (61) can be seen as the algebraic sum of three second order determinants with a's as coefficients, or

$$= \begin{vmatrix} a_1 & b_1 & c_1 \\ a_2 & b_2 & c_2 \\ a_3 & b_3 & c_3 \end{vmatrix} = a_1 \begin{vmatrix} b_2 & c_2 \\ b_3 & c_3 \end{vmatrix} - a_2 \begin{vmatrix} b_1 & c_1 \\ b_3 & c_3 \end{vmatrix} + a_3 \begin{vmatrix} b_1 & c_1 \\ b_2 & c_2 \end{vmatrix}, \tag{62}$$

which is the *expansion by minors* of the third order determinant. Detailed inspection of (62) shows that the second order determinant with a_1 as coefficient can be found by crossing out the row and column containing a_1 in the third order determinant; the second order determinant with $-a_2$ as coefficient can be found by crossing out the row and column containing a_2, and the second order determinant with a_3 as coefficient can be found by crossing out the row and column containing a_3. Expression (62) shows the third order determinant expanded into minors along a column; such expansions are possible along rows and diagonals; selective manipulation of (57) into the minor form (62) will bear this out.

EXAMPLE 28. Using minors, evaluate the determinant given in Example 26.

Solution: Using (62), we have

$$\begin{vmatrix} 1 & 3 & 2 \\ 0 & 2 & -2 \\ 2 & -1 & 0 \end{vmatrix} = 1 \begin{vmatrix} 2 & -2 \\ -1 & 0 \end{vmatrix} - 0 \begin{vmatrix} 3 & 2 \\ -1 & 0 \end{vmatrix} + 2 \begin{vmatrix} 3 & 2 \\ 2 & -2 \end{vmatrix}$$

$$= 1(0 - 2) - 0(0 + 2) + 2(-6 - 4)$$

$$= -2 - 20 = -22.$$

Note: Any higher order determinant can be reduced to determinants of lower order by use of the method of minors. Any third order determinant (or second) can be evaluated by the diagonal product method.

Caution: The diagonal product method is restricted to determinants of third or second order. Determinants of fourth order or higher must be reduced by the method of minors.

EXAMPLE 29. Evaluate the determinant

$$\Delta = \begin{vmatrix} 1 & 2 & 3 & 0 \\ 2 & 1 & 0 & 3 \\ 3 & 0 & 1 & 2 \\ 4 & 3 & 2 & 1 \end{vmatrix}.$$

Solution: Expanding to third order minors, we have

$$\Delta = \begin{vmatrix} 1 & 0 & 3 \\ 0 & 1 & 2 \\ 3 & 2 & 1 \end{vmatrix} - 2 \begin{vmatrix} 2 & 3 & 0 \\ 0 & 1 & 2 \\ 3 & 2 & 1 \end{vmatrix} + 3 \begin{vmatrix} 2 & 3 & 0 \\ 1 & 0 & 3 \\ 3 & 2 & 1 \end{vmatrix} - 4 \begin{vmatrix} 2 & 3 & 0 \\ 1 & 0 & 3 \\ 0 & 1 & 2 \end{vmatrix}$$

$$= 1(-12) - 2(12) + 3(12) - 4(-12) = 48.$$

A host of additional properties of determinants is available; however, the student is referred to other texts for them. The discussion in this section is sufficient to provide the student with the tools to solve determinants derived from certain physical situations, particularly electrical circuits.

Exercises

In Exercises 1–9 evaluate the given determinant by use of the method of minors.

1. $\begin{vmatrix} 2 & 3 & 1 \\ 1 & 3 & 2 \\ 3 & 0 & 0 \end{vmatrix}.$ *Ans.* 9.

2. $\begin{vmatrix} 1 & 2 & 1 \\ 2 & 0 & 3 \\ 4 & 0 & 5 \end{vmatrix}.$

3. $\begin{vmatrix} 2 & 3 & 0 \\ -2 & 5 & 0 \\ -1 & 1 & 6 \end{vmatrix}.$ *Ans.* 96.

4. $\begin{vmatrix} 0 & -1 & -2 \\ 0 & 2 & 3 \\ -1 & 2 & 2 \end{vmatrix}.$

5. $\begin{vmatrix} 0 & 4 & 5 \\ 1 & 0 & 6 \\ 2 & 3 & 0 \end{vmatrix}.$ *Ans.* 63.

6. $\begin{vmatrix} 1 & 2 & 3 \\ 1 & 2 & 3 \\ 1 & 2 & 3 \end{vmatrix}.$

7. $\begin{vmatrix} 1 & 2 & 5 & 6 \\ 0 & 3 & 2 & 1 \\ 0 & -1 & 8 & 0 \\ 0 & 2 & -3 & 0 \end{vmatrix}.$ *Ans.* −13.

8.
$$\begin{vmatrix} 1 & 2 & 0 & 4 \\ 1 & 0 & 1 & 0 \\ 1 & 0 & -1 & -1 \\ 1 & 3 & 0 & 1 \end{vmatrix}.$$

9.
$$\begin{vmatrix} 1 & -2 & 0 & 3 \\ -1 & 2 & 0 & 1 \\ 1 & -2 & 3 & 2 \\ -1 & 2 & 0 & 2 \end{vmatrix}. \qquad\qquad\qquad\qquad Ans.\ 0.$$

In Exercises 10–13 use determinants to solve the given systems.

10. $x + y - z = 1,$
$\qquad\quad y + 4z = 0,$
$\quad 3x + y \qquad = 0,$.

11. $m + n + 3p = 3,$
$\quad 2m - n \qquad = 0,$
$\qquad\qquad 4n - p = 8.$ $\qquad\qquad\qquad Ans.\ (1, 2, 0).$

12. $a + 2b + c = 2,$
$\quad 3a + 3b \qquad = 0,$
$\quad 2a \qquad - c = -1.$

13. $w + x - y + z = 2,$
$\quad 2w - x - 3y + 4z = -2,$
$\qquad\quad x - 2y + 2z = 0,$
$\quad w \qquad - 3y + 6z = 1.$ $\qquad\qquad Ans.\ (1, 2, 2, 1).$

14. $3r + s + 4t = 1,$
$\quad 10r + s - t = -1,$
$\qquad r - 3s - 15t = 1.$

15. $2a - b \qquad + 2d = 2,$
$\quad 4a - 2b + 3c \qquad = -7,$
$\qquad\qquad b + c + d = 6,$
$\quad 6a \qquad - 4c + 5d = 23.$ $\qquad\qquad Ans.\ (\tfrac{3}{2}, 5, -1, 2).$

In Exercises 16–20, given the determinant in expression (57).

16. Show that $\Delta = 0$ if $a_1 = a_2 = a_3 = 0.$

17. Show that $\Delta = 0$ if $b_1 = ka_1, b_2 = ka_2,$ and $b_3 = ka_3.$

18. Show that $\Delta = a_1(b_2c_3 - b_3c_2)$ if $a_2 = a_3 = 0.$

19. Find Δ if $a_1 = b_2 = c_3 = 0.$

20. Interchange the a column and the b column and determine the effect on $\Delta.$

21. Given the two determinants

$$\begin{vmatrix} a & b & c \\ d & e & f \\ g & h & i \end{vmatrix} \quad \text{and} \quad \begin{vmatrix} a+kb & b & c \\ d+ke & e & f \\ g+kh & h & i \end{vmatrix}$$

where the second determinant is created from the first by multiplying each element of the second column by the factor k and adding the results to the corresponding elements of the first column. Show that the two determinants are of equal value.

22. As a challenge to the assertion that the diagonal method does not work for determinants of order greater than three, try to evaluate Exercise 9 by the diagonal method and compare the result with that obtained by the method of minors.

In Chap. 1 we discussed positive and negative powers of the base 10 in standard notation. In this chapter we will introduce the general laws of exponents, using any suitable base, and operations involving radicals. These operations will be the fundamental ones including addition, subtraction, multiplication, and division. First, we will give certain appropriate laws and definitions.

6 EXPONENTS AND RADICALS

6-1 Definitions and the Laws of Exponents

Many problems arise in mathematics where a number is multiplied by the same factor several times. An example is the case of starting today with one penny, doubling the amount to two pennies tomorrow, doubling again on the following day to four pennies, and so forth. After ten such doubling operations, the amount may be described as

$$1 \cdot 2 \cdot 2 \cdot 2 \cdot 2 \cdot 2 \cdot 2 \cdot 2 \cdot 2 \cdot 2 \cdot 2 \tag{1}$$

pennies. Expression (1) is seen to contain the factor 2 a total of ten times. If we called for 100 doubling operations, it would be tedious to write an expression with 100 factors in the form of (1). For this and other reasons, exponential notation is introduced. Expression (1) is compactly written as

$$1 \cdot (2)^{10},$$

where the number 2 is called the *base*, the number 10 is called the *exponent*, and the total expression $(2)^{10}$ is called "the tenth power of 2."

If we wish to indicate the product of n like factors where each factor is of value a, we have the definition

$$\underset{n \text{ factors}}{a \cdot a \cdot a \cdot \ \cdots \ \cdot a} = a^n. \tag{2}$$

EXAMPLE 1. Evaluate (*a*) $(3)^4$ and (*b*) $(\frac{1}{2})^3$.

Solution:

(*a*) $(3)^4 = 3 \cdot 3 \cdot 3 \cdot 3 = 81$, by definition (2).

(*b*) $(\frac{1}{2})^3 = \frac{1}{2} \cdot \frac{1}{2} \cdot \frac{1}{2} = \frac{1}{8}$, by definition (2).

Several laws of exponents are listed in Table 6-1; the laws are tabulated there for ready reference. Discussion and examples of these laws follow.

Table 6-1

LAWS OF EXPONENTS

(a and b are any nonzero numbers; m and n are integers)

Law 1:	$a^m \cdot a^n = a^{m+n}$	
Law 2a:	$\dfrac{a^m}{a^n} = a^{m-n}$	$(a \neq 0)$
Law 2b:	$a^0 = 1$	
Law 2c:	$\dfrac{1}{a^n} = a^{-n}$	$(a \neq 0)$
Law 3:	$(a^m)^n = a^{mn}$	
Law 4:	$(ab)^n = a^n b^n$	
Law 5:	$\left(\dfrac{a}{b}\right)^n = \dfrac{a^n}{b^n}$	$(b \neq 0)$

Referring to Table 6-1, we have the following verbal statements for the laws given:

Law 1. *In multiplying powers of like bases, add the exponents.*

Law 2a. *In dividing powers of like bases, subtract the exponent of the divisor from the exponent of the dividend.*

Law 2b. *Any nonzero base raised to the zero power has the value 1.*

Law 2c. *A power in the denominator of a fraction can become a factor of the numerator by changing the sign of the exponent.*

Law 3. *To raise a power to a power, multiply exponents.*

Law 4. *The power of the product of two numbers is the product of the powers of the two numbers.*

Law 5. *The power of the quotient of two numbers is the quotient of the powers of the two numbers.*

Law 1 is readily apparent from definition (2). We have

$$a^m \cdot a^n = \underbrace{a \cdot a \cdot a \cdot \; \cdots \; \cdot a}_{n \text{ factors}} \cdot \underbrace{a \cdot a \cdot a \cdot \; \cdots \; \cdot a}_{m \text{ factors}} = a^{m+n}, \tag{3}$$

where the number of factors in (3) is apparently $m + n$.

Law 2 is also apparent from definition (2). We have

$$\frac{a^m}{a^n} = \frac{a \cdot a \cdot a \cdot \; \cdots \; \cdot a \quad (m \text{ factors})}{a \cdot a \cdot a \cdot \; \cdots \; \cdot a \quad (n \text{ factors})} = a^{m-n}. \tag{4}$$

From expression (4), several factors of the middle equality will cancel; the exact number that will cancel is either m or n, depending upon which is the smaller. If $m > n$, then $m - n > 0$. If $m < n$, $m - n < 0$. If $m = n$, $m - n = 0$ and Law 2b holds.

Accepting Laws 2a and 2b, Law 2c follows:

$$\frac{1}{a^n} = \frac{a^0}{a^n} = a^{0-n} = a^{-n}.$$

Let us pause here to consider some example problems involving Laws 1 through 2c from Table 6-1.

EXAMPLE 2. In parts (a) through (f) we show solved examples which require application of the laws of exponents drawn from Table 6-1. In each case the object is simplification.

(a) $x^2 \cdot x^4 = x^{2+4} = x^6$ (Law 1)

(b) $x^{n+1} \cdot x^{n-1} = x^{(n+1)+(n-1)} = x^{2n}$ (Law 1)

(c) $\dfrac{y^3}{y^{-5}} = y^{3-(-5)} = y^{3+5} = y^8$ (Law 2a)

(d) $\dfrac{1}{x^{-2}} = x^{-(-2)} = x^2$ (Law 2c)

(e) $(a + b)^0 = 1$ (Law 2b)

(f) $p^{-m+2} \cdot p^{m-2} = p^{-m+2+m-2} = p^0 = 1$ (Laws 1 and 2b)

Continuing now to demonstrate the laws in Table 6-1, we refer to Law 3:

$$(a^m)^n = \underbrace{a^m \cdot a^m \cdot a^m \cdots \cdot a^m}_{n \text{ factors}} = a^{mn}. \qquad (5)$$

From (5) we see that there are n factors each containing m identical a factors, or a total of mn identical a factors.

From Law 4, we see that

$$(ab)^n = (ab \cdot ab \cdot ab \cdots \cdot ab)$$
$$= \underbrace{(a \cdot a \cdot a \cdots \cdot a)}_{n \text{ factors}} \cdot \underbrace{(b \cdot b \cdot b \cdots \cdot b)}_{n \text{ factors}} = a^n b^n, \qquad (6)$$

where $(ab)^n$ is the product of n factors with each factor of value ab; this means that both a and b are present n times as factors, or the last term of (6) holds. Law 5 can be discussed in terms similar to those used for Law 4.

More examples illustrating the use of the laws of exponents follow.

EXAMPLE 3. Simplify the given expressions using the laws of exponents in Table 6-1.

(a) $(k^2)^4 = k^{2 \cdot 4} = k^8$ (Law 3)

(b) $(6x)^2 = 6^2 x^2 = 36x^2$ (Law 4)

(c) $\left(\dfrac{3k}{2p}\right)^3 = \dfrac{27k^3}{8p^3}$ (Law 5)

Many simplification operations require use of more than one of the laws in Table 6-1. Some are shown in Example 4.

EXAMPLE 4. Simplify the expression

$$\frac{(3ab)^2}{6a^2b^3} \cdot \frac{9(a^2b)^3}{(3ab^2)^3}.$$

Solution. Removing parentheses by laws 3 and 4, we have

$$\frac{9 \cdot a^2 \cdot b^2 \cdot 9 \cdot a^6 \cdot b^3}{6 \cdot a^2 \cdot b^3 \cdot 27 \cdot a^3 \cdot b^6}. \tag{7}$$

Now expression (7) reduces to expression (8) by Law 1,

$$\frac{9 \cdot 9 \cdot a^8 \cdot b^5}{6 \cdot 27 \cdot a^5 \cdot b^9}, \tag{8}$$

and expression (8) simplifies, by Law 2a, to the solution

$$\frac{a^3}{2b^4}.$$

Occasionally products and quotients of *unlike* bases can be simplified by changing to similar bases and applying Laws 1, 2a, and 3. Observe Example 5.

EXAMPLE 5. Simplify the expression

$$\frac{(2)^{3x-3} \cdot (4)^{4x+2}}{(8)^{2x+5}}. \tag{9}$$

Solution. The laws of multiplication and division in Table 6-1 are not appropriate here because they pertain only to powers of like bases. We note that the bases in (9) are 2, 4, and 8, which are not alike. However, 4 and 8 can be expressed as powers of the base 2, Now,

$$4 = (2)^2 \text{ and } (4)^{4x+2} = (2^2)^{4x+2} = (2)^{8x+4}$$

and

$$8 = (2)^3 \text{ and } (8)^{2x+5} = (2^3)^{2x+5} = (2)^{6x+15}$$

and (9) becomes

$$\frac{(2)^{3x-3} \cdot (4)^{4x+2}}{(8)^{2x+5}} = \frac{(2)^{3x-3} \cdot (2)^{8x+4}}{(2)^{6x+15}} = \frac{(2)^{11x+1}}{(2)^{6x+15}} = (2)^{5x-14}.$$

The method employed in Example 5 is very important to the understanding of logarithms in a later chapter. In Example 5 we converted all of the bases to the same base 2. We chose the base 2 simply because it seemed to be the most convenient base; that is, all of the other bases were powers of the number 2. Tables of logarithms are set up in such a way that, through the table, we may rapidly convert all of the bases to the base used in the table of logarithms. Two bases are popular in tables of logarithms, namely the base 10 or the *common* base, and the base *e*, or the *natural* base. We will discuss this extensively in the chapter on logarithms.

Exercises

Perform the indicated operations by the laws of exponents. Reduce answers to the simplest terms.

1. $m^2 \cdot m^4$.   *Ans.* m^6.   **2.** $p^3 \cdot p^2 \cdot p$.

3. $(3m^2)^2$.   *Ans.* $9m^4$.   **4.** $-(\frac{1}{2}x^2)^3$.

5. $3(m^2)^2$.   *Ans.* $3m^4$.   **6.** $-\frac{1}{2}(x^2)^3$.

7. $3(m^2 + 2)^0$.   *Ans.* 3.   **8.** $5(b + 2)^0/10$.

9. $[4(p^2 + 2p)]^0$.   *Ans.* 1.   **10.** $m^2 n^3 \div mn$.

11. $(z^2 \cdot z^3)^2$.   *Ans.* z^{10}.   **12.** $a^5 \div a^{-3}$.

13. $(z^3/z^{-2})^2$.   *Ans.* z^{10}.   **14.** $(r_1 r_2^2)^2$.

15. $(-4F/F^2)^3$.   *Ans.* $-64/F^3$.   **16.** $(m^{-1}n^{-2}/2n)^3$.

17. $(b^3 \cdot b^2 \cdot b^{-5})^5$.   *Ans.* 1.   **18.** $[(m^2 - n^2)(p + 2)]^0$.

19. $\dfrac{b^2}{ac} \cdot \dfrac{a^2 c}{b} \cdot \dfrac{c}{2b}$.   *Ans.* $\dfrac{ac}{2}$.   **20.** $(-b)(-b^2)(-b)^3$.

21. $b^{-x} \cdot b^{1+x}$.   *Ans.* b.   **22.** $b^{3x} \cdot b^{x-2}$.

23. $R^{2x+5} \cdot R^{x-5}$.   *Ans.* R^{3x}.   **24.** $R^{2x} \cdot R^{x-3} \cdot R^{-x+2}$.

25. $(ab)^{2k-3} \div (ab)^{3k-4}$. *Ans.* $(ab)^{1-k}$.   **26.** $(y^{c-6})(y^5) \div y^{c+2}$.

27. $(x^2 y^n)^{-5} \div 5x^3 y^{3n}$.
         Ans. $1/(5x^{13}y^{8n})$.   **28.** $[(x^2)^2]^3$.

29. $(m^m)^m$.   *Ans.* m^{m^2}.   **30.** $(5)^{k+2} \cdot (25)^k$.

31. $(3)^{2c+4} \cdot (9)^{1-c}$.   *Ans.* $(3)^6$.   **32.** $(9)^2 \cdot (3)^{k-4}$.

33. $(125)^{m-n} \cdot (25)^{m+n} \cdot (5)^2$.   **34.** $(p^{2+k}) \div (p^{3+k})$.
         Ans. $(5)^{5m-n+2}$.

35. $\dfrac{(36)^{q-3} \cdot (6)^{q+7}}{(216)^q}$.   *Ans.* 6.   **36.** $(k^{m+2}/k^{2m-1})^2$.

37. $(b^{3k+2}/b^{2k-2})^3$.   *Ans.* b^{3k+12}.   **38.** $(x^{k-3}/x^{k+3}) \div (x)^3$.

39. $(m^{2n-p}/m^{p+n}) \div (m^{p+3n}/m^{2n-3p})$.   **40.** $(p^2 - p^{-2})(p^2 + p^{-2})$.
         Ans. $1/m^{6p}$.

6-2   Radicals and Fractional Exponents

In Sec. 6-1 we treated only integral exponents, both positive and negative; we made no reference to fractional exponents. In this section we will introduce fractional exponents. Here we will elaborate, also, on the relationship between radical quantities and quantities raised to fractional powers.

If we are given the expression

$$y = b^n \qquad (b > 0), \tag{10}$$

where n is a positive integer, then

$$y = b \cdot b \cdot b \cdot \; \cdots \; \cdot b \tag{11}$$
$$n \text{ factors}$$

according to definition (2). Now, from (10), the number y (more specifically, y to the first power) can be expressed as the product of n factors,

$$y^{1/n} \cdot y^{1/n} \cdot y^{1/n} \cdot \; \cdots \; \cdot y^{1/n} = (y^{1/n})^n = y^1, \tag{12}$$
$$n \text{ factors}$$

and (10) can be written, from (11) and (12), as

$$y^{1/n} \cdot y^{1/n} \cdot y^{1/n} \cdot \; \cdots \; \cdot y^{1/n} = b \cdot b \cdot b \cdot \; \cdots \; \cdot b. \tag{13}$$
$$n \text{ factors} \qquad\qquad n \text{ factors}$$

From (13) there is a one-to-one correspondence between the positive factors $y^{1/n}$ and b, such that we have

$$y^{1/n} = b. \tag{14}$$

Now from (10) and (14), if y is the product of n factors each of value b, then b is of value $y^{1/n}$. We can state that if y is the nth power of b, then b is the nth root of y.

The nth root of y is symbolized as $y^{1/n}$ as in (14) and is also symbolized in radical form as $\sqrt[n]{y}$, where y is called the *radicand*, the symbol $\sqrt{}$ is a *radical*, and n is the *index*. We have the equivalency

$$y^{1/n} = \sqrt[n]{y}. \tag{15}$$

EXAMPLE 6. Express one of the five equal positive factors of r in both the radical and exponent form.

Solution. In the exponent form we have $r^{1/5}$ as one of the five equal factors of r because the product involving five such factors has the value r, or

$$(r^{1/5})(r^{1/5})(r^{1/5})(r^{1/5})(r^{1/5}) = (r^{1/5})^5 = r.$$

In the radical notation, from (15) we have

$$r^{1/5} = \sqrt[5]{r}.$$

Referring back to (15), we note that the denominator of the fractional exponent is the index (or indicates the order) of the radical. It is possible that the exponent does not have a unity numerator, as in $y^{2/3}$. By law 3 in Table 6-1, where

$$(a^m)^n = a^{mn},$$

we have

$$y^{2/3} = (y^2)^{1/3} = (y^{1/3})^2. \tag{16}$$

The center portion of (16) asserts that y to the $\frac{2}{3}$ power is the same as the cube root of y^2 and the right portion of (16) asserts that y to the $\frac{2}{3}$ power is the same as the square of the cube root of y. Writing (16) in radical notation, we have

$$y^{2/3} = \sqrt[3]{y^2} = (\sqrt[3]{y})^2.$$

In general, it can be seen that the following equalities are true:

$$a^{m/n} = \sqrt[n]{a^m} = (\sqrt[n]{a})^m. \tag{17}$$

EXAMPLE 7. Evaluate $(16)^{3/2}$.

Solution. From (17), we see that

$$(16)^{3/2} = \sqrt[2]{(16)^3},$$

(that is, $(16)^{3/2}$ equals the square root of the cube of 16) or

$$(16)^{3/2} = (\sqrt[2]{16})^3$$

(that is, $(16)^{3/2}$ equals the cube of the square root of 16). Of the two above choices we select the latter purely for its simplicity, because the square root of 16 is 4 and the cube of 4 is 64, or

$$(16)^{3/2} = (\sqrt[2]{16})^3 = (4)^3 = 64.$$

Two more laws regarding radicals require some inspection. Let us consider the nth root of the product of two factors. Here

$$\sqrt[n]{ab} = (ab)^{1/n} = a^{1/n} \cdot b^{1/n} = \sqrt[n]{a} \cdot \sqrt[n]{b}, \tag{18}$$

where (18) asserts that the positive nth root of the product of two factors is the same as the product of the positive nth roots of the two factors. Also,

$$\sqrt[n]{\frac{a}{b}} = \left(\frac{a}{b}\right)^{1/n} = \frac{a^{1/n}}{b^{1/n}} = \frac{\sqrt[n]{a}}{\sqrt[n]{b}}, \tag{19}$$

where (19) asserts that the nth root of the quotient of two factors is the quotient of the nth roots of the two factors.

Now (12), (15), (17), (18), and (19) are compiled into Table 6-2.

Table 6-2

LAWS OF RADICALS

(a and b are positive numbers; m and n are integers)

Definition 1:	$a^{1/n} = \sqrt[n]{a}$
Definition 2:	$(a^{1/n})^n = (a^n)^{1/n} = a$
Law 1:	$a^{m/n} = \sqrt[n]{a^m} = (\sqrt[n]{a})^m$
Law 2:	$\sqrt[n]{ab} = \sqrt[n]{a} \cdot \sqrt[n]{b}$
Law 3:	$\sqrt[n]{\dfrac{a}{b}} = \dfrac{\sqrt[n]{a}}{\sqrt[n]{b}}$

EXAMPLE 8. Employing the laws of exponents and radicals we show here some simplification operations.

(a) $\sqrt[3]{27a^6b^3} = (3^3a^6b^3)^{1/3} = 3^{3/3}a^{6/3}b^{3/3} = 3a^2b$.

(b) $(64)^{2/3} = (4^3)^{2/3} = 4^{6/3} = 4^2 = 16$.

(c) $\sqrt[2]{\dfrac{a^4c^2}{b^6}} = \dfrac{\sqrt[2]{a^4c^2}}{\sqrt[2]{b^6}} = \dfrac{(a^4c^2)^{1/2}}{(b^6)^{1/2}} = \dfrac{a^2c}{b^3}$.

In all of the parts of Example 8, the entire radicand was removable from under the radical sign; this constituted a step in simplification. In many cases only portions of the radicand can be removed; once again this is simplification, but it is not as complete in that some radical quantities will still remain in the final simplified form.

EXAMPLE 9. Simplify (a) $\sqrt{48}$, (b) $\sqrt[3]{a^4b^5}$, and (c) $\sqrt[4]{32a^7/c^4}$.

Solution. In (a) and (b) we use law 2 of Table 6-2 and definition 2 of the same table.

$$\sqrt{48} = \sqrt{16 \cdot 3} = \sqrt{16} \cdot \sqrt{3} = 4\sqrt{3}.$$

Note that the number 48 is expressed as the product of the two factors 16 and 3, where 16 is the largest perfect square that is a factor of 48. The reason for choosing the factor 16 lies in definition 2 of Table 6-2 since

$$\sqrt{16} = (16)^{1/2} = (4^2)^{1/2} = 4.$$

In part (*b*), we must select the largest perfect *cube* that is contained as a factor of the radicand since we are taking a cube root, hence

$$\sqrt[3]{a^4 b^5} = \sqrt[3]{a^3 b^3 \cdot ab^2} = ab\sqrt[3]{ab^2}.$$

In part (*c*), we must select the largest fourth-power factor of the radicand, or

$$\sqrt[4]{\frac{32a^7}{c^4}} = \frac{\sqrt[4]{32a^7}}{\sqrt[4]{c^4}} = \frac{\sqrt[4]{16a^4 \cdot 2a^3}}{\sqrt[4]{c^4}} = \frac{2a\sqrt[4]{2a^3}}{c}.$$

In some examples where simplification is requested by removing a factor from the radicand, the index involved is literal. The procedures involved are similar to those in Example 9.

EXAMPLE 10. We show here three examples of simplification of radicals with literal indices and provide some discussion.

(*a*) $\sqrt[n]{c^{n+3}} = \sqrt[n]{c^n \cdot c^3} = \sqrt[n]{c^n} \cdot \sqrt[n]{c^3} = c\sqrt[n]{c^3}.$

(*b*) $\sqrt[n+1]{b^{2n+7}} = \sqrt[n+1]{a^{2n+2} \cdot b^5} = \sqrt[n+1]{b^{2n+2}} \cdot \sqrt[n+1]{b^5}$

$\qquad = b^2 \left(\sqrt[n+1]{b^5} \right).$

(*c*) $\sqrt[2n-1]{\frac{a^{2n+1}}{b^{4n-2}}} = \sqrt[2n-1]{\frac{a^{2n-1} \cdot a^2}{b^{4n-2}}} = \sqrt[2n-1]{\frac{a^{2n-1}}{b^{4n-2}}} \cdot \sqrt[2n-1]{a^2}$

$\qquad = \frac{a}{b^2} \left(\sqrt[2n-1]{a^2} \right).$

In all of the parts of Example 10, one intermediate goal is evident. In each case the radicand is factored into two factors. One of these factors has an exponent that is an integral multiple of the index, and the exponent of the other factor is such that the sum of the exponents of the two factors equals the original exponent. To point this out, we see in part (*b*) that the radicand is b^{2n+7} and the index is $n + 1$. The radicand is expressed as $b^{2n+2} \cdot b^5$, where $2n + 2$ is exactly twice $n + 1$ and $2n + 2 + 5$ adds to the original exponent $2n + 7$.

In Examples 9 and 10 simplification of the radical quantities was performed by removing a factor of the radicand from the radicand and making it a multiplier of the remaining radical quantity. Before introducing a set of exercises, we will introduce another simplification procedure; this one involves fractional radicands or radical quantities in the denominators of fractions. From Law 3 of Table 6-2 we have

$$\sqrt[n]{\frac{a}{b}} = \frac{\sqrt[n]{a}}{\sqrt[n]{b}},$$

where the left side shows that the root of a quotient of two numbers is the quotient of the roots of the two numbers. In the simplified form, it is desirable to eliminate fractions from radicands and to eliminate radical quantities from denominators. Refer to Examples 11 and 12 for illustrations.

EXAMPLE 11. Simplify the quantity $\sqrt[4]{ab^2/cd^2}$.

Solution. Using law 3 of Table 6-2, we have

$$\sqrt[4]{\frac{ab^2}{cd^2}} = \frac{\sqrt[4]{ab^2}}{\sqrt[4]{cd^2}},$$

where the denominator of the right side is a radical quantity. The process of eliminating the radical in the denominator is called *rationalizing the denominator* and can be accomplished by multiplying the denominator by a conveniently chosen quantity. If the exponents of c and d in the denominator were each 4 (or integral multiples of the index 4), then the fourth root of the radicand would not involve a radical. If we multiply the denominator by $\sqrt[4]{c^3d^2}$, the new denominator will be

$$\sqrt[4]{cd^2} \cdot \sqrt[4]{c^3d^2} = \sqrt[4]{c^4d^4} = cd,$$

where cd is rational. We must recall, however, that if we multiply the denominator of a fraction by a factor, we must provide the numerator with the same factor so that the value of the original fraction will be unchanged. Proceeding,

$$\sqrt[4]{\frac{ab^2}{cd^2}} = \frac{\sqrt[4]{ab^2} \cdot \sqrt[4]{c^3d^2}}{\sqrt[4]{cd^2} \cdot \sqrt[4]{c^3d^2}} = \frac{\sqrt[4]{ab^2c^3d^2}}{cd}.$$

EXAMPLE 12. We show here three more examples involving the process of rationalizing denominators.

$$(a) \quad \frac{3}{\sqrt{2}} = \frac{3}{\sqrt{2}} \cdot \frac{\sqrt{2}}{\sqrt{2}} = \frac{3\sqrt{2}}{2}.$$

$$(b) \quad \frac{3}{\sqrt[3]{2}} = \frac{3}{\sqrt[3]{2}} \cdot \frac{\sqrt[3]{4}}{\sqrt[3]{4}} = \frac{3\sqrt[3]{4}}{2}.$$

$$(c) \quad \frac{3}{\sqrt[5]{2}} = \frac{3}{\sqrt[5]{2}} \cdot \frac{\sqrt[5]{16}}{\sqrt[5]{16}} = \frac{3\sqrt[5]{16}}{2}.$$

Note in Example 12 that the rationalizing factor varies according to the nature of the root in the original denominator. In (*a*) the rationalizing factor involves a square root, in (*b*) a cube root, and in (*c*) a fifth root.

Exercises

The quantities given in Exercises 1–5 are in exponent form. Express them in radical form.

1. $b^{3/2}$.

Ans. $\sqrt[2]{b^3}$.

2. $(m + n)^{2/3}$.

3. $(c^2 d)^{2/5}$.

Ans. $\sqrt[5]{(c^2 d)^2}$.

4. $m^{1/4} n^{3/4} p^{-1/4}$.

5. $\left(\dfrac{1 + x^2}{x}\right)^{2/3}$.

Ans. $\sqrt[3]{\left(\dfrac{1 + x^2}{x}\right)^2}$.

The quantities given in Exercises 6–10 are in radical form. Express them in exponent form.

6. $\sqrt[3]{b^2 c}$.

7. $\sqrt[4]{a^3 b}$.

Ans. $a^{3/4} b^{1/4}$.

8. $\sqrt[3]{(m + n)^2}$.

9. $\sqrt[4]{\dfrac{b}{(c + d)^3}}$.

Ans. $b^{1/4}(c + d)^{-3/4}$.

10. $\sqrt[5]{p^2 q^{-3} m}$.

Simplify the expressions in Exercises 11–40 by removing factors from the radicands.

11. $\sqrt{12}$. Ans. $2\sqrt{3}$. **12.** $\sqrt{18}$.

13. $\sqrt{24}$. Ans. $2\sqrt{6}$. **14.** $\sqrt{72}$.

15. $\sqrt{75}$. Ans. $5\sqrt{3}$. **16.** $\sqrt{54}$.

17. $\sqrt{27}$. Ans. $3\sqrt{3}$. **18.** $\sqrt{288}$.

19. $\sqrt{125}$. Ans. $5\sqrt{5}$. **20.** $\sqrt{108}$.

21. $\sqrt[3]{54}$. Ans. $3\sqrt[3]{2}$. **22.** $\sqrt[3]{81}$.

23. $\sqrt[3]{24}$. Ans. $2\sqrt[3]{3}$. **24.** $\sqrt[3]{128}$.

25. $\sqrt[4]{32}$. Ans. $2\sqrt[4]{2}$. **26.** $\sqrt[3]{320}$.

27. $\sqrt[4]{162}$. Ans. $3\sqrt[4]{2}$. **28.** $\sqrt[4]{48}$.

29. $\sqrt[6]{576}$. Ans. $2\sqrt[6]{9}$. **30.** $\sqrt[4]{a^5 b}$.

31. $\sqrt[3]{a^5 b^4 c^3}$. Ans. $abc\sqrt[3]{a^2 b}$. **32.** $\sqrt{ab^2 c^3}$.

33. $\sqrt{12m^3 p^5}$. Ans. $2mp^2\sqrt{3mp}$. **34.** $\sqrt[3]{12m^3 p^5}$.

35. $\sqrt[4]{243a^{13}b^{14}}$. Ans. $3a^3 b^3\sqrt[4]{3ab^2}$. **36.** $\sqrt[n]{x^{3n} y^{n+1}}$.

37. $\sqrt[n]{2^{n+1}x^{4n+5}}$.   *Ans.* $2x^4\sqrt[n]{2x^5}$.   **38.** $\sqrt[n+1]{a^{2+n}b^{2n+3}}$.

39. $\sqrt[2n-1]{a^{2n}b^{4n-1}}$.   *Ans.* $ab^2\sqrt[2n-1]{ab}$.   **40.** $\sqrt[2n+1]{a^{2n+2}b^{3n+5}}$.

Simplify Exercises 42–70 by rationalizing denominators.

41. $\dfrac{1}{\sqrt{3}}$.   *Ans.* $\dfrac{\sqrt{3}}{3}$.   **42.** $\sqrt{\frac{4}{9}}$.

43. $\sqrt{\frac{1}{2}}$.   *Ans.* $\dfrac{\sqrt{2}}{2}$.   **44.** $\sqrt{\frac{3}{4}}$.

45. $\sqrt{\frac{3}{2}}$.   *Ans.* $\dfrac{\sqrt{6}}{2}$.   **46.** $\sqrt{\dfrac{4.5}{2}}$.

47. $\sqrt{\frac{5}{4}}$.   *Ans.* $\dfrac{\sqrt{5}}{2}$.   **48.** $\sqrt{\dfrac{24}{1.5}}$.

49. $\sqrt{\frac{5}{32}}$.   *Ans.* $\dfrac{\sqrt{10}}{8}$.   **50.** $\sqrt{\frac{40}{18}}$.

51. $\sqrt{\frac{7}{8}}$.   *Ans.* $\dfrac{\sqrt{14}}{4}$.   **52.** $\sqrt{\frac{5}{8}}$.

53. $\sqrt{\dfrac{a^2}{bc}}$.   *Ans.* $\dfrac{a\sqrt{bc}}{bc}$.   **54.** $\sqrt{\dfrac{4b^3}{9c^3}}$.

55. $\sqrt{\dfrac{9ab}{98c^3}}$.   *Ans.* $\dfrac{3\sqrt{2abc}}{14c^2}$.   **56.** $\sqrt[3]{\dfrac{2x^2}{9y^4}}$.

57. $\sqrt[4]{\dfrac{b^{4n}}{c^{3n}}}$.   *Ans.* $\dfrac{b^n(\sqrt[4]{c^n})}{c^n}$.   **58.** $\sqrt[n]{\dfrac{1}{x^{n-1}}}$.

59. $\sqrt[n+1]{\dfrac{1}{x^n}}$.   *Ans.* $\dfrac{\sqrt[n+1]{x}}{x}$.   **60.** $\sqrt[2n+1]{\dfrac{x^2}{y^{4n+4}}}$.

61. $\dfrac{1}{\sqrt[3]{3}}$.   *Ans.* $\dfrac{\sqrt[3]{9}}{3}$.   **62.** $\dfrac{\sqrt{3}}{\sqrt{8}}$.

63. $\dfrac{\sqrt[4]{3}}{\sqrt[4]{4}}$.   *Ans.* $\dfrac{\sqrt[4]{12}}{2}$.   **64.** $\sqrt{\dfrac{m+n}{m-n}}$.

65. $\sqrt{\dfrac{m-n}{m+n}}$.   *Ans.* $\dfrac{\sqrt{m^2-n^2}}{m+n}$.   **66.** $\sqrt[3]{\dfrac{m}{3n+2}}$.

67. $\sqrt{\dfrac{5}{72}}$.   *Ans.* $\dfrac{\sqrt{10}}{12}$.   **68.** $\sqrt{\dfrac{x^2+4x^2y}{8}}$.

69. $\sqrt{\dfrac{(a+b)^3}{a}}$.

   Ans. $\dfrac{(a+b)\sqrt{a(a+b)}}{a}$.   **70.** $\sqrt[3]{\dfrac{1}{4x^2y}}$.

6-3 Multiplication and Division of Radical Quantities

The laws that are most useful in the multiplication and division of radical quantities are

$$\sqrt[n]{a} \cdot \sqrt[n]{b} = \sqrt[n]{ab}, \tag{20}$$

$$\sqrt[n]{a} \div \sqrt[n]{b} = \sqrt[n]{\frac{a}{b}}. \tag{21}$$

Observe that (20) and (21) have similar indices and different radicands. This observation is very valuable in identifying the proper procedure to use.

Appropriate also are the laws of exponents where

$$a^m \cdot a^n = a^{m+n}, \tag{22}$$

$$a^m \div a^n = a^{m-n}. \tag{23}$$

Expressions (22) and (23) are applied to radical quantities which, after they are converted to exponent form, have unlike exponents and similar bases.

We can organize our material to involve four cases for multiplication and division of radical quantities:

Case 1. If the radicands are different and the indices are the same, apply (20) or (21).

Case 2. If the radicands are the same and the indices different, convert to the exponential form and apply (22) or (23).

Case 3. If the radicands are the same and the indices the same, apply (20), (21), (22), or (23).

Case 4. If the radicands are different and the indices are different, similar indices may be obtained by converting to the exponential form and establishing an LCD of the exponents, then converting back to radicals and applying (20) or (21). If the bases are numerical, and the indices are different, conversion to the base 10 can be made through logarithm tables and (22) or (23) can be applied.

EXAMPLE 13. We will give here three examples. In each the indices are the same and the radicands are different. This condition suggests that Case 1 is appropriate and we will use either (20) or (21) in the solution.

(*a*) $\sqrt{2} \cdot \sqrt{3} = \sqrt{6}$.

(*b*) $\sqrt[3]{5a^2b} \cdot \sqrt[3]{50a^2b^2} = \sqrt[3]{250a^4b^3} = \sqrt[3]{125a^3b^3} \cdot \sqrt[3]{2a} = 5ab\sqrt[3]{2a}$.

(*c*) $\sqrt[n]{6a^{2n-3}} \div \sqrt[n]{3a^{n-6}} = \sqrt{\frac{6a^{2n-3}}{3a^{n-6}}} = \sqrt[n]{2a^{n+3}} = a\sqrt[n]{2a^3}$.

Observe in Example 13 that, with the indices the same and the radicands different, we multiply or divide the radicands without modification of the index.

EXAMPLE 14. In this example we give two examples where the radicands are similar and the indices different. Here Case 2 is appropriate.

(a) $\sqrt[2]{2} \cdot \sqrt[3]{2} = 2^{1/2} \cdot 2^{1/3} = 2^{(1/2)+(1/3)} = 2^{5/6} = \sqrt[6]{2^5} = \sqrt[6]{32}.$

(b) $\sqrt[3]{18a} \div \sqrt[4]{18a} = (18a)^{1.3} \div (18a)^{1/4} = (18a)^{(1/3)-(1/4)}$
$= (18a)^{1/12} = \sqrt[12]{18a}.$

Here the bases were the same and the indices were different. Upon conversion to the exponent form, we added or subtracted the exponents by conversion to an LCD. After the collection of the exponents, we converted back to the radical form.

EXAMPLE 15. We present here a single example of the multiplication of two quantities where the radicands are similar and the indices are similar. This is Case 3. By (20),

$$\sqrt[5]{3a^2b} \cdot \sqrt[5]{3a^2b} = \sqrt[5]{9a^4b^2},$$

or by (22),

$$\sqrt[5]{3a^2b} \cdot \sqrt[5]{3a^2b} = (3a^2b)^{1/5} \cdot (3a^2b)^{1/5} = (3a^2b)^{2/5} = \sqrt[5]{9a^4b^2}.$$

Note that this is perhaps the simplest of the operations. It amounts merely to a squaring operation.

EXAMPLE 16. Here we will consider two examples where the radicands and indices are different. This is Case 4. This case can be solved by converting to the exponent form, adding the exponents, then converting back to the radical form.

(a) $\sqrt[3]{4} \cdot \sqrt[2]{2} = (4)^{1/3} \cdot (2)^{1/2} = (4)^{2/6} \cdot (2)^{3/6} = (4^2)^{1/6} \cdot (2^3)^{1/6}$
$= \sqrt[6]{4^2 \cdot 2^3} = 2\sqrt[6]{2}.$

(b) $\sqrt[5]{6} \div \sqrt[3]{3} = (6)^{1/5} \div (3)^{1/3} = (6)^{3/15} \div (3)^{5/15}$
$= (6^3)^{1/15} \div (3^5)^{1/15} = \sqrt[15]{6^3/3^5} = \sqrt[15]{8/9}$
$= \frac{1}{3}\sqrt[15]{8 \cdot 3^{13}}.$

Exercises

Perform the indicated operations. Simplify the results wherever possible.

1. $\sqrt{3} \cdot \sqrt{15}.$ *Ans.* $3\sqrt{5}.$

2. $\sqrt{6} \cdot \sqrt{15}.$

3. $\sqrt[3]{4} \cdot \sqrt[3]{12}$.   *Ans.* $2\sqrt[3]{6}$.

4. $\sqrt[4]{12} \cdot \sqrt[4]{20}$.

5. $\sqrt{3x^3y} \cdot \sqrt{6xy^5}$.   *Ans.* $3x^2y^3\sqrt{2}$.

6. $\sqrt[4]{x^5y^5} \cdot \sqrt[4]{x^3y^7}$.

7. $\sqrt{8x^3y^3} \div \sqrt{2xy^3}$.   *Ans.* $2x$.

8. $\sqrt{50} \div \sqrt{2}$.

9. $\sqrt{48ab} \div \sqrt{12ab}$.   *Ans.* 2.

10. $\sqrt[3]{a^2b} \div \sqrt[3]{ab}$.

11. $\sqrt[2]{6} \cdot \sqrt[3]{12}$.   *Ans.* $2\sqrt[6]{486}$.

12. $\sqrt[3]{12} \div \sqrt[2]{6}$.

13. $\sqrt[4]{54} \div \sqrt[2]{27}$.   *Ans.* $\sqrt[4]{6}\,/\,3$.

14. $\sqrt{32} \cdot \sqrt{32}$.

15. $\sqrt[3]{35} \div \sqrt[3]{35}$.   *Ans.* 1.

16. $(2\sqrt[3]{5})^3$.

17. $(\sqrt[3]{9x^2})^2$.   *Ans.* $3x\sqrt[3]{3x}$.

18. $(\sqrt{5} - \sqrt{3})^2$.

19. $(\sqrt{2} + \sqrt{3})^2$.   *Ans.* $5 + 2\sqrt{6}$.

20. $(3 - \sqrt{2})^2$.

21. $(3 + \sqrt{2})(3 - \sqrt{2})$.   *Ans.* 7.

22. $(2\sqrt{3} + 4)(2\sqrt{3} - 4)$.

23. $(\sqrt{3} - 3)(\sqrt{12} + 2)$.   *Ans.* $-4\sqrt{3}$.

24. $(\sqrt{x+y} + z)(\sqrt{x+y})$.

25. $\sqrt{3 - \sqrt{3}} \cdot \sqrt{3 + \sqrt{3}}$.   *Ans.* $\sqrt{6}$.

26. $\sqrt{A/\pi} \cdot \sqrt{\pi/A}$.

27. $(\sqrt{x^2 - y^2} - \sqrt{x^2 + y^2})^2$.   *Ans.* $2x^2 - 2\sqrt{x^4 - y^4}$.

28. $\sqrt[3]{a^2b} \div \sqrt[2]{ab^2}$.

29. $\sqrt[2]{a^3b} \div \sqrt[3]{ab}$.   *Ans.* $a\sqrt[6]{ab}$.

30. $\sqrt[4]{m^3n} \div \sqrt[3]{mn}$.

31. $\sqrt[n]{x^{n+1}y^{n-1}} \cdot \sqrt[n]{x^ny^{n+3}}$.   *Ans.* $x^2y^2\sqrt[n]{xy^2}$.

32. $\sqrt[n]{a^2b} \div \sqrt[n]{ab}$.

33. $\sqrt[n+1]{a^{n-1}b^n} \div \sqrt[n]{a^{n+1}b^{n-1}}$.   *Ans.* $\sqrt[n^2+n]{a^{-3n-1}b}$.

34. $\sqrt[n]{a^{n+1}b^{n-1}} \div \sqrt[n-1]{a^nb^n}$.

Two radical quantities are alike only if their radicands are the same and their indices are the same. If the quantities are expressed in exponential form, they are alike only if the bases are the same and the exponents are the same. *Radical quantities can be added or subtracted only if they are alike or can be made alike.*

EXAMPLE 17. Perform the indicated operations:

(*a*) $\sqrt{3} + 2\sqrt{3}$.

(*b*) $\sqrt{2} + \sqrt{50} - \sqrt{18}$.

(*c*) $2\sqrt{a^3} - \sqrt{a^5} - 3\sqrt{a}$.

Solutions. (*a*) Since the radicands are the same and both of the quantities involve the same (square) root, the radical quantities are of the same kind and can be added by adding the coefficients.

$$\sqrt{3} + 2\sqrt{3} = 3\sqrt{3}.$$

(*b*) The indices are the same but the radicands appear different. If we remove factors from the last two radicands, we will have similar radicands as shown:

$$\sqrt{2} + \sqrt{50} - \sqrt{18} = \sqrt{2} + 5\sqrt{2} - 3\sqrt{2} = 3\sqrt{2}.$$

(*c*) The method of solution here is similar to that used in part (*b*); that is, factors are removed from the radicands.

$$2\sqrt{a^3} - \sqrt{a^5} - 3\sqrt{a} = 2a\sqrt{a} - a^2\sqrt{a} - 3\sqrt{a}$$
$$= -\sqrt{a}\,(a^2 - 2a + 3).$$

EXAMPLE 18. Perform the indicated operation:

$$5\sqrt{6} - 4\sqrt{\tfrac{3}{2}} + 2\sqrt[4]{36}.$$

Solution. Similar indices and similar radicands can be obtained by standard simplification procedures:

$$5\sqrt{6} - 4\sqrt{\tfrac{3}{2}} + 2\sqrt[4]{36} = 5\sqrt{6} - 4\sqrt{\tfrac{6}{4}} + 2(36)^{1/4}$$
$$= 5\sqrt{6} - \tfrac{4}{2}\sqrt{6} + 2(6^2)^{1/4}$$
$$= 5\sqrt{6} - 2\sqrt{6} + 2\sqrt{6} = 5\sqrt{6}.$$

Note that $\sqrt[4]{36}$ was modified to $\sqrt[2]{6}$. Changing from the higher index 4 to the lower index 2 is called *reduction in order*.

Exercises

Perform the indicated addition and subtraction operations wherever possible.

1. $\sqrt{3} - 3\sqrt{3} + 4\sqrt{3}$.   *Ans.* $2\sqrt{3}$.

2. $3\sqrt[3]{5} + 2\sqrt[3]{5} - \sqrt[3]{5}$.

3. $a\sqrt[n]{x} - b\sqrt[n]{x} + c\sqrt[n]{x}$.   *Ans.* $(a - b + c)\sqrt[n]{x}$.

4. $\sqrt{4x} - \sqrt{x}$.

5. $\sqrt{2} - \sqrt{8}$.   *Ans.* $-\sqrt{2}$.

6. $\sqrt{3} - \sqrt{27}$.

7. $\sqrt{12} - \sqrt{3}$.   *Ans.* $\sqrt{3}$.

8. $\sqrt{32} - \sqrt{18}$.

9. $\sqrt{27} + \sqrt{\frac{1}{3}}$.   *Ans.* $\dfrac{10\sqrt{3}}{3}$.

10. $3\sqrt{32} - 2\sqrt{50}$.

11. $3\sqrt{50} - 2\sqrt{8}$.   *Ans.* $11\sqrt{2}$.

12. $\sqrt{8} + \sqrt{\frac{1}{2}}$.

13. $2\sqrt{98} + 3\sqrt{72} - 5\sqrt{50}$.   *Ans.* $7\sqrt{2}$.

14. $\sqrt{80} - \sqrt{20} - \sqrt{\frac{5}{4}}$.

15. $2\sqrt{48} + \sqrt{75} - 2\sqrt{27}$.   *Ans.* $7\sqrt{3}$.

16. $\sqrt{12} + \sqrt{27} - \sqrt{\frac{1}{3}}$.

17. $\sqrt{28} - \sqrt{\frac{7}{9}} + \sqrt{\frac{1}{7}}$.   *Ans.* $\dfrac{38\sqrt{7}}{21}$.

18. $\sqrt[3]{16} + \sqrt[3]{54} - \sqrt[3]{128}$.

19. $\sqrt[3]{32} + \sqrt[3]{500}$.   *Ans.* $7\sqrt[3]{4}$.

20. $2\sqrt[3]{\frac{1}{2}} + 3\sqrt[3]{\frac{4}{27}}$.

21. $3\sqrt[3]{\frac{1}{4}} - 2\sqrt[3]{\frac{2}{27}} + \sqrt[3]{\frac{4}{27}}$.   *Ans.* $13\dfrac{\sqrt[3]{2}}{12}$.

22. $\sqrt{a^2b} - \sqrt{a^4b^3} + 2\sqrt{b^5}$.

23. $\sqrt{x^3y} - \sqrt{xy^3} + \sqrt{xy}$.   *Ans.* $(x - y + 1)\sqrt{xy}$.

24. $\sqrt{x^5y^4} + \sqrt{x^3y^6}$.

25. $\sqrt[3]{a^4b^5} - 3\sqrt[3]{a^7b^5} + 2\sqrt[3]{a^4b^2}$.   *Ans.* $\sqrt[3]{ab^2}(ab - 3a^2b + 2a)$.

26. $\sqrt[3]{(m + n)^2} - 2\sqrt[3]{1/(m + n)}$.

27. $\sqrt{a + b} - 2\sqrt{\dfrac{1}{a + b}}$.   *Ans.* $\dfrac{(a + b - 2)\sqrt{a + b}}{a + b}$.

28. $3\sqrt[3]{40x} + \sqrt[3]{135y^3x}.$

29. $\sqrt[4]{(a^2 - b^2)^2} + \frac{1}{3}\sqrt{a^2 - b^2}.$ *Ans.* $4\sqrt{a^2 - b^2}/3.$

30. $\sqrt{mn} - \sqrt{m^3n} + 4\sqrt{\dfrac{n}{m}}.$

31. $\sqrt{75a^2x - 50a^4} + \sqrt{48x^5 - 32a^2x^4}.$ *Ans.* $(5a + 4x^2)\sqrt{3x - 2a^2}.$

32. $4\sqrt[3]{24c^4d^2} + 3\sqrt[3]{81cd^2}.$

33. $\sqrt{\dfrac{1}{m}} - 3\sqrt{\dfrac{1}{m^3}} + 2\sqrt{\dfrac{1}{m^5}}.$ *Ans.* $\sqrt{m}(m - 2)(m - 1)/m^3.$

34. $\sqrt{\dfrac{a - b}{a + b}} - \sqrt{\dfrac{a + b}{a - b}}.$

35. $\sqrt[9]{(x + y)^{12}} + \sqrt[3]{64xy^3 + 64y^4}.$

36. $\sqrt{(a + b)^3} - \sqrt{a^3b^2 + a^2b^3}.$

37. $\sqrt{m^2 - m^2n^2} - \sqrt{\dfrac{1 + n}{1 - n}} + \sqrt{n^2 - n^4}.$

               Ans. $\dfrac{(m + n - mn - 1 - n^2)\sqrt{1 - n^2}}{1 - n}.$

38. $\sqrt[3]{1 - \dfrac{1}{x}} - \dfrac{1}{x}\sqrt[3]{x^3 - x^2}.$

39. $\dfrac{x^2}{2}\sqrt{\dfrac{2y^3}{x^5}} - \sqrt{\dfrac{y^3}{2x}} + x\sqrt{\dfrac{y^3}{2x^3}}.$ *Ans.* $\dfrac{y\sqrt{2xy}}{2x}.$

40. $3\sqrt[4]{\dfrac{a^2}{4b^2}} + \dfrac{b^2}{2}\sqrt{\dfrac{2a^3}{b^5}}.$

6-5   More on Rationalizing Denominators—a Summary

When radical expressions arise, a question regarding their simplification also arises. A primary reason for certain standards in simplification is to leave results in the same form. Often two students will arrive at equivalent answers to a problem, but will fail to recognize the equivalency of their answers because the answers are left in two different algebraic forms. Other reasons for certain simplification standards are given also. If a student is without computation aids such as the slide rule or tables, numerical radicands are best expressed in small numbers; that is, given

$$\sqrt{12} = \sqrt{4} \cdot \sqrt{3} = 2\sqrt{3},$$

it is less likely that the student knows the approximate decimal value of $\sqrt{12}$ than the decimal value of $\sqrt{3}$.

There are also cases involving division of radicals. Once again, if we are without computation aids, given

$$\frac{1}{\sqrt{3}} = \frac{1}{\sqrt{3}} \cdot \frac{\sqrt{3}}{\sqrt{3}} = \frac{\sqrt{3}}{3} = \frac{1.732}{3} = 0.577$$

it is easier to divide 1.732 by 3 than to divide unity by 1.732. Hence, we attempt to eliminate radicals from denominators.

There are four simplification operations which we will summarize here. We will accept them as operations that are standard but not absolutely essential.

1. *Reduce radicands to the simplest form.* When factors can be removed from radicands, remove them. Such simplifications depend upon the law:

$$\sqrt[n]{ab} = \sqrt[n]{a} \cdot \sqrt[n]{b}.$$

Many exercises were provided in Sec. 6-2.

2. *Do not leave a fraction under a radical sign.* Given the nth root of a fraction, express this as the quotient of the nth roots of the numerator and denominator, then rationalize the denominator. That is,

$$\sqrt[n]{\frac{a}{b}} = \frac{\sqrt[n]{a}}{\sqrt[n]{b}} = \frac{\sqrt[n]{a}}{\sqrt[n]{b}} \cdot \frac{\sqrt[n]{b^{n-1}}}{\sqrt[n]{b^{n-1}}} = \frac{\sqrt[n]{ab^{n-1}}}{b}. \tag{24}$$

The preceding operation involved the division of a radical expression. Many exercises were provided in Secs. 6-2 and 6-3.

3. *Rationalize denominators whenever it is done simply.* There are two common operations involved here. In (24) we saw a denominator containing a monomial quantity $\sqrt[n]{b}$. The procedure used in simplification there has been previously discussed with examples in Secs. 6-2 and 6-3. It is emphasized that those examples embraced only monomial denominators.

The second operation regarding rationalization of denominators involves a binomial denominator where either or both of the terms in the denominator involve a square root radical. Before showing some examples, let us reflect upon a certain algebraic operation: if the sum of two numbers is multiplied by the difference of the same two numbers, the product is the difference of the squares of the two numbers. If either or both of the numbers is a square root, the operation eliminates the square root radical. That is,

$$(\sqrt{a} + b)(\sqrt{a} - b) = a - b^2,$$
$$(a + \sqrt{b})(a - \sqrt{b}) = a^2 - b,$$
$$(\sqrt{a} + \sqrt{b})(\sqrt{a} - \sqrt{b}) = a - b.$$

Any two numbers of the forms $x + \sqrt{y}$ and $x - \sqrt{y}$ are *conjugate* numbers. That is, $x + \sqrt{y}$ is the conjugate of $x - \sqrt{y}$ and $x - \sqrt{y}$ is the conjugate of $x + \sqrt{y}$.

EXAMPLE 19. Rationalize the denominators of the expressions

$$(a) \ \frac{3}{3 - \sqrt{5}}, \ (b) \ \frac{\sqrt{2}}{\sqrt{2} + 1}, \ (c) \ \frac{\sqrt{2} - \sqrt{3}}{\sqrt{2} + \sqrt{3}}.$$

Solution. In each case rationalization is accomplished by multiplying the denominator by the conjugate of the denominator. In order to preserve the value of the fraction, the numerator is multiplied by the same quantity.

$$(a) \ \frac{3}{3 - \sqrt{5}} \cdot \frac{3 + \sqrt{5}}{3 + \sqrt{5}} = \frac{3(3 + \sqrt{5})}{3^2 - (\sqrt{5})^2} = \frac{9 + 3\sqrt{5}}{9 - 5}$$
$$= \frac{9 + 3\sqrt{5}}{4}.$$

$$(b) \ \frac{\sqrt{2}}{\sqrt{2} + 1} \cdot \frac{\sqrt{2} - 1}{\sqrt{2} - 1} = \frac{\sqrt{2}(\sqrt{2} - 1)}{(\sqrt{2})^2 - 1^2} = \frac{2 - \sqrt{2}}{2 - 1}$$
$$= 2 - \sqrt{2}.$$

$$(c) \ \frac{\sqrt{2} - \sqrt{3}}{\sqrt{2} + \sqrt{3}} \cdot \frac{\sqrt{2} - \sqrt{3}}{\sqrt{2} - \sqrt{3}} = \frac{(\sqrt{2} - \sqrt{3})^2}{(\sqrt{2})^2 - (\sqrt{3})^2}$$
$$= \frac{2 - 2\sqrt{6} + 3}{2 - 3} = -5 + 2\sqrt{6}.$$

4. *Reduction of order.* The last standard operation discussed here is called reduction of order. A cube root is a radical of third order, a square root is of second order, etc. Often a higher-order expression may be reduced to a lower order by methods which follow in Example 20.

EXAMPLE 20. Reduce to simpler order the expressions $(a) \ \sqrt[4]{25}$, $(b) \ \sqrt[6]{81}$, $(c) \ \sqrt[8]{a^4 b^{12}}$.

Solutions.

$$(a) \ \sqrt[4]{25} = (25)^{1/4} = (5^2)^{1/4} = 5^{2 \cdot \tfrac{1}{4}} = 5^{1/2} = \sqrt{5}.$$
$$(b) \ \sqrt[6]{81} = (81)^{1/6} = (3^4)^{1/6} = (3)^{4/6} = (3)^{2/3} = (3^2)^{1/3} = \sqrt[3]{9}.$$
$$(c) \ \sqrt[8]{a^4 b^{12}} = b\sqrt[8]{a^4 b^4} = b(ab)^{4/8} = b(ab)^{1/2} = b\sqrt{ab}.$$

In general, we have the problem of reducing in order the expression $\sqrt[n]{N}$. If N can be written in the form $N = (M)^a$, then

$$\sqrt[n]{N} = \sqrt[n]{M^a} = M^{a/n}.$$

Now, if a/n is reducible to a simpler form, then $\sqrt[n]{N}$ can be reduced in order.

Exercises

In Exercises 1–27 simplify the given expressions.

1. $\sqrt{\frac{2}{5}}$.   *Ans.* $\frac{1}{5}\sqrt{10}$.   2. $\sqrt{\frac{3}{5}}$.

3. $\sqrt{\frac{3}{8}}$.   *Ans.* $\frac{1}{4}\sqrt{6}$.   4. $\sqrt{\frac{4}{5}}$.

5. $\sqrt{\frac{5}{8}}$.   *Ans.* $\frac{1}{4}\sqrt{10}$.   6. $\sqrt{\frac{3}{16}}$.

7. $\sqrt{\frac{5}{12}}$.   *Ans.* $\frac{1}{6}\sqrt{15}$.   8. $\sqrt{\frac{5}{9}}$.

9. $\sqrt[3]{\frac{5}{8}}$.   *Ans.* $\frac{1}{2}\sqrt[3]{5}$.   10. $\sqrt{\frac{3}{32}}$.

11. $\dfrac{1}{\sqrt{2}}$.   *Ans.* $\dfrac{\sqrt{2}}{2}$.   12. $\dfrac{2}{\sqrt{3}}$.

13. $\dfrac{2}{\sqrt{8}}$.   *Ans.* $\dfrac{\sqrt{2}}{2}$.   14. $\dfrac{3}{\sqrt{5}}$.

15. $\dfrac{3}{\sqrt[3]{2}}$.   *Ans.* $3\dfrac{\sqrt[3]{4}}{2}$.   16. $\dfrac{6}{\sqrt[3]{4}}$.

17. $\dfrac{4}{\sqrt[4]{8}}$.   *Ans.* $2\sqrt[4]{2}$.   18. $\dfrac{5}{\sqrt[5]{16}}$.

19. $\dfrac{1}{2+\sqrt{5}}$.   *Ans.* $\sqrt{5}-2$.   20. $\dfrac{8}{6+\sqrt{6}}$.

21. $\dfrac{4}{4-\sqrt{2}}$.   *Ans.* $\dfrac{8+2\sqrt{2}}{7}$.   22. $\dfrac{5}{5-\sqrt{5}}$.

23. $\dfrac{3}{\sqrt{3}+\sqrt{2}}$.   24. $\dfrac{1}{2\sqrt{2}-\sqrt{3}}$.

Ans. $3\sqrt{3}-3\sqrt{2}$.

25. $\dfrac{5}{5\sqrt{3}-2\sqrt{5}}$.   26. $\dfrac{\sqrt{2}-\sqrt{3}}{\sqrt{2}+\sqrt{3}}$.

Ans. $\dfrac{5\sqrt{3}+2\sqrt{5}}{11}$.

27. $\dfrac{\sqrt{5}-\sqrt{3}}{\sqrt{5}+2\sqrt{3}}$.

Ans. $\dfrac{3\sqrt{15}-11}{7}$.

Reduce the order of the given expressions.

28. $\sqrt[4]{4}$.

29. $\sqrt[6]{27}$.   *Ans.* $\sqrt{3}$.   30. $\sqrt[10]{32}$.

31. $\sqrt[8]{16}$.   *Ans.* $\sqrt{2}$.   32. $\sqrt[4]{64}$.

33. $\sqrt[6]{a^3b^6c^9}$.   *Ans.* $bc\sqrt{ac}$.   **34.** $\sqrt[6]{a^4b^{10}}$.

35. $\sqrt[4]{4a^2b^6}$.   *Ans.* $b\sqrt{2ab}$.   **36.** $\sqrt[n]{a^{n/2}b^{3n/2}}$.

37. $\sqrt[3n]{a^3b^6}$.   *Ans.* $\sqrt[n]{ab^2}$.

6-6   The Number j

The square root of a positive number is defined as one of the two equal factors of that number. If $N = 9$, then the square root of N is $+3$ since $(+3)(+3) = 9$. Also $(-3)(-3) = 9$ where the two equal factors of 9 are integers. The two equal factors of 6 are $\pm\sqrt{6}$, which is irrational. The two equal factors of -6 are $\pm\sqrt{-6}$ which have no *real* meaning and are therefore called *imaginary*.

The square root of -1 is the most elementary imaginary number. It is called the *imaginary unit* and is represented by the symbol j. (Many texts use the symbol i; however, in technical mathematics the symbol i is reserved for electrical current.) Now,

$$j = \sqrt{-1} \tag{25}$$

and

$$j^2 = -1.$$

Operations involving the j quantity will be discussed in considerable detail in the chapter on complex numbers. We have presented here the definition of the j quantity (25). Any time we have the square root of a negative number we can use the j notation, as in

$$\sqrt{-9} = \sqrt{(-1)(9)} = \sqrt{-1}\cdot\sqrt{9} = 3j,$$
$$\sqrt{-20} = \sqrt{(4)(-1)(5)} = 2\sqrt{-1}\cdot\sqrt{5} = 2j\sqrt{5}.$$

Limited use of the j quantity will be made in the following chapter on quadratics.

In the preceding material we have been concerned primarily with linear equations, i.e., equations of first degree. In many applications equations of degree greater than one appear; their study is essential in a program of technical mathematics. The simplest of the equations of degree greater than one is the quadratic equation, which we will define and discuss in this chapter.

QUADRATIC EQUATIONS 7

7-1   Definitions—the Incomplete Quadratic

We will initiate the study of quadratic equations by discussing the quadratic in one unknown. A *quadratic equation* is defined here as an equation of second degree. The highest power to which any of the terms is raised is the degree of the equation. For an equation with one variable, the degree of a term is the degree of the variable in the term. Based on the preceding definitions, the general quadratic in one unknown will be given here in the form

$$ax^2 + bx + c = 0 \qquad (a \neq 0), \tag{1}$$

where a, b, and c are constants and x is the variable. The condition $a \neq 0$ in equation (1) is essential since (1) must be of second degree. If $a = 0$, the term of highest degree is the bx term, causing (1) to be a first- or lower-degree equation.

Note in (1) that no nonzero condition is mentioned regarding b or c. If $b = 0$ or $c = 0$ or $b = c = 0$, then (1) is called an *incomplete quadratic*. Methods of solving incomplete quadratics follow in three cases.

Case 1. Let $b = 0$; then (1) becomes the incomplete quadratic

$$ax^2 + c = 0, \tag{2}$$

from which

$$x^2 = -\frac{c}{a},$$

and we have the two solutions

$$x = \pm\sqrt{-\frac{c}{a}}. \tag{3}$$

Note in equation (3) that if c and a are of the same sign, then x is the square root of a negative number and we say that we have no *real* solutions for x. If a and c are of different signs, two real solutions of x exist. These solutions are equal but opposite in sign.

EXAMPLE 1. Solve $3x^2 - 12 = 0$.

Solution 1. Since

$$3x^2 - 12 = 0,$$

then

$$3x^2 = 12$$

and

$$x^2 = \tfrac{12}{3} = 4,$$

from which

$$x = \pm\sqrt{4} = \pm 2. \tag{4}$$

Solution. 2. The problem may also be solved by factoring. Removing the common monomial factor, we have

$$3x^2 - 12 = 3(x^2 - 4) = 0.$$

Now, $x^2 - 4$ is the difference of two squares and we can factor it, showing the fully factored, incomplete quadratic as

$$3(x - 2)(x + 2) = 0 \tag{5}$$

From (5) we have the product of three numbers equal to zero, where the numbers are 3, $x - 2$, and $x + 2$. Reflecting that when factors multiply to equal zero, at least one of the factors must be zero, then we have either

$$x - 2 = 0. \tag{6}$$

or

$$x + 2 = 0. \tag{7}$$

(Note that the factor 3 cannot be zero.) From (6) and (7), $x = 2$ or $x = -2$, agreeing with the solutions in (4).

EXAMPLE 2. A 12-ft. ladder is inclined against a vertical wall as shown in Fig. 7-1. The inclination is such that the distance from the base of the wall to the top of the ladder is three times the distance from the base of the wall to the base of the ladder. What is the distance from the base of the wall to the top of the ladder?

FIGURE 7-1

Solution. Referring to Fig. 7-1, by the Pythagorean theorem we have the equation

$$(3x)^2 + (x)^2 = (12)^2. \tag{8}$$

Squaring where indicated in (8), we have

$$9x^2 + x^2 = 144,$$

from   which

$$10x^2 = 144$$

and

$$x = \pm\sqrt{14.4} = \pm 3.795.$$

The original problem requested $3x$; therefore, we have the solution

$$3x = 3(3.795) = 11.385.$$

Even though $x = -3.795$ is a solution of (8) it is rejected here because physically it makes no sense.

Case 2. Referring to (1), let $c = 0$ and we have the incomplete quadratic

$$ax^2 + bx = 0. \tag{9}$$

Factoring (9) by removing the common monomial, we have

$$(x)(ax + b) = 0. \tag{10}$$

Setting each factor of (10) equal to zero and solving for x, we have the solutions

$$x = 0 \text{ and } x = -\frac{b}{a}.$$

EXAMPLE 3. Solve $3y^2 - 4y = 0$.

Solution. Factoring, we have

$$y(3y - 4) = 0,$$

from which, upon equating each factor to zero, we have

$$y = 0 \text{ and } y = \tfrac{4}{3}.$$

EXAMPLE 4. An object is thrown into the air with an initial velocity (upward) $v_0 = -128$ ft./sec. The distance-time equation is given as

$$s = v_0 t + \tfrac{1}{2} g t^2. \tag{11}$$

If $g = 32$ ft./sec./sec., at what times (t in seconds) does $s = 0$?

Solution. Substituting the given data into (11), we have the incomplete quadratic

$$0 = -128t + \tfrac{1}{2}(32)t^2. \tag{12}$$

Clearing parentheses in (12) gives us

$$16t^2 - 128t = 0. \tag{13}$$

Factoring (13), we have

$$16t(t - 8) = 0,$$

from which we have the solutions $t = 0$ sec. and $t = 8$ sec. The solutions here are physically explained as those times when the distance is zero or those times when the object is at the altitude of the launch point. At $t = 0$ sec., the object is at the launch altitude heading upward; at $t = 8$ sec., the object is at the launch altitude heading downward.

Case 3. The third and last case of the incomplete quadratic has $b = c = 0$ in (1). This produces the trivial case

$$ax^2 = 0.$$

With a any nonzero constant, x must be zero since the product of a and x^2 equals zero.

   Later we will point out that the number of solutions of a quadratic of the form of (1) must be *two* solutions, not necessarily distinct. In Examples 1–4, two solutions were shown. In the generalization of Case 3, x has two values, both of which are zero.

Exercises

In Exercises 1–21, solve for the quantity indicated. In equations where only one literal quantity appears, solve for that quantity.

1. $2x^2 - 7 = 25$. *Ans.* $x = \pm 4$.

2. $3(x^2 + 4) = x^2 + 16$,

3. $-5x^2 + 2x = 0$. *Ans.* $x = 0, \tfrac{2}{5}$.

4. $36 - 4x^2 = 0$.

5. $2(x^2 + 7) = 112$. *Ans.* $x = \pm 7$.

6. $6(x^2 - 2) = 204$.

7. $3(11 - 3x^2) - 15 = 0$.   *Ans.* $x = \pm 2$

8. $4(3 - x^2) = 3x^2 - 16$.

9. $2(3x^2 - 4) = 3x^2 + 19$.   *Ans.* $x = \pm 3$.

10. $6(x^2 - \frac{1}{2}) = 47 + 4x^2$.

11. $(m + 4)^2 = 16$.

12. $a^2 - y^2 = b^2$ (for y).   *Ans.* $y = \pm \sqrt{a^2 - b^2}$.

13. $r^2 - a^2 r = 0$ (for r).

14. $ar^2 + br^2 + a - b = 0$ (for r).   *Ans.* $r = \pm \sqrt{(b - a)(b + a)}/(b + a)$.

15. $(x + y)^2 - 5(x + y) = 0$ (for $x + y$).

16. $(\sin \phi)^2 - \frac{1}{4} = 0$ (for $\sin \phi$).   *Ans.* $\sin \phi = \pm \frac{1}{2}$.

17. $9(\cos \theta)^2 = \cos \theta$ (for $\cos \theta$).

18. $\tan \phi (\tan \phi - 1) = 3 \tan \phi$ (for $\tan \phi$).   *Ans.* $\tan \phi = 0, 4$.

19. $\dfrac{at + r}{t} = \dfrac{t}{at - r}$ (for r, t).

20. $\dfrac{3x + 4}{x} = \dfrac{x}{3x - 4}$.   *Ans.* $x = \pm \sqrt{2}$.

21. $0.0125t^2 - 2t = 0$.

22. Given a square of side s, show that the diagonal d of the square is $d = s\sqrt{2}$.

23. Given an equilateral triangle of side s, show that the altitude h of the triangle is $h = s\sqrt{3}/2$.

24. The compound interest law is given as

$$A = P(1 + r)^n,$$

where A is the amount to which the principal P will accumulate in n years at an interest rate r. If a \$5000 investment accumulates by compound interest to \$5618 in two years, what is the interest rate?   *Ans.* $r = 0.06$.

25. A curve represented by the equation

$$y = 2x^3 - \tfrac{1}{2}x^2 + 4$$

has a slope y' for all x where

$$y' = 6x^2 - x.$$

For what two values of x does the slope equal zero? For what two values of y does the slope equal zero?   *Ans.* $x = 0, \frac{1}{6}; y = 4, \frac{863}{216}$.

26. A square of side t and a circle of radius r are formed separately from two pieces of wire. If the two pieces of wire are made into a single wire and subsequently this single wire is shaped into a larger square of side s, how long is s in terms of r and t?   *Ans.* $s = t + \frac{1}{2}\pi r$.

27. In electricity, power p equals the product of the intensity i and electromotive force e. Also, $e = ir$, where r is the resistance. Give an expression for i in terms of p and r only.   *Ans.* $i = \sqrt{p/r}$.

28. Given the equation

$$s = v_0 t + \tfrac{1}{2}gt^2,$$

show that $t = 0$, $-2v_0/g$ when $s = 0$.

29. A brick with six rectangular faces is such that the length exceeds the width by 2 and the height is 1 less than the width. The total surface area of the brick is 24 less than 6 times the width. Show that the width of the brick is 2.

7-2 Solution of the General Quadratic by Factoring

Many quadratics may be solved by a device called *factoring. A* trinomial equation such as

$$ax^2 + bx + c = 0. \tag{14}$$

has two linear factors of the form $x + r$ and $x + s$, so that (14) may be written in the form

$$(x + r)(x + s) = 0. \tag{15}$$

Now, from (15), since the product of two factors equals zero, either of the factors may be zero. Therefore, from (15) we have the statements

$$x + r = 0 \text{ from which } x = -r.$$
$$x + s = 0 \text{ from which } x = -s.$$

EXAMPLE 5. Solve for m if $m^2 - 2mn - 15n^2 = 0$.

Solution. We recognize that the given expression may be factored as

$$(m - 5n)(m + 3n) = 0.$$

Setting each factor equal to zero and solving for m, we have the solutions

$$m = 5n, \ -3n.$$

The factoring device is definitely a time saver in the solution of a quadratic when the factors of the quadratic are readily recognized. However, many quadratics have irrational and even imaginary roots, so that the factors may be difficult to recognize and the factoring device would be of little use. In glancing back through Examples 1–5, we note that the factoring device is useful for incomplete quadratics and complete quadratics; it is useful for quadratics with literal or numerical coefficients. It is also useful for solving equations of degree greater than two; once again, however, the obviousness of the factors of the expression dictates the use of the device.

7-3   Solution of the Quadratic
by Completing the Square

A general approach to the solution of a quadratic equation is a method called *completing the square*. This name accurately describes the procedure of the method because it involves the square of a binomial. Let us examine such a square.

EXAMPLE 6. Expand the quantities $(x - 5)^2$ and $(x + k)^2$.

Solution. We recognize from previous work that

$$(x - 5)^2 = x^2 - 10x + 25$$

and

$$(x + k)^2 = x^2 + 2kx + k^2.$$

Examination of the expansions above reveals certain features. First, we might recognize one restriction: note that each is the square of a *binomial* and that each has a unity coefficient for x. In the expansions, three facts should be apparent:

1. The x^2 term has a unity coefficient.
2. The coefficient of the first-degree term is twice the value of the second term of the binomial; i.e., -10 is twice -5 and $2k$ is twice k.
3. The last term of the expansion is the square of the second term of the binomial and is also the square of half of the coefficient of the second term of the trinomial expansion.

We may assert here that any quadratic that possesses the three properties listed above is the square of a binomial.

EXAMPLE 7. Given the quadratic expression $x^2 - 6x + 9$. Examine the expression to determine whether it is the square of a binominal and, if so, determine the binomial.

Solution. We use two of the three properties above as a test for the square. First, the coefficient of x^2 is unity. Second, the last term, 9, is the square of one-half of the coefficient of the center term, -6. With this simple test, the quadratic is shown to be the square of a binomial. The particular binomial is $x - 3$, where the -3 term is chosen using either the second or third property above. The solution then is

$$x^2 - 6x + 9 = (x - 3)^2.$$

Any quadratic of the form $x^2 + bx + c = 0$ can be solved by completing the square. The method is discussed in Example 8.

EXAMPLE 8. Solve for x by completing the square if

$$x^2 - 6x - 16 = 0.$$

Solution. First, re-write the given expression as

$$x^2 - 6x = 16. \tag{16}$$

Now complete the square on the left side of (16). To obtain a square there, the constant, $+9$, must be added. The $+9$ is determined by taking one-half of the coefficient of the first degree term and squaring the result. Addition of $+9$ to the left side of the equation requires addition of the same quantity to the right side in order to retain the equality; therefore, (16) becomes

$$x^2 - 6x + 9 = 16 + 9,$$

or, after factoring and combining terms,

$$(x - 3)^2 = 25. \tag{17}$$

The addition of $+9$ to the left side of (16) was the critical step and it completed the square of the binomial shown in (17). Taking the square root of both sides of (17), we have

$$x - 3 = \pm 5$$

or

$$x = 3 \pm 5,$$

from which we obtain the two solutions

$$x = 3 + 5 = 8$$

and

$$x = 3 - 5 = -2.$$

The student may inquire as to why this seemingly roundabout method of completing the square was used when the given expression in Example 8 could have been solved more readily by factoring. The reason is twofold: first, many quadratics are not readily factorable; second, the method of completing the square will be used in the next section to develop the quadratic formula, which is useful in solving the general quadratic.

Exercises

Solve · Exercises 1–20 by factoring. In exercises where the factors are not readily apparent, solve by completing the square.

1. $x^2 - 4x - 21 = 0$.   *Ans.* $x = 7, -3$.

2. $2m^2 - 9m - 5 = 0$.

3. $6t^2 - 5t - 6 = 0$.   *Ans.* $t = -\frac{2}{3}, \frac{3}{2}$.

4. $12\phi^2 + \phi - 35 = 0$.

5. $24k^2 - k - 44 = 0$.   *Ans.* $k = -\frac{4}{3}, \frac{11}{8}$.

6. $x^2 + 4x - 20 = 0$.

7. $m^2 + 6m + 6 = 0$.   *Ans.* $m = -3 \pm \sqrt{3}$.

8. $2m^2 - 3m - 6 = 0$.

9. $3b^2 + 4b + 1 = 0$.   *Ans.* $b = -1, -\frac{1}{3}$.

10. $4k^2 + 11k - 4 = 0$.

11. $x^2 - 4x - 32 = 0$.   *Ans.* $x = 8, -4$.

12. $4k^2 - 4k - 3 = 0$.

13. $m^2 - 9m + 14 = 0$.   *Ans.* $m = 7, 2$.

14. $b^2 - 8b + 12 = 0$.

15. $t^2 + 2t - 3 = 0$.   *Ans.* $t = 1, -3$.

16. $2x^2 - 9x + 9 = 0$.

17. $2k^2 - 5k - 12 = 0$.   *Ans.* $k = 4, -\frac{3}{2}$.

18. $b^2 - 13 = 6b - 6$.

19. $t^2 + 4t + 2 = 0$.   *Ans.* $t = -2 \pm 2$.

20. $t^2 - 6t + 4 = 0$.

Solve Exercises 21–26 for the quantity indicated. Use factoring or completion of the square, whichever seems appropriate.

21. $a^2b^2 - 3ab - 4 = 0$ (for a).   *Ans.* $a = 4/b,\ -1/b$.

22. $a^2 - 3ab - 4b^2 = 0$ (for a).

23. $(a + b)^2 + 5(a + b) - 6 = 0$ (for a).   *Ans.* $a = -6 - b,\ 1 - b$.

24. $c^2(b - 1)^2 - c(b - 1) - 2 = 0$ (for c).

25. $6(\sin \phi)^2 - \sin \phi - 1 = 0$ (for $\sin \phi$).   *Ans.* $\sin \phi = -\tfrac{1}{3}, \tfrac{1}{2}$.

26. $(a^2 - b^2)^2 + 2(a^2 - b^2) + 1 = 0$ (for b).

27. The standard form of a circle is given as

$$(x - h)^2 + (y - k)^2 = r^2.$$

By completing the square, assemble the equation

$$x^2 + y^2 + 4x - 6y - 12 = 0$$

into the standard form and identify h, k, and r.

Ans. $(x + 2)^2 + (y - 3)^2 = 25,\ h = -2,\ k = 3,\ r = 5$.

28. Given the equation

$$a^2 + 2ab + b^2 - 3ac - 3bc + 2c^2 = 0,$$

show that it may be factored into the form

$$(a + b - c)(a + b - 2c) = 0.$$

29. What is the equation of a quadratic whose solutions are $m = -4$ and $m = 3$?

Ans. $m^2 + m - 12 = 0$.

30. Identify the equation which has the solutions $x = 1, -1, 2$.

7-4   The Quadratic Formula

We are reminded that the complete quadratic equation in one unknown is of the form

$$ax^2 + bx + c = 0. \tag{18}$$

Let us solve (18) for x by the method of completing the square as discussed in Sec. 7-3. First, the coefficient of the x^2 term must be unity, so we divide (18) by a, giving

$$x^2 + \frac{b}{a}x + \frac{c}{a} = 0. \tag{19}$$

Next, rewrite (19) as

$$x^2 + \frac{b}{a}x = -\frac{c}{a}. \tag{20}$$

Now complete the square in (20) by adding to both sides the square of one-half of the coefficient of x. Here the coefficient of x is b/a; one-half of the coefficient of x is $b/2a$ and the square of one-half of the coefficient of x is $b^2/4a^2$. Now

$$x^2 + \frac{b}{a}x + \frac{b^2}{4a^2} = \frac{b^2}{4a^2} - \frac{c}{a}, \tag{21}$$

and the square is completed.

Next, express the left side of (21) as the square of a binominal and place the right side over a least common denominator, or

$$\left(x + \frac{b}{2a}\right)^2 = \frac{b^2 - 4ac}{4a^2}. \tag{22}$$

Taking the square root of both sides of (22),

$$x + \frac{b}{2a} = \frac{\pm\sqrt{b^2 - 4ac}}{2a}. \tag{23}$$

Solving for x in (23), we have

$$x = \frac{-b \pm \sqrt{b^2 - 4ac}}{2a}, \tag{24}$$

where (24) is called the *quadratic formula* and is useful in solving any quadratic of the form (18).

Certain features of (18) must be recognized before applying (24). First, the quantity which we call a is the coefficient of the square term. Second, the quantity which we call b is the coefficient of the first-degree term. Third, c is the constant. Fourth, all nonzero terms of (18) are on one side of the equal sign.

EXAMPLE 9. Using the quadratic formula, solve for x if

$$x = 3x^2 - 2.$$

Solution. First, we must rearrange the given equation into the form of (18) so that we can identify *a*, *b*, and *c*. Placing all of the nonzero terms on one side of the equal sign, we have

$$3x^2 - x - 2 = 0. \tag{25}$$

Comparing (25) to (18), we have $a = 3$, $b = -1$, and $c = -2$. Substituting these values into (24), we have

$$x = \frac{-(-1) \pm \sqrt{(-1)^2 - 4(3)(-2)}}{2(3)}$$

$$= \frac{1 \pm \sqrt{25}}{6} = \frac{1 \pm 5}{6} = \frac{1}{6} \pm \frac{5}{6},$$

from which

$$x = \frac{1}{6} + \frac{5}{6} = 1$$

or

$$x = \frac{1}{6} - \frac{5}{6} = -\frac{2}{3}.$$

In Example 9 the coefficients and constants were numerical quantities; this is not necessary in applying (24) since (24) is also useful for quantities where *a*, *b*, and *c* are literal. Consider Example 10.

EXAMPLE 10. Using the quadratic formula, solve for *z* if

$$m^2 z^2 + 3mnz - 4n^2 = 0.$$

Solution. Inspecting the given equation and comparing it to (18) shows that $a = m^2$, $b = 3mn$, and $c = -4n^2$. Substituting into (24), we have

$$z = \frac{-3mn \pm \sqrt{(3mn)^2 - 4(m^2)(-4n^2)}}{2m^2}. \tag{26}$$

Simplification of (26) gives the solutions

$$z = \frac{n}{m}, \, -\frac{4n}{m}.$$

Further generality of the quadratic formula as it applies to (18) can be demonstrated. In Example 9 we saw that the quadratic formula was useful when the coefficients of (18) were numerical. In Example 10 it proved useful when the coefficients were literal. It is also useful when the unknown is something other than a monomial or some quantity other than a simple alphabetic letter. Consider Examples 11 and 12.

EXAMPLE 11. Solve for $\sin \phi$ if

$$6(\sin \phi)^2 + \sin \phi - 2 = 0.$$

Solution. Here the unknown is the quantity $\sin \phi$, comparable to x in (18). Also, $a = 6$, $b = 1$, and $c = -2$. Substituting these data into (24),

$$\sin \phi = \frac{-1 \pm \sqrt{(1)^2 - 4(6)(-2)}}{2(6)} = \frac{-1 \pm \sqrt{49}}{12},$$

and $\sin \phi = \frac{1}{2}, -\frac{2}{3}$ are the resulting solutions.

EXAMPLE 12. Solve for m if

$$2m^2 + 4mn + 2n^2 - m - n - 15 = 0. \tag{27}$$

Solution. Equation (27) may seem hopelessly complicated and it may appear unlikely that it could be rendered into the form of (18). However, after collecting terms by twice completing the square, it may be written in the form

$$2(m + n)^2 - (m + n) - 15 = 0. \tag{28}$$

Comparing (28) and (18), we have the variable $m + n$, with $a = 2$, $b = -1$, and $c = -15$. Applying (24), we have

$$m + n = \frac{-(-1) \pm \sqrt{(-1)^2 - 4(2)(-15)}}{2(2)} = \frac{1 \pm 11}{4} = 3, -\frac{5}{2}.$$

Now, since

$$m + n = 3, \quad \text{then} \quad m = 3 - n,$$

and, since

$$m + n = -\frac{5}{2}, \quad \text{then} \quad m = -\frac{5}{2} - n.$$

Examples 11 and 12 were introduced here to show the broad usage of the quadratic formula.

Applications involving the quadratic equation seldom commence with a neatly organized equation of the form of (18), where simple substitution into the quadratic formula completes the solution. Instead, the quadratic equation is often the by-product of algebraic manipulation of some given data. Consider Example 13.

EXAMPLE 13. A rectangular field 250 ft. long and 180 ft. wide has a sidewalk bordering it. If the sidewalk is of uniform width and its area is 2616 sq. ft., what is the width of the sidewalk?

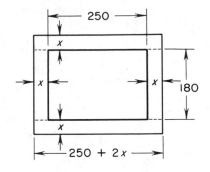

FIGURE 7–2

Solution. Refer to the sketch in Fig. 7-2. The sidewalk can be considered to be composed of four rectangles. Two have the dimensions x by 250 + 2x and two have the dimensions x by 180, where x is the width of the sidewalk. Adding the areas of the four rectangles, we have the equation

$$2(x)(250 + 2x) + 2(x)(180) = 2616. \tag{29}$$

Equation (29) reduces to the quadratic

$$x^2 + 215x - 654 = 0,$$

which may be factored as

$$(x - 3)(x + 218) = 0,$$

from which we obtain two solutions $x = 3, -218$, where $x = 3$ is chosen as the acceptable solution.

Checking the solution, the dimensions of the four rectangles are now

$$x \text{ by } 250 + 2x \text{ or } 3 \text{ by } 256$$

and

$$x \text{ by } 180 \qquad \text{or } 3 \text{ by } 180.$$

the total area is

$$2(3)(256) + 2(3)(180) = 1536 + 1080 = 2616.$$

Exercises

Solve Exercises 1–10 for the unknown indicated by using the quadratic formula except where factoring may prove to be an easier method.

1. $2m^2 + 5m - 25 = 0.$ *Ans.* $m = \frac{5}{2}, -5.$

2. $m^2 + 5m - 15 = 0.$

3. $bx^2 + 3x - 4 = 0$ (for x).   *Ans.* $x = (-3 \pm \sqrt{9 + 16b})/2b$.

4. $x^2 + 3bx - 4 = 0$ (for x).

5. $\dfrac{1}{x+2} - \dfrac{1}{3} = \dfrac{2}{x+4}$.   *Ans.* $x = -1, -8$.

6. $\dfrac{9}{2y+6} + \dfrac{5}{2y-2} = 2$.

7. $s = v_0 t + \frac{1}{2}gt^2$ (for t).   *Ans.* $t = (-v_0 \pm \sqrt{v_0^2 + 2gs})/g$.

8. $A = 2\pi rh + 2\pi r^2$ (for r).

9. $x^2 + 2ax + a^2 = b^2$ (for x).   *Ans.* $x = -a - b, -a + b$.

10. $a^2 x^2 + a^2 x + ab - b^2 = 0$ (for x).

11. The sum of the squares of two consecutive integers is 85. What are the integers?
Ans. 6, 7.

12. The difference of the cubes of two consecutive integers is 61. What are the integers?

13. One leg of a right triangle exceeds the other leg by 4 in. The hypotenuse is 20 in. long. How long are the legs?   *Ans.* 12 in., 16 in.

14. Given the quadratic equation

$$x^2 + kx + 9 = 0,$$

what is the value of k if the solutions of the quadratic are equal? Equal but opposite in sign?

15. Given the quadratic equation

$$x^2 + 8x + k = 0,$$

for what values of k
(*a*) are the roots equal?   *Ans.* $k = 16$.
(*b*) is one root zero?   *Ans.* $k = 0$.
(*c*) is one root $+4$?   *Ans.* $k = -48$.

16. Find the radius r of the circle shown in Fig. 7-3 if $\angle ABC = 90°$ and the dimensions shown are in inches.   *Ans.* $r = 5$ in.

17. The quadratic equation

$$r^2 - 6r + 5 = 0$$

arises in Exercise 16; from it the solution $r = 5$ is found. The other solution of the quadratic is not a radius of the circle O shown in Fig. 7-3, but is the radius of another circle which, like O, is tangent to AB, tangent to BC, and passes through

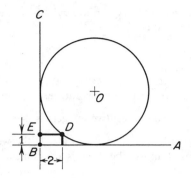

FIGURE 7-3

D. Describe the location of the center of the second circle and the radius of the circle.

18. The cosine law is given as

$$a^2 = b^2 + c^2 - 2bc \cos A$$

where a, b, and c are the sides of a triangle. Find c if $a = 1.5$, $b = 1.4$, and $\cos A = 0.50$.   *Ans. $c = 1.58$.*

19. In Exercise 18, if all other conditions are the same, with $b = 1.8$, the solution of the quadratic in c results in a negative quantity under the radical sign, meaning that there is no real solution. With reference to the triangle, explain why no real solution is possible. (If $\cos A = 0.5$, then angle $A = 60°$.)
                                       Ans. It is impossible to construct such a triangle.

20. Two like magnetic poles of strengths m_1 and m_2 at a distance d apart are repelled from each other by a force F according to the equation

$$F = \frac{m_1 m_2}{d^2}.$$

If one pole is of strength 40 and the other is of strength 30 and the force of attraction is 12, what is the distance between the poles?

21. The current in a circuit flows according to the equation

$$i = 12 - 12t^2$$

where i is the current and t is time in seconds.
(a) Find i when $t = 0$.   *Ans. 12.*
(b) Find t when $i = 0$.   *Ans. 1.*
(c) If t changes from $t = 0.1$ to $t = 0.6$, what is the change in i?
                                                                        Ans. 4.20.

22. The maximum theoretical temperature starting from 0°C to which the products of combustion of hydrogen with oxygen are raised by the heat liberated is given approximately by the equation

$$t = \frac{2600}{0.34 + 0.00015t}.$$

Solve for t, the maximum theoretical temperature. *Ans.* 3180°C.

23. The product of what two consecutive integers is 240?

24. A rectangle is 3 units longer than it is wide. If the width is doubled and the length is diminished by 4 units, the area is unchanged. What are the original dimensions? *Ans.* Length = 8, width = 5.

25. The power output of a generator armature is given by the equation

$$P_0 = E_g I - r_g I^2.$$

Find I, given $P_0 = 120$, $E_g = 16$, and $r_g = 0.5$. *Ans.* $I = 20, 12$.

26. Given the reactance of an electric circuit as

$$x = 2\pi f L - \frac{1}{2\pi f C},$$

solve for f. *Ans.* $f = (Cx \pm \sqrt{C^2 x^2 + 4LC})/4\pi LC$.

27. Given the quadratic equation

$$y = x^2 - 2x - 3,$$

find x if $y = 0, -3, -4$.
Ans. $y = 0$, $x = 3, -1$; $y = -3$, $x = 0, 2$; $y = -4$, $x = 1, 1$.

7-5 Equations of the Quadratic Type

Previous discussions of the quadratic in one unknown have been limited to the form

$$ax^2 + bx + c = 0, \tag{30}$$

where the unknown x was present in degree two and was a monomial in most cases. We defined the quadratic as being of degree two and developed the method of solution accordingly.

Any equation of the form

$$ax^{2n} + bx^n + c = 0 \tag{31}$$

can be solved by methods applicable to the quadratic (30); for this reason we may call (31) an *equation of quadratic type*. In (31), x is not restricted to being a first-degree monomial; it may be a polynomial, one or more trigonometric functions, a logarithmic quantity, or an exponential—to mention a few possibilities. The number n in (31) need not be a positive integer; it can be positive, negative, integral, or fractional. The condition that must be met regarding n in (31) is that the exponent of the variable in one of the terms be exactly twice that in another term.

EXAMPLE 14. Solve for z where

$$3z^{-1/2} - 2z^{-1/4} - 1 = 0. \tag{32}$$

Solution 1. Equation (32) is readily compared to (31) since $-\frac{1}{2}$ is twice $-\frac{1}{4}$, or one of the exponents of the variable is twice the other. Now (32) may be rewritten in the form of (30) as

$$3(z^{-1/4})^2 - 2(z^{-1/4}) - 1 = 0 \tag{33}$$

where $a = 3$, $b = -2$, $c = -1$, and the variable is not x but is $z^{-1/4}$. If we apply the quadratic formula to (33), we will not solve for x but will solve for $z^{-1/4}$ instead. Solving, we have

$$z^{-1/4} = \frac{-(-2) \pm \sqrt{(-2)^2 - 4(3)(-1)}}{2(3)} = \frac{2 \pm 4}{6}.$$

from which

$$z^{-1/4} = 1 \quad \text{or } z = 1$$

and

$$z^{-1/4} = -\tfrac{1}{3} \text{ or } z = 81.$$

Solution. 2. We may choose to solve (32) by using a preliminary substitution that was suggested in Solution 1. Comparing (32) to (31), if we let

$$x = z^{-1/4}, \tag{34}$$

then

$$x^2 = z^{-1/2}$$

and, by substitution, (32) becomes $3x^2 - 2x - 1 = 0$, which has the solution $x = 1$, $-\frac{1}{3}$. These solutions in x have their equivalents in z through (34),

$$x = 1 = z^{-1/4} \quad \text{and } z = 1$$
$$x = -\tfrac{1}{3} = z^{-1/4} \quad \text{and } z = 81.$$

Solution 3. Equation (32) may be factored as

$$(3z^{-1/4} + 1)(z^{-1/4} - 1) = 0,$$

which, when each factor is equated to zero, has the solutions previously shown.

EXAMPLE 15. Solve for $m + n$ where

$$(m + n)^4 - 13(m + n)^2 + 36 = 0. \tag{35}$$

Solution. Equation (35) may be written as

$$[(m + n)^2]^2 - 13[m + n]^2 + 36 = 0. \tag{36}$$

Comparing (36) to (30), we have $a = 1$, $n = -13$, $c = 36$, and the variable is the expression $(m + n)^2$. Now (36) can be solved by any of the methods displayed in Example 14. We will choose here the substitution method shown in Solution 2. We let

$$x = (m + n)^2,$$

from which (36) becomes

$$x^2 - 13x + 36 = 0$$

which has the intermediate solutions $x = 4, 9$. Returning to $m + n$, we have

$$(m + n)^2 = 4 \text{ and } (m + n)^2 = 9,$$

from which we obtain the desired solutions

$$m + n = \pm 2 \text{ and } m + n = \pm 3.$$

It is worth noting that equation (35) in Example 15 was of fourth degree in $m + n$ and that four solutions were found for $m + n$. There is a theorem from the theory of equations that asserts that an equation of the form

$$a_0 x^n + a_1 x^{n-1} + a_2 x^{n-2} + \cdots + a_{n-1} x + a_n = 0, \tag{37}$$

where all of the a's are constants and n is a positive integer, has n solutions. Equations of form (37) that satisfy the conditions cited are called *polynomial equations*. These remarks are made here in anticipation of equations with several solutions that will be found in subsequent exercises. Further, note that the solutions of (37) need not be real solutions; i.e., some may be imaginary. Imaginary solutions of quadratic equations will be discussed in Sec. 7-7.

Exercises

In the following exercises, if one literal quantity is present, solve the given equation for that quantity. If two or more literal quantities are present, solve for the quantity indicated in parentheses. The answers given show only the real solutions.

1. $x^4 - 2x^2 - 3 = 0$.   *Ans.* $x = 3$.

2. $k^4 + 3k^2 - 4 = 0$.

3. $y^4 - 5y^2 - 6 = 0$.   *Ans.* $y = 6$.

4. $b^6 + 7b^3 - 8 = 0$.

5. $t + 4t^{1/2} + 3 = 0$.   *Ans.* $t = 1, 9$.

6. $2b - 3b^{1/2} - 2 = 0$.

7. $m^{-2/3} - m^{-1/3} - 2 = 0$.   *Ans.* $m = -1, \frac{1}{8}$.

8. $p^{-2} - p^{-1} - 42 = 0$.

9. $x^{-4} - 2x^{-2} - 3 = 0$.   *Ans.* $x = \dfrac{\sqrt{3}}{3}$.

10. $2y^{-4} - 3y^{-2} - 2 = 0$.

11. $\dfrac{1}{(m + \frac{1}{2})^2} + \dfrac{4}{m + \frac{1}{2}} + 4 = 0$.   *Ans.* $m = -1, -1$.

12. $\dfrac{1}{(a + b)^2} + \dfrac{6}{a + b} - 7 = 0$ (for $a + b$).

13. $\dfrac{2}{(x - \frac{1}{2})^2} + \dfrac{1}{(x - \frac{1}{2})} - 3 = 0$.   *Ans.* $x = \frac{3}{2}, -\frac{1}{16}$.

14. $\dfrac{2}{(x + y)^2} - \dfrac{5}{(x + y)} - 3 = 0$ (for $x + y$).

15. $\dfrac{1}{x^2} - \dfrac{1}{4a^2} = 0$ (for x)   *Ans.* $x = 2a$.

16. $x^{-2} - 6(x)(m - n)^{-1} + 8(m - n)^{-2} = 0$ (for $m - n$).

17. $2y^2 - 5y(a - b)^{-1} + 3(a - b)^{-2} = 0$ (for $a - b$).

       Ans. $a - b = 1/y, 3/2y$.

18. $\dfrac{3}{k^2} - \dfrac{1}{3b^2} = 0$. (for k).

19. $(a + b)^2(x)^{-2/3} - (a + b)(y)(x)^{-1/3} = 12y^2$ (for x).

       Ans. $x = (a + b)^3/64y^3, -(a + b)^3/27y^3$.

20. $(I_{max} \sin \phi)^4 - 2(I_{max} \sin \phi)^2 - 3 = 0$ (for $I_{max} \sin \phi$).

21. $(3 + \tan \phi)^6 - 9(3 + \tan \phi)^3 + 8 = 0$ (for $\tan \phi$).

Ans. $\tan \phi = -1, -2$.

7-6   Graphing the Quadratic

In previous sections of this chapter discussion was directed toward solutions of the quadratic equation in one unknown. In this section we will extend our discussion of the quadratic to graphing a particular quadratic in two unknowns, namely

$$y = ax^2 + bx + c, \tag{38}$$

where $a \neq 0$ and a, b, and c are real constants.

One method of graphing equations of the form of (38) would be to assign arbitrarily selected values to x (called the *independent variable*) and to obtain the corresponding values that are forced upon y (called the *dependent variable*). This procedure will obtain several (x, y) pairs which can be plotted on an (x, y) plane. The method described here is somewhat uncertain in that many (x, y) pairs may be required before the shape of the curve is determined and certain critical features of the curve may not be revealed.

We choose here to graph equations of the form of (38) by determining four properties of the curve; these properties are:

1. the roots or x-intercepts (if they exist),

2. the y-intercept,

3. the axis of symmetry,

4. the extreme point.

Let us discuss each of these briefly.

The Roots or x-intercepts

These are the points where the curve intercepts the x-axis. Since these intercepts are on the x-axis, the value of y at these points is zero. Therefore, it follows that the roots of (38) can be found by letting $y = 0$ and then solving for x. This involves solving the quadratic equation

$$ax^2 + bx + c = 0,$$

as in previous sections.

The y-intercept

This is the point where (38) crosses the y-axis; here $x = 0$. Therefore, to find the y-intercept of (38), let $x = 0$ and solve for y. In all cases, this solution will be $y = c$, which asserts that the y-intercept of (38) is at $y = c$.

The Axis of Symmetry

The axis of symmetry is an "axis of reflection"; it divides the curve into two portions that are mirror images of each other. Figure 7-4 shows a curve

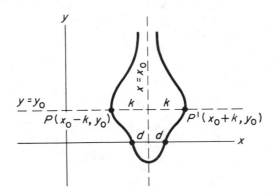

FIGURE 7-4

which is symmetrical about the line $x = x_0$. Notice a particular feature demonstrated in Fig. 7-4. An ordinate line $y = y_0$ intersects the curve in two points P and P', which points are symmetrically located with respect to the axis of symmetry $x = x_0$. Another way of saying this is that P is as far to the left of $x = x_0$ as P' is to the right of it; this distance is shown in Fig. 7-4 as k. Now, since the abscissa of the axis of symmetry is $x = x_0$, then P has the abscissa $x_0 - k$ and P' has the abscissa $x_0 + k$. Through the preceding discussion we can observe that the abscissas of the points where $y = y_0$ crosses the curve are $x = x_0 \pm k$. We see further that the curve has x-intercepts (or roots) at $x = x_0 \pm d$, where the roots straddle the axis of symmetry.

Now let us examine the roots of (38). If we let $y = 0$, we may write the roots of (38) as

$$x = -\frac{b}{2a} \pm \frac{\sqrt{b^2 - 4ac}}{2a}. \tag{39}$$

Examining (39) carefully, we see that the two roots straddle the value $x = -b/2a$ by an amount $\sqrt{b^2 - 4ac}/2a$. Should we choose to determine where the graph of (38) crosses any horizontal line $y = y_0$, we will have the equation

$$y_0 = ax^2 + bx + c, \quad \text{or}$$

$$ax^2 + bx + c - y_0 = 0$$

which has the solutions

$$x = -\frac{b}{2a} \pm \frac{\sqrt{b^2 - 4a(c - y_0)}}{2a}. \tag{40}$$

Now (40) shows that, for any preselected value y_0, the values of x straddle the value $x = -b/2a$, which shows that $x = -b/2a$ is the axis of symmetry of (38). One of the possible graphs of (38) is shown in Fig. 7-5; note the axis of symmetry and the disposition of the roots about that axis.

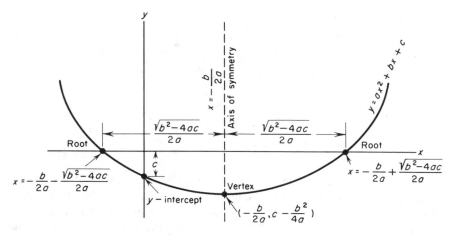

FIGURE 7-5

The Extreme Point

The extreme point on a curve is defined here as the highest or lowest point in the neighborhood. For (38) this point lies on the axis of symmetry and therefore has an abscissa value $x = -b/2a$. Substituting $x = -b/2a$ into (38), we have

$$y = a\left(-\frac{b}{2a}\right)^2 + b\left(-\frac{b}{2a}\right) + c,$$

from which

$$y = c - \frac{b^2}{4a},$$

and the coordinates of the extreme point of (38) are

$$x = -\frac{b}{2a}, \qquad y = c - \frac{b^2}{4a}. \tag{41}$$

In many cases, the quadratic may be graphed adequately by plotting the y-intercept, roots, and extreme point. It may be helpful to plot an extra point or two with the assistance of the axis of symmetry, to add detail. Consider an example.

EXAMPLE 16. Plot the graph of the quadratic

$$y = x^2 - 2x - 3. \tag{42}$$

Solutions. Let us follow the four-step procedure suggested and described in the preceding paragraphs.

Roots. Let $y = 0$; then

$$x^2 - 2x - 3 = 0,$$

from which

$$(x - 3)(x + 1) = 0$$

and we have the roots $x = 3, -1$. This means that the graph crosses the x-axis at $x = 3$ and $x = -1$. Refer to Fig. 7-6.

The y-intercept. Let $x = 0$ in (42), from which $y = -3$. This means that the graph crosses the y-axis at $y = -3$.

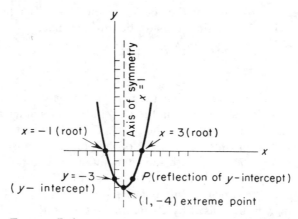

FIGURE 7-6

Axis of symmetry. Comparing (42) to (38) we have the constants $a = 1$ and $b = -2$. Now the axis of symmetry is at

$$x = -\frac{b}{2a} = \frac{-(-2)}{2(1)} = +1.$$

We may find the axis of symmetry another way; it lies midway between the roots, or midway between $x = -1$ and $x = +3$. This mid-value is found by adding the roots together and taking one-half of the sum, or $(-1 + 3) \div 2 = +1$.

Extreme point. The extreme point is on the axis of symmetry where $x = 1$. Substituting $x = 1$ into (42) we find that $y = -4$. This extreme point with coordinates $(1, -4)$ also may be located by using (41), where $a = 1$, $b = -2$, and $c = -3$.

We can add another point to the graph readily; this point is designated as P in Fig. 7-6 and is the reflection, across the axis of symmetry, of the y-intercept. This applies to any other point which is plotted; it will have a companion across the axis of symmetry. This means that only one-half of the curve need be plotted since the other half is a mirror copy.

Note that the quadratic graphed in Fig. 7-6 is shaped like the cross section of the reflector of a flashlight or an automobile headlight. This general shape is characteristic of all quadratics of the form of (38) and is called a *parabola*.

In the examples that follow it is shown that, by modifying certain parts of (38), the parabola may be made to open downward, upward, left, or right.

EXAMPLE 17. Plot the graph of the quadratic

$$y = -x^2 - 2x + 8. \tag{43}$$

Solution. Let us look first for the roots and the axis of symmetry. Letting $y = 0$ and solving the remaining quadratic for x, we have

$$x = -\frac{2}{2} \pm \frac{\sqrt{(-2)^2 - 4(-1)(8)}}{2} = -1 \pm 3. \tag{44}$$

Inspecting (44) closely, we see that the axis of symmetry is at $x = -1$ and the roots are **3** units to the right and left of the axis of symmetry or at $x = 2, -4$. See Fig. 7-7 for a plot of the roots. To find the extreme point, let $x = -1$ in (43), from which $y = 9$. All of the points previously determined are shown in Fig. 7-7, along with the companion or reflection point of the y-intercept. Note that the parabolas in Fig. 7-6 and Fig. 7-7 have the same basic shapes, but they open in different directions. This reversal of the direction of opening can be caused by changing the sign of the coefficient of the second-degree term.

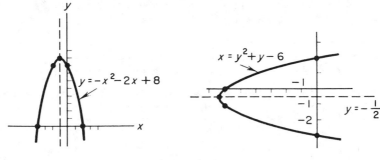

FIGURE 7-7   FIGURE 7-8

EXAMPLE 18. Plot the graph of the equation

$$x = y^2 + y - 6. \tag{45}$$

Solution. Comparing (45) with (38), we observe that the variables, x and y, are interchanged. This suggests that the properties that hold for x in (38) now hold for y in (45) and vice versa.

The roots are on the y-axis for (45) and are found by letting $x = 0$; they are $y = -3, +2$ (see Fig. 7-8). The axis of symmetry is the line $y = -\frac{1}{2}$, which is midway between the two roots. The x-intercept is found by letting $y = 0$, from which we obtain $x = -6$ as the horizontal intercept. The extreme point is now the leftmost point and is at $x = -6\frac{1}{4}$, which is found by letting $y = -\frac{1}{2}$ in (45).

The graph of (45), as shown in Fig. 7-8, is shaped like a parabola but has a horizontal axis of symmetry. The horizontal position of the parabola is the result of interchanging the x and y variables in (38).

Exercises

Graph the quadratic given in Exercises 1–10. Plot the axis of symmetry, intercepts of both coordinate axes, and extreme point in all cases.

1. $y = x^2 - 4$.   **2.** $y = x^2 - 2x$.

3. $y = x^2 - 3x - 10$.   **4.** $y = -x^2 + 4x$.

5. $y = -x^2 + 3x + 4$.   **6.** $y = 2x^2 - 3x - 2$.

7. $x = y^2 + 3y$.   **8.** $x = -y^2 + 8$.

9. $x = -2y^2 - y + 3$.   **10.** $x = y^2 - 3y - 4$.

11. A free-falling body thrown vertically travels according to the equation

$$s = \tfrac{1}{2}gt^2 + v_0 t + s_0$$

where s is distance, t is time, and g, v_0, s_0 are constants. What are the values of s and t when s is an extreme value?   *Ans.* $t = -v_0/g$, $s = s_0 - v_0^2/2g$.

12. In Exercise 11, if t is the abscissa and s the ordinate, the (s, t) curve plots as a parabola opening upward or downward, depending upon the sign of which constant? Changing which constant modifies the s-intercept?

13. A ball thrown vertically from the ground with an initial velocity of 144 ft./sec. has its distance from the ground measured according to the equation

$$s = -16t^2 + 144t$$

where s is distance in feet and t is elapsed time in seconds. At what two times does $s = 0$? At what time does the ball reach maximum height? What is the maximum height?   *Ans.* $t = 0, 9$ sec.; $t = 4.5$ sec.; $s = 324$ ft.

14. A 40-volt generator with an internal resistance of 4 ohms delivers power to an external circuit amounting to $40i - 4i^2$ watts where i is the current in amperes. For what current will the generator deliver maximum power?

15. A company successfully sells 500 units daily of a certain item at \$1.20 per item. In order to increase sales, it is found that 50 additional items per day can be sold for each 10-cent decrease in the sale price of the item. What number of items at what unit price will provide maximum daily receipts?
         Ans. 550 items at \$1.10 each.

7-7   More on Graphs of Quadratics—the Discriminant

In the preceding section, all of the quadratics discussed in the examples and appearing in the exercises had two real, distinct roots; that is, the equation of the form

$$y = ax^2 + bx + c \tag{46}$$

was such that its graph crossed the x-axis twice. However, this circumstance need not hold. Referring to Fig. 7-9, we see the graphs of

$$y = x^2 - 2x + c,$$

where $c = -3$, $+1$, and $+3$. When $c = -3$ as in Fig. 7-9(a), the curve crosses the x-axis in two distinct points. In Fig. 7-9(b), when $c = +1$, the curve is tangent to the x-axis. In Fig. 7-9(c), when $c = +3$, the curve fails to intercept the x-axis.

If we accept an argument that an equation of the form of (46) has two algebraic solutions, then the solutions can be (from Fig. 7-9)

    1. real, rational, and unequal, as in (a),
    2. real, rational, and equal, as in (b),

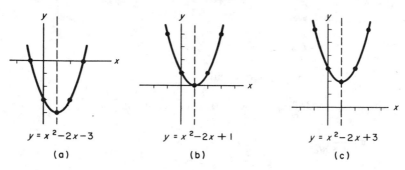

$y = x^2 - 2x - 3$ $y = x^2 - 2x + 1$ $y = x^2 - 2x + 3$

(a)   (b)   (c)

FIGURE 7–9

3. imaginary, as in (c),

4. real, irrational, and unequal, not pictured in Fig. 7-9.

The above situations regarding the reality, equality, and rationality of the roots of (46) can be observed from the quadratic formula. Let $y = 0$ in (46), whence

$$x = -\frac{b}{2a} \pm \frac{\sqrt{b^2 - 4ac}}{2a}, \tag{47}$$

where we will call the portion $b^2 - 4ac$ the *discriminant*. Now inspect (47) carefully for the nature of the roots:

1. If the discriminant is positive ($b^2 - 4ac > 0$) and is a perfect square, then $\sqrt{b^2 - 4ac}/2a$ is a rational number. Added to or subtracted from $-b/2a$ (which is also rational), we see that (47) has two roots, distinct (different) from each other, and both are real (as opposed to imaginary) and both are rational (as opposed to irrational). This case is pictured in Fig. 7-9(a), where

$$b^2 - 4ac = 16$$

and the roots are

$$x = -\frac{-2}{2} \pm \frac{\sqrt{16}}{2} = 1 \pm 2.$$

2. If the discriminant is positive ($b^2 - 4ac > 0$), but is not a perfect square, then roots of (46) still exist (that is, they are real), are distinct, but are irrational. Consider the equation

$$y = x^2 - 2x - 2,$$

from which

$$\sqrt{b^2 - 4ac} = \sqrt{12} = 2\sqrt{3}$$

and the solutions are

$$x = 1 \pm \sqrt{3},$$

both of which are real but irrational.

3. If the discriminant equals zero, then the roots of (46) are

$$x = -\frac{b}{2a} + 0 \quad \text{and} \quad x = -\frac{b}{2a} - 0,$$

which means that the roots are equal, rational, and real. This case is shown in Fig. 7-9(b), where equal roots indicate tangency.

4. In Fig. 7-9(c), it is apparent from the sketch that y cannot be zero since the curve never crosses or is tangent to the x-axis. If we try to solve (46) by the quadratic formula, we have automatically introduced the condition $y = 0$. In effect, we have imposed a condition that the equation cannot accept; theorefore, we can not expect a real result. If

$$y = x^2 - 2x + 3,$$

and we let $y = 0$, the roots are

$$x = -\frac{-2}{2} \pm \frac{\sqrt{-8}}{2} = 1 \pm j\sqrt{2},$$

where the roots are imaginary. Since the roots are imaginary, we cannot expect to plot them on the real (x, y) plane. When $b^2 - 4ac < 0$, the roots are always imaginary.

The preceding information assembles into Table 7-1.

Table 7-1

NATURE OF ROOTS OF A QUADRATIC
FOR $y = ax^2 + bx + c$

Discriminant	Nature of roots	Graph
$b^2 - 4ac > 0$ and a perfect square	Real, distinct, rational	Crosses the x-axis twice at rational values of x
$b^2 - 4ac > 0$ and not a perfect square	Real, distinct, irrational	Crosses x-axis twice at irrational values of x
$b^2 - 4ac = 0$	Real, equal, rational	Is tangent to x-axis
$b^2 - 4ac < 0$	Imaginary	Does not cross x-axis

EXAMPLE 19. Give the nature of the roots of

$$y = 2x^2 - 3x - 6.$$

Solution. First evaluate $b^2 - 4ac$. Referring to the given equation and comparing it with (46), we have $a = 2$, $b = -3$, and $c = -6$, from which

$$b^2 - 4ac = 9 + 48 = 57.$$

Now 57 is positive, so the roots are real; it is not a perfect square, so the roots are irrational; it is not zero, so the roots are unequal.

EXAMPLE 20. Given the equation

$$y = 2x^2 - kx + 8, \tag{48}$$

what condition regarding k is necessary if the roots of (48) are equal?

Solution. If the roots of (48) are to be equal, the discriminant must be zero. Now, $a = 2$, $b = k$, and $c = 8$ so that

$$b^2 - 4ac = k^2 - 64,$$

from which

$$k^2 - 64 = 0$$

and $k = \pm 8$, which are the requested solutions.

Exercises

In Exercises 1–10 describe the nature of the roots of the given equation. Also plot the graph of the equation.

1. $y = x^2 - 5x.$ *Ans.* Real, unequal, rational.

2. $y = 3x^2 + 4x.$

3. $y = 2x^2 - 6.$ *Ans.* Real, unequal, irrational.

4. $y = x^2 - 8.$

5. $y = x^2 - 6x + 9.$ *Ans.* Real, equal, rational.

6. $y = x^2 + 4x + 4.$

7. $y = 2x^2 + 4x + 6.$ *Ans.* Imaginary.

8. $y = 3x^2 + x + 1.$

9. $y = 4x^2 - 5x - 9$. *Ans.* Real, unequal, rational.

10. $y = 3x^2 + x - 1$.

11. From the equation $y = x^2 - 6x + c$, determine the value of c for which the roots of the equation are equal. *Ans.* $c = 9$.

12. From the equation $y = ax^2 + 3x + 2$, determine the value of a for which the roots of the equation are equal.

13. The quadratic $y = x^2 - 5x + c$ has roots such that one root is twice the other. Determine c. *Ans.* $c = \frac{50}{9}$.

14. For the quadratic equation $y = 3x^2 + bx + 3$, what range of values of b will permit the roots of the quadratic to be real?

Determine the nature of the roots in Exercises 15–18.

15. $y = x^4 - 13x^2 + 36$. *Ans.* Four roots, all real.

16. $y = x^4 - 5x^2 - 36$. *Ans.* Two real, two imaginary roots.

17. $y = x^4 + 13x^2 + 36$. *Ans.* Four imaginary roots.

18. $y = x^4$. *Ans.* Four equal roots.

19. Given the equation

$$y = x^2 - 3x - 4,$$

substitute $x = w - 2$ and obtain an equation in y and w. Show that the roots of the (y, x) equation are each 2 less than the roots of the (y, w) equation. Note that the substitution merely shifts the location of the graph horizontally by 2 units.

20. For the quadratic equation $y = 2x^2 + bx + 8$, what range of values of b will permit the roots of the quadratic to be real?

7-8 Radical Equations—Extraneous Roots

Applied problems in mathematics frequently involve equations in which one or more of the terms is a radical quantity; the most common radical involves a square root. Such equations are called *radical equations*; their solutions can involve quadratics in that a squaring operation that is intended to eliminate a radical may give rise to a second-degree expression. Then, too, it often occurs that manipulation of a radical equation may give rise to solutions that are legitimate for some intermediate expression but are not appropriate for the original expression; these solutions are called *extraneous*.

The process of solving radical equations calls for arranging the radical expressions in such a manner that successive squaring of the sides of the given equality will eliminate the radicals. This successive squaring assumes that the radicals present are square roots.

EXAMPLE 21. Solve for x if

$$\sqrt{2x + 5} - x + 5 = 0. \qquad (49)$$

Solution. Squaring (49) in its given form will not eliminate the radical; however, if the radical quantity is isolated on one side of the equal sign and all of the other terms are transposed to the other side of the equal sign, then a single squaring operation will eliminate the radical. Hence,

$$\sqrt{2x + 5} = x - 5.$$

If we square both sides, then

$$2x + 5 = x^2 - 10x + 25.$$

Collecting like terms, we have

$$x^2 - 12x + 20 = 0, \qquad (50)$$

which has the solutions $x = 10, 2$.

If we accept only the *positive* value of $\sqrt{2x + 5}$, then the only acceptable solution of (49) will be $x = 10$. The quantity $x = 2$, although an acceptable solution of the intermediate equation (50), is *not* a solution of (49) and will therefore be regarded as extraneous.

EXAMPLE 22. Solve for y if

$$\sqrt{6y + 7} = 6 + \sqrt{2y - 13}. \qquad (51)$$

Solution. No single squaring operation will eliminate both of the radicals in (51). Squaring both sides, we have

$$6y + 7 = 36 + 12\sqrt{2y - 13} + 2y - 13. \qquad (52)$$

Collecting like terms in (52) and dividing by 4, we have

$$y - 4 = 3\sqrt{2y - 13}.$$

If we square again, then

$$y^2 - 8y + 16 = 18y - 117,$$

which has the solutions $y = 19, 7$, where, accepting again only the positive values of the square root, neither root is extraneous.

EXAMPLE 23. Three circles are blended according to the dimensions shown in Fig. 7-10. Solve for the radius r of the center circle.

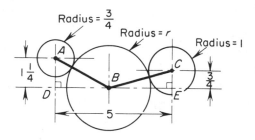

FIGURE 7–10

Solution. Since the radius r is the unknown quantity for which we are to solve, an equation relating r and the known data is required. From the right triangles shown, a Pythagorean relationship is suggested. Now $AB = r + \frac{3}{4}$ and $BC = r + 1$. From $\triangle ABD$,

$$DB = \sqrt{(r + \tfrac{3}{4})^2 - (\tfrac{5}{4})^2},$$

and for $\triangle CBE$,

$$BE = \sqrt{(r + 1)^2 - (\tfrac{3}{4})^2}.$$

Now $DB + BE = 5$, or

$$\sqrt{(r + \tfrac{3}{4})^2 - (\tfrac{5}{4})^2} + \sqrt{(r + 1)^2 - (\tfrac{3}{4})^2} = 5. \tag{53}$$

Solution of equation (53) for r now involves the solution of a radical equation. As in previous examples, radicals are eliminated by successive squaring operations. Transposing the second term of (53) to the right member, we have

$$\sqrt{(r + \tfrac{3}{4})^2 - (\tfrac{5}{4})^2} = 5 - \sqrt{(r + 1)^2 - (\tfrac{3}{4})^2}.$$

Removing parentheses, we have

$$\sqrt{r^2 + \tfrac{3}{2}r - 1} = 5 - \sqrt{r^2 + 2r + \tfrac{7}{16}}.$$

Squaring both sides,

$$r^2 + \tfrac{3}{2}r - 1 = 25 - 10\sqrt{r^2 + 2r + \tfrac{7}{16}} + r^2 + 2r + \tfrac{7}{16}.$$

Collecting like terms and clearing fractions,

$$8r + 423 = 160\sqrt{r^2 + 2r + \tfrac{7}{16}}.$$

Squaring both sides and collecting like terms, we have the quadratic

$$25{,}536r^2 + 44{,}432r - 167{,}729 = 0,$$

which, using slide rule accuracy, has the positive solution $r = 1.84$.

Exercises

In Exercises 1–10 solve for the literal quantity. Disregard extraneous roots.

1. $\sqrt{m-3} = 6.$ *Ans. 39.*

2. $12 = \sqrt{m+100}.$

3. $\sqrt{3z+4} = z.$ *Ans. 4.*

4. $2z - 1 = \sqrt{z^2 + 8z + 16}.$

5. $\sqrt{y+13} - 3 = \sqrt{2y-5}.$ *Ans. 3.*

6. $\sqrt{3m+28} - \sqrt{3m-5} \mid 3.$

7. $-\sqrt{8k} + 15 - \sqrt{2k} = 12/\sqrt{2k}.$ *Ans. 8, $\frac{1}{2}$.*

8. $\sqrt{m+95} - 5 = \sqrt{m}.$

9. $\sqrt{k^2 + 15} - 4 = \sqrt{k^2 - 4k - 5}.$ *Ans. 7, -1.*

10. $\sqrt{2r+5} = \sqrt{r} + \sqrt{5}.$

11. Two numbers differ by 24. The square root of the larger number differs from the square root of the smaller number by 2. What are the numbers?   *Ans. 49, 25.*

12. Determine the value of AB in Fig. 7-11 if $DC = 8$, $AC = 3$, and DB exceeds AB by 2. (Figure not to scale.)   *Ans. 4.15.*

13. In Fig. 7-12 find BD, given $AD = 12$, $AB = 8$, and $DC = 3$.   *Ans. 4.69.*

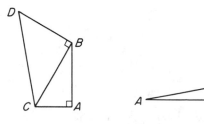

FIGURE 7–11   FIGURE 7–12

14. In Fig. 7-13 find BE, given $AB = 5$, $BC = 9$, $ED = 3$, and $AE + DC = 12$.
Ans. 2.07.

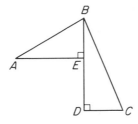

FIGURE 7-13

In Exercises 15–20 solve for the quantity indicated.

15. $v = \sqrt{\dfrac{g\alpha}{2\pi}}$ (for α).
 Ans. $\alpha = 2\pi v^2/g$.

16. $z = \sqrt{R^2 + (X_L - X_C)^2}$ (for R).

17. $m = \dfrac{m_0}{\sqrt{1 - (v/c)^2}}$ (for v).
 Ans. $v = \dfrac{c\sqrt{m^2 - m_0^2}}{m}$.

18. $t = \dfrac{-v_0 \pm \sqrt{v_0^2 - 2sg}}{g}$ (for s).

19. $A = \pi(R^2 - r^2)$ (for R).
 Ans. $R = \sqrt{(A + \pi r^2)/\pi}$.

20. $r = \dfrac{-\pi h \pm \sqrt{\pi^2 h^2 + A\pi}}{\pi}$ (for A).

21. Show that the expression $x + a = \sqrt{y^2 + (x - a)^2}$ may be reduced to the expression $y^2 = 4ax$.

22. Show that the expression

$$\sqrt{(x + f)^2 + y^2} + \sqrt{(f - x)^2 + y^2} = 2a$$

may be reduced to the expression

$$\frac{x^2}{a^2} + \frac{y^2}{b^2} = 1,$$

where $b^2 = a^2 - f^2$.

Additional Exercises

1. In the given equations find the values of a, b, and c for which the roots of the quadratic are equal.

(a) $5x^2 + 4x + c = 0.$

(b) $3x^2 + bx + 8 = 0.$ *Ans.* $b = \pm 4\sqrt{6}.$

(c) $ax^2 + x - 6 = 0.$

(d) $ax^2 - 4x + a = 0.$ *Ans.* $a = \pm 2.$

2. Given the quadratic equation

$$2x^2 - 3x + k = 0.$$

(a) For what value of k are the roots such that one root exceeds the other by unity?
Ans. $k = \frac{5}{8}.$

(b) For what value of k are the roots such that one root is twice the other?

3. A runner of width 3 ft. is placed over a 9′ by 12′ rectangular rug as shown in Fig. 7-14(a). Find the area of the runner.   *Ans.* 36.09 ft².

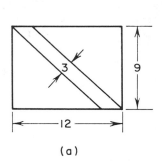

(a)

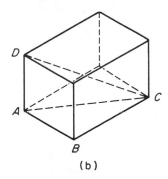

(b)

FIGURE 7–14

4. Two circles are such that the sum of their circumferences is 24π ft. and the sum of their areas is 84π ft². What are the radii of the circles?
Ans. $6 + \sqrt{6}, 6 - \sqrt{6}.$

5. Solve for L if

$$n = \sqrt{\frac{R^2}{4L^2} - \frac{1}{LC}}.$$

6. Referring to Fig. 7-15,

(a) Find the lengths AC, AE, BD, DC, and DE.
Ans. $BD = 4.40''; \ DC = 3.76''.$

(b) There is a point F on AD such that $FB = 1.2FE$. Show that F is either 2.61 or 21.0 in. from A.

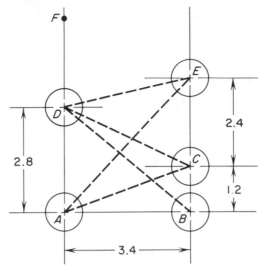

FIGURE 7–15

7. Figure 7-14(b) shows a prism with six rectangular faces. Note by the Pythagorean theorem that

$$(AB)^2 + (BC)^2 = (AC)^2$$

and that

$$(AC)^2 + (AD)^2 = (DC)^2$$

from which

$$(DC)^2 = (AB)^2 + (BC)^2 + (AD)^2.$$

(a) Find DC if $AD = AB = 5.2$ and $BC = 2AB$.
(b) Find AB if $BC = AD$, DC exceeds BC by 2, and BC exceeds AB by 1.

Ans. $AB = (1 + \sqrt{15})/2$.

(c) If the prism is a perfect cube, show that $DC = AB\sqrt{3}$.

8. It can be shown from Graham's Law of Gaseous Diffusion that, under similar conditions of temperature and pressure, the ratio of the rates of diffusion of two gases is the reciprocal of the ratio of the square roots of the molecular weights. That is,

$$\frac{D_a}{D_b} = \frac{\sqrt{M_b}}{\sqrt{M_a}}$$

where D is the rate of diffusion and M is molecular weight.

(a) If $D_a = 1.12D_b$, show that $M_a = 0.796M_b$.

(b) Find D_a/D_b where Gas a is oxygen (molecular weight 32) and Gas b is nitrogen (molecular weight 28). *Ans.* 0.936.

9. A best estimate of standard error of the difference between the means of two random samples is given as

$$\sigma = \sqrt{\frac{S_1^2}{N_1 - 1} + \frac{S_2^2}{N_2 - 1}}.$$

Show that

$$S_1 = \sqrt{\frac{N_1 - 1}{N_2 - 1}(\sigma^2 N_2 - \sigma^2 - S_2^2)}.$$

10. The equivalent resistance of two resistors in parallel is

$$R = \frac{R_1 R_2}{R_1 + R_2}.$$

A constant resistance R_1 is placed in parallel with a thermistor R_2 which has a resistance of 27 ohms at 20°C and 4 ohms at 80°C. Find the value of R_1 which will cause the equivalent resistance of the cold circuit to be 0.8 ohms greater than that of the hot circuit. *Ans.* $R_1 = 2.6$ ohms.

11. An object with initial velocity v undergoes an acceleration a for time t. The displacement s of the object for this time is given by the equation

$$s = vt + \tfrac{1}{2}at^2.$$

(a) Solve for t.

(b) Find t if $s = 100$ ft., $v = 20$ ft./sec., and $a = 8$ ft./sec².

12. A force F in Fig. 7-16 is attempting to shear a rivet across its circular cross section area $\pi D^2/4$ where the diameter D is unknown. The maximum force that the rivet can endure safely is 15,000 times the rivet's cross sectional area, where the area is expressed in square inches. The force F is also attempting to pull the bar apart (tension failure) at its weakest cross sectional area, located at the rivet hole. The maximum force that the bar can endure safely is 20,000 times the bar's

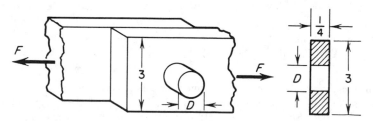

FIGURE 7–16

cross-sectional area, taken at the weakest section. Find the rivet diameter required to make the load-carrying ability of the rivet equal to that of the bar.

Ans. $D = 0.94$ in.

13. In equations (53.1) and (53.2), S_x and S_y represent respectively the horizontal and vertical components of displacement of a projectile.

$$S_x = (V \cos \theta)(t) \tag{53.1}$$

$$S_y = (V \sin \theta)(t) - \tfrac{1}{2} g t^2 \tag{53.2}$$

(a) Eliminate t (time in flight) from the equation for S_y.

$$\text{Ans. } S_y = S_x \left(\frac{\sin \theta}{\cos \theta} \right) - \frac{g S_x^2}{2(V \cos \theta)^2}.$$

(b) From the answer in part (a) above, let $\theta = 30°$, $\sin \theta = \tfrac{1}{2}$, $\cos \theta = \sqrt{3}/2$, $g = 32$ ft./sec², and $V = 400$ ft./sec. Solve for S_x when $S_y = 300$ ft.

Ans. $S_x = 606$ ft. or 3730 ft.

(c) When the assumed values for part (b) are substituted into the answer for part (a), the equation

$$S_y = (0.577)S_x - (0.000133)S_x^2$$

is obtained. Solve for S_x when $S_y = 0$. Graph the equation with S_x on the horizontal axis and S_y on the vertical axis.

Ans. $S_x = 0$ ft. and 4330 ft.

(d) Calculate the maximum value of S_y in part (c) and compare the result with that shown on the graph. *Ans.* $S_{y(\text{max})} = 625$ ft.

14. A circuit is designed with a switching device that places two resistors either in parallel or series. The parallel resistance $R_p = R_1 R_2 /(R_1 + R_2)$ is 10 ohms and the series resistance $R_s = R_1 + R_2$ is 48 ohms. Find R_1 and R_2.

Ans. 14.2 and 33.8 ohms.

15. A company has N machines of equal capacity that produce a total of 180 pieces each work day. If two machines break down, the work load of the remaining machines is increased by 3 pieces each per day to maintain production. Find N.

Ans. $N = 12$.

16. The total power developed in a 100-volt electric generator is the product of the generated voltage and current, or $100I$, where I is in amperes. Part of the total power and voltage is lost in the generator, due to the current flow through the internal resistance R_i of 5 ohms. The internal power loss is $I^2 R_i$, or $5I^2$ watts. Consequently, the output power $P = 100I - 5I^2$. Find the current that gives the maximum output power. Find the maximum power.

Ans. $I = 10$ amps, $P = 500$ watts.

17. In Exercise 16 show that the output power is maximum when $I =$ (generated voltage)$/2R_i$, and that this power equals the quotient of the generated voltage squared and $4R_i$. Show that the output power is maximum when it equals one-half of the total power generated.

18. A nozzle directs a jet of water tangent to a hydraulic turbine wheel to hit turbine buckets and drive a generator. The jet speed is J ft./sec. and the peripheral speed of the buckets is B ft./sec. The turbine power P is proportional to the product of the bucket speed and the difference between the jet and bucket speeds, or $P = KB(J - B)$. When $J = 100$ and $B = 70$, the power is 210 kw. If the jet speed is constant, what bucket speed gives maximum power and what is the maximum power?   *Ans.* $B = 50$ ft./sec., $P = 250$ kw.

19. A beam of length L shown in Fig. 7-17 is supported by reaction forces R_1 and R_2 which vary while two wheels of a travelling crane roll across the beam from left to right. Forces P_1 and P_2 are the constant wheel loads, and x is the varying distance from the left end of the beam to the load P_1. As the wheels move

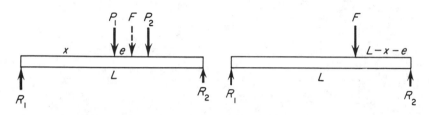

FIGURE 7–17   FIGURE 7–18

across the beam, there is for each value of x a value of the bending effect (bending moment) inside the beam directly under P_1. The general expression for this bending moment is $M = R_1 x$. Since R_1 changes with x, a function of x may be substituted for R_1. Referring to Fig. 7-18, it may be shown from mechanics that

$$R_1 = F(L - x - e)/L$$

where F is the resultant load effect of P_1 and P_2, and is located some constant distance e from P_1. F, L, and e remain constant. Show that the maximum value of M, under load P_1, occurs when $x = (L - e)/2$.

7-9   The General Quadratic—Conics

The general quadratic is represented by the second degree equation

$$Ax^2 + Bxy + Cy^2 + Dx + Ey + F = 0, \tag{54}$$

where, in order to remain second degree, A, B, and C cannot all be zero. The quadratic familiar to students of more elementary mathematics was second degree in one variable only and was generally of the form $Ax^2 + Dx + F = 0$, where $B = C = E = 0$, or of the form $Cy^2 + Ey + F = 0$, where $A = B = D = 0$. Modification of the constants A–F in (54) result in equations which, when graphed, describe a group of curves called the *conic sections.* Several of these modifications are discussed in subsequent sections from the point of view of inspecting for mathematical types and graphing the curves.

Circle

The *circle* is defined as the locus of points equidistant from a given point. If a circle of radius r has its center on the origin [see Fig. 7-19(a)] then

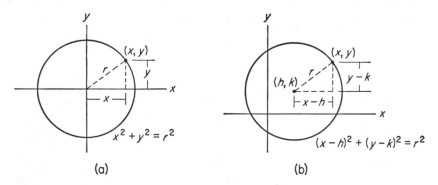

(a)   (b)

FIGURE 7–19

$x^2 + y^2 = r^2$ is the equation of the circle by the Pythagorean theorem. This is a modification of equation (54) such that $Ax^2 + Cy^2 + F = 0$, where $A = C$ and $B = D = E = 0$. The equation of a circle with center on the origin can, therefore, be readily identified by the presence of the sum of two squares with equal coefficients. Thus,

$$x^2 + y^2 = 49$$

is an origin-centered circle of radius 7 and

$$2x^2 + 2y^2 = 72$$

is an origin-centered circle of radius 6.

If the center of the circle is at a point other than the origin, say (h, k), as in Fig. 7-19(b), the equation of the circle, again by the Pythagorean theorem, is

$$(x - h)^2 + (y - k)^2 = r^2. \tag{55}$$

This is the *standard form* of the circle. If equation (55) is expanded, we have

$$x^2 + y^2 - 2hx - 2ky + h^2 + k^2 - r^2 = 0, \tag{56}$$

where, by comparison with equation (54), we have

$$B = 0, A = C, D = -2h, E = -2k, \text{ and } F = h^2 + k^2 - r^2;$$

therefore,

$$Ax^2 + Ay^2 + Dx + Ey + F = 0 \qquad (57)$$

is an expression equivalent to equation (55) and is called the *general form* of the circle.

EXAMPLE 24. Give the equation of the circle with radius 3 and center at $(4, -2)$.

Solution. Substituting into equation (55) the values $r = 3$, $h = 4$, and $k = -2$, we have

$$(x - 4)^2 + (y + 2)^2 = 3^2.$$

EXAMPLE 25. Describe the circle whose equation is

$$x^2 + y^2 - 10x + 2y = -10.$$

Solution. This equation is given in the general form and can be made more meaningful by reverting to the standard form. Completing the square, we have

$$(x - 5)^2 + (y + 1)^2 = 4^2,$$

which is a circle of radius 4 and center at $(5, -1)$.

Exercises

Assemble Exercises 1–8 into the standard form. Identify the center and radius and sketch the graph.

1. $2x^2 + 2y^2 = 162.$

2. $3x^2 + 3y^2 = 27.$

3. $x^2 + y^2 + 8x = 0.$

4. $x^2 + y^2 - 8y = 0.$

5. $x^2 + y^2 + 6x + 4y = 0.$

6. $x^2 + y^2 + 3x - 7y = \frac{1}{4}.$

7. $36x^2 + 36y^2 + 108x - 96y + 1 = 0.$

8. $9x^2 + 9y^2 + 6y - 24 = 0.$

Find the equations of the following circles:

9. With center on origin and radius 10.

10. With center at $(3, -8)$ and radius $\sqrt{5}$.

11. With center $(10, 0)$ and tangent to $y = x$.

12. With center $(-5, 12)$ and passing through the origin.

Ellipse

An ellipse is defined as the locus of points, the sum of whose distances to two fixed points is constant. These fixed points are called *foci* and are pictured in Fig. 7-20 as F and F'. From Fig. 7-20, the horizontal and vertical distances

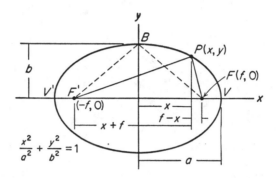

FIGURE 7–20

between P and F' are $x + f$ and y, respectively, while the corresponding distances between P and F are $f - x$ and y. The sum of the slanting distances PF' and PF must equal $2a$, for if P rests at V,

$$PF = a - f \text{ and } PF' = a + f.$$

From this,

$$PF + PF' = 2a.$$

Also, by the locus definition of an ellipse, $PF + PF'$ must remain fixed. With P anywhere on the curve, then, we have the equation

$$\sqrt{(x + f)^2 + y^2} + \sqrt{(f - x)^2 + y^2} = 2a,$$

from which

$$\frac{x^2}{a^2} + \frac{y^2}{a^2 - f^2} = 1.$$

Since the vertical axis of the ellipse in Fig. 7-20 is the perpendicular bisector of FF', point B is equidistant from F and F' with the consequence that $BF = a$, and hence, the Pythagorean relationship $b^2 = a^2 - f^2$. This makes the *standard form* of the ellipse either

$$\frac{x^2}{a^2} + \frac{y^2}{b^2} = 1 \qquad (a^2 > b^2)$$

or $\qquad\qquad\qquad\qquad\qquad\qquad\qquad\qquad\qquad\qquad\qquad\qquad\qquad$ (58)

$$\frac{y^2}{a^2} + \frac{x^2}{b^2} = 1. \qquad (a^2 > b^2)$$

The second equation above is the case where the major axis is vertical rather than the horizontal case pictured in Fig. 7-20. The distance a is always measured from the center to the vertex, and, from the relationship $b^2 = a^2 - f^2$, the requirement that $a^2 > b^2$ is apparent. Note that the equations (58) are modifications of the general quadratic equation (54) with $B = D = E = 0$.

It can further be shown that an ellipse with center (h, k) will be of the form

$$\frac{(x - h)^2}{a^2} + \frac{(y - k)^2}{b^2} = 1 \qquad (a^2 > b^2)$$

or $\qquad\qquad\qquad\qquad\qquad\qquad\qquad\qquad\qquad\qquad\qquad\qquad\qquad$ (59)

$$\frac{(y - k)^2}{a^2} + \frac{(x - h)^2}{b^2} = 1. \qquad (a^2 > b^2)$$

It should be noted that if equations (59) are expanded to the form of the equation (54), the characteristic of the equation of the ellipse is seen to be the sum of two squares with the coefficients of the square terms unlike.

Consider these example problems employing some of the properties of the ellipse and the standard forms.

EXAMPLE 26. Give the equation of the ellipse with horizontal axis 6 units, vertical axis 12 units, and center at $(-3, 4)$.

Solution. Here, because the long axis is vertical, we employ the latter of equations (4) with $h = -3$, $k = 4$, $a^2 = 36$, and $b^2 = 9$. Substituting, we have

$$\frac{(y - 4)^2}{36} + \frac{(x + 3)^2}{9} = 1.$$

EXAMPLE 27. Describe the ellipse represented by the equation

$$25x^2 + 4y^2 - 100x + 24y + 36 = 0.$$

Solution. Completing the square,

$$25(x^2 - 4x + 4) + 4(y^2 + 6y + 9) = -36 + 100 + 36,$$

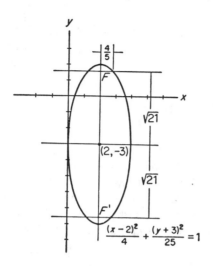

FIGURE 7–21

from which

$$\frac{(x - 2)^2}{4} + \frac{(y + 3)^2}{25} = 1.$$

This is recognized as an ellipse with center $(2, -3)$. The graph is shown in Fig. 7-21. The major axis is vertical and is ten units long, placing the vertices at $(2, 2)$ and $(2, -8)$. The minor axis is 4 units long. The foci are (from $f^2 = a^2 - b^2 = 25 - 4 = 21$) located $\sqrt{21}$ units above and below the center and therefore have the coordinates $(2, -3 + \sqrt{21})$ and $(2, -3 - \sqrt{21})$. The alert student will recognize that the ellipses

$$\frac{(x - 2)^2}{4} + \frac{(y + 3)^2}{25} = 1 \quad \text{and} \quad \frac{x^2}{4} + \frac{y^2}{25} = 1$$

differ only in one respect, namely, the locations of their centers. Their dimensions are identical. Since the latter form is easier to graph, it would be advisable in Example 27 to assume the ellipse to be origin-centered, graph it accordingly, then move the origin away from the center of the ellipse to its proper relative position.

Exercises

Collect the ellipses in Exercises 1–7 into the standard form. Plot the center, vertices, and foci of each and sketch the graph.

1. $4x^2 + 9y^2 = 36$.

2. $4x^2 + y^2 = 16$.

3. $5x^2 + y^2 - 50x + 100 = 0$.

4. $x^2 + 4y^2 + 16y = 0$.

5. $2x^2 + 3y^2 + 12x - 30y + 81 = 0$.

6. $5x^2 + 4y^2 - 60x + 72y + 464 = 0.$

7. $6x^2 + 3y^2 - 72x + 24y + 222 = 0.$

Determine the equation of the ellipse in each of the following from the given properties.

8. Center at $(1, -5)$, horizontal major axis 12 units long and minor axis 4 units.

9. Center at $(\frac{1}{2}, 1)$, vertical major axis of length 6 and minor axis of length 3.

10. Center at $(5, 0)$, one focus at $(0, 0)$, major axis 12 units long.

11. Vertices at $(-3, 2)$ and $(3, 2)$, minor axis half the major axis.

Hyperbola

The *hyperbola* is defined as the locus of points, the difference of whose distances to two fixed points is constant.

The equation of the hyperbola is derived in a manner somewhat similar to that of the ellipse; the *standard form* of a hyperbola with center (h, k) is given as either of the following:

$$\frac{(x-h)^2}{a^2} - \frac{(y-k)^2}{b^2} = 1,$$

$$\frac{(y-k)^2}{a^2} - \frac{(x-h)^2}{b^2} = 1. \tag{60}$$

From equations (60), if $h = k = 0$, we have the origin-centered equations shown in Fig. 7-22. We choose the origin-centered hyperbola for a more detailed study primarily because it is less cumbersome, and, as in the case of

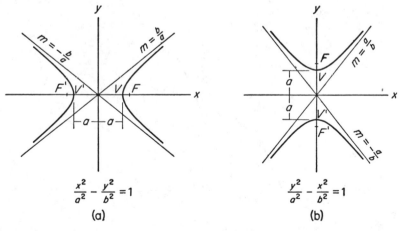

$$\frac{x^2}{a^2} - \frac{y^2}{b^2} = 1$$

(a)

$$\frac{y^2}{a^2} - \frac{x^2}{b^2} = 1$$

(b)

FIGURE 7-22

the ellipse, the relocation of the center in no way affects the shape of the conic.

The student will notice these features from Fig. 7-22:

(*a*) Only one of the coordinate axes intercepts the origin-centered hyperbola. This axis becomes the *transverse axis* as opposed to the *conjugate axis.*

(*b*) The vertices are $\pm a$ from the center along the transverse axis.

(*c*) The foci are also on the transverse axis. In deriving the distance from the center to the focus, we obtain $f = \pm\sqrt{a^2 + b^2}$. (The derivation is left as a problem for the student.)

(*d*) The hyperbola approaches limiting lines whose slopes are $\pm a/b$ or $\pm b/a$ according to the direction of the transverse axis.

The limiting lines suggested above are called *asymptotes;* they are lines which a curve approaches but never reaches.

The equations of these asymptotes and other properties of the hyperbola are better discussed through an example problem.

EXAMPLE 28. Discuss and graph the hyperbola

$$\frac{x^2}{4} - \frac{y^2}{9} = 1.$$

Solution. Reference here is made to Fig. 7-23. To find the intercepts, we let $y = 0$ and obtain $x = \pm 2$ as the x-intercepts. If we let $x = 0$, we discover that the y-intercepts do not exist.

If the equation is solved for y, we have

$$y = \pm\sqrt{\tfrac{9}{4}x^2 - 9}.$$

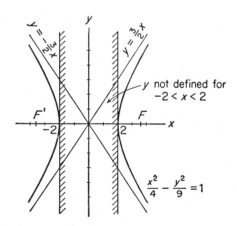

FIGURE 7–23

Two interesting things are noted here:

(*a*) If $9x^2/4 - 9$ is negative, y is imaginary. This means that, to have a defined y, $9/4\ x^2 \geqq 9$ and the absolute value of x equals or exceeds 2, that is, $|x| \geqq 2$. See Fig. 7-23. This is the domain of x for which y is defined and is accordingly called the *domain of definition* of y.

(*b*) As x becomes very large, $9x^2/4$ dominates the radicand, and the constant -9 has but a trifling effect on the value of y. For large abscissas then, $y = \pm 3x/2$ is a near-correct description of the hyperbola, becoming still closer to correct as x continues to enlarge. It is by this reasoning that $y = \pm 3x/2$ are the limiting lines of the hyperbola, or asymptotes.

If equations (60) are expanded, the result is of the general form

$$Ax^2 + Cy^2 + Dx + Ey + F = 0,$$

where in every case, A and C differ in sign. The characteristic of the equation of a hyperbola is, then, for purposes of rapid identification, the difference of the squares of the variables.

EXAMPLE 29. Graph the equation $xy = 12$.

Solution. This equation asserts that the product of the abscissa and ordinate equals 12. Immediately suggested are such coordinate pairs as

$$(12, 1),\ (3, 4),\ (-6, -2),\ (-4, -3),\ \text{etc.,}$$

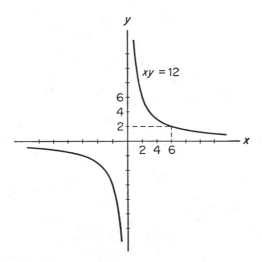

FIGURE 7–24

where it is apparent that the ordinate and abscissa must be of the same sign, forcing the graph to exist only in the first and third quadrants. This information, combined with the condition that the coordinate axes are the asymptotes, produces the graph in Fig 7-24.

The equation $xy = c$ takes on the form

$$(x - h)(y - k) = c$$

by shifting the center to the point (h, k). When expanded, this takes on the form

$$xy + Dx + Ey + F = 0,$$

which is a modification of the general quadratic equation.

Exercises

Assemble Exercises 1–7 into the standard form. Locate the center, foci, and vertices. Sketch the asymptotes and the curve.

1. $x^2 - 4y^2 = 36$.

2. $y^2 - 6x^2 = 24$.

3. $y^2 - 9x^2 + 8y - 20 = 0$.

4. $4x^2 - 9y^2 - 24x - 108y - 432 = 0$.

5. $x^2 - y^2 - 4x - 12 = 0$.

6. $xy = -16$.

7. $xy - 3y + 4x = 0$.

Determine the equations of the following hyperbolas with horizontal transverse axes.

8. Asymptotes of slopes ± 1, center $(0, 0)$, distance between vertices 6.

9. Center $(0, 0)$, vertex $(\frac{3}{2}, 0)$, asymptotes of slopes ± 2.

10. Center $(0, 0)$, passing through $(4, 1)$, $a = \sqrt{15}$.

Simultaneous systems involving conics

In Section 5-7 the solution of simultaneous linear systems was discussed. There it was demonstrated that two straight lines in a plane are parallel, intersecting, or coincident, yielding, respectively, no, one, or an indefinite number of solutions. We will discuss here the solutions of systems involving (1) a straight line and a conic and (2) two conics.

A straight line and a conic can intersect in no, one, or two distinct points, as demonstrated in Fig. 7-25. The number of real solutions is dependent upon whether the line fails to intersect the conic, is tangent to it, or cuts it as a secant. A theorem from the theory of equations states that the number of solutions of two equations equals the products of their degrees. Figure 7-25(a)

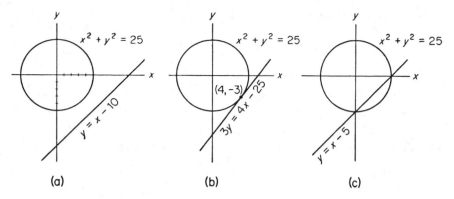

(a)   (b)   (c)

FIGURE 7–25

shows no *real* solutions; any effort to obtain the solutions algebraically would produce an (x, y) set of which either x or y or both are imaginary because the quadratic resulting from eliminating one of the unknowns will contain a negative discriminant. An algebraic example of this situation follows.

EXAMPLE 30. Solve the system containing

$$x^2 + y^2 = 25 \text{ and } y = x - 10.$$

Solution. By substitution,

$$x^2 + (x - 10)^2 = 25.$$

Expanding,

$$2x^2 - 20x + 75 = 0.$$

This quadratic in x produces the coordinates

$$x = \frac{10 \pm 5\sqrt{-2}}{2} \quad \text{and} \quad y = \frac{-10 \pm 5\sqrt{-2}}{2}.$$

This shows the solutions to be imaginary. A graph of the system is approximated in Fig. 7-25(a), where the line and circle fail to intersect.

When the line is tangent to the circle as shown in Fig. 7-25(b), an attempt to solve the system algebraically would result in a quadratic in one unknown whose discriminant is zero. An example of this situation follows.

EXAMPLE 31. Solve the system containing

$$x^2 + y^2 = 25 \text{ and } y = \frac{4x}{3} - \frac{25}{3}.$$

Solution. By substitution,

$$x^2 + \left(\frac{4x}{3} - \frac{25}{3}\right)^2 = 25,$$

from which

$$x^2 - 8x + 16 = 0,$$

which has the roots 4, 4 and produces the points of intersection

$$\begin{pmatrix} x = & 4 \\ y = & -3 \end{pmatrix}, \begin{pmatrix} x = & 4 \\ y = & -3 \end{pmatrix}.$$

The multiple roots indicate a tangency situation.

When the line intersects the circle in two distinct points, the student would properly anticipate two distinct solutions when solving algebraically. The quadratic resulting in the elimination of one unknown will have a positive discriminant, indicating real and distinct roots. An example of this situation follows.

EXAMPLE 32. Solve the system containing

$$x^2 + y^2 = 25 \text{ and } y = x - 5.$$

Solution. By substitution,

$$x^2 + (x - 5)^2 = 25$$

or

$$2x^2 - 10x = 0,$$

producing roots

$$\begin{pmatrix} x = & 0 \\ y = & -5 \end{pmatrix}, \begin{pmatrix} x = 5 \\ y = 0 \end{pmatrix}.$$

These roots show that the intersections are real and distinct. Figure 7-25(c) illustrates this example.

The preceding situations are duplicated and expanded for the systems involving two non-coincident conics, which can intersect in 0, 1, 2, 3, or 4, distinct points. A theorem from the theory of equations states that imaginary roots occur in pairs. In eliminating one of the unknowns from a system of

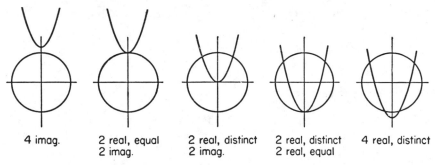

| 4 imag. | 2 real, equal
2 imag. | 2 real, distinct
2 imag. | 2 real, distinct
2 real, equal | 4 real, distinct |

FIGURE 7-26   Solutions of a parabola and a circle.

simultaneous quadratics, four solutions will always result; none, two, or four of these can be imaginary. The others will be real or infinite and, in the case of tangencies, will be multiple. The separate situations involving a circle and a parabola are pictured in Fig. 7-26.

EXAMPLE 33. Solve the system containing

$$x^2 + y^2 = 25 \quad \text{and} \quad y = \frac{4x^2}{9}.$$

Solution. Substituting,

$$y^2 + \frac{9y}{4} - 25 = 0,$$

from which

$$\left(\begin{matrix} y = & 4 \\ x = \pm 3 \end{matrix} \right), \quad \left(\begin{matrix} y = -\dfrac{25}{4} \\ x = \pm\dfrac{15}{4}j \end{matrix} \right).$$

This is the situation of 4 roots of which 2 are imaginary and 2 are real and distinct, as pictured in the middle sketch in Fig. 7-26.

Exercises

Solve Exercises 1–8 both graphically and algebraically.

1. $9x^2 + 4y^2 = 36,$
   $2y - 3x = 6.$

2. $x^2 - y^2 = 12,$
   $2y - x = 0.$

3. $4y^2 - x^2 = 36,$
   $x^2 + y^2 = 9.$

4. $4x - 8 = y^2,$
   $x^2 + 9y^2 = 4.$

5. $9x = 4y^2 - 40y + 100,$
$x^2 + y^2 - 10y = 0.$

6. $x^2 - 2x + y^2 = 24,$
$x^2 - y^2 = 16.$

7. $9x^2 + 16y^2 - 36x - 64y = 0,$
$3x^2 - 12x - 2y = 0.$

8. $x^2 - 4x + 4y^2 = 0,$
$x^2 - 4x = y.$

Solve the following systems algebraically.

9. $x^2 + xy = 3,$
$4xy + y^2 = 12.$

10. $xy + y = 10,$
$x + xy = 6.$

11. $x^2 + 2xy + y^2 = 64,$
$x^2 + 4xy + 4y^2 = 100.$

12. $x^3 + y^3 = 26,$
$x + y = 2.$

13. $\dfrac{1}{x} + \dfrac{1}{y} = 5,$

$\dfrac{1}{2x} - \dfrac{1}{6y} = -1.$

14. $x + \dfrac{1}{x} = y,$

$x - \dfrac{2}{x} = 2y.$

In the preceding chapter we discovered that quadratic equations often have roots which are irrational in nature. The irrational roots of a quadratic are inexact when expressed in decimal form. This same inexactness may occur in logarithmic, trigonometric, and exponential forms; it also may occur in many algebraic forms.

Third-degree and fourth-degree polynomial equations, like quadratic equations, have radical solutions. These radical solutions are often very involved and might better be obtained in decimal form by approximate methods. There is no general radical solution available for equations of fifth degree and higher.

In this chapter we will introduce methods of identifying roots, isolating roots, and approximating roots.

IDENTIFICATION AND APPROXIMATION OF ROOTS 8

8-1   Introduction

In discussions involving approximate solutions it is convenient to use the term *function*. We have already gained sufficient background to enable us to define a function. We recall from previous chapters that, for equations such as

$$y = x - 5, \tag{1}$$

$$y = \tfrac{1}{2}x^2 + x - 6, \tag{2}$$

the assignment of a numerical value to x imposes a unique value upon y. In each case we arrive at an (x, y) pair which satisfies the equation in question. In each (1) and (2) we may state that y is the value of a function of x; we may call the right-hand member of (1) the *f*-function of x and of (2) the *g*-function of x, giving us new symbols:

$$y = f(x) = x - 5,$$
$$y = g(x) = \tfrac{1}{2}x^2 + x - 6.$$

The symbols $f(x)$ and $g(x)$ simply mean *f*-function of x and *g*-function of x and do not imply multiplication. Going back to the (x, y) pairs, we may define a *function* as *a set of ordered pairs of numbers (x, y) such that to each value of the first variable (x) there corresponds a unique value of the second variable (y).*

The composite of all (x, y) pairs which satisfy (1) can be shown as a straight

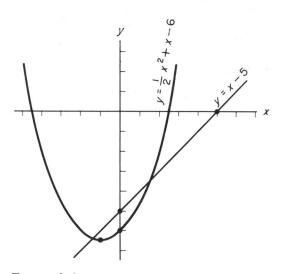

FIGURE 8–1

line on a graph, while the composite of (x, y) pairs which satisfy (2) can be shown as a parabola, as in Fig. 8-1. We note a particular property of the two functions. First, we observe that for *all* real values of x there is a real value for y. Second, as a consequence the graphs in Fig. 8-1 are smooth and *continuous*. We will describe a continuous function here in terms of the graphical representation of that function: *if the graph of a function possesses no unusual "leaps" or "breaks," the function represented by that graph is continuous.* Figure 8-2 pictures some graphs which contain the "leaps" or "breaks" cited and gives the accompanying equations. Note in Fig. 8-2(a)

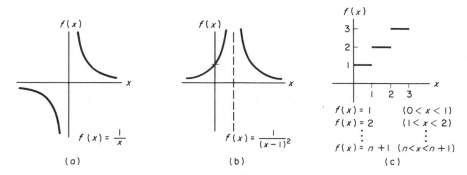

FIGURE 8–2

that $f(x)$ is infinitely large for $x = 0$; in Fig. 8-2(b) $f(x)$ is infinitely large for $x = 1$. In each case, $f(x)$ "leaps" to "infinity" for certain values of x. In Fig. 8-2(c), $f(x)$ does not exist when x is exactly an integer and the graph "leaps" in steps.

8-2   Polynomial Equations—Integral Roots—Synthetic Division

We will now turn our attention to the special function

$$f(x) = x^n + a_1 x^{n-1} + a_2 x^{n-2} + \cdots + a_n. \tag{3}$$

We will impose certain conditions upon (3); first, n is a positive integer and $a_1, a_2, a_3, \cdots, a_n$ are constants. If we set the right side of (3) equal to zero, then

$$x^n + a_1 x^{n-1} + a_2 x^{n-2} + \cdots + a_n = 0, \tag{4}$$

where (4) is *an integral rational equation of the nth degree in x* and $f(x)$ from (3) is called *a polynomial of the nth degree in x.* We assert here that (3) is continuous for all x.

Let us discuss a certain simple integral rational equation with a view to obtaining its roots. Given

$$y = f(x) = x^2 - 2x - 3, \tag{5}$$

we have an integral rational equation of degree 2 in x. Let us find the roots of (5); we recall that the roots may be defined as the x-intercepts and that y has the value zero at the x-intercept. Therefore, if we wish the roots of (5), we let $y = 0$ and we have

$$x^2 - 2x - 3 = 0, \tag{6}$$

which is now a polynomial of second degree in x.

Recalling the factoring method of solving (6), we have

$$x^2 - 2x - 3 = (x - 3)(x + 1) = 0.$$

Now, since the product of $(x - 3)$ and $(x + 1)$ is zero, then either

$$x - 3 = 0 \quad \text{or} \quad x + 1 = 0$$

and we have the roots $x = 3$, $x = -1$.

Observe that the root $x = 3$ is obtained from the factor $x - 3$; similarly, $x = -1$ is obtained from the factor $x + 1$. Likewise, a root $x = r$ would be obtained from the factor $x - r$. Note also from the original polynomial $x^2 - 2x - 3$ that the roots 3 and -1 are factors of the constant term -3.

In the general case of a quadratic, if we have the roots $x = r_1$ and $x = r_2$, then $x - r_1$ and $x - r_2$ are factors of the original quadratic, and the original quadratic is

$$(x - r_1)(x - r_2) = x^2 - (r_1 + r_2)x + r_1 r_2,$$

where it is again noted that the roots r_1 and r_2 are factors of the constant $r_1 r_2$.

This is broadened to include the cubic, quartic, and the general equation (4), such that we may say that if (4) has integral roots, these roots are factors of a_n.

EXAMPLE 1. Determine by inspection whether

$$y = x^3 - 2x^2 + 2x - 4 \tag{7}$$

has any integral roots.

Solution. In view of the preceding material, we recall first that a number is a root of (7) if it satisfies the equation

$$x^3 - 2x^2 + 2x - 4 = 0. \tag{8}$$

Second, if (8) has an *integral* root, that root is a factor of the constant term -4. This limits our choice to $x = \pm 4, \pm 2, \pm 1$. Substituting these six values of x into (7), we have

$$
\begin{array}{c|c|c|c|c|c|c}
x & +4 & -4 & +2 & -2 & +1 & -1 \\
\hline
y & \neq 0 & \neq 0 & 0 & \neq 0 & \neq 0 & \neq 0
\end{array},
$$

where our interest is that of determining the exact value of y only if $y = 0$. If $y \neq 0$, we have no concern about its exact value.

Our conclusion here is that $x = 2$ is a root of (7) because $y = 0$ when $x = 2$.

Reverting again to (4), the nth-degree polynomial has n roots r_1, r_2, $r_3, \cdots, r_n$. This asserts that it has n factors, such that (4) can be written

$$
x^n + a_1 x^{n-1} + a_2 x^{n-2} + \cdots + a_n
$$
$$
= (x - r_1)(x - r_2)\cdots(x - r_n) = 0. \qquad (9)
$$

Now in (9) the right member is the product of n factors, and we assert that if we divide both members of (9) by any one of those n factors (say, $x - r_1$), we have the new polynomial

$$
x^{n-1} + b_1 x^{n-2} + b_2 x^{n-3} + \cdots + b_{n-1}
$$
$$
= (x - r_2)(x - r_3)\cdots(x - r_n) = 0, \qquad (10)
$$

where the left member of (10) equated to zero is called a *depressed equation* since it is the equation (4) with one factor removed. Note that removal of the linear factor $x - r_1$ reduces the degree of (4) by unity. This suggests a ready method of solving certain third-degree equations. Observe Example 2.

EXAMPLE 2. Inspect the equation

$$
y = x^3 + 6x^2 + 7x - 2 \qquad (11)
$$

for integral roots. If an integral root in found, depress the equation to a quadratic and then solve the quadratic, thus obtaining all of the roots of (11).

Solution. From (11), if $y = 0$ then

$$
x^3 + 6x^2 + 7x - 2 = 0. \qquad (12)
$$

Now the only integral roots of (12) are factors of -2, suggesting $x = \pm 1$, $x = \pm 2$. Trying all of these, we have

$$
\begin{array}{c|c|c|c|c}
x & 1 & -1 & 2 & -2 \\
\hline
y & \neq 0 & \neq 0 & \neq 0 & 0
\end{array}.
$$

Now we have ascertained that $x = -2$ is a root of (12) and $x + 2$ is a factor of $x^3 + 6x^2 + 7x - 2$. Dividing the third-degree expression by $x + 2$, we have

$$
\begin{array}{r}
x^2 + 4x \ - \ 1 \\
x + 2 \overline{\smash{\big)}\ x^3 + 6x^2 + 7x - 2} \\
\underline{x^3 + 2x^2\phantom{{}+ 7x - 2}} \\
4x^2 + 7x\phantom{{}- 2} \\
\underline{4x^2 + 8x\phantom{{}- 2}} \\
-x - 2 \\
\underline{-x - 2}
\end{array}
$$

where the quotient $x^2 + 4x - 1$ is the other factor of the third-degree expression. Thus,

$$ x^3 + 6x^2 + 7x - 2 = (x + 2)(x^2 + 4x - 1) = 0. \tag{13} $$

Now each factor of (13) may be zero so that

$$ x^2 + 4x - 1 = 0, $$

from which

$$ x = -2 \pm \sqrt{5}, $$

and the three roots of (11) are

$$ x = -2, $$
$$ x = -2 + \sqrt{5} = 0.236, $$
$$ x = -2 - \sqrt{5} = -4.236. $$

By successively depressing a polynomial equation, all of the integral roots may be determined. If the equation can be depressed to a quadratic, the last two roots may be readily obtained through the quadratic formula regardless of the character of those roots, i.e., whether the remaining roots are real or imaginary, equal or unequal, rational or irrational.

Synthetic Division

A speedy and convenient means of dividing a polynomial by a binomial is a process called *synthetic division*. As an introduction to the process, we observe that

$$ \frac{P(x)}{x - r} = q(x) + \frac{R}{x - r} $$

or

$$P(x) = (x - r)q(x) + R$$

where these equations assert that division of a polynomial $P(x)$ by a binomial $x - r$ results in a quotient $q(r)$ and a remainder R. With R independent of x, $q(x)$ will be a depressed polynomial of degree one less than that of $P(x)$. Note from the latter equation above that $P(x) = R$ when $x = r$, meaning that the remainder is the value of the function $P(r)$.

We will show here how synthetic division is derived from the long division process outlined in Section 2-7. A model of that process is given here:

$$
\begin{array}{r}
3x^3 + 10x^2 + 20x + 5 \\
1x - 2 \overline{\smash{\big)}\ 3x^4 + 4x^3 + 0x^2 - 35x - 7} \\
\end{array}
$$

$3x^4 - 6x^3$	(3)
$10x^3 + 0x^2$	(0)
$10x^3 - 20x^2$	(10)
$20x^2 - 35x$	(−35)
$20x^2 - 40x$	(20)
$5x - 7$	(−7)
$5x - 10$	(5)
3	

This demonstrates division of the polynomial $P(x) = 3x^4 + 4x^3 - 35x - 7$ by the binomial $x - 2$ to obtain the quotient $q(x) = 3x^3 + 10x^2 + 20x + 5$ and remainder $R = 3$.

Let us now make three changes in the division display above. First, omit all of the powers of x. Second, avoid the duplication of showing the "brought down" numbers 0, −35, and −7 shown in parentheses at the right. Third, avoid duplicating the sub-product numbers 3, 10, 20, and 5. Now compress into three lines the numbers which remain and we have the new array

$$
\begin{array}{r|rrrrr}
1 - 2 & 3 & 4 & 0 & -35 & -7 \\
& & -6 & -20 & -40 & -10 \\
\hline
& & 10 & 20 & 5 & 3 \\
\end{array}
$$

Let us now drop the coefficient 1 from the divisor (it is always 1 due to our condition of dividing by $1x - r$) and, for convenience, duplicate the 3 of the first line onto the third line.

$$
\begin{array}{r|rrrrr}
-2 & 3 & 4 & 0 & -35 & -7 \\
& & -6 & -20 & -40 & -10 \\
\hline
& 3 & 10 & 20 & 5 & 3 \\
\end{array}
$$

From the above array we observe that we may *multiply* any number on the third line by −2 of the divisor to obtain the next number of the second line. Also, we obtain any number in the third line by *subtracting* the second line number from the first line number in the column above it. Since *multiplication by* -2 and *subtraction* is the equivalent of *multiplication by* $+2$ and *addition*, we may make final modifications in the array, providing the model for *synthetic division*:

$$\underline{2\,|}\ \begin{array}{rrrrr} 3 & 4 & 0 & -35 & -7 \\ & 6 & 20 & 40 & 10 \\ \hline 3 & 10 & 20 & 5 & 3 \end{array}$$

Note the components of the last array when compared to important portions of the original problem. The dividend $P(x)$ is expressed without powers of x; however, those powers of x assisted in ordering the sequence of the coefficients. The quotient $q(x)$ appears in the last line, as does the remainder $R = 3$. Observe that all columns are added and that all second-row entries are obtained by multiplying the previous third-row entry by the divisor. Let us try two examples.

EXAMPLE 2.1. Using synthetic division, divide

$$(x^3 + 6x^2 + 7x - 2) \div (x + 2).$$

Solution. Using the simplified array suggested, duplicate the coefficients of the dividend and show the divisor as -2.

$$\underline{-2\,|}\ \begin{array}{rrrr} 1 & 6 & 7 & -2 \end{array}$$

$$\begin{array}{c} \hline 1 \end{array}$$

Draw a line under what will become the second line and "bring down" the lead coefficient 1 as the first coefficient on the third line. Now multiply the third-line coefficient 1 by the divisor -2 and place the product -2 under the first line coefficient 6.

$$\underline{-2\,|}\ \begin{array}{rrrr} 1 & 6 & 7 & -2 \\ & -2 & & \\ \hline 1 & 4 & & \end{array}$$

Add the 6 and -2 to obtain the second coefficient, 4, in the third line. Multiply 4 by the divisor -2 and place the product -8 under the first line coefficient 7 and add to obtain the third line coefficient -1.

$$\underline{-2\,|}\ \begin{array}{rrrr} 1 & 6 & 7 & -2 \\ & -2 & -8 & \\ \hline 1 & 4 & -1 & \end{array}$$

Multiply -1 by -2 and place the product 2 under the first line coefficient -2 and add to obtain 0.

$$
\begin{array}{r|rrrr}
-2 & 1 & 6 & 7 & -2 \\
   &   & -2 & -8 & 2 \\
\hline
   & 1 & 4 & -1 & 0
\end{array}
$$

This finishes the synthetic division process and leaves only an interpretation of the results. We observe that the quotient is $q(x) = x^2 + 4x - 1$ and the remainder is $R = 0$; all of this information is obtained from the third line.

EXAMPLE 2.3. Is $x = 5$ a root of $x^3 + 2x^2 - 23x + 60 = 0$?

Solution. If $x = 5$ is a root, then $x - 5$ is an exact divisor of the cubic, meaning that the remainder will be $R = 0$. Applying synthetic division, we have

$$
\begin{array}{r|rrrr}
5 & 1 & 2 & -23 & 60 \\
  &   & 5 & 35 & 60 \\
\hline
  & 1 & 7 & 12 & 120
\end{array}
$$

From this operation, the quotient is $q(x) = x^2 + 7x + 12$ and the remainder is $R = 120$, showing that $x = 5$ is not a root of the cubic.

Exercises

In Exercises 1–10 divide the polynomial by the binomial. Express both the quotient and the remainder. Use synthetic division.

1. $x^2 - 2x - 3$ by $x + 1$.   *Ans.* $q(x) = x - 3$, $R = 0$.

2. $x^2 + 4x - 5$ by $x - 1$.

3. $3x^3 + 8x^2 + 3x - 1$ by $x + 2$.   *Ans.* $q(x) = 3x^2 + 2x - 1$, $R = 1$.

4. $2x^3 - 5x^2 + 7x - 4$ by $x + 3$.

5. $63m + 4m^3 - 6$ by $m - 4$.   *Ans.* $q(m) = 4m^2 + 16m + 127$, $R = 502$.

6. $5p + 9 - p^3$ by $p + 6$.

7. $k^4 - 1$ by $k + 2$.   *Ans.* $q(k) = k^3 - 2k^2 + 4k - 8$, $R = 15$.

8. $y^4 + 8$ by $y - 1$.

9. $-6x^3 + 2x^2 - 3x^3 + 4x^4 - 5$ by $x + 1$.
             Ans. $q(x) = 4x^3 - 13x^2 + 15x - 15$, $R = +10$.

10. $9y^4 - 6 + 5y^2 - 3y$ by $y - 1$.

11. Show that $x = -3$ is a root of $x^3 + 5x^2 + 8x + 6 = 0$.

12. Is $x - 1$ a factor of $x^5 - 2x + 1$?

13. Given $P(x) = 4x^3 + x - 110$. Show that $R > 0$ for $P(3)$ and $R < 0$ for $P(2)$.

14. Given $P(x) = x^3 + ax^2 - 3x + 4$. For what value of a is $P(x)$ exactly divisible by $x - 1$?

15. By synthetic division find the value of $P(x) = 3x^4 + 4x^3 + x - 18$ for $x = -1$. Compare this remainder to $P(-1)$.

In Exercises 16–28, identify the integral roots of the given polynomial equations (if they possess integral roots). When an integral root is identified, depress the equation. If the equation is depressible to a quadratic, find all of the roots regardless of their character.

16. $y = x^3 - 2x + 1$.   *Ans.* $x = 1, -\frac{1}{2} \pm \frac{1}{2}\sqrt{5}$.

17. $y = x^3 + 2x + 3$.

18. $y = x^3 - x^2 - 4x - 6$.   *Ans.* $x = 3, -1 \pm j$.

19. $y = x^3 + 5x^2 + 8x + 6$.

20. $y = x^4 - x^3 - 4x^2 - 5x - 3$.   *Ans.* $x = 3, -1, -\frac{1}{2} \pm \frac{1}{2}j\sqrt{3}$.

21. $y = x^4 + 3x^3 - x - 3$.

22. $y = x^3 - 1$.   *Ans.* $x = 1, -\frac{1}{2} \pm \frac{1}{2}j\sqrt{3}$.

23. $y = x^3 + 1$.

24. $y = x^4 - 1$.   *Ans.* $x = 1, -1, j, -j$.

25. $y = x^4 + 1$.

26. $y = x^3 + 3x^2 - 5x + 12$.   *Ans.* No integral roots.

27. $y = x^4 - 3x^2 - 4$.

28. $y = x^3 + 4x^2 - 5x$.   *Ans.* $x = 0, -5, 1$.

29. The rectangular sheet of tin in Fig. 8-3 has equal squares cut from its corners. The resulting sheet is folded along the dotted lines to form a topless box. What three different dimensions can each square have so that the volume of the box is 16 cu. in.?

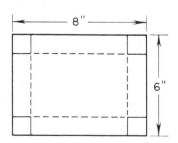

Ans. $2, (5 \pm \sqrt{17})/2$.

30. The length, width, and height of the large rectangular bin shown in Fig. 8-4 are each increased by the same amount. The increases change the volume of the bin by 864 cu. ft. What are the new dimensions of the bin?

FIGURE 8–3

31. The sum of the volume and total

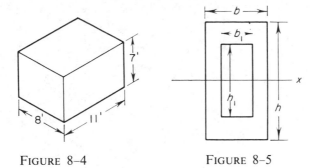

FIGURE 8–4   FIGURE 8–5

surface area of a certain cube is 275. What are the dimensions of the cube?

Ans. 5 × 5 × 5.

32. The dimensions of a box are such that it is one inch taller than it is wide and one inch longer than it is tall. The sum of the volume and surface area is 604. What are the dimensions of the box?

33. The amount of inertia about the x-axis of the thin hollow rectangular plate shown in Fig. 8-5 is given as

$$I_x = \frac{bh^3}{3} - \frac{b_1 h_1 (3h^2 + h_1^2)}{12}.$$

What height h must a designer choose if he wishes to have a moment of inertia $I_x = \frac{400}{3}$ with $b_1 = 2$, $b = 3$, and $h_1 = 4$?   *Ans.* $h = 6$.

**8-3   Isolation of Roots Between Consecutive
         Integers**

In the preceding section we discussed integral roots of a polynomial equation. Special care was used to avoid examples and exercises where a polynomial equation had no integral roots. We will extend our discussion now to include the case of polynomial equations with no integral roots and will eventually extend it to include equations (whether polynomial or not) that possess no integral roots and that may have discontinuities, but discontinuities that are not sufficiently close to a root to disturb the methods of solution that we will discuss.

A completely continuous function $y = f(x)$ may have a root $x = r$ where r is irrational and none of its other roots are rational. Let us assume that the root r is between two consecutive integral values of x, such that $k < r < k + 1$. Referring to Fig. 8-6, we see three graphs of different continuous

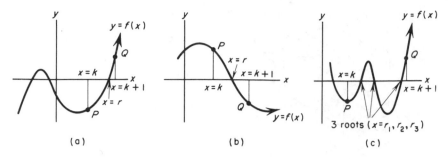

FIGURE 8–6

functions $y = f(x)$. In each case a root at $x = r$ is shown and in each case $k < r < k + 1$ where k is an integer. Note in Fig. 8-6(a) that when $x = k$, $y < 0$; when $x = r$, $y = 0$; and when $x = k + 1$, $y > 0$. Note in Fig. 8-6(b) that when $x = k$, $y > 0$; when $x = r$, $y = 0$; and when $x = k + 1$, $y < 0$. What is suggested here is the following fact: *if a function $y = f(x)$ is continuous in the interval from $x = k$ to $x = k + 1$ and sign of y is different at $x = k$ from the sign of y at $x = k + 1$, then at least one root of $y = f(x)$ exists between $x = k$ and $x = k + 1$.* When there is a sign change we say that we have *isolated* a root between $x = k$ and $x = k + 1$.

The reason for the assertion in the preceding statement that *at least one root* exists between $x = k$ and $x = k + 1$ is pictured in Fig. 8-6(c). There may be *more than one* root. Inspection will bear out the assertion that the number of roots will be an *odd* number.

In Fig. 8-7 we observe that the signs of y at $x = k$ and $x = k + 1$ are

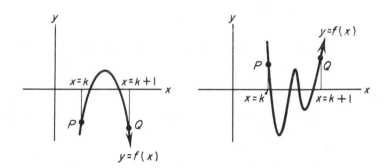

FIGURE 8–7

unchanged. The *lack* of a sign change does not prove that there is no root between $x = k$ and $x = k + 1$ because there may be an even number of roots in the interval.

Let us put the preceding observation to use with an example problem.

EXAMPLE 3. The equation

$$y = x^3 - 3x^2 - 19x - 15 \qquad (14)$$

possesses one positive root. Isolate the root between consecutive integers.

Solution. Let us commence with arbitrarily chosen integral values of x and determine the sign of y. We emphasize that the magnitude of y is not important; only the *sign* is important. We observe that y is negative for $0 < x < 6$,

x	0	1	2	3	4	5	6	7
y	−	−	−	−	−	−	−	+

but y is positive for $x = 7$. This asserts that there is at least one root where $6 < r < 7$. The graph of the important portion of (14) is shown in Fig. 8-8. The actual numerical value of the root in question is $x = 2 + \sqrt{19}$ or $x = 6.359$.

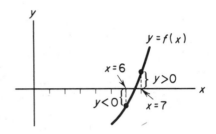

FIGURE 8-8

8-4   Approximation of Roots

In Sec. 8-3 we discussed a method of isolating a root between consecutive integers. It may be desirable to describe the root more accurately, perhaps correct to the nearest tenth or hundredth or thousandth. We can broaden the method in Sec. 8-3 to embrace further refinement; in that section we stated that for $y = f(x)$, if $f(k)$ and $f(k + 1)$ differ in sign, then there is a root $x = r$ such that $k < r < k + 1$. We restricted k to integral values, and the x-interval was one unit wide with k on the left edge of the interval and $k + 1$ on the right edge.

Actually, we need not be so restrictive about the edges of the interval. We may say that *a continuous function $y = f(x)$ has a root $x = r$ in the interval $a < x < b$ if the signs of $f(a)$ and $f(b)$ are different.* In Fig. 8-9 we show the interval $a < x < b$ where $f(a) < 0$ and $f(b) > 0$. It is important to note that

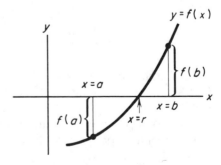

FIGURE 8-9

a and *b* need not be integers; the quantity *b* − *a* may be small or large. If we wish to obtain *r* correct to hundredths or thousandths, it is important that *b* − *a* be a small quantity, perhaps in the order of tenths or hundredths.

A method of refining the estimate of the value of a root is suggested here. This method presumes that there is only one root in the interval *a* < *x* < *b*; it also presumes continuity in the interval. We shall call this the *method of linear interpolation* and shall discuss it with reference to Fig. 8-10. Presume

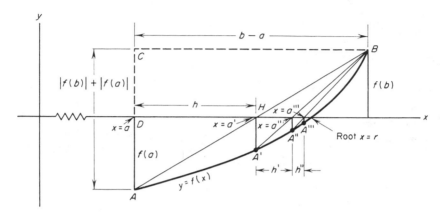

FIGURE 8–10

that we have isolated the root between *x* = *a* and *x* = *b* such that *f*(*a*) and *f*(*b*) are of opposite sign. The curve *y* = *f*(*x*) is shown as a curved line. Draw the chord *AB* which will intersect the *x*-axis between *a* and *b* at *H*. Ignoring signs, we have △*ADH* similar to △*ACB*, from which

$$\frac{DH}{DA} = \frac{CB}{AC} \text{ or } \frac{h}{|f(a)|} = \frac{|b-a|}{|f(b)|+|f(a)|},$$

from which

$$h = \frac{|b-a||f(a)|}{|f(b)|+|f(a)|}, \tag{15}$$

where *h* is an *adjustment* away from *a* toward *b*. Absolute values are used in (15) because of possibilities of modifications of the signs of *a*, *b*, *f*(*a*), and *f*(*b*).

Expression (15) may be used repeatedly to refine the estimate of the root. After one application of (15) the root is *a'*, where

$$a' = a + h.$$

For the next refinement we consider the interval from a' to b where (15) remains unchanged except that we are obtaining a second adjustment h', using a' as a reference so that (15) is

$$h' = \frac{|b - a'|\,|f(a')|}{|f(b)| + |f(a')|} \tag{15a}$$

and the second estimate of the root is

$$a'' = a' + h' = a + h + h'.$$

Let us use the method of linear interpolation in an example problem.

EXAMPLE 4. Use the method of linear interpolation to determine the positive root of

$$y = x^3 - 4x^2 - 12x - 6 = f(x) \tag{16}$$

correct to thousandths.

Solution. First, we isolate the root of (16) between consecutive integers by substituting consecutive integral values of x into (16) and looking for a change in the sign of y.

$$\frac{x}{y}\;\begin{array}{|c|c|c|c|c|c|c|c|}0 & 1 & 2 & 3 & 4 & 5 & 6 & 7 \\ \hline - & - & - & - & - & - & -6 & +57\end{array}. \tag{17}$$

We note that a root exists such that $+6 < r < +7$ because $f(6) < 0$ and $f(7) > 0$.

Next, we observe from Fig. 8-11 (drawn out of scale) that the root possibly favors the left side of the interval bounded on the left by $x = 6$ and on the right by $x = 7$. We have not yet assigned the a and b of equation (15). Let us first narrow the interval by estimating a value $x = b$ with $6 < b < 7$ such that $f(b) > 0$ but $f(b)$ is nearer zero than $+57$. It seems logical to try

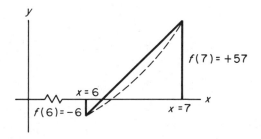

FIGURE 8-11

$b = 6.2$ so that

$$f(b) = f(6.2) = (6.2)^3 - 4(6.2)^2 - 12(6.2) - 6 = +4.168. \qquad (18)$$

Now we make our assignments appropriate to (15), letting $a = +6$, with $f(a) = f(6) = -6$ from (17), letting $b = 6.2$ with $f(b) = f(6.2) = +4.168$ from (18). Substituting these facts into (15),

$$h = \frac{|6.2 - 6||-6|}{|4.168| + |-6|} = \frac{(0.2)(6)}{10.168} = 0.12.$$

Refer to Fig. 8-12 for a graph involving a, b, $f(a)$, $f(b)$, and h.

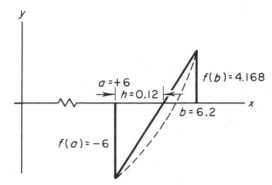

FIGURE 8–12

Now the new estimate of the root is

$$a' = a + h = 6 + 0.12 = 6.12.$$

To find the second estimate we apply (15a) with $b = 6.2$, $f(b) = +4.168$, $a' = 6.12$, and

$$f(a') = f(6.12) = (6.12)^3 - 4(6.12)^2 - 12(6.12) - 6 = -0.036672,$$

so now

$$h' = \frac{|6.2 - 6.12||-0.036672|}{|4.168| + |-0.036672|} = \frac{(0.08)(0.036672)}{4.204672}$$

$$= \frac{0.00293376}{4.204672} = 0.0007.$$

Our new estimate of the root is

$$a'' = a' + h' = 6.12 + 0.0007 = 6.1207.$$

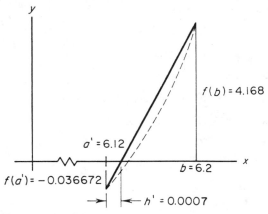

FIGURE 8–13

and we conclude that the desired root of (16), correct to thousandths, is 6.121. Refer to Fig. 8-13 for a graph involving $a', f(a'), b, f(b),$ and h'.

The method of linear interpolation need not converge on a root as rapidly as was shown in Example 4. It will always converge on the root as long as the function is continuous for $a < x < b$ and $f(a), f(a'), f(a''),$ etc. are different in sign from $f(b)$, but will converge rather slowly if the curve nearly parallels the x-axis near a or b. See Fig. 8-14.

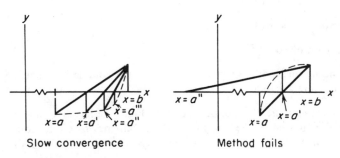

Slow convergence   Method fails

FIGURE 8–14

Exercises

In Exercises 1–15, isolate the indicated root using procedures given in the previous section. After isolation, refine the approximation of the root correct to thousandths.

1. $y = x^3 - 4x^2 - 3x - 29$, the real root.   *Ans.* 5.503.

2. $y = x^3 - 4x^2 - 3x - 28$, the real root.

3. $y = x^3 - 4x^2 - 3x - 7$, the real root.   *Ans.* 4.903.

4. $y = x^3 - 4x^2 - 3x - 6$, the real root.

5. $y = x^3 - 4x^2 - 3x + 1$, the negative root.   *Ans.* −0.858.

6. $y = x^3 - 4x^2 - 3x + 3$, the negative root.

7. $y = x^3 - 4x^2 - 3x + 10$, the smaller positive root.   *Ans.* 1.485.

8. $y = x^3 - 4x^2 - 3x + 11$, the larger positive root.

9. $y = x^3 - 4x^2 - 3x + 20$, the real root.   *Ans.* −2.078.

10. $y = x^3 - 4x^2 - 3x + 22$, the real root.

11. $y = 3x^4 + x - 66$, the positive root.   *Ans.* 2.148.

12. $y = 4x^3 + x - 112$, the real root.

13. $x^2y = x^3 - 45$, the positive root.   *Ans.* $x = 3.557$.

14. $x^2y = x^3 - 73$, the positive root.

15. $y = x^5 - 100x^3 + 42{,}200$, the negative root.   *Ans.* −11.350.

In Exercises 16–20 find the root indicated using the method of linear interpolation.

16. Cube root of 12.

17. Cube root of 23.   *Ans.* 2.844.

18. Two fourth roots of 36.

19. Two fourth roots of 50.   *Ans.* ±2.659.

20. Fifth root of 100.

21. By adding one foot to each side of a cube, the volume of the cube is doubled. How long were the sides of the original cube?   *Ans.* Approx. 3.846 ft.

22. The right cylindrical container shown in Fig. 8-15 has a volume of 25 gallons where one gallon equals 231 cu. in. Find the dimensions of the container to the nearest tenth of an inch if the height exceeds the radius by 3 inches.
         Ans. $r = 11.3$ in.; $h = 14.3$ in.

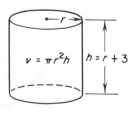

FIGURE 8–15

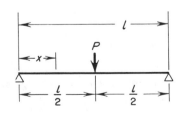

FIGURE 8–16

23. The deflection at P, σ_x, of a simple beam with a concentrated load at the center is given by the equation

$$\sigma_x = \frac{Px}{48EI}(3l^2 - 4x^2),$$

where the situation described is pictured in Fig. 8-16. Find l if $l = 2x$, $P = 4000$ lb., $E = 3 \times 10^7$, $I = 10.2$, and $\sigma_x = 0.02$.   *Ans.* $l = 42.02$ in.

24. In Fig. 8-17 a simple beam is loaded with a load that increases uniformly from one end to the other. The deflection, σ_x, at some distance x from the end A, is given by

$$\sigma_x = \frac{Wx}{180EI\,l^2}(3x^4 - 10l^2x^2 + 7l^4).$$

Find x if $W = 5000$ lb., $E = 3 \times 10^7$, $I = 11.2$, $\sigma_x = 0.03$, and $l = 100$.
           Ans. $x = 32.1$ approx.

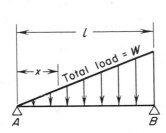

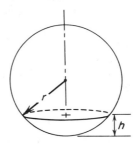

FIGURE 8–17   FIGURE 8–18

25. The value V of a certain quantity is given by the expression

$$V = 1 + x + \frac{x^2}{2!} + \frac{x^3}{3!} + \frac{x^4}{4!} + \cdots + \frac{x^n}{n!} + \cdots,$$

where $n!$ is the product of all integers from 1 through n. Using the first seven terms of the expansion on the right, find an approximate value for x if $V = 0.15$.
           Ans. $x = -1.9$ approx.

26. The volume of a spherical segment shown in Fig. 8-18 is given as

$$V = \pi h^2 \left(r - \frac{h}{3}\right),$$

where r is the radius of the sphere and h is the thickness of the segment. A sphere of radius 10 feet contains 390 gallons of water (231 cu. in. $= 1$ gal.). What is the greatest depth of the water, correct to hundredths?   *Ans.* $h = 1.32$ ft.

8-5   Imaginary and Multiple Roots

In Chap. 5 we introduced the simultaneous solutions of linear equations; there we showed that a simultaneous solution of two straight lines can be interpreted as the point where the two lines intersect. In determining an x-intercept (or root) of a linear equation, we can interpret this as the simultaneous solution of the given line and the x-axis; in other words, the root of $ax + by = c$ can be interpreted as the solution of the system

$$ax + by = c, \qquad y = 0,$$

where $y = 0$ is the equation of the x-axis.

This same interpretation can be made regarding the roots of a quadratic; we may find the roots (x-intercepts) of a quadratic by solving the system

$$y = ax^2 + bx + c, \qquad y = 0.$$

An important point arises here; perhaps, for the given quadratic, y cannot be zero. Yet we are, in attempting the simultaneous solution, imposing the condition that y is zero! We must, therefore, obtain no real solutions. In this case we will obtain imaginary roots.

A theorem from the theory of equations asserts that two equations of degree m and n will have $m \cdot n$ solutions. Thus, if $y = f(x)$ is of degree n and is solved simultaneously with the first-degree equation $y = 0$, there will be $n \cdot 1 = n$ solutions. We attempt to interpret all n of these solutions as being points of intersection of $y = f(x)$ with the x-axis (or x-intercepts) but the curve need not cross the x-axis n times. Consider the three equations

$$y = x^3 - 3x^2 - x + 3, \tag{19}$$

$$y = x^3 - 3x^2 + 4, \tag{20}$$

$$y = x^3 - 3x^2 + x + 5, \tag{21}$$

which graph as shown in Fig. 8-19. In Fig. 8-19 we see the intersections of (19), (20), and (21) with the x-axis. In Fig. 8-19(a) observe that (19) intersects the x-axis in three distinct points; therefore, we say that (19) has three real, distinct roots. In Fig. 8-19(b) observe that (20) intersects the x-axis at $x = -1$ and is tangent to the x-axis at $x = 2$; we say that (20) has three real roots with a root of multiplicity two at $x = 2$. In Fig. 8-19(c) we see that (21) intersects the x-axis only once; therefore, (21) has one real root and two imaginary roots; any effort to locate these imaginary roots on the x-axis would be in vain because they do not exist.

The roots of (21) are shown by factoring as

$$x^3 - 3x^2 + x + 5 = (x + 1)(x^2 - 4x + 5) = 0,$$

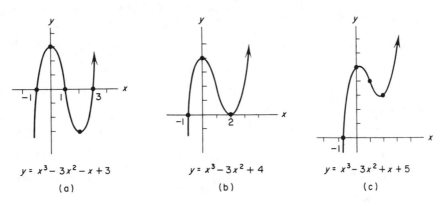

$y = x^3 - 3x^2 - x + 3$

(a)

$y = x^3 - 3x^2 + 4$

(b)

$y = x^3 - 3x^2 + x + 5$

(c)

FIGURE 8–19

from which $x = -1$ and $x = 2 \pm j$, where the roots $x = 2 + j$ and $x = 2 - j$ are called *complex conjugates*. General complex conjugates are of the form $a + jb$ and $a - jb$. A theorem from the theory of equations asserts that imaginary roots occur in complex conjugate pairs.

The general shape of a quartic (fourth-degree polynomial equation) is shown in Fig. 8-20. Various positions of the quartic display some combinations of imaginary and real roots. Not listed is the possibility of four roots at one point; this is a distorted quartic whose shape is like a parabola.

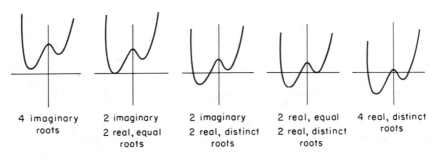

| 4 imaginary roots | 2 imaginary 2 real, equal roots | 2 imaginary 2 real, distinct roots | 2 real, equal 2 real, distinct roots | 4 real, distinct roots |

FIGURE 8–20

Exercises

Describe the nature of the roots of the given equations in Exercises 1–21. Graph the equation in each case.

1. $y = x^2$. *Ans.* Two real, equal.

2. $y = x^2 - 4$.

3. $y = x^2 + 4$. *Ans.* Two imaginary.

4. $y = x^3$.

5. $y = x^3 - 8$. *Ans.* One real, two imaginary.

6. $y = x^3 + 8$.

7. $y = x^4 - 16$. *Ans.* Two real, two imaginary.

8. $y = x^4 + 16$.

9. $y = x^3 + 2x - 3$. *Ans.* One real, two imaginary.

10. $y = x^3 - 4x^2 - 3x + 18$.

11. $y = (x - 1)^3$. *Ans.* Three real, equal.

12. $y = x^2 + 3x - 7$.

13. $y = 5x^2 - 24x + 17$. *Ans.* Two real.

14. $y = 3x^2 + 10$.

15. $y = x^3 + x^2 - 8x + 6$. *Ans.* Three real.

16. $y = x^2 + 25x - 25$.

17. $y = x + \dfrac{1}{x} - 1$. *Ans.* Two imaginary.

18. $y = x + \dfrac{1}{x} - 3$.

19. $y = x + \dfrac{1}{x} - 2$. *Ans.* Two real, equal.

20. $y = x^2 + 6x + 10$.

21. $y = x^2 + 6x + 8$. *Ans.* Two real.

Give the polynomial equation of the form $Z = f(s)$ which has the roots given in Exercises 22–28.

22. $s = 2, -2$. *Ans.* $Z = s^2 - 4$.

23. $s = 2, -2 \pm j$.

24. $s = 0, 0, 0, 0$. *Ans.* $Z = s^4$.

25. $s = \pm 3j$.

26. $s = 6, 3, \pm j$. *Ans.* $Z = s^4 - 9s^3 + 19s^2 - 9s + 18$.

27. $s = \pm 2, 3$.

28. $s = 1 \pm j, 2 \pm 3j$. *Ans.* $Z = s^4 - 6s^3 + 23s^2 - 34s + 26$.

In preceding sections, discussions were limited to algebraic expressions and groups of equations which might be classified as algebraic equations. Our ultimate goal is that of discussing the elementary functions, which include algebraic, exponential, logarithmic, and trigonometric functions. In this chapter we will discuss the second and third of these functions, namely the exponential and logarithmic functions. Exponentials are involved in investment, bacterial growth, radioactivity, sound, and many other areas. They are intimately related to logarithms through a simple device which is used to convert an expression from the exponential form to the logarithm form.

EXPONENTIALS
AND LOGARITHMS   9

9-1 Definitions—How Exponential Expressions Arise

Frequently the question is asked, "Which would you rather have, a million dollars or the amount obtained by starting on the first of the month with one cent and doubling your holdings each day for the entire month?" The answer lies in the amount obtained in the doubling operation; call the amount at any time A. If we double at the end of each day,

$$A_1 = 2 = (2)^1 \text{ at the end of the first day,}$$
$$A_2 = 4 = (2)^2 \text{ at the end of the second day,}$$
$$A_3 = 8 = (2)^3 \text{ at the end of the third day.}$$

We observe that the power of 2 is the same as the number of the day; therefore,

$$A_x = (2)^x \text{ at the end of the xth day.}$$

Thus, dropping the subscript, we have the equation

$$A = (2)^x, \tag{1}$$

where A is the amount at the end of a given day and the exponent x is the day number. Expression (1) is called an *exponential equation*. In answer to our original problem, if the month is considered to have 30 days in it, then $x = 30$ and (1) becomes

$$A = (2)^{30} = 1,073,741,824\cent = \$10,737,418.24. \tag{2}$$

The choice between the offered million and the amount shown in (2) is easy to make.

In (1), A is called the *amount* or *number*, 2 is called the *base*, and x is the *exponent*. A general expression for the *exponential equation* is

$$y = (b)^x, \tag{3}$$

where y is the number, b is the base, and x is the exponent. We note in (3) that x and y are variables and the base is constant. The fact that we have a variable exponent with a constant base is the identifying feature of the *exponential form*. This is in opposition to the *power form* which has a variable base and a constant exponent, such as $y = x^2$.

The base in (1) can be any constant, including both negative and positive choices. If b is positive and other than 1, then the exponent x can take on an alternative name *logarithm;* we will begin study of these in Sec. 9–4.

Another illustration which shows how exponentials arise is the case of compound interest. Let us start with the assumption that $5000 is invested in a financial program which guarantees 6 per cent interest compounded annually. This means that the amount in the account at the end of any year is 1.06 times the amount at the beginning of that year. Thus, the amount A is

$$A = 5000(1.06) \text{ at the end of year 1,}$$
$$A = 5000(1.06)^2 \text{ at the end of year 2,}$$
$$A = 5000(1.06)^3 \text{ at the end of year 3,}$$
$$A = 5000(1.06)^n \text{ at the end of year } n. \tag{4}$$

Thus, the expression in (4) is a modification of (3) with the base a decimal quantity. In general, for compound interest, if a principal P is compounded annually at a yearly interest rate i, then the amount A is given by

$$A = P(1 + i)^n \tag{5}$$

where n is the number of years.

If the interest rate in (5) is considered to be negative, we have *depreciation*. Thus, if the value of machinery is depreciating at 10 per cent per year, this means that the value of the machinery at the end of a given year is 90 per cent of its value at the beginning of that year and (5) becomes

$$A = P(1 - i)^n.$$

Formulation involving exponentials is important. Exercises involving formulation and definitions follow.

Exercises

1. Evaluate 3^x for $x = 2, 3, 4$.   *Ans.* 9, 27, 81.

2. Evaluate $(\frac{1}{3})^x$ for $x = 2, 3, 4$.

3. Evaluate 3^{-x} for $x = 1, 2, 3$.   *Ans.* $\frac{1}{3}, \frac{1}{9}, \frac{1}{27}$.

4. Evaluate $(\frac{1}{3})^{-x}$ for $x = 1, 2, 3$.

5. Evaluate $(2^x)^2$ for $x = 3$.   *Ans.* 64.

6. Evaluate 2^{x^2} for $x = 3$.

7. Evaluate 0.5^x for $x = 2, 3, 4$.   *Ans.* .25, .125, .0625.

8. Evaluate $(1 - 0.1)^x$ for $x = 1, 2, 3$.

9. Evaluate $(1 + 0.1)^x$ for $x = 3$.   *Ans.* 1.331.

10. Evaluate 9^x for $x = 1.5, 2.5$.

11. A savings bank offers a compound interest rate of $3\frac{1}{2}$ per cent yearly with the compounding taking place at the end of each year. Give an expression showing the amount to which an initial account of $150 accumulates in 6 years.

Ans. $A = 150(1.035)^6$.

12. A radioactive material decays in such a way that it loses one-half of its radioactive component every 7.8 years. How many years are required for 32 grams to decay to 2 grams? *Ans.* 31.2 years.

13. Assume that the population of a bacteria culture doubles every 50 hours. A culture of 5000 units will be how large at the end of 350 hours?

Ans. 640,000.

14. Assume that the atmospheric pressure at sea level measures 30 inches of mercury. If each increase in altitude of one kilometer is accompanied by a 14 per cent fall in the pressure, what is the predicted pressure at a height of 3 kilometers? *Ans.* 19.08 inches.

15. Show that $a^{-x} = b^x$ where $a = 1/b$. This asserts that reciprocating the base changes the sign of the exponent.

16. Which of the given forms are exponential, as opposed to the power form?

(a) $W = \eta\beta^{1.6}$.

(b) $k = (I/A)^{1/2}$.

(c) $A = 100(1.05)^i$.

(d) $\delta = Wl^3/15EI$.

(e) $i = I(1 - e^{-kt})$.

(f) $y = (3.05)^{-2x}$.

17. A man starts stepping toward a wall which is initially 10 feet away. If his steps are such that each step covers one-half of the distance remaining to the wall, what is the size of his fifth step? What is the equation relating d, the length of a given step, and n, the step number? *Ans.* $\frac{10}{32}$ ft.; $d = 10(\frac{1}{2})^n$.

9-2 Graphs of Exponential Equations

Graphs of exponentials display growth or decay of the dependent variable. From the general exponential form

$$y = ab^x, \tag{6}$$

x is the *independent* variable and y is the *dependent* variable. These are so named because assignment of arbitrarily chosen values of x imposes values upon y. Let us graph an equation of the form of (6) by plotting arbitrarily chosen points.

EXAMPLE 1. Graph the equation

$$y = 10(\tfrac{1}{2})^x. \tag{7}$$

Solution. Let us choose several values of the independent variable x and compute the corresponding values of y, arranging them as follows:

x	-3	-2	-1	0	1	2	3	4	5
y	80	40	20	10	5	$\frac{5}{2}$	$\frac{5}{4}$	$\frac{5}{8}$	$\frac{5}{16}$

Note from the chart that when x increases by unity, the value of y is multiplied by $\frac{1}{2}$; this factor is the base in (7) and is often called the *decrement* or rate of decay for a decreasing exponential like (7). The graph of (7) is shown in Fig. 9-1, where the axes are intentionally drawn out of scale to show the

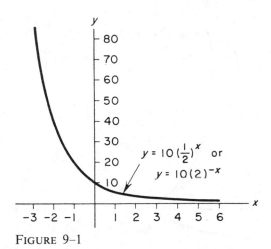

FIGURE 9–1

complete range of values drawn from the chart. Observe that as x increases to large positive values, y becomes very small, suggesting that the curve approaches the x-axis, but will never reach it. This means that the x-axis is a limiting line, or an *asymptote*.

EXAMPLE 2. Graph the equation

$$y = 10(2)^{-x}. \tag{8}$$

Solution. Before attempting to graph (8), let us manipulate the expression.

First, we know that

$$2 = (\tfrac{1}{2})^{-1},$$

therefore,

$$(2)^{-x} = [(\tfrac{1}{2})^{-1}]^{-x} = (\tfrac{1}{2})^{x}$$

by a law of exponents. Now, by substitution, (8) may be rewritten as

$$y = 10(2)^{-x} = 10(\tfrac{1}{2})^{x}.$$

Now (8) and (7) are identical and the graph of (8) is exactly as shown in Fig. 9-1. We have demonstrated here the reciprocation of the base of an exponential form changes the sign of the exponent. Thus, for the exponential (6),

$$y = a(b)^{x} = a\left(\frac{1}{b}\right)^{-x}.$$

Examining (6) for its properties, we see that:

    (*a*) If $0 < b < 1$, *y* decreases as *x* increases and the curve is shaped as (a) in Fig. 9-2.

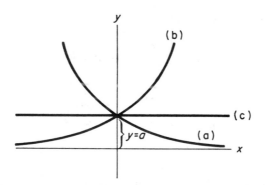

FIGURE 9–2

    (*b*) If $b > 1$, *y* increases as *x* increases and the curve is shaped as (*b*) in Fig. 9-2.

    (*c*) If $b = 1$, $y = a$ for all *x* as in (*c*) in Fig. 9-2.

    (*d*) In all cases, the *y*-intercept is $y = a$.

Consider another graph which is particularly useful in electricity. Refer to Example 3.

EXAMPLE 3. Graph the equation

$$y = k(1 - b^{-x}) \qquad (b > 1).$$ (9)

Solution. Equation (9) can be written in the form

$$y = k - kb^{-x}.$$ (10)

If we graph $y_1 = k$ and $y_2 = kb^{-x}$ as shown by the dotted lines in Fig. 9-3,

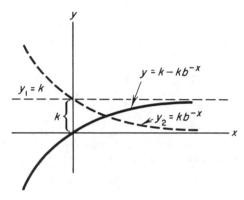

FIGURE 9–3

we see that the desired y in (10) is the difference $y_1 - y_2$. Here y is obtained by subtracting from a fixed $y_1 = k$ an ever-diminishing quantity obtained from $y_2 = kb^{-x}$. Thus, the greater the value of x, the closer the value of y in (10) is to the fixed value $y_1 = k$.

Exponential equations are readily formulated from given data. It is useful (for the sake of simplicity) if the given values of one of the variables are uniformly spaced. Consider an example.

EXAMPLE 4. From the data given in the accompanying chart, formulate an equation whose graph will pass through the given points.

x	-2	-1	0	1	2	3	4
y	81	27	9	3	1	$\frac{1}{3}$	$\frac{1}{9}$

Solution. Upon inspection of the given data, we see that a unit increase in x is accompanied by a decrease in y which is a factor $\frac{1}{3}$. Hence, continual multiples by $\frac{1}{3}$ are appropriate and an exponential with base $\frac{1}{3}$ is suggested.

Also, when $x = 0$, $y = 9$, suggesting a constant factor 9. Combining this information, we have the equation

$$y = 9(\tfrac{1}{3})^x. \qquad (11)$$

Applying values of x drawn from the given chart, we see that each (x, y) pair satisfies (11).

In the more general form, if we are given the (x, y) pairs (x_1, y_1), (x_2, y_2), $(x_3, y_3), \cdots, (x_i, y_i)$, and the x values are uniformly spaced, then

$$\frac{y_2}{y_1} = \frac{y_3}{y_2} = \frac{y_4}{y_3} = \cdots = \frac{y_i}{y_{i-1}} = b,$$

where b is the base in the form

$$y = ab^x.$$

Exercises

In Exercises 1–15 show the graphs of the given equations. When more than one literal quantity is present, the variables are indicated at the right.

1. $y = 2^x$.   **2.** $y = 2^{-x}$.

3. $y = -2^x$.   **4.** $y = -2^{-x}$.

5. $x = 2^y$.   **6.** $x = 2^{-y}$.

7. $x = -2^y$.   **8.** $x = -2^{-y}$.

9. $y = 1 - (3)^{-x}$.   **10.** $y = 4(1 - 2^{-x})$.

11. $p = p_0(0.86)^h$ (p, h).   **12.** $A = P(1.06)^n$ (A, n).

13. $A = P(0.94)^n$ (A, n).   **14.** $i = I(1 - e^{-t})$ $(i, t; e = 2.7)$.

15. $y = \sqrt{64}$.

In Exercises 16–20, develop the equation of an exponential passing through the given (x,y) points.

16.

x	0	1	2	3	4	5
y	4.4	2.2	1.1	0.55	0.275	0.1375

Ans. $y = 4.4(\tfrac{1}{2})^x$.

17.

x	0	$\tfrac{1}{3}$	$\tfrac{2}{3}$	1	$\tfrac{4}{3}$	$\tfrac{5}{3}$
y	4.4	2.2	1.1	0.55	0.275	0.1735

18.

x	0	-2	-4	-6	-8	-10
y	4.4	2.2	1.1	0.55	0.275	0.1375

Ans. $y = 4.4(\tfrac{1}{2})^{-x/2}$.

19.

x	1.5	2.5	3.5	4.5	5.5	6.5
y	4.4	2.2	1.1	0.55	0.275	0.1375

20.

x	-3	-1	1	3	5	7
y	4.4	2.2	1.1	0.55	0.275	0.1375

Ans. $y = 4.4(\frac{1}{2})^{(x+3)/2}$.

21. A financial amount A is such that at the end of each year it is 96 per cent of its amount at the beginning of the same year. Give an expression for A if the initial amount was P and the number of years is n. Give an expression for the amount by which P has been depleted in n years.

22. In compound interest problems, the amount is usually given by the equation

$$A = P(1 + i)^n, \tag{12}$$

where i is the yearly interest rate and n is the number of years. In many cases compounding is done more than once yearly, say m times per year. In these cases, the interest rate is i/m and the exponent is mn, so that (12) becomes

$$A = P\left(1 + \frac{i}{m}\right)^{mn}.$$

Given $P = 1$, $i = 0.04$, and $n = 1$, approximate values for A with $m = 1, 2, 4,$ 80, 1600. Does it appear that, as m becomes large, A approaches 0 or 1 or some other number?　　　　　　　　　　　　　　*Ans.* A approaches $2.718\cdots$.

23. In simple interest problems, interest is computed yearly on only the *original* principal. Thus, in 5 years at rate 3 per cent with a principal of $100, the interest accumulated is

$$(\$100)(0.03)(5) = \$15$$

and the amount is

$$A = \$100 + \$15 = \$115.$$

Formulate an expression for the amount A derived from a principal P if the simple interest rate is i and is applied for n years. Compare this expression to (12). Graph both of them on the same set of axes. Is the simple interest formula an exponential?

9-3　　Changing Bases—the Base e—the Base 10

In preceding sections we applied the exponential to a variety of bases, including integral and fractional numbers. With the aid of a table of logarithms or a slide rule containing LL scales, bases can be readily interchanged. We will postpone to a later section those changes which require tables; in this section we will discuss, with certain exceptions, only those base changes which require no special tables. Change of bases is especially easy if the old base is some simple power of the new base; we say some *simple* power because any positive number can be expressed as a power of another positive number; however, the powers involved are often difficult to obtain.

EXAMPLE 5. Express (a) $(\frac{1}{2})^{3x}$, (b) $4^{-0.6x}$, (c) $64^{-x/4}$ as exponentials using the base 8.

Solution. In all cases we must determine the power of 8 that is the equivalent of the given base.

(a) We want to determine what power of 8 is of value $\frac{1}{2}$. Therefore, we are asking to find k where

$$8^k = \tfrac{1}{2}. \tag{13}$$

We may rewrite (13) in such a way as to express both sides as powers of the same base. The convenient new base is the base 2, thus,

$$8^k = (2^3)^k = (2)^{3k} \tag{14}$$

and $\quad \frac{1}{2} = (2)^{-1}.$ (15)

Equating the last two members of (14) and (15), we have

$$2^{3k} = 2^{-1}. \tag{16}$$

Now, with the bases in (16) equal, the exponents are also equal and

$$3k = -1,$$

from which

$$k = -\tfrac{1}{3}.$$

Substituting $k = -\frac{1}{3}$ into (13), we have

$$(8)^{-1/3} = \tfrac{1}{2}.$$

Replacing the base $\frac{1}{2}$ by the number $(8)^{-1/3}$ in the given expression $(\frac{1}{2})^{3x}$, we have

$$(\tfrac{1}{2})^{3x} = (8^{-1/3})^{3x} = 8^{-x}, \tag{17}$$

where (17) shows the conversion of the given expression from the base $\frac{1}{2}$ to the base 8.

(b) If we proceed as in part (a), we must determine what power of 8 the number 4 is. Thus,

$$8^k = 4$$

from which

$$2^{3k} = 2^2$$

and $k = \frac{2}{3}$. Now

$$4 = 8^{2/3}$$

and

$$4^{-0.6x} = (8^{2/3})^{-0.6x} = 8^{-0.4x}.$$

(c) To find the power of 8 to which $64^{-x/4}$ corresponds, we need not go through the intermediate base 2 as done in parts (a) and (b). Since $64 = 8^2$, then

$$64^{-(1/4)x} = (8^2)^{-(1/4)x} = 8^{-(1/2)x}.$$

EXAMPLE 6. Given that

$$2 = 10^{0.30103}, \quad 3 = 10^{0.47712} \quad \text{and} \quad 5 = 10^{0.69897},$$

express the following numbers as powers of 10: (a) 16, (b) 15, (c) $\sqrt{6}$, (d) $\sqrt[3]{30}$.

Solution. In each case we will convert the given number to a power of 10 through use of the three powers of 10 shown.

(a) $\quad 16 = 2^4 = (10^{0.30103})^4 = 10^{1.20412}$.

(b) $\quad 15 = 3 \cdot 5 = (10^{0.47712})](10^{0.69897}) = 10^{1.17609}$.

(c) $\quad \sqrt{6} = (2 \cdot 3)^{1/2} = (10^{0.30103} \cdot 10^{0.47712})^{1/2} = 10^{0.77815/2} = 10^{0.38907}$.

(d) $\quad \sqrt[3]{30} = (2 \cdot 3 \cdot 5)^{1/3} = (10^{0.30103} \cdot 10^{0.47712} \cdot 10^{0.69897})^{1/3} = 10^{1.47712/3}$
$\quad \quad = 10^{0.49237}$.

In Example 6 a group of numbers was converted to the base 10. In computations with common logarithms, the base 10 is used throughout. Tabular entries in the table of common logarithms simply indicate the power of 10 which represents the number in question. The number 10, familiar to all of us, is called the *common base*. Computations are also made using the base e, where e is called the *natural base* and is a rather strange number. We will define e here and show how it is obtained.

The number e is defined as a limit; it is the limit of the quantity $(1 + x)^{1/x}$ as x goes to zero; this is written as

$$e = \lim_{x \to 0} (1 + x)^{1/x}. \tag{18}$$

Inspecting (18), two incorrect views are often brought forth. One person views the base $1 + x$, remarks that the base goes to unity as x goes to zero and that unity raised to any power is unity, suggesting that e has the value unity. Another person views the exponent $1/x$ and remarks that as $x \to 0$, $1/x \to \infty$, suggesting that e is infinitely large. Neither viewpoint is correct. If we substitute successively smaller values of x into (18), say $x = 0.1$, $x = 0.001$, $x = 0.00001$, and so forth, e appears to converge on the value $e = 2.718\cdots$; this is the value of e which we will accept without proof.

Exercises

In Exercises 1–10, convert the given expression into another expression in the base indicated in parentheses.

1. 9^{2x} (3).   *Ans.* 3^{4x}.   **2.** $16^{3.5x}$ (2).

3. 2^{-8x} (16).   *Ans.* 16^{-2x}.   **4.** $3^{-0.3x}$ (27).

5. 32^{-2y} (8).   *Ans.* $8^{-10y/3}$.   **6.** $64^{-0.1y}$ (2).

7. $0.3^{7.2y}$ (0.09).   *Ans.* $(0.09)^{3.6y}$.   **8.** $2500^{-1.26t}$ (50).

9. 8^{2t-3} (16).   *Ans.* $16^{(6t-9)/4}$.   **10.** 16^{t+4} (8).

In Exercises 11–30, given the values

$$2 = 10^{0.30103}, \qquad 5 = 10^{0.69897}, \qquad 10 = e^{2.30259},$$
$$3 = 10^{0.47712}, \qquad e = 10^{0.43429}, \qquad \pi = 10^{0.49715},$$

express the given numbers as powers of the base indicated in parentheses.

11. 2π (10).   *Ans.* $10^{0.79818}$.   **12.** 5π (10).

13. 50 (10).   *Ans.* $10^{1.69897}$.   **14.** 15 (10).

15. 9 (10).   *Ans.* $10^{0.95424}$.   **16.** 25 (10).

17. 36 (10).   *Ans.* $10^{1.55630}$.   **18.** 8 (10).

19. $15,000$ (10).   *Ans.* $10^{4.17609}$.   **20.** 810 (10).

21. $\frac{1}{3}$ (10).   *Ans.* $10^{-0.47712}$.   **22.** $\frac{1}{2}$ (10).

23. 0.6 (10).   *Ans.* $10^{-0.22185}$.   **24.** $\frac{2}{3}$ (10).

25. 100 (e).   *Ans.* $e^{4.60518}$.   **26.** 1000 (e).

27. $\sqrt[3]{10}$ (e).   *Ans.* $e^{0.76753}$.   **28.** $\sqrt{10}$ (e).

29. $10\pi/e$ (10).   *Ans.* $10^{1.06286}$.   **30.** $12\pi^2$ (10).

In Exercises 11–30, the operations involved adding, subtracting, doubling, halving, etc., the given exponents. In view of those operations, provide answers to the questions in Exercises 31–35.

31. If we multiply two numbers a and b which are in the power form, how is the exponent of the product ab related to the exponents of a and b?

Ans. Using the base 10, the exponents can be called the logarithms and

$$\log_{10} ab = \log_{10} a + \log_{10} b.$$

This asserts that the logarithm of a product of two factors is the sum of the logarithms of the two factors.

32. If we divide a by b, how is the logarithm of $a \div b$ related to the logarithms of a and b? Assume base 10. *Ans.* $\log_{10} a/b = \log_{10} a - \log_{10} b$.

33. If we raise a to the nth power, how is the logarithm of a^n related to the logarithm of a? *Ans.* $\log_{10} a^n = n \log_{10} a$.

34. If we take the nth root of a, how is the logarithm of $\sqrt[n]{a}$ related to the logarithm of a? *Ans.* $\log_{10} \sqrt[n]{a} = (1/n) \log_{10} a$.

35. Given the number $N = a^2 b^3 / 5c$, give an expression for $\log_{10} N$.
Ans. $\text{Log}_{10} N = 2 \log_{10} a + 3 \log_{10} b - (\log_{10} 5 + \log_{10} c)$.

9-4   Logarithms

In preceding sections in this chapter we have discussed exponentials; particularly appropriate were those discussions which suggested that exponents may be called *logarithms* as long as the base being considered is a positive base other than 1. Any number may be expressed as a power of a base; for example, the number 64 may be expressed as $(2)^6$, or

$$64 = (2)^6. \tag{19}$$

In (19), 64 is the *number*, 2 is the *base*, and 6 is the exponent or *logarithm*. This may be stated in the inverse form as "6 is the logarithm to the base 2 of the number 64" and written

$$6 = \log_2 64. \tag{20}$$

In general, a number y may be considered to be the xth power of a base b. The general form of (19) may be written as

$$y = b^x. \tag{21}$$

Now (21) can be written in the logarithmic form (20) where the general logarithmic form of (21) is

$$x = \log_b y. \tag{22}$$

In (21) the base b is assumed to be constant and both the logarithm x and the number y are variables. Once again, the description distinguishes the exponential form from the power form.

Expressions (22) and (20) assert that a quantity is a logarithm of a second quantity with a third quantity as a base. A given number may be the logarithm of many different numbers, depending upon the choice of base. Consider the case of several squares:

$$9 = 3^2 \quad \text{and} \quad 2 = \log_3 9,$$
$$100 = 10^2 \quad \text{and} \quad 2 = \log_{10} 100,$$
$$10 = 3.162^2 \quad \text{and} \quad 2 = \log_{3.162} 10.$$

In each of the preceding illustrations, the logarithm of the given number is 2. The numbers differ and the bases differ also.

In common usage two bases are used—the base 10 and the base e. Our initial discussion here will be with reference to the *common* or *Briggsian* base 10. In each case cited we will make our considerations using the base 10. In Appendix C we are given a *Table of Common Logarithms of Numbers*. This table lists a number and its logarithm, using the base 10. It is emphasized here that Appendix C does not give the *entire* logarithm, but only a part of the logarithm called the *mantissa*. More on this later.

Let us examine a logarithm more closely with the objective of using Appendix C and analyzing the complete logarithm. First, logarithms of integral powers of 10 are integers. We have

$$
\begin{aligned}
1 &= 10^0 \quad \text{and} \quad 0 = \log_{10} 1, \\
10 &= 10^1 \quad \text{and} \quad 1 = \log_{10} 10, \\
100 &= 10^2 \quad \text{and} \quad 2 = \log_{10} 100, \\
1000 &= 10^3 \quad \text{and} \quad 3 = \log_{10} 1000, \\
10{,}000 &= 10^4 \quad \text{and} \quad 4 = \log_{10} 10{,}000
\end{aligned}
\tag{23}
$$

From expressions (23) we see that the logarithms of positive powers of 10 are positive integers (using the base 10). Similarly, from expressions (24), we observe that the logarithms of negative powers of 10 are negative integers.

$$
\begin{aligned}
0.1 &= \tfrac{1}{10} = 10^{-1} \quad &&\text{and} \quad -1 = \log_{10} 0.1, \\
0.01 &= \tfrac{1}{100} = 10^{-2} \quad &&\text{and} \quad -2 = \log_{10} 0.01, \\
0.001 &= \tfrac{1}{1000} = 10^{-3} \quad &&\text{and} \quad -3 = \log_{10} 0.001, \\
0.0001 &= \tfrac{1}{10000} = 10^{-4} \quad &&\text{and} \quad -4 = \log_{10} 0.0001.
\end{aligned}
\tag{24}
$$

Certain general facts are seen from (23) and (24):

(a) If a number N is greater than unity, then $\log_{10} N$ is greater than zero; that is, if

$$N > 1 \quad \text{then} \quad \log_{10} N > 0.$$

(b) If a number N is between 0 and 1, then $\log_{10} N$ is negative; that is, if

$$0 < N < 1 \quad \text{then} \quad \log_{10} N < 0. \tag{25}$$

(c) If a number $N = 1$, then $\log_{10} N = 0$.

For the next portion of our discussion we draw particular attention to (25). In expressions (23) and (24) we considered only those numbers which are integral powers of 10. Now let us consider the logarithms of some numbers which are not integral powers of the base 10.

EXAMPLE 7. Find $\log_{10} N$ if (a) $N = 2$, (b) $N = 20,000$, (c) $N = 0.002$.

Solution. Referring to the table of common logarithms in Appendix C, we find no entry in the N column listed as 2, or 20,000, or 0.002. There is a listing for a number designated by the digits 2000 (where the digits are *not* intended to mean the number "two thousand"). The tabular entry under 2000 is 30103. This means simply that there is a number whose one significant digit, 2, is identified with a logarithm with significant digits 30103. Now, in view of (23) and (25) we can be more explicit.

(a) Since $N = 2$, then $0 < \log_{10} N < 1$. Actually, from Appendix C, we then have

$$2 = 10^{0.30103} \quad \text{or} \quad 0.30103 = \log_{10} N.$$

(b) Here $N = 20,000$. We can write 20,000 in standard notation as

$$20,000 = 2 \times 10^4.$$

In part (a) and from Appendix C we have

$$2 = 10^{0.30103}$$

so that we now have

$$20,000 = 2 \times 10^4 = 10^{0.30103} \times 10^4 = 10^{0.30103+4}. \tag{26}$$

The exponent (logarithm) in (26) is written in a seemingly unusual fashion. From (26) we have

$$\log_{10} 20,000 = 0.30103 + 4, \tag{27}$$

where the portion 0.30103 of the logarithm was obtained from the table and is called the *mantissa* of the logarithm, and the $+4$ portion was obtained through standard notation. The $+4$ portion is called the *characteristic* of the logarithm; it was *not* obtained from the table and serves simply to indicate the position of the decimal point.

(*c*) Here $N = 0.002$. Written in standard notation,

$$N = 0.002 = 2 \times 10^{-3}.$$

Now,

$$0.002 = 2 \times 10^{-3} = 10^{0.30103} \times 10^{-3} = 10^{0.30103-3},$$

from which we have

$$\log_{10} 0.002 = 0.30103 - 3.$$

Here the characteristic is the negative number -3.

It is noteworthy that any number in decimal form can be written in standard notation. If we accept the fact that proper standard notation requires that a number be written as the product of two parts, the first part being a quantity between 1 and 10 and the second part being a power of 10 which properly locates the decimal point, then we can make the observations that

1. the table of logarithms will provide the mantissa, and
2. the characteristic *is* the exponent in the power of 10 shown in the standard notation.

Consider another example.

EXAMPLE 8. Find $\log_{10} N$ if (*a*) $N = 987,000$, (*b*) $N = 0.00155$.

Solution. (*a*) First, express the number in standard notation, thus,

$$N = 987,000 = 9.87 \times 10^5.$$

Now, from the table of logarithms,

$$\log_{10} 9.87 = 0.99432 \quad \text{or} \quad 9.87 = 10^{0.99432}$$

and $\quad N = 9.87 \times 10^5 = 10^{0.99432} \times 10^5 = 10^{0.99432+5}$

and we have the statement

$$\log_{10} 987000 = 0.99432 + 5$$

(b) Proceeding more rapidly with the problem of finding the logarithm, we have

$$N = 0.00155 = 1.55 \times 10^{-3} = 10^{0.19033-3}$$
and $$\log_{10} 0.00155 = 0.19033 - 3.$$

where the mantissa, 0.19033, was found in Appendix C.

Observation: In part (a) *both* the characteristic and the mantissa are positive for

$$\log_{10} 987000 = 0.99432 + 5. \tag{28}$$

It would not be confusing or improper to write (28) as

$$\log_{10} 987000 = 5.99432, \tag{29}$$

where the characteristic in (29) *precedes* the mantissa, as opposed to (28) where the characteristic follows the mantissa. We assert that interchanging the positions of the characteristic and mantissa in (28) is not confusing; however, in part (b) it may be confusing to make the interchange. Thus, if

$$\log_{10} 0.00155 = 0.19033 - 3, \tag{30}$$

we have a *positive* mantissa and a *negative* characteristic. If we wrote (30) by interchanging the positions of the characteristic and mantissa, we would have

$$\log_{10} 0.00155 = -3.19033, \tag{31}$$

where in (31) it is difficult to understand that the mantissa is positive and the characteristic is negative. Therefore, other conventions are adopted. Some references use the standard

$$\log_{10} 0.00155 = \bar{3}.19033$$

to show that the negative sign belongs *only* with the characteristic. A more common convention writes the characteristic in two parts, one before the mantissa and the other trailing, with the trailing portion usually the number -10. Thus, since $-3 = 7 - 10$, we can write (30) as

$$\log_{10} 0.00155 = 7.19033 - 10. \tag{32}$$

It is remarked here that the leading and trailing portions of the characteristic in (32) can be *any* two numbers that add to -3; for example, $97 - 100, 41 - 44$, etc. Flexibility in the choice of parts will be useful later.

Exercises

In Exercises 1–20 find the logarithm of the given number. Provide both the characteristic and the mantissa. Split the characteristic into two parts with the trailing part the number −10. Use the table of common logarithms in Appendix C.

1. 3.   *Ans.* 10.47712 − 10.   **2.** 30.

3. 3000.   *Ans.* 13.47712 − 10.   **4.** 0.3.

5. 0.00003.   *Ans.* 5.47712 − 10.   **6.** 48.

7. 0.48.   *Ans.* 9.68124 − 10.   **8.** 4850.

9. 48.50.   *Ans.* 11.68574 − 10.   **10.** 485.4.

11. 4.854.   *Ans.* 10.68610 − 10.   **12.** 9273.

13. 0.009273.   *Ans.* 7.96722 − 10.   **14.** 7.25×10^{-5}.

15. 6.22×10^{-7}.   *Ans.* 3.79379 − 10.   **16.** 622×10^{-5}.

17. 7250×10^{-3}.   **18.** 10^{-5}.

Ans. 10.86034 − 10.

19. 10^{-9}.   *Ans.* 1.00000 − 10.   **20.** 10^3

In Exercises 21–40 find the number whose logarithm is given. Express the number in standard notation.

21. 0.84510.   *Ans.* 7.   **22.** 0.74036.

23. 3.84510.   *Ans.* 7×10^3.   **24.** 4.74036.

25. 6.84510 − 10.   *Ans.* 7×10^{-4}.   **26.** 7.74036 − 10.

27. 14.84510 − 8.   *Ans.* 7×10^6.   **28.** 12.74036 − 7.

29. 0.84510 − 27.   *Ans.* 7×10^{-27}.   **30.** 0.74036 − 21.

31. 4.85126.   *Ans.* 7.10×10^4.   **32.** 3.17609.

33. 0.85552 − 5.   *Ans.* 7.17×10^{-5}.   **34.** 0.19173 − 6.

35. 19.85600 − 20.   **36.** 9.20003 − 10.

Ans. 7.178×10^{-1}.

37. 19.86004 − 10.   **38.** 12.28081 − 10.

Ans. 7.245×10^9.

39. 0.87035.   *Ans.* 7.419.   **40.** 3.39707.

9-5   Interpolation

The table of logarithms of numbers in Appendix C gives logarithms of numbers to the base 10 according to the equation

$$N = 10^x, \tag{33}$$

where N is the *number* listed to three significant figures in the N-column (with the fourth significant figure obtained under additional columns shown) and x is the logarithm of the number; the mantissa of x is obtained from the table. Equation (33) graphs as shown in Fig. 9-4. Note that consecutive

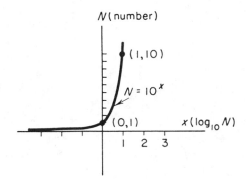

FIGURE 9–4

values of N listed are given to four places. By a method called *interpolation*, $\log_{10} N$ may be found for N given to *five* places; here $\log_{10} N$ will be approximate. Consider Example 9.

EXAMPLE 9. Find log 3.5264 using the table of logarithms in Appendix C.

Solution 1. From Appendix C we find entries for $N = 3.526$ and $N = 3.527$, but none for $N = 3.5264$. We see that

$$\log 3.5260 = 0.54728,$$
$$\log 3.5270 = 0.54741.$$

Now, log 3.5264 lies between log 3.5260 and log 3.5270, or

$$0.54728 < \log 3.5264 < 0.54741.$$

We are interested in a tiny portion of the graph in Fig. 9-4. This portion of the graph of equation (33) is shown in Fig. 9-5 where

$$3.5260 < N < 3.5270 \quad \text{and} \quad 0.54728 < x < 0.54741.$$

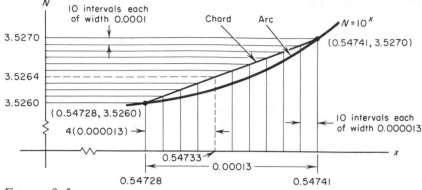

FIGURE 9–5

In Fig. 9-5 we have drawn a chord between the points (0.54728, 3.5260) and (0.54741, 3.5270). This chord is a reasonable approximation of the arc of the curve in the brief interval concerned. The N-interval is divided into 10 equal parts; we wish to proceed $\frac{4}{10}$ of the way through this interval; i.e., from 3.5260 to 3.5264. By projecting 10 equal subdivisions of the N-interval to the chord, then downward to the x-axis, we divide the x-interval into 10 parts. Since the x-interval is 0.00013 in width, each of the 10 equal parts is 0.000013 in width. We require four of these parts, or

$$4(0.000013) = 0.00005.$$

Now we displace our value of x from 0.54728 to the right by an amount 0.00005 and find that

$$\log 3.5264 = 0.54728 + 0.00005 = 0.54733.$$

We note that the value 0.54733 is not exact since we used the chord instead of the arc, but it is accurate enough in most cases to be useful.

Solution 2. A second method of interpolation is shown here; it does not use the graph of the curve directly, but embraces the same idea as that used in solution 1. This second method is perhaps the more popular one.

List both tabular values as before, and the desired quantity between them:

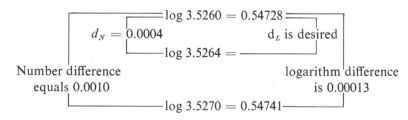

From the preceding format we can set up the ratio

$$\frac{0.0004}{0.0010} = \frac{d_L}{0.00013},$$

from which $d_L = 0.00005$. Now,

$$\log 3.5264 = 0.54728 + 0.00005 = 0.54733.$$

The method in solution 2 determines the portion of the interval through which the number passes, then moves through the logarithm interval the same portion. Linearity (chord) is again assumed.

Interpolation can also be used in finding the number whose logarithm is given. This number is called the *antilogarithm* of the given logarithm. Methods used are identical with those shown in Example 9. Consider an example.

EXAMPLE 10. Find N given $\log N = 3.41269$.

Solution. From the table of logarithms, we list the two logarithms straddling the given logarithm, along with their antilogarithms. The characteristic is also supplied.

From the preceding format we have the proportion

$$\frac{d_N}{10} = \frac{6}{17},$$

from which $d_N = 3.53 = 0.4$. Now,

$$N = 2586.0 + 0.4 = 2586.4.$$

Note that we did not indicate the base 10 in the logarithm notation in Examples 9 and 10. We will adopt the conventions

(a) $\log N$ indicates the *common logarithm*, base 10.

(b) $\ln N$ indicates the *natural logarithm*, base e.

(c) $\log_b N$ indicates logarithms to any base, where the base b is specified.

In summary, we state that the table of logarithms gives only the mantissa.

The characteristic is obtained through standard notation. Errors in the characteristic produce errors only in the location of the decimal point. Mantissa errors produce errors in the significant digits of the antilogarithm. Interpolation procedures described here extend the logarithm tables to five-place tables.

Exercises

In Exercises 1–10 find the logarithm of the given number by interpolation. Use the table of logarithms in Appendix C.

1. $N = 2.5045$.   *Ans.* Log $N = 0.39872$.

2. $N = 5.4135$.

3. $N = 30.004$.   *Ans.* Log $N = 1.47718$.

4. $N = 72.443$.

5. $N = 0.030908$.   *Ans.* Log $N = 8.49007 - 10$.

6. $N = 0.022493$.

7. $N = 16892$.   *Ans.* Log $N = 4.22768$.

8. $N = 84241$.

9. $N = 0.00072498$.   *Ans.* Log $N = 6.86033 - 10$.

10. $N = 0.0059293$.

In Exercises 11–20 find the antilogarithm of the given logarithm by interpolation. Use Appendix C.

11. Log $N = 0.36403$.   *Ans.* $N = 2.3122$.

12. Log $N = 0.48257$.

13. Log $N = 2.25969$.   *Ans.* $N = 181.84$.

14. Log $N = 3.37282$.

15. Log $N = 8.81021 - 10$.   *Ans.* $N = 0.064597$.

16. Log $N = 7.92225 - 10$.

17. Log $N = 4.92222$.   *Ans.* $N = 83602$.

18. Log $N = 1.10035$.

19. Log $N = 16.16161$.   *Ans.* 1.4508×10^{16}.

20. Log $N = 10.00029$.

9-6   Multiplication and Division with Logarithms

From the laws of exponents we have

$$a^m \cdot a^n = a^{m+n}, \tag{34}$$

$$a^m \div a^n = a^{m-n}, \tag{35}$$

where (34) asserts that powers of like bases can be multiplied by adding the exponents and (35) asserts that powers of like bases can be divided by subtracting the exponent of the divisor from the exponent of the dividend. The table of logarithms in Appendix C is constructed using the base 10; therefore, if we are to use the table of logarithms, it would be useful to modify (34) and (35) to read

$$10^m \cdot 10^n = 10^{m+n}, \tag{36}$$

$$10^m \div 10^n = 10^{m-n}. \tag{37}$$

Now, in (36) and (37), the exponents m and n are logarithms which can be obtained through the table of logarithms. Let us consider an example.

EXAMPLE 11. Find $N = 2 \times 3$ by use of logarithms.

Solution 1. Using the table of logarithms to convert the numbers 2 and 3 to powers of the base 10, we have

$$N = 2 \times 3 = 10^{0.30103} \times 10^{0.47712}$$
$$= 10^{0.30103 + 0.47712} = 10^{0.77815}. \tag{38}$$

Now in (38) we have a statement that $N = 10^{0.77815}$. If we enter the table to find the number whose logarithm is 0.77815, we find that $N = 6$.

Solution 2. In computational practice, displaying the given factors as powers of 10 as in (38) is not commonly done. It was done in (38) to show that the multiplication operation is performed by adding logarithms. In common practice, we realize that the base is 10 and that we are dealing with logarithms, so that we simply reduce the operation to the following format:

$$
\begin{array}{ll}
\log 2 = 0.30103 & \text{(from the table)} \\
+\log 3 = 0.47712 & \text{(from the table)} \\
\hline
\log N = 0.77815 & \text{(by addition)} \\
N = 6.0000 & \text{(by antilogarithm)}
\end{array}
$$

EXAMPLE 12. Find N if $N = 6.8327 \div 0.46263$.

Solution. Here we have division, which calls for the subtraction of logarithms.

Using the format shown in Example 11, we have

$$
\begin{array}{lll}
\log 6.8327 & = 10.83459 - 10 & \text{(table, interpolation)} \\
-\log 0.46263 & = 9.66524 - 10 & \text{(table, interpolation)} \\
\hline
\log N & = 1.16935 & \text{(subtraction)} \\
N & = 14.769 & \text{(antilogarithm)}
\end{array}
$$

It is important to note in Example 12 that we resorted to the device of breaking the characteristic into two parts. This is especially necessary if the divisor is greater than the dividend. We may have to resort to some unusual breakdowns of the characteristic when circumstances require.

Combined operations involving multiplication and division require expansion of our format somewhat. Such operations are mere extensions of simple multiplications or divisions. Let us show an example problem which calls for combined operations and some juggling of the characteristic.

EXAMPLE 13. Find N if

$$
N = \frac{0.325 \times 4.695}{15.46 \times 0.673 \times 8.882}.
$$

Solution. Here we have the quotient of products; by usual division we have

$$
\log N = \log S - \log T,
$$

where S is the numerator and T is the denominator, or

$$
\log N = (\log 0.325 + \log 4.695) - (\log 15.46 + \log 0.673 + \\
\log 8.882).
$$

Introducing a format, we have

$$
\begin{array}{ll}
\begin{array}{ll}
\log 0.325 = 29.51188 - 30 \\
+\log 4.695 = 10.67164 - 10 \\
\hline
\log S \quad\;\; = 40.18352 - 40 \\
-\log T \quad\;\; = 31.96574 - 30 \\
\hline
\log N \quad\;\; = 8.21778 - 10 \\
N \quad\quad\;\;\, = 0.016511
\end{array}
&
\begin{array}{ll}
\log 15.46 = 11.18921 - 10 \\
+\log 0.673 = 9.82802 - 10 \\
+\log 8.882 = 10.94851 - 10 \\
\hline
\log T \quad\;\;\; = 31.96574 - 30
\end{array}
\end{array}
$$

Note in Example 13 that the characteristic of $\log 0.325$ was chosen as 29 minus 30. This made it possible to have the leading part of the characteristic of the logarithm of the numerator greater than the leading part of the characteristic of the denominator, enabling the subtraction of the logarithms of the numerator and denominator. We chose to do the juggling with $\log 0.325$;

actually, this juggling could have been done at other points in the solution without loss of accuracy.

At this point we introduce two laws of logarithms namely

$$\log_b MN = \log_b M + \log_b N, \tag{39}$$

$$\log_b \frac{M}{N} = \log_b M - \log_b N. \tag{40}$$

We applied laws (39) and (40) in Examples 11, 12, and 13. The laws are shown here for the sake of generality.

Exercises

Evaluate the expressions in Exercises 1–25 by using the logarithm tables in Appendix C. Express the results correct to accuracy that can be achieved by interpolation.

1. 23.427×653.26.   *Ans.* 15304.

2. 14.296×185.35.

3. 692.04×0.0042763.   *Ans.* 2.9594.

4. 312.29×0.0092932.

5. $0.092959 \times 0.0062935$.   *Ans.* 5.8504×10^{-4}.

6. $0.0083259 \times 0.00085262$.

7. $613.52 \div 4.9526$.   *Ans.* 123.88.

8. $900.08 \div 2.6004$.

9. $\pi \div 57.3$.   *Ans.* 0.054827.

10. $3.0986 \div 292.14$.

11. $0.0049424 \div \pi$.   *Ans.* 0.0015732.

12. $0.0082953 \div 0.079673$.

13. $(315.20 \times 404.26)/1859.2$.   *Ans.* 68.537.

14. $(418.12 \times 3.4626)/(17.155 \times 255.67)$.

15. $(96.665 \times 4.2477)/3.9196\pi$.   *Ans.* 33.344.

16. $1 \div 792.6$.

17. $1 \div 3.982$.   *Ans.* 0.2512.

18. 6344.8×0.12345.

19. $920.28 \div 2.4763$.   *Ans.* 371.64.

20. 0.0062651×12.272.

21. $(157.60 \times 60.639)/92.960$.   *Ans.* 102.81.

22. $(727.55 \times 1.4692)/20.266$.

23. $0.98848 \div \pi$.   *Ans.* 0.31464.

24. $4.6821 \div 0.031395$.

25. 979.89×46.854.   *Ans.* 45912.

26. The density of mercury is given as 13.546 grams per cubic centimeter. There are 16.387 cubic centimeters per cubic inch. What is the weight of a column of mercury filling a right circular cylinder with a base of area 0.04255 sq. in. and height 3.295 in.?

27. Give the logarithm for the reciprocal of π.   *Ans.* $9.50285 - 10$.

28. There is one dyne of gravity force acting on 1.0197×10^{-3} grams of mass at the earth's surface. Find the number of grams which has a weight of one poundal if the poundal is 1.3825×10^{-4} dynes.

29. Find the area of a trapezoid with bases of lengths $b_1 = 3.2952$ in. and $b_2 = 5.6271$ in. and altitude $h = 2.7919$ in. if the area A is

$$A = (h/2)(b_1 + b_2).$$

Ans. $A = 12.455$.

30. The location of the centroid of a trapezoid is given by the equation

$$h = \frac{h(2b_1 + b_2)}{3(b_1 + b_2)},$$

where h is measured from b_2. Find h for the trapezoid described in Exercise 29.

31. A point is on the rim of a wheel 14.375 inches from the center of the wheel. If the wheel rotates at the rate of 218 revolutions each 32.5 seconds, find the speed of the point in inches per second.   *Ans.* 605.86 in./sec.

32. By using logarithms find the approximate value of 10! where 10! (ten factorial) is the product of all of the integers from 1 through 10.

33. The pH value of a substance is defined as the negative of the logarithm of the hydrogen ion concentration. If a substance is such that only one part in one hundred million is ionized hydrogen, what is the pH value?   *Ans.* pH = 8.

9-7   Powers and Roots

The definition of a power of a number combines with the law of multiplication by use of logarithms to present a method of computing powers of numbers by logarithms. If

$$N = b^k \qquad (k \text{ an integer, } b \neq 1),$$

then, by the definition of a power,

$$N = b \cdot b \cdot b \cdot \cdots \cdot b \qquad (k \text{ factors})$$

and, by the law of multiplication by logarithms in the preceding section,

$$\log N = \log b + \log b + \log b + \cdots + \log b \qquad (k \text{ addends})$$

or $\qquad \log N = k \log b.$

Thus, we have a law of logarithms of powers

$$\log_b M^n = n \log_b M. \qquad (41)$$

Law (41) can be worded in a specific example as "the logarithm of the cube of a number is three times the logarithm of the number." Examples are

$$\log_{10} 5^2 = 2 \log_{10} 5,$$
$$\log_{10} (0.0034)^{1.25} = 1.25 \log_{10} 0.0034,$$
$$\log_7 (4.25)^{-2.3} = -2.3 \log_7 4.25.$$

EXAMPLE 14. Find N if $N = (0.8325)^4$.

Solution. Using (41) to express the given quantity as an equation of logarithms,

$$\log N = 4 \log 0.8325.$$

Using a format for computations,

$$\log 0.8325 = \quad 9.92038 - 10$$
$$\underline{\times 4}$$
$$\log N = 39.68152 - 40$$
$$N = 0.48031.$$

The preceding example illustrated a case where the exponent was integral. A slight bit of juggling of the characteristic is useful if the exponent is not integral. The trailing portion of the characteristic is wisely chosen in such a way that the product of that portion of the characteristic and the exponent is an integer; this is not necessary, but often has a simplifying effect. Consider Example 15.

EXAMPLE 15. Evaluate N if $N = (0.1265)^{3.12}$.

Solution. Since the exponent contains a decimal to hundredths, the trailing portion of the characteristic is wisely chosen as 100; therefore, from

$$\log N = 3.12 \log 0.1265.$$

we have the format

$$\log 0.1265 = \begin{array}{r} 99.10209 - 100 \\ \times 3.12 \\ \hline \end{array}$$
$$\begin{array}{rl} \log N & = 309.19852 - 312 \\ N & = \quad 1.5795 \times 10^{-3}. \end{array}$$

It is interesting to note, at the risk of confusion, that the product of 99.10209 by 3.12 in Example 15 could have been obtained by the use of logarithms, adding log 99.10209 and log 3.12. The sum would not have been log N, but would have been log 309.19852 (shortened by the limitations of the table of logarithms). The antilogarithm of log 309.19852 would be log N, which in turn is such that the antilogarithm of log N is N. In the preceding discussion, the location of the decimal point in N is ignored.

Roots by logarithms can be computed in the same manner as powers if we wish. The indicated root can be expressed as a power. Thus, if

$$N = \sqrt[4]{3.26},$$

then

$$N = (3.26)^{1/4} = (3.26)^{0.25}$$

and we can apply (41). As an alternative, we may use the law

$$\log_b \sqrt[n]{M} = \frac{1}{n} \log_b M. \tag{42}$$

In applying (42) it is useful to have the trailing portion of the characteristic divisible by n with no remainder.

EXAMPLE 16. Evaluate $N = \sqrt[6]{0.009642}$.

Solution. By (42), we have

$$\begin{array}{rl} \log N & = \tfrac{1}{6} \log 0.009642 \\ & = \tfrac{1}{6} (3.98417 - 6) \\ & = 0.66403 - 1, \\ N & = 0.46135. \end{array}$$

Combined operations involving roots and powers are performed by selecting appropriate laws among (39), (40), (41), and (42). Thus, if

$$N = \sqrt[3]{\frac{a^2b}{5cd^4}},$$

then

$$\log N = \log\left(\frac{a^2b}{5cd^4}\right)^{1/3}$$

and

$$\log N = \tfrac{1}{3}(\log a^2b - \log 5cd^4)$$
$$= \tfrac{1}{3}(2\log a + \log b - \log 5 - \log c - 4\log d). \tag{43}$$

It is often useful to express a problem in the logarithmic form (43). It is further useful to establish a format which will provide an organized plan for the sequence of operations, showing the intended steps of addition, subtraction, etc. The advantages of a format are orderliness and the fact that, once the format is completely built, there is no longer reason to switch back and forth between the problem and the table of logarithms. Such switching is often confusing and tends toward disorganization.

Exercises

Evaluate the expressions in Exercises 1–26. Use the table of logarithms in Appendix C.

1. $(9.826)^2$.   *Ans.* 96.552.   2. $(4.735)^2$.

3. $(0.1629)^3$.   *Ans.* 4.3227×10^{-3}.   4. $(0.02404)^3$.

5. $(4.913)^2$.   *Ans.* 24.138.   6. $(8.219)^3$.

7. $(3.276 \times 0.0907)^2$.   8. $(0.01345 \times 0.0615)^2$.

                Ans. 8.8288×10^{-2}.

9. $(3.258)^3$.   *Ans.* 34.582.   10. $(5.417 \times 0.196)^2$.

11. $\sqrt{819.4}$.   *Ans.* 28.625.   12. $\sqrt{1006.4}$.

13. $\sqrt[3]{1.842}$.   *Ans.* 1.2258.   14. $\sqrt[3]{76.68}$.

15. $\sqrt[4]{0.0003294}$.   *Ans.* 0.13472.   16. $\sqrt[5]{0.08275}$.

17. $\sqrt{204.85}$.   *Ans.* 14.312.   18. $\sqrt[6]{4096}$.

19. $\sqrt{\dfrac{94.05}{275.47}}$.   *Ans.* 0.58431.   20. $\left(\dfrac{0.0615}{57.53}\right)^2$.

21. $(2.166\pi)^2$.   *Ans.* 46.304.   22. $\left(\dfrac{57.53}{0.0615}\right)^2$.

23. $\dfrac{31.35}{826.4}$.   *Ans.* 0.19477.   **24.** $\sqrt{\dfrac{9.254}{10.985}}$.

25. $\left(\dfrac{43.26 \times 125.67}{2.14 \times 6.285}\right)^2$.   **26.** $\left(\dfrac{99.04}{34.62 \times 0.2163}\right)^3$.

Ans. 1.6339×10^5.

27. Given a circle of radius 6.245, find

(*a*) circumference C.

(*b*) area A.

(*c*) moment of inertia I_A about one of the diameters if $I_A = \pi r^4/4$.

Ans. 1194.6.

28. By use of logarithms find $\sqrt{7}$ to five figures.

29. The moment of inertia I_A of an annulus (ring) about a diameter is given as

$$I_A = \pi \frac{r_1^4 - r_2^4}{4},$$

where r_2 is the inside radius and r_1 is the outside radius. Find I_A if $r_2 = 1.356$ and $r_1 = 2.138$.   *Ans.* 13.756.

30. Using the compound interest law $A = P(1 + i)^n$, find A if $P = \$9500$, $n = 20$, and $i = 0.055$.

31. Find the volume of a sphere of radius $r = 1.254$ in.   *Ans.* $V = 8.2600$ in.^{3}

32. What is the characteristic of log N if (a) $N = 1 \times 10^{-27}$? (b) $N = 1.62 \times 10^{-27}$?

33. By using logarithms, find the hypotenuse of the right triangle with legs 3.406 in. and 5.866 in.   *Ans.* 6.7832.

34. Find CB in Fig. 9-6 if $AB = 1.495$, $EB = 0.8925$, and $DC = 1.666$.

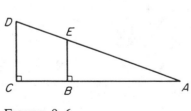

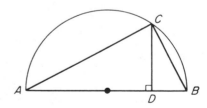

FIGURE 9–6   FIGURE 9–7

35. In Fig. 9-7, triangle ABC is inscribed in a semicircle. If CD is perpendicular to diameter AB with $AD = 4.182$ inches and $DB = 1.369$ inches, find CD.

36. If R dollars per year are placed into a fund for n years and interest accumulates at rate i, the amount K is given as

$$K = Rs_{\overline{n}|},$$

where $s_{\overline{n}|}$ is

$$s_{\overline{n}|} = \frac{(1 + i)^n - 1}{i}.$$

This yearly payment into a fund is called an annuity. Find K if \$200 per year is deposited for 6 years at 4 per cent.   *Ans.* $K = \$1326.60$.

37. If a man sets up an account today and wishes to withdraw R dollars annually from it for n years, the initial value of the account must be

$$A = Ra_{\overline{n}|},$$

where

$$a_{\overline{n}|} = \frac{1 - (1 + i)^{-n}}{i}.$$

Here A is the present amount of an annuity. Find A if \$1000 is to be taken from the account yearly for 10 years, with the account yielding 3.5 per cent.

Ans. \$8316.60.

In this chapter we shall introduce several special topics involving exponentials and logarithms. Among these are special topics which will facilitate certain operations with logarithms, solution of exponential and logarithmic equations, use of the log-log scales on the slide rule, applications and curve rectification. The basic notions advanced here rely upon methods and laws established in Chap. 9.

MISCELLANEOUS TOPICS IN EXPONENTIALS AND LOGARITHMS

10

10-1   Cologarithms

A *cologarithm* of a number is defined here as the logarithm of the reciprocal of the number; it is abbreviated as colog. Thus,

$$\operatorname{colog}\left(\frac{1}{N}\right) = \log N$$

or

$$\operatorname{colog} N = \log\left(\frac{1}{N}\right). \tag{1}$$

From (1) we can determine another relationship between colog N and log N since (1) can be written

$$\operatorname{colog} N = \log 1 - \log N$$

but log $1 = 0$, therefore

$$\operatorname{colog} N = -\log N, \tag{2}$$

where (2) asserts that the colog of a number is the negative of the logarithm of the number. Cologs are useful in computations where use of logarithms requires extensive manipulation of the characteristic. Let us observe two examples; the first involves finding a colog and the second utilizes the colog in a computation.

EXAMPLE 1. Find (*a*) colog 76, (*b*) colog 0.000372.

Solution. (*a*) from (2),

$$\operatorname{colog} 76 = -\log 76.$$

From the table of logarithms,

$$\log 76 = 1.88081$$

so that

$$\operatorname{colog} 76 = -(1.88081). \tag{3}$$

Now (3) is written in such a way as to indicate that both the characteristic and mantissa are negative. This is permissible and sometimes useful. Expression (3) can be written in the more popular form by adding and subtracting 10, such that

$$\operatorname{colog} 76 = 10 - (1.88081) - 10$$
$$= 8.11919 - 10, \tag{4}$$

where (4) is the more popular form.

(*b*) From (2),

$$\text{colog } 0.000372 = -\log 0.000372$$
$$= -(6.57054 - 10)$$
$$= 10 - 6.57054$$
$$= 3.42946.$$

It is again asserted here that negative mantissas are permissible in logarithms. Thus, if

$$N = \frac{1}{\sqrt{10}} = (10)^{-1/2} = 10^{-0.50000}$$

then $\log_{10} N = -0.50000$ where 50000 is the mantissa and is negative. It is also permissible to defy former usage and have a positive characteristic with a negative mantissa. Thus, if

$$N = \frac{10^3}{\sqrt{10}} = 10^3 \cdot 10^{-0.50000}$$

then $\log_{10} N = 3 - 0.50000$, where $+3$ is the characteristic and -0.50000 is the mantissa.

EXAMPLE 2. Find N if $N = (0.00493)^{-2.14}$.

Solution. By the laws of exponents, we can write the given expression as

$$N = (1/0.00493)^{+2.14}. \tag{5}$$

A reason for rewriting in the form of (5) is that the original problem has a negative exponent and the logarithm of the base is negative. Multiplication of these two can be confusing because of the minus signs. Now from (5),

$$\log N = 2.14 \log (1/0.00493), \tag{6}$$

and from (2), (6) can be written

$$\log N = 2.14(-\log 0.00493).$$

Now

$$-\log 0.00493 = -(7.69285 - 10)$$
$$= +2.30715$$

and

$$\log N = (2.14)(2.30715) = 4.93730$$

from which

$$N = 86556.$$

10-2   Solutions by Logarithms Where Some Quantities Are Negative

In the preceding chapter we established the requirement that we will not consider the logarithm of a negative number. However, in computations, since numbers used are negative, preliminary manipulation to determine the final outcome of the sign can assist us. Consider Example 3.

EXAMPLE 3. Evaluate N if $N = \sqrt[3]{(-4.17)^2/-8.65}$.

Solution. By examination of the given expression we see that $N = \sqrt[3]{a}$, where a is negative; therefore, N is negative. We could rewrite the given expression as

$$-N = \sqrt[3]{(4.17)^2/8.65}, \tag{7}$$

where preliminary manipulation eliminates the negative signs in the radicand and we know that $-N$ is positive because N is negative. Now we can proceed, knowing that we will not be taking the logarithms of negative numbers. Thus from (7),

$$\begin{aligned}
\log(-N) &= \tfrac{1}{3}[2\log 4.17 - \log 8.65] \\
&= \tfrac{1}{3}[2(0.62014) - 0.93702] \\
&= \tfrac{1}{3}[1.24028 - 0.93702] \\
&= \tfrac{1}{3}(0.30326) = 0.10109,
\end{aligned}$$

from which

$$-N = 1.2621$$

and

$$N = -1.2621.$$

Extending this discussion somewhat, if we have the form

$$N = \sqrt[k]{a},$$

where k is an odd integer and a is positive, no special manipulation is necessary. If a is negative when k is odd, manipulation such as that shown in Example 3 is necessary. If k is even and a is positive, again no manipulation is necessary. If k is even and a is negative, we are faced with an even root of a negative number; this will involve removing a factor $\sqrt{-1} = j$ and then proceeding as usual.

10-3   Expressions Involving Sums and Differences

Logarithms can be used to compute certain quantities that involve sums and differences. Their use, with certain exceptions, is not direct and, therefore, is often quite laborious. This section is introduced to show some manipulations involving sums and differences and certain short cuts.

Among the common applications involving differences is the Pythagorean theorem. From that theorem,

$$b = \sqrt{c^2 - a^2}, \tag{8}$$

where c is the hypotenuse and a and b are the legs of a right triangle. Now from (8),

$$b = \sqrt{c^2 - a^2} = \sqrt{(c + a)(c - a)}$$

and

$$\log b = \tfrac{1}{2}[\log (c + a) + \log (c - a)], \tag{9}$$

where (9) is direct as compared with other methods of finding $\log b$. If we did not employ (9), we would have to square c by logarithms, then square a by logarithms, subtract the squares, then take the square root by logarithms. A logarithmic representation of the procedure mentioned is

$$\log b = \tfrac{1}{2} \log [\text{antilog} (2 \log c) - \text{antilog} (2 \log a)].$$

EXAMPLE 4. In Fig. 10-1, find b.

Solution. From Fig. 10-1,

$$b = \sqrt{(6.254)^2 - (4.929)^2}. \tag{10}$$

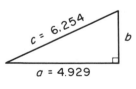

$a = 4.929$

FIGURE 10-1

Factoring the radicand, (10) becomes

$$b = \sqrt{(6.254 + 4.929)(6.254 - 4.929)} = \sqrt{(11.183)(1.325)},$$

from which we have

$$\log b = \tfrac{1}{2}[\log 11.183 + \log 1.325]$$
$$= \tfrac{1}{2}[1.04856 + 0.12222]$$
$$= \tfrac{1}{2}(1.17078) = 0.58539$$

and

$$b = 3.8494.$$

Whenever possible, it is desirable to factor the radicand to facilitate direct use of logarithms so as to avoid intermediate antilogarithms. The process of factoring is not always possible; however, some simplicity can be gained by other devices.

EXAMPLE 5. Find $\log c$ if $c = \sqrt{a^2 + b^2}$.

Solution. From $c = \sqrt{a^2 + b^2}$ we have

$$c = \sqrt{\frac{a^2(a^2 + b^2)}{a^2}} = a\sqrt{1 + \left(\frac{b}{a}\right)^2}$$

and

$$\log c = \log a + \tfrac{1}{2} \log [1 + \text{antilog} (2 \log b - 2 \log a)].$$

Here we have reduced the number of antilogarithms to one, which is a useful reduction in the amount of work required for computation.

Exercises

In Exercises 1–6 find the colog of the given number.

1. 0.286.   *Ans.* 0.54363.

2. 0.619.

3. 0.000355.   *Ans.* 3.44977.

4. 0.0000572.

5. 14.06.   *Ans.* $8.85201 - 10$.

6. 27.18.

In Exercises 7–16 evaluate the given expressions by use of logarithms.

7. $\left(\dfrac{-4.35}{6.19}\right)^2$.   *Ans.* 0.49386.

8. $\left(\dfrac{4.98}{-3\pi}\right)^2$.

9. $\sqrt[3]{\dfrac{-285}{1.16 \times 3.29}}$.   *Ans.* -4.2110.

10. $\sqrt{\dfrac{(-14.9)(27.6)}{1.385}}$.

11. $(+0.0032)^{-1.25}$.   *Ans.* 1313.9.

12. $(-12.36)^{2/3}$.

13. $(14.6)^{-3}(-0.045)^{-5}$.   *Ans.* -1741.4.

14. $(0.0969)^{-32.9}$.

15. $(\tfrac{1}{8})^{-4.51}$.   *Ans.* 1.1829×10^4.

16. $(\tfrac{1}{2})^{-0.05}$.

In Exercises 17–30 evaluate the given expressions by use of logarithms. Use the values $a = 5.623$, $b = 4.995$, $c = 1.629$.

17. $\sqrt{a^2 - b^2}$.   *Ans.* 2.5846.

18. $\sqrt{b^2 - c^2}$.

19. $a^2 + c^2 - b^2$.   *Ans.* 9.322.

20. $a^2 + b^2 - c^2$.

21. $\sqrt{2ab - a^2}$.   *Ans.* 4.9553.

22. $\sqrt{s(s - a)(s - b)(s - c)}$ where $s = \tfrac{1}{2}(a + b + c)$.

23. $ab + bc$.   *Ans.* 36.224.

24. $\sqrt{3a(a + 2b)}$.

25. $a^2 + 2ab - 3b^2$.   *Ans.* 12.942.

26. $a^2 - 3ac + 2c^2$.

27. $a^2 - 4c^2$.   *Ans.* 21.005.

28. $a^3 - 3a^2c + 2ac^2$.

29. $\dfrac{a^2 + c^2 - 2ac}{2ab}$.   *Ans.* 0.28397.

30. $\sqrt[3]{c^2 - 3ac}$.

10-4 Miscellaneous Applications of Logarithms

pH Value

In chemistry the pH value of a solution is defined as the negative of the logarithm of the hydrogen ion concentration (using base 10). Thus, if a_{H}

is the hydrogen ion concentration, then the pH of the solution is

$$pH = -\log_{10} a_{\mathrm{H}}.$$

Thus, if the hydrogen ion concentration of a solution is given as $a_{\mathrm{H}} = 3 \times 10^{-3}$, then

$$pH = -\log(3 \times 10^{-3}) = -\log(0.003)$$
$$= -(7.48 - 10) = -(-2.52) = 2.52.$$

The greater the hydrogen ion concentration, the more acid the solution. A solution of $pH = 7$ is considered neutral.

If a pH value is known, the hydrogen ion concentration can be determined. Thus, if a substance has $pH = 9.8$, then from the definition of pH,

$$-\log_{10} a_{\mathrm{H}} = 9.8 \quad \text{and} \quad \log_{10} a_{\mathrm{H}} = -9.8.$$

Now since 10 is the base and -9.8 is the logarithm, we have

$$a_{\mathrm{H}} = 10^{-9.8} = 10^{-10} \times 10^{+0.2}.$$

From the table of logarithms $10^{+0.2} = 1.58$; then

$$a_{\mathrm{H}} = 1.58 \times 10^{-10}.$$

It is pointed out here that the number of significant figures involved in pH and concentrations is usually not beyond three; hence, the five-place tables in Appendix C are more than sufficient.

Decibels

M is the sound initially produced by a source, and N is a new sound produced by the same source after a change. If P_M and P_N are the power levels of the two sounds, the difference in loudness between M and N is measured in decibels by the expression

$$\text{decibel gain or loss} = 10 \log_{10} \frac{P_N}{P_M}. \tag{11}$$

If the ratio $0 < P_N/P_M < 1$, then $\log_{10} P_N/P_M < 0$, and we have a decibel loss. This occurs when the power has been diminished. In the case of a gain, the later power is greater than the initial power.

EXAMPLE 6. A loudspeaker is supplied by 2.5 watts producing a certain sound volume in an enclosure. If the power is increased to 3.5 watts, what is the gain in decibels?

Solution. Here $P_M = 2.5$ and $P_N = 3.5$. Substituting into (11), decibel gain (db) is

$$db = 10 \log_{10} \frac{3.5}{2.5} = 10 \log_{10} 1.4 = 10(0.146) = 1.46.$$

The power in sound-level studies can be described indirectly; that is, $P = I^2 R$ in electricity where I is intensity and R resistance. Also, $E = IR$ where E is electromotive force. Combination of E, I, and R can be given from which P is derived.

Radioactive Decay

The intensity of radioactivity is measured at intervals referred to as *half-life* intervals. The half-life is the time period required for the material's activity to decay by 50 per cent. Thus, if a material has a level of activity today of L, then the time period lapsing between now and the time when the activity level is $\frac{1}{2}L$ is called its half-life. The radioactive level of a substance is a measure of the amount of radioactive material present; therefore, 10 mg. of radioactive material will decompose to 5 mg. in a half-life.

An example of radioactive material is radium, which has a half life of 1580 years. This does not presume that full decay occurs in 2(1580) years, for such would be an assumption that the decay is linear as opposed to exponential. Actually, the amount at the end of 2(1580) year is $(\frac{1}{2})(\frac{1}{2})$ of the original amount. The amount after t years is given as

$$A = A_0(\tfrac{1}{2})^{t/1580},$$

where A is the instantaneous amount, A_0 is the amount at $t = 0$, and t is the time in years.

EXAMPLE 7. How many years are required for 10 mg. of radium to decay to 4 mg.?

Solution. Using the information from the preceding paragraph, $A = 4$ and $A_0 = 10$, so

$$4 = 10(\tfrac{1}{2})^{t/1580}$$

from which

$$0.4 = \left(\frac{1}{2}\right)^{t/1580} \quad \text{and} \quad \frac{t}{1580} \log\left(\frac{1}{2}\right) = \log 0.4.$$

Using base 10,

$$\frac{t}{1580}(-0.301) = -0.398,$$

from which we have the solution $t = 2190$ years.

Exercises

1. The pH value of a solution is given in parts (a) through (d). What are the hydrogen ion concentrations?

(a) 8.5.   *Ans.* 3.16×10^{-9}.

(b) 9.6.

(c) 3.2.   *Ans.* 6.31×10^{-4}.

(d) 4.6.

2. The hydrogen ion concentration of a solution is given in parts (a) through (d). What is the pH value in each case?

(a) 1.65×10^{-12}.   *Ans.* 11.8.

(b) 3.86×10^{-10}.

(c) 6.19×10^{-9}.   *Ans.* 8.2.

(d) 8.37×10^{-7}.

3. In parts (a) through (d) a loudspeaker is initially supplied with a power of P watts and the power is later changed to R watts. What is the gain (or loss) of decibels for the values of P and R given?

(a) $P = 4.3$, $R = 6.5$.   *Ans.* 1.8.

(b) $P = 1.3$, $R = 4.2$.

(c) $P = 5.2$, $R = 2.5$.   *Ans.* -3.2.

(d) $P = 8.4$, $R = 2.1$.

4. From electricity we have $P = I^2 R$ where P is power, I is intensity (amps.), and R is resistance (ohms). Also, $E = IR$, where E is electromotive force (volts). If an amplifying system has a resistance of 10 ohms and the voltage is changed from E_1 to E_2, find the decibel change if

(a) $E_1 = 50$, $E_2 = 100$.   *Ans.* 6.

(b) $E_1 = 100$, $E_2 = 50$.

(c) $E_1 = 75$, $E_2 = 52$.   *Ans.* -5.2.

(d) $E_1 = 108$, $E_2 = 126$.

5. If actinium has a half-life of 0.002 sec., 3 mg. of actinium will decay to what amount after 0.10 sec.?   *Ans.* 2.665×10^{-15} mg.

6. If a radioactive material has a half-life of 6 minutes, in how many seconds will it decay by 10%?

10-5   Exponential and Logarithmic Equations

An *exponential equation* is defined here as an equation where the variable is present in the exponent. Such equations can readily be solved by use of logarithms. It is generally less confusing to use logarithms to the base e rather than the base 10, but once again manipulation of the characteristic in base 10 can permit solutions. We will obtain our solutions in base 10.

Two devices are useful in solving exponential equations: (1) if feasible, take the logarithm of both sides of the equation or (2) retain the exponential form, changing all of the bases to the same base. These two devices actually are the same device if the logarithms in (1) are of the same base as the base used in (2). Consider an example.

EXAMPLE 8. Solve for x if

$$2^{3x-4} = 7^x$$

Solution 1. If we take the logarithm of both sides of the given equation we have

$$(3x - 4) \log 2 = x \log 7,$$

from which

$$(3x - 4)(0.30103) = x(0.84510).$$

Now we have a linear expression in x from which

$$0.05799x = 1.20412,$$
$$x = \frac{1.20412}{0.05799} = 20.764.$$

It is interesting to note that the division of 1.20412 by 0.05799 can be done by logarithms, despite the fact that those numbers are obtained from logarithms.

Solution 2. Given $2^{3x-4} = 7^x$, we can convert each base (2 and 7) to powers of the same base. If we use the table of logarithms in Appendix C, the base is 10. We could use base e or any other base. Thus, $2 = 10^{0.30103}$ and $7 = 10^{0.84510}$, so that we have

$$[(10)^{0.30103}]^{3x-4} = [(10)^{0.84510}]^x.$$

Now, with the bases alike, the exponents can be equated, and

$$0.30103(3x - 4) = 0.84510x.$$

The remainder of the solution is identical to Solution 1.

Sometimes the bases involved can be converted to the same base, which is neither 10 nor e. Consider Example 9.

EXAMPLE 9. Find x if $(2)^{x-1} = 8$.

Solution. Here we observe that both bases are powers of 2, hence we have $(2)^{x-1} = (2)^3$. Now, equating exponents because the bases are alike, $x - 1 = 3$, $x = 4$.

10-6   Logarithmic Equations

A *logarithmic equation* is defined here as an equation where at least one term involves a logarithmic expression of one or more variables. We will confine our work to expressions involving only one variable. Solutions depend upon fundamental properties of logarithms and often involve conversion to the exponential form. Consider some examples.

EXAMPLE 10. Find y if

$$\log (y + 3) + \log (y + 1) = \log 2 + \log (y + 3).$$

Solution. By the laws of logarithms, the given expression can be converted to

$$\log (y + 3)(y + 1) = \log 2(y + 3)$$

since the sum of the logarithms is the logarithm of the product. Now we take the antilogarithm of both sides, giving

$$(y + 3)(y + 1) = 2(y + 3),$$

which can be solved as a quadratic to yield solutions $y = -3$, $y = +1$. Only the solution $y = 1$ is permissible since $y = -3$ would involve the logarithm of a negative number.

EXAMPLE 11. Find x if $\log (5x + 20) = 2$.

Solution. Convert the given expression to the exponential form using base 10. Here 2 is the exponent, 10 is the base, so that $10^2 = 5x + 20$, from which $5x + 20 = 100$, $x = 16$.

Exercises

In Exercises 1–20 solve the given exponential equation for the variable present. Use whatever base seems to be most convenient.

1. $2^x = 8$.   *Ans.* $x = 3$.   **2.** $3^x = 81$.

3. $2^x = \frac{1}{16}$.   *Ans.* $x = -4$.   **4.** $4^x = \frac{1}{16}$.

5. $3^{-2x} = 27$.   *Ans.* $x = -3/2$.   **6.** $2^{-3x} = 16$.

7. $4^{x-1} = 2^{3x-1}$.   *Ans.* $x = 4$.   **8.** $3^{2x+4} = 9^{-x-1}$.

9. $81^{(x/2)+1} = 27^{4x-1}$.   *Ans.* $x = 0.7$.   **10.** $25^{Z+4} = 125^{3Z-2}$.

11. $4^{2Z+2} = 3^{Z-1}$.   *Ans.* $Z = -2.32$.   **12.** $2^{x-2} \cdot 3^{2x+1} = 1$.

13. $(0.4)^{0.5Z} = (1.9)^{2Z+3}$.

14. $\sqrt[K]{25} = 5$.

$$Ans.\ Z = -1.1.$$

15. $\sqrt[3K]{81} = 3$. $Ans.\ K = \frac{4}{3}$.

16. $\sqrt[K]{3} \times \sqrt[2K]{6} = 4$.

17. $\sqrt[m]{5} \times \sqrt[3m]{63} = 12$.

18. $\sqrt[2]{0.004} = 3^m$.

$$Ans.\ m = 1.21.$$

19. $\sqrt[3]{0.0065} = 4^n$.

20. $\sqrt[n]{4} = (4)^n$.

$$Ans.\ n = -1.21.$$

In Exercises 21–27 we are given the compound interest formula

$$A = P(1 + i)^n,$$

where A *is amount,* P *is principal,* i *is interest rate per year, and* n *is the number of years.*

21. What is the interest rate if an amount of $968 results from compounding a principal of $850 for 4 years?   *Ans.* 3.3%.

22. What is the interest rate if an amount of $255 results from compounding a principal of $225 for 3 years?

23. What principal is required to accumulate to an amount of $10,000 in 10 years at 5% interest rate?   *Ans.* $6139.00.

24. What principal is required to accumulate to an amount of $3000 in 5 years at 5% interest rate?

25. In how many years at 3.5% will a principal of $7000 accumulate to $10,000?   *Ans.* 10.37 years.

26. In how many years at 5% will a principal double?

27. If a man wishes to double his money in 12 years, what would be the interest rate required?   *Ans.* 5.96%.

In Exercises 28–30, apply the formula

$$i = \frac{V}{R}(1 - e^{-Rt/L}),$$

where V *is a steady voltage applied to an inductance* L *in series with a resistance* R *with* i = *current and* t = *time.*

28. At what time does $i = 3$ amp. if $V = 120$, $R = 12$, and $L = 0.3$? $(e = 2.718 = 10^{0.4343})$.   *Ans.* $t = 0.00895$.

29. What voltage V is required if $i = 5$ when $t = 0.006$ with $R = 10$ and $L = 0.5$?   *Ans.* $V = 443$.

30. Determine L for a system where $V = 100$, $R = 2$, and $i = 5$ when $t = 0.01$.

Ans. $L = 0.19$.

In Exercises 31–38 solve the given logarithmic equation for the variable present.

31. $\text{Log}_{10} x^2 = 4$. *Ans. $x = \pm 100$.*

32. $\text{Log}_{10} (x - 4) = 1$.

33. $\text{Log}_2 A + \log_2 (A + 6) = 4$. *Ans. $A = 2$.*

34. $1 + \log_{10} x = \log_{10} (x + 1)$.

35. $2 + \log_2 k = \log_2 (k + 5)$. *Ans. $k = 5/3$.*

36. $\text{Log } A - \log P = n \log (1 + i)$ (solve for P).

37. $\text{Log } x = (1/n) \log A$. *Ans. $A = x^n$.*

38. $bn \log x = \log y - \log a$. (solve for y).

10-7 Conversions Between Bases

Let us assume that we are given an exponential in one base (base a) and wish to convert this expression to an exponential in another base (base b). We will start with the expression

$$y = a^x \tag{12}$$

and will convert it to another expression

$$y = b^z. \tag{13}$$

If we take the logarithm (to any base, say the base c) of (12) and of (13) we have

$$\log_c y = x \log_c a \quad \text{and} \quad \log_c y = z \log_c b. \tag{14}$$

Now, by substitution, we have

$$x \log_c a = z \log_c b$$

so that

$$z = x(\log_c a)/(\log_c b)$$

and we have

$$a^x = b^{z \,(\log_c a)/(\log_c b)} \tag{15}$$

In the preceding paragraph it is unnecessary in most cases to introduce a third base c. The logarithm taken to obtain (14) might more wisely have been to the base a or b, from which (15) becomes either

$$a^x = b^{x\,(\log_a a)/(\log_a b)} = b^{x/\log_a b} \tag{16}$$

or

$$a^x = b^{x\,(\log_b a)/(\log_b b)} = b^{x\,\log_b a}. \tag{17}$$

For conversions between base 10 and base e, from (16) let $a = 10$ and $b = e$, so that

$$10^x = e^{x/\log_{10} e}. \tag{18}$$

Now in (18) $\log_{10} e = \log_{10} 2.718 = 0.4343$ and (18) becomes

$$10^x = e^{x/0.4343}, \tag{19}$$

where (19) asserts that: *to change a logarithm from base 10 to base e, divide the logarithm by 0.4343.* Also, from (19), if we raise both sides to the 0.4343 power, we have

$$10^{0.4343x} = e^x, \tag{20}$$

where (20) asserts that: *to change a logarithm from base e to base 10, multiply the logarithm by 0.4343.*

EXAMPLE 12. Express the number 12 as a power of the base e.

Solution. Since we have only the base 10 logarithms in Appendix C, we will express 12 as a power of base 10. Hence

$$12 = 10^{1.07918}. \tag{21}$$

Now from (19),

$$10^{1.07918} = e^{1.07918/0.4343} = e^{2.48491}. \tag{22}$$

From Example 12 we have a method of using a table of common logarithms to find the natural (base e) logarithms of numbers. From (21) and (22), we can say that

$$\log_e 12 = 2.48491.$$

Convention. *It is a common convention to express $\log_e$ N by another notation ln N, where ln is used to indicate natural (or base e) logarithms.*

EXAMPLE 13. If ln $N = 2.0000$, find N using Appendix C.

Solution. From ln $N = 2.0000$ we have the exponential $e^2 = N$, but from (20),

$$e^2 = 10^{2(0.4343)} = 10^{0.8686} = 7.389.$$

Exercises

Solve the given equation for the variable present by taking the logarithm to the base 10 of both sides.

1. $10^2 = 3^y$.   *Ans.* $y = 4.192$.   **2.** $10^3 = 6^y$.

3. $10^{2.5} = e^y$.   *Ans.* $y = 5.756$.   **4.** $10^{1.8} = e^y$.

5. $6^3 = 10^y$.   *Ans.* $y = 2.334$.   **6.** $2^{3.6} = 10^y$.

7. $e^4 = 10^x$.   *Ans.* $x = 1.737$.   **8.** $e^{2.5} = 10^x$.

9. $3^{10} = 6^y$.   *Ans.* $y = 6.131$.   **10.** $2^{1.1} = 8^x$.

11. $6^{-2} = 3^y$.   *Ans.* $y = 3.262$.   **12.** $15^{-.55} = 2^y$.

13. $y = \log_4 100$.   *Ans.* $y = 3.322$.   **14.** $x = \log_{0.5} 10$.

15. $x = \log_2 3^{1.5}$.   *Ans.* $x = 2.377$.

10-8   The L and LL Scales on the Slide Rule

At this point it is worthwhile to discuss more on the slide rule. The standard slide rule is constructed using logarithms; the A, B, C, D, Cl, Dl, ClF, D1F, K, S, T, and ST scales are constructed in such a way that the entries there are not equally spaced, but are spaced according to the logarithm of the entry. The only scale on which the entries are equally spaced is the L-scale.

The L-Scale

The L-scale is perhaps the least-used scale on a slide rule; it is so seldom used that it is often omitted on the less-detailed models available. However, as previously stated, most of the scales on the slide rule rely upon an L-scale. The L-scale is frequently given the legend "log x" where the C and D scales are given the legend "x". Hence, if x is on the C-scale, a direct transfer to the L-scale finds log x; more specifically, this transfer finds $\log_{10} x$.

For purpose of plotting, let

$$y = \log_{10} x, \tag{23}$$

from which we have

$$x = 10^y. \tag{24}$$

Now (23) and (24) are different forms of the same function. The graph of (23) is shown normally graphed in Fig. 10-2.

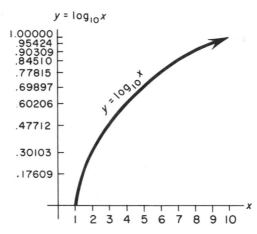

FIGURE 10–2

In Fig. 10-3 we have located on the y-axis the positions $\log_{10} 1 = 0.00000$, $\log_{10} 2 = 0.30103$, $\log_{10} 3 = 0.47712$, etc. and have projected these positions horizontally to the line $y = x$, then vertically to the x-axis. We note that such a method of projection creates an unequally spaced set of numbers 1, 2, 3, 4, etc. The spacing on the x-axis is identical with that on the C-scale of the slide rule. If the x-axis were rotated through $90°$ to meet the y-axis (this characterizes placing the C-scale opposite the L-scale), then the number 2 would be exactly opposite $\log_{10} 2$, 3 would be opposite $\log_{10} 3$, etc. We can say, then, that the entries on the C-scale are not equally spaced according to the integers 1, 2, 3, etc., but are equally spaced according to the logarithms of those integers.

EXAMPLE 13. Using the slide rule find $\log_{10} 17$.

Solution. Here $x = 17$ is found on the C-scale and $\log_{10} x = \log_{10} 17$ is found directly opposite on the L-scale. Thus, from Fig. 10-4, we place the hairline over 17 on the C-scale and read $\log_{10} 17 = 1.230$ from the L-scale under the hairline. (Note that 0.230 is read from the L-scale where 0.230 is the *mantissa*. The characteristic is supplied as usual by the operator.) Thus, $\log_{10} 17 = 1.230$.

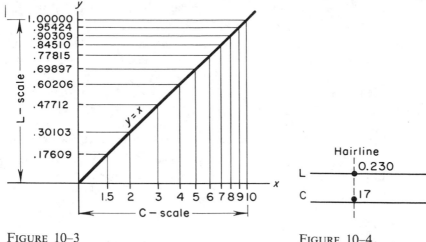

FIGURE 10-3

FIGURE 10-4

Since the entries on the L-scale are equally spaced and the entries on the C and D scales correspond, arithmetic addition on the C and D scales performs addition of logarithms or multiplication. Arithmetic subtraction on the C and D scales performs division.

It is worth noting here that (since the A-scale is a double scale) all entries on the A-scale are positioned not where $\log x$ would be but where $2 \log x$ would be. Hence, the squaring property of the A-scale. The K scale is a triple scale, hence its cubing property.

The LL-Scales

The LL-scales are referred to as the "log-log" scales. More properly they should be called the "log-ln" scales according to our convention of using ln to designate natural logarithms. Slide rules vary as to the number of LL-scales which they contain; this once again is a matter of completeness and space available. We will assume here a slide rule with *eight* LL-scales, namely, the LL_0, LL_1, LL_2, LL_3, LL_{00}, LL_{01}, LL_{02}, and LL_{03} scales. Inspection of those scales reveals:

(1) The LL_1 is an extension of the LL_0, the LL_2 is an extension of the LL_1, etc. Also, the LL_{01} is an extension of the LL_{00}, the LL_{02} is an extension of the LL_{01}, etc.

(2) The ranges of values of numbers shown on the LL-scales are:
   (*a*) The LL_0 through LL_3 have entries ranging from 1.001 to 4×10^4, depending on scale extensions.
   (*b*) The LL_{00} through LL_{03} have entries ranging from 0.999 to 3×10^{-4}, depending on scale extensions.

(3) The numbers on the LL-scales are complete in the sense that decimal points are provided.

Entries on the LL-scales are powers of the natural base e. Thus, an entry can be called e^x, and the LL-scales are so constructed that the exponent x

Table 10-1

POWERS OF e AS GIVEN ON THE LL-SCALES ($1 < x < 10$)

Scale	Power of e	Range of Values of Power of e			
LL_3	x	e^1	to e^{10}	or	2.718 to 4×10^4
LL_2	$0.1x$	$e^{0.1}$	to e^1	or	1.1 to 2.718
LL_1	$0.01x$	$e^{0.01}$	to $e^{0.1}$	or	1.01 to 1.1
LL_0	$0.001x$	$e^{0.001}$	to $e^{0.01}$	or	1.001 to 1.01
LL_{00}	$-0.001x$	$e^{-0.001}$	to $e^{-0.01}$	or	0.999 to 0.99
LL_{01}	$-0.01x$	$e^{-0.01}$	to $e^{-0.1}$	or	0.99 to 0.91
LL_{02}	$-0.1x$	$e^{-0.1}$	to e^{-1}	or	0.91 to 0.4
LL_{03}	$-x$	e^{-1}	to e^{-10}	or	0.4 to 3×10^{-4}

is vertically opposed on the D-scale. Since $x = \ln e^x$, x is on the D-scale, and entries on the L-scale are $\log_{10}$ of those on the D-scale, we can understand the name "log-ln" previously referred to.

Assuming that $1 < x < 10$, then the entries on the LL-scales are as shown in Table 10-1. *Note*: Some slide rules are so constructed that negative powers of e are oriented from the B-scale while positive powers are oriented from the D-scale, making portions of Table 10-1 inappropriate.

EXAMPLE 14. Find the value of $e^{0.45}$.

Solution. The exponent is on the D-scale, hence we place the hairline over 45 on the D-scale as in Fig. 10-5. There are eight LL-scales over which the hairline rests, posing the problem of the proper choice of LL-scales from which to obtain $e^{0.45}$. From Table 10-1 we see that with $1 < x < 10$, the LL_2-scale

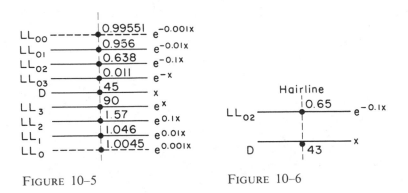

FIGURE 10-5   FIGURE 10-6

has a power of e called $0.1x$ so that $0.1 < 0.1x < 1$. Now 0.45 is in this range, hence we read $e^{0.45} = 1.57$ from the LL_2 scale.

EXAMPLE 15. What power of e is the number 0.65?

Solution. Here we can set up the equation $e^k = 0.65$, where we wish to find k. Since powers of e are entered on the LL-scales complete with decimal points, we scan the LL-scales to find the number 0.65. We find it on the LL_{02}-scale and place the hairline over it as in Fig. 10-6. Under the hairline we read from the D-scale the number whose significant figures are 43. The only remaining problem is to determine the sign and decimal-point location of the exponent; since 0.65 came from the LL_{02}-scale, where the exponent is of the order $-0.1x$ (where $1 < x < 10$), then our exponent is -0.43, and we have the solution $k = -0.43$ or $e^{-0.43} = 0.65$.

It is noted here that since e^k is the reciprocal of e^{-k}, then direct transfer from, say, the LL_{01}-scale to its reciprocal companion LL_1 reciprocates the hairlined number.

The LL-scales can be used (within certain limits) to evaluate powers of any base. This means that we are not limited to the base e. Consider some examples.

EXAMPLE 16. Find N if $N = (0.31)^{-0.25}$.

Solution. First, we will express the base 0.31 as a power of e. Place the hairline over 0.31 on the LL_{03}-scale and read $0.31 = e^{-1.17}$ from the D-scale under the hairline as in Fig. 10-7. Now we have the expression

$$N = (0.31)^{-0.25} = (e^{-1.17})^{-0.25}. \tag{25}$$

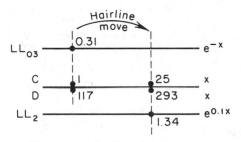

FIGURE 10-7

In expression (25) we must multiply the exponents according to the laws of logarithms. Since, in Fig. 10-7, the hairline is over 117 on the D-scale, place the C-index opposite 117 and then move the hairline over 25 on the C-scale. Under the hairline on the D-scale we find $-1.17 \times -0.25 = 0.293$, where the operator provided the proper sign and decimal point. Now (25) reads

$$N = (0.31)^{-0.25} = (e^{-1.17})^{-0.25} = e^{0.293}.$$

Since we now have the hairline over the exponent 0.293 on the D-scale, transfer along the hairline to the LL_2-scale gives us

$$N = e^{0.293} = 1.34.$$

EXAMPLE 17. Find b if $0.94 = b^{1.86}$.

Solution. Call b some power of e, say $b = e^k$ so that we have

$$0.94 = e^{1.86k}. \tag{26}$$

Now in (26), express 0.94 as a power of e and equate exponents. Using the LL_{01}-and D-scales, as shown in Fig. 10-8, we have $0.94 = e^{-0.0619}$, and

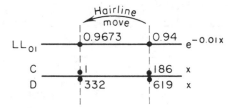

FIGURE 10–8

(26) becomes

$$e^{-0.0619} = e^{1.86k}. \tag{27}$$

Now, from Fig. 10-8 we have the hairline over 619. With the exponents of (27) equated,

$$1.86k = -0.0619, \tag{28}$$

and we must divide 0.0619 by 1.86 to obtain k. Place 1.86 of the C-scale under the hairline opposite 619 on the D-scale and move the hairline to the C-index. Now read the solution of (28),

$$k = -0.0332,$$

from the D-scale under the hairline. Our original substitution had

$$b = e^k = e^{-0.0332}. \tag{29}$$

The hairline, from Fig. 10-8, is now over 332 on the D-scale and $e^{-0.0332}$ is read from the LL_{01}-scale as

$$b = e^{-0.0332} = 0.9673,$$

where $b = 0.9673$ is the desired base.

EXAMPLE 18. Find k if $36.5 = (0.92)^k$.

Solution. Let us first express 36.5 and 0.92 as powers of e so that we have $e^{3.6} = 36.5$ from the D- and LL_3-scales and $e^{-0.0832} = 0.92$ from the D- and LL_{01}-scales. Now

$$e^{3.6} = (e^{-0.0832})^k = e^{-0.0832k}. \qquad (30)$$

Equating exponents in (30), we have $3.6 = -0.0832k$, from which $k = -43.2$, the desired solution.

Exercises

Find the literal quantity by use of the slide rule.

1. $e^{4.2} = N.$ *Ans.* $N = 66.7.$ **2.** $e^{-8.6} = N.$

3. $e^{0.047} = N.$ *Ans.* $N = 1.0481.$ **4.** $e^{-0.37} = N.$

5. $e^{-0.096} = N.$ *Ans.* $N = 0.9084.$ **6.** $(1.04)^{4.2} = N.$

7. $(0.95)^{-3.6} = N.$ **8.** $(0.02)^{-0.02} = N.$

            Ans. $N = 1.2025.$

9. $\sqrt[25]{4216} = N.$ *Ans.* $N = 1.397.$ **10.** $\sqrt[10]{0.00385} = N.$

11. $e^x = 4.5.$ *Ans.* $x = 1.504.$ **12.** $e^x = 0.025.$

13. $(0.04)^x = 27.$ *Ans.* $x = -1.025.$ **14.** $(0.982)^x = 0.02.$

15. $b^{2.7} = 48.2.$ *Ans.* $b = 4.2.$ **16.** $b^{-0.09} = 1.06.$

17. $(0.619)^{1.95} = N.$ *Ans.* $N = 0.392.$ **18.** $(2 \times 10^{-5})^{0.033} = N.$

19. $(0.775)^{-3.4} = N.$ *Ans.* $N = 2.38.$ **20.** $e^{14.3} = N.$

21. $e^{-12.7} = N.$ **22.** $e^{22.7} = N.$

            Ans. $N = 3.1 \times 10^{-6}.$

23. $(12.4)^{9.8} = N.$ **24.** $(0.092)^{0.00042} = N.$

            Ans. $N = 5.19 \times 10^{10}.$

25. $\sqrt[5]{12,800} = N.$ *Ans.* $N = 6.62.$ **26.** $(0.985)^{15.6} = N.$

Additional Exercises

1. When a switch is closed to apply a constant voltage E to a circuit containing an inductance L and a resistance R, the current i increases from zero to a maximum value. The instantaneous value of current at any time t seconds after the switch is closed is given by

$$i = \frac{E}{R}(1 - e^{-Rt/L}).$$

If L is 0.8 henrys, R is 16 ohms, and E is 32 volts, find i when t is 0.03 seconds.

Ans. $i = 0.9$ amperes.

2. Referring to the equation of Exercise 1, show that $i = 0$ when $t = 0$, and that i approaches E/R as a maximum value when t is increased. (Try $t = 1$ second.)

3. Find t in Exercise 1 when $i = 90\%$ of its maximum value.

Ans. $t = 0.115$ seconds.

4. A convenient measure of the rapidity of current increase in the circuit of Exercise 1 is the value of time t numerically equal to the ratio L/R, known as the time constant. Show, for any such circuit, that the current has increased to 63.2% of its maximum value when t equals L/R seconds.

5. From the relation $\ln N = \ln N_0 - kt$, show that $N = N_0 e^{-kt}$.

6. The atoms of a radioactive material disintegrate, forming a new substance and reducing the amount of active material present. In the equation below, N_0 is the original amount of radioactive material in a sample at some time. N is the amount remaining t seconds later.

$$N = N_0 e^{-kt}$$

If N_0 is 3.5 grams and the decay constant k for the material is $3.2(10)^{-6}$, find the amount remaining two days later.

7. The half-life of a radioactive material is the time required for half of the atoms to disintegrate. From the equation of Exercise 6 show that the half-life equals $0.693/k$.

8. Five per cent of a radioactive sample has disintegrated in 10 days. Using the equation of Exercise 6 find the total time in days required for disintegration of 80% of the original amount. The decay constant and the time may be solved for using days for time units.

9. An annual payment P, invested at the end of each year for n years and earning interest at i per cent compounded annually, will build a "sinking fund" S. The annual payment required is

$$P = \frac{Si}{(1 + i)^n - 1}.$$

If a company has just purchased a $30,000 machine and wishes to have a sinking fund available in 15 years to replace it, what annual payment must be made? Interest is at 5 per cent, or $i = 0.05$.

10. The expression for sound level in decibels is $DB = 10 \log (I/I_0)$, where I is the intensity of sound power in watts/cm.^{2} at the point of interest. I_0 is 10^{-16} watts/cm.^{2}, a reference value approximating a barely audible sound. If the sound level is 80 db. at a certain distance R from a small source, what would the sound level be at a distance five times as great? The intensity of sound power varies inversely as the square of distance from the source, or $I_1/I_2 = R_2^2/R_1^2$.

11. If people begin life as a single biological cell, and by cell division become fully grown with about ten billion cells, how many generations of cell division are required? Neglect the effect of cell deaths and assume that all cells require the same time from one division to the next. *Ans.* 34.

12. The electrical resistance R of a thermistor decreases as its temperature T is increased, according to the relation

$$R = (R_a)e^{B\left(\frac{1}{T} - \frac{1}{T_a}\right)}.$$

R_a is the resistance at temperature T_a. Find R when T is 370°K if R_a is 25 ohms at 300°K. The constant B, which depends on the type of thermistor, has the value 3530.

13. At what temperature T would the thermistor in Exercise 12 have a resistance R of 10 ohms? *Ans.* $T = 325°K$.

14. From the equation of Exercise 12 make a graph of R vs. T for values of T from 300 to 370°K. Four points may be sufficient. Use the given values for B, R_a, and T_a.

15. If the work put into compressing a gas is done at the same rate at which energy is removed from the gas by a cooling system, there is no change in gas temperature and the process is called isothermal compression. The work required is

$$W = P_1 V_1 \ln \frac{V_2}{V_1}.$$

Find the foot-pounds of work required if the initial pressure P_1 is 2100 lb/ft², the initial volume V_1 is 5 ft³, and the final volume V_2 is 1.2 ft³. A negative answer indicates work is done on the gas. *Ans.* $W = -15,000$ ft-lb.

16. Referring to Exercise 15, what initial volume V_1 can be isothermally compressed by twice the amount of work in Exercise 15? Use the same initial pressure and final volume. A trial-and-error procedure may be required.

17. If a principal P is invested at interest rate $i = 0.04$ compounded annually, in how many years will the investor's money double? In how many years will it triple? Use the compound interest formula

$$A = P(1 + i)^t.$$

Ans. Doubles in 17.7 years

18. Given $i = 120$, solve for t in the equation

$$i = 240e^{t^2 - 2t}.$$

Ans. $t = 0.445, 1.555.$

19. The population of a certain city doubles every 40 years. If the population in 1900 was 10,000, what was the population in 1960? *Ans.* 28,500

20. A sequence of terms is given as

$$100, 90, 81, 72.9, \cdots$$

where each term is 90 per cent of the previous term. Calculate the value of the tenth term of the sequence; the 51st term. Use logarithms for the computations.

Ans. 38.74; 0.515.

21. Solve for t in Exercise 1.

22. The temperature of the atmosphere in a certain room is 70°F. A vat of liquid at temperature 180°F is brought into the room. The liquid cools in such a way that its temperature falls, during any 30-minute interval, to a reading half-way between the room temperature and the liquid temperature at the beginning of the 30-minute time period. That is, during the first 30 minutes, the liquid temperature falls $(180° - 70°)/2 = 55°$ to a reading of 125°F; during the second 30 minutes the temperature falls $(125° - 70°)/2 = 27.5°$ to a reading of $125° - 27.5° = 97.5°$F, etc. In how many minutes will the temperature of the liquid fall from 180°F to 75°F, assuming that the room temperature remains at 70°F? *Ans.* 132.3 mins.

In this chapter trigonometric functions will be introduced. Definitions of the trigonometric functions, reciprocal and cofunctional relationships will be discussed. The approach is vectorial in nature, with vectors placed on the Cartesian coordinate plane. Emphasis is placed on the determination of horizontal and vertical components of vectors, with a view to applications in mechanics, physics, surveying, and electricity.

TRIGONOMETRY OF
RIGHT TRIANGLES 11

11-1   Vectors on the Cartesian Coordinate Plane

Quantities such as light, mass, area, volume, and so forth, which are characterized by magnitude only, are given the name *scalars*. Scalars are usually discussed in conjunction with *vectors*, quantities which are characterized by both magnitude and direction. A vector is usually represented by a straight line; the length of the line is intended to represent the magnitude of the quantity involved, and a direction is assigned. Physical quantities such as velocity, acceleration, and force are examples of vectors.

In Fig. 11-1 conventions regulating the description of vectors on the Cartesian coordinate plane are displayed. In all cases, the vectors originate at the origin, O, and terminate at P_1, P_2, or P_3. Length units on the vector, consistent with those on the x-axis and the y-axis, are shown. The arrowhead or barb at the terminal end of the vector conveys direction, or perhaps more explicitly, *sense*. Note that OP_1 is of magnitude 5, OP_2 is of magnitude 4, and OP_3 is of magnitude approximately 4.5.

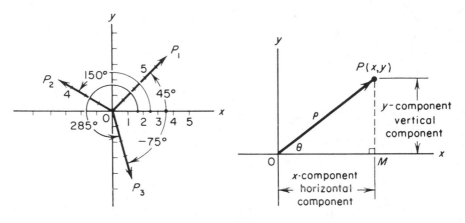

FIGURE 11–1   FIGURE 11–2

Directions of the vectors in Fig. 11-1 are shown in angular units (degrees in this case) and are consistently measured from the right-hand horizontal, with the counterclockwise direction being called positive and the clockwise direction negative. The angle between the right-hand horizontal and the vector is called the *reference angle*. Thus, OP_1 is of magnitude 5 and has a reference angle of 45°. Note that OP_3 has a magnitude of approximately 4.5 and has a reference angle of either $+285°$ or $-75°$.

For our purposes here we will consider the magnitudes of all vectors as positive; this is merely a convention to be used here and is not universally adopted. We will depart from the convention in a later chapter on the *j*-operator. The general designation that we will assign to the magnitude of the vector is ρ (the Greek letter "rho") and the general reference angle is θ (the Greek letter "theta").

In Fig. 11-2, we see a vector **OP** with initial end at O and terminal end at P. The point P is at a position designated by the coordinates (x, y). If a vertical line MP is drawn from P perpendicular to the x-axis, two sides of a right triangle OPM are formed. MP is called the y-*component* or *vertical component* of **OP**. The length of MP is exactly the ordinate of P, namely, y. OM is called the x-*component* or *horizontal component*; its length is exactly the abscissa of P, namely, x.

It is important for us to recognize that, even though the magnitude ρ is, by our convention, always positive, the horizontal and vertical components can be either negative or positive, according to the size of θ. Referring to Fig 11-3(a), we observe the following: if OP terminates in quadrant II ($90° < \theta < 180°$) then the vertical component is positive and the horizontal component is negative. If OP terminates in quadrant IV ($270° < \theta < 360°$) the vertical component is negative and the horizontal is positive. From Fig. 11-3(b), we see that both components are positive in quadrant I ($0° < \theta < 90°$) and both are negative in quadrant III ($180° < \theta < 270°$).

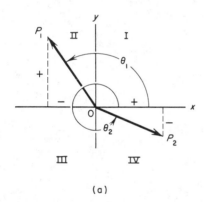
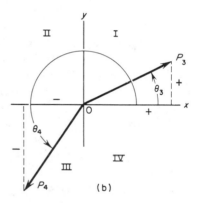

(a) (b)

FIGURE 11–3

Exercises

1. Calling the magnitude of a vector ρ (always positive), the horizontal component x and the vertical component y, we have six possible ratios involving the division of one of these quantities by another, namely

$$\frac{y}{\rho}, \quad \frac{x}{\rho}, \quad \frac{y}{x}, \quad \frac{\rho}{y}, \quad \frac{\rho}{x}, \quad \frac{x}{y}.$$

Determine the sign of each of these six ratios for a vector which initiates at the origin and terminates in the (*a*) First quadrant.   *Ans.* All positive.

(*b*) Second quadrant.

(*c*) Third quadrant.   *Ans.* *x/y, y/x* positive, rest negative.

(*d*) Fourth quadrant.

2. If two vectors are exactly 180° apart, compare the signs of their horizontal components; vertical components; magnitudes; ratio of horizontal to vertical components.

What positive reference angle, less than 360°, is the equivalent of the angle given in Exercises 3–8?

3. 400°.   *Ans.* 40°.

4. −80°.

5. 725°.   *Ans.* 5°.

6. 1000°.

7. −885°.   *Ans.* 195°.

8. −718°.

11-2   Definitions of the Trigonometric Functions

We consider six trigonometric functions. Each is a ratio of two sides of the triangle sketched in Fig. 11-4 and each is a function of the angle θ. These

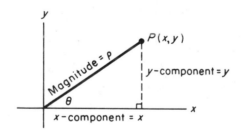

FIGURE 11-4

functions are purely definitions and must therefore be memorized. Taking our symbols from Fig. 11-4 we will define the trigonometric functions as

$$\text{sine of } \theta = \sin \theta = \frac{y}{\rho}, \tag{1}$$

$$\text{cosine of } \theta = \cos \theta = \frac{x}{\rho}, \tag{2}$$

$$\text{tangent of } \theta = \tan \theta = \frac{y}{x}, \tag{3}$$

$$\text{cosecant of } \theta = \csc \theta = \frac{\rho}{y}, \tag{4}$$

$$\text{secant of } \theta = \sec \theta = \frac{\rho}{x}, \tag{5}$$

$$\text{cotangent of } \theta = \operatorname{ctn} \theta = \frac{x}{y}. \tag{6}$$

We note that the six definitions given made reference to a vector drawn on a Cartesian coordinate plane and the components of the vector. Many students are acquainted with geometrically slanted definitions which employ the terms "side opposite," "side adjacent," and "hypotenuse"; these terms are shown in Fig. 11-5 and have their equivalents in Fig. 11-4. It is worthwhile to draw comparisons here. In Fig. 11-5(a) we are given a right triangle with the hypotenuse, the side opposite the angle θ, and the side adjacent to the angle θ shown. In Fig. 11-5(b) the same triangle is placed on a Cartesian

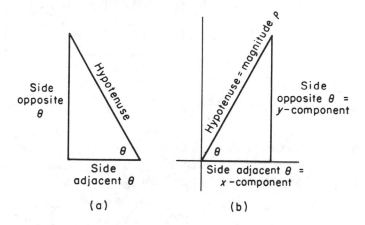

FIGURE 11-5

coordinate plane, showing the equivalencies of the hypotenuse, side opposite, and side adjacent to the magnitude, y-component, and x-component, respectively.

In view of the comparative nomenclature drawn from Fig. 11-5, we may redefine the trigonometric functions in terms of the hypotenuse, side opposite, and side adjacent as:

$$\sin \theta = \frac{\text{side opposite } \theta}{\text{hypotenuse}}, \tag{7}$$

$$\cos \theta = \frac{\text{side adjacent } \theta}{\text{hypotenuse}}, \tag{8}$$

$$\tan \theta = \frac{\text{side opposite } \theta}{\text{side adjacent } \theta}, \tag{9}$$

$$\csc \theta = \frac{\text{hypotenuse}}{\text{side opposite } \theta}, \tag{10}$$

$$\sec \theta = \frac{\text{hypotenuse}}{\text{side adjacent } \theta}, \tag{11}$$

$$\text{ctn } \theta = \frac{\text{side adjacent } \theta}{\text{side opposite } \theta}. \tag{12}$$

EXAMPLE 1. Give the numerical values of the six trigonometric functions of θ in Fig. 11-6(a).

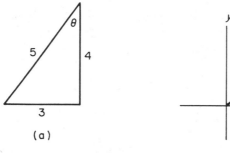

(a) (b)

FIGURE 11–6

Solution. Using notation consistent with Fig. 11-4 and definitions (1) through (6), we place the given triangle on a Cartesian coordinate plane as in Fig. 11-6(b). Now, $x = 4$, $y = 3$, and $\rho = 5$, so that

$$\sin \theta = \frac{y}{\rho} = \frac{3}{5} = 0.600, \qquad \csc \theta = \frac{\rho}{y} = \frac{5}{3} = 1.667,$$

$$\cos \theta = \frac{x}{\rho} = \frac{4}{5} = 0.800, \qquad \sec \theta = \frac{\rho}{x} = \frac{5}{4} = 1.250,$$

$$\tan \theta = \frac{y}{x} = \frac{3}{4} = 0.750, \qquad \text{ctn } \theta = \frac{x}{y} = \frac{4}{3} = 1.333.$$

In Example 1 we could have said that the side opposite θ is 3, the side adjacent θ is 4, and the hypotenuse is 5, then applied definitions (7) through (12).

Let us now examine the components of vectors whose reference angles are 30°, 45°, and 60°. These special angles will provide opportunity for additional exercises involving the trigonometric functions, without reference to the tables of trigonometric functions.

Functions of 30° and 60°

An equilateral triangle may be assumed to have sides of length $2s$; its angles are all 60°. If a perpendicular is drawn to one side from the opposing vertex, as the dotted line in Fig. 11-7(a), it bisects that side. If we call the altitude

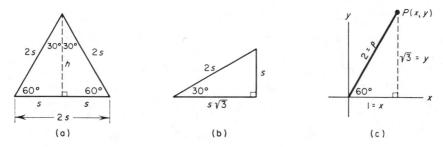

FIGURE 11-7

h, we have the Pythagorean relationship

$$(h)^2 + (s)^2 = (2s)^2$$

from which

$$h^2 = 4s^2 - s^2 = 3s^2$$

and

$$h = s\sqrt{3}. \tag{13}$$

Expression (13) shows that either triangle formed by the bisector can be shown as the triangle in Fig. 11-7(b), where the ratio of the sides of a 30°-60° right triangle is $s : 2s : s\sqrt{3}$, or $1 : 2 : \sqrt{3}$ where the smallest side (s) is opposite the 30° angle, the largest side $(2s)$ is the hypotenuse, and the remaining side $(s\sqrt{3})$ is opposite the 60° angle.

EXAMPLE 2. Find tan 60°, sec 60°, and csc 60°.

Solution. Sketch a vector with reference angle 60° measured from the right-hand horizontal in a counterclockwise direction. From the terminal end of the vector drop a perpendicular to the x-axis as shown in Fig. 11-7(c). Since the resulting right triangle is a 30°-60° right triangle, assign values in the proper $1 : 2 : \sqrt{3}$ ratio as shown. Now,

$$\tan 60° = \frac{y}{x} = \frac{\sqrt{3}}{1} = \sqrt{3},$$

$$\sec 60° = \frac{\rho}{x} = \frac{2}{1} = 2,$$

$$\csc 60° = \frac{\rho}{y} = \frac{2}{\sqrt{3}} = \frac{2\sqrt{3}}{3}.$$

Functions of 45°

If a diagonal is drawn in a square of side s, it divides the square into two right triangles with angles 45°, 45°, and 90°. The sides of the 45° right triangle can be shown to be in the ratio $1 : 1 : \sqrt{2}$, as shown in Fig. 11-8(a). (The proof is left as an exercise for the student.) The sides s and s (or 1 and 1) are opposite the 45° angles and the side $s\sqrt{2}$ is opposite the 90° angle.

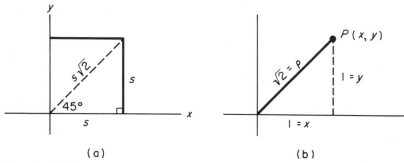

(a)   (b)

FIGURE 11–8

EXAMPLE 3. Find cos 45°, ctn 45°, and sin 45°.

Solution. From Fig. 11-8, we see the components $x = 1$, $y = 1$, and magnitude $\rho = \sqrt{2}$. Now,

$$\cos 45° = \frac{x}{\rho} = \frac{1}{\sqrt{2}} = \frac{\sqrt{2}}{2},$$

$$\text{ctn } 45° = \frac{x}{y} = \frac{1}{1} = 1,$$

$$\sin 45° = \frac{y}{\rho} = \frac{1}{\sqrt{2}} = \frac{\sqrt{2}}{2}.$$

Exercises

1. Complete the chart shown. Rationalize denominators. Recall the ratios given in Fig. 11–7 and Fig. 11–8.

θ	$\sin \theta$	$\cos \theta$	$\tan \theta$	$\csc \theta$	$\sec \theta$	$\operatorname{ctn} \theta$
30°	$\frac{1}{2}$					
45°		$\sqrt{2}/2$		$\sqrt{2}$		
60°					2	

2. Given the triangle in Fig. 11–9, give all six of the trigonometric functions of each θ and ϕ. Since θ and ϕ are *complementary* angles, determine which functions of θ and ϕ are equal; this might provide a lead to the prefix *co-* on three of the trigonometric functions.

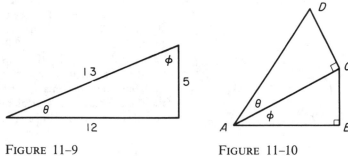

FIGURE 11–9   FIGURE 11–10

3. Given two points on a Cartesian coordinate plane with descriptions $P_1(-3, -4)$ and $P_2(2, 3)$, what is the tangent of the angle θ formed by a horizontal line drawn to the right through P_1 and by the line $P_1 P_2$? *Ans.* Tan $\theta = \frac{7}{5}$.

4. Given Fig. 11–10 with $AB = 1$, $BC = 2$, and $CD = 2$. Find sec ϕ and cos θ.
Ans. Sec $\phi = \sqrt{5}$; $\cos \theta = \frac{1}{3}\sqrt{5}$.

5. Given a 30°–60° right triangle with hypotenuse 10. Find the lengths of the legs of the triangle, using the definitions of the sine and cosine functions.

6. In Fig. 11–4 we have the Pythagorean relationship

$$x^2 + y^2 = \rho^2. \tag{14}$$

If we divide through by ρ^2, we have

$$\frac{x^2}{\rho^2} + \frac{y^2}{\rho^2} = 1$$

or

$$\left(\frac{x}{\rho}\right)^2 + \left(\frac{y}{\rho}\right)^2 = 1, \tag{15}$$

where, by (2), $\cos \theta = x/\rho$ and, by (1), $\sin \theta = y/\rho$. Substituting these into (14) or (15), we have the identity

$$(\cos \theta)^2 + (\sin \theta)^2 = 1,$$

which asserts that the sum of the squares of the sine and cosine functions of any angle equals unity. By using similar techniques in dividing (14) by x^2, establish the identity

$$1 + (\tan \theta)^2 = (\sec \theta)^2.$$

Also divide (14) by y^2 and obtain the identity

$$1 + (\text{ctn } \theta)^2 = (\csc \theta)^2.$$

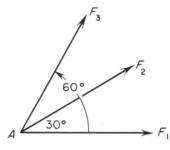

FIGURE 11–11

7. Three forces, $F_1, F_2,$ and F_3 are applied to an object A in the directions shown in Fig. 11–11. The magnitudes of the forces are $F_1 = 10$ lb., $F_2 = 12$ lb., and $F_3 = 15$ lb. If AF_1 is parallel to the x-axis, find the sum of the horizontal components contributed by the three forces; the vertical sum.

Ans. Horiz. $= 27.89$ lb.;
vert. $= 18.99$ lb.

8. In Exercise 7, resolve the three forces into a single force whose horizontal and vertical components are the sums given as answers. Find the cosine function of the reference angle of the new vector. *Ans.* Cos $\theta = 0.833.$

11-3 Functions of Angles Reducible to First-Quadrant Angles

In preceding sections our discussions were restricted primarily to first-quadrant angles, that is, to angles between 0° and 90°. In this section we will en-

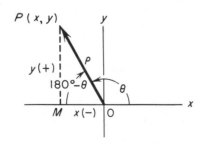

FIGURE 11–12

large our discussions to include angles in all quadrants. We will use reference angles which are multiples of 30° and 45°.

In Sec. 11-1 we established the convention that reference angles are measured from the x-axis. In Fig. 11-12 we see a vector **OP** with reference angle θ. If θ is sufficiently large (as in Fig. 11-12) to place the vector in the second quadrant, then right triangle *OPM* has an acute angle 180° − θ, with a vertical component which is positive and a negative horizontal component. Since 180° − θ is now less than 90°, we have reduced the second-quadrant angle θ to a first-quadrant angle 180° − θ and we may proceed to describe the trigonometric functions of θ using the proper signs of the components.

EXAMPLE 4. Find (*a*) tan 135°, (*b*) sin 210°, (*c*) sec 300°.

Solution. Let us follow the four-step procedure:
1. Sketch the vector in the proper position.
2. Drop a perpendicular from the end of the vector to the *x*-axis.
3. Determine the signs of the components of the vector.
4. Use the definitions to determine the values of the trigonometric functions of the angle involved.

(*a*) To find tan 135°, sketch the vector **OP** with reference angle 135° as in Fig. 11-13(a). The perpendicular drawn from *P* to the *x*-axis forms a 45°

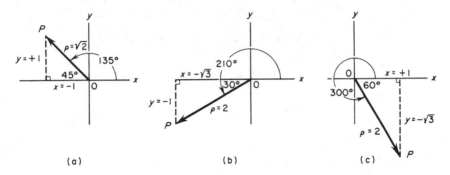

(a)   (b)   (c)

FIGURE 11–13

right triangle with horizontal component $x = -1$, vertical component $y = +1$, and magnitude $\rho = \sqrt{2}$ (this assumes the ratio $s:s:s\sqrt{2}$ and proper signs). Now, by definition (3)

$$\tan 135° = \frac{y}{x} = \frac{+1}{-1} = -1.$$

(*b*) To find sin 210° sketch the vector **OP** as in Fig. 11-13(b). The right triangle formed by dropping a perpendicular from *P* to the *x*-axis is a 30°-60° right triangle, and we consider the angle reduced to the first-quadrant angle 30° with components $x = -\sqrt{3}$, $y = -1$ and magnitude $\rho = 2$. By definition (1),

$$\sin 210° = \frac{y}{\rho} = \frac{-1}{2} = -\frac{1}{2}.$$

(c) To find sec 300°, sketch the vector **OP** as in Fig. 11-13(c). Assign signs and numbers to the components and magnitude, as dictated by the fourth-quadrant position of the 60° angle. Now, by definition (5),

$$\sec 300° = \frac{\rho}{x} = \frac{2}{+1} = 2.$$

For angles greater than 360° or for negative angles, we proceed in the fashion discussed in Example 4. Sketch the vector in its appropriate position, drop a perpendicular from the end of the vector to the x-axis, determine the signs of the components, then apply the definitions.

EXAMPLE 5. Find (a) ctn 930°, (b) csc (−420°).

Solution. (a) In Fig. 11-14(a) we see that the vector with reference angle

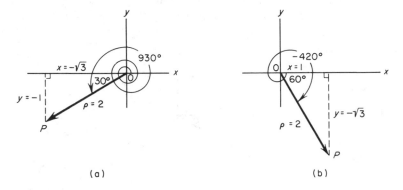

(a)   (b)

FIGURE 11-14

930° is two complete revolutions plus 210° more removed from the zero position. This places the vector in the third quadrant, 30° past the 180° position. Resolving the components and applying the proper definition, we have

$$\text{ctn } 930° = \text{ctn } 210° = \frac{x}{y} = \frac{-\sqrt{3}}{-1} = \sqrt{3}.$$

(b) From Fig. 11-14(b), the reference angle sends us −420° or one full revolution in the clockwise direction, plus 60° more. This places the vector at −60° (or +300°) in the fourth quadrant. Applying previous procedures, we have

$$\csc (-420°) = \csc (-60°) = \csc 300° = \frac{\rho}{y} = \frac{2}{-\sqrt{3}} = -\frac{2\sqrt{3}}{3}.$$

We are now ready to apply the reverse of Examples 4 and 5. We may be given the components of a vector and asked to find the reference angle. For this discussion we will confine ourselves to positive values of θ less than 360°. Actually there will be an infinite number of values of θ available; discussion of all of the values will follow in a later section.

EXAMPLE 6. Find θ if (a) $\tan \theta = -1/ + 1$, (b) $\sec \theta = -(2/\sqrt{3})$.

Solution. (a) From the given information and definition (3),

$$\tan \theta = \frac{-1}{+1} = \frac{y}{x}.$$

This suggests the components $y = -1$ and $x = +1$. Sketching these components, we have only one position available for P, as shown in Fig. 11-15(a).

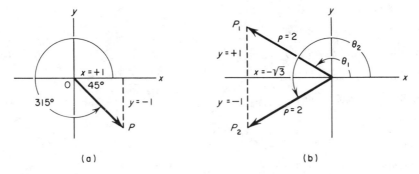

(a)   (b)

FIGURE 11-15

Therefore, when $\tan \theta = -1/+1$, then $\theta = 315°$.

(b) From the given information and definition (5),

$$\sec \theta = -\frac{2}{\sqrt{3}} = \frac{\rho}{x}.$$

Now, by convention, ρ is always positive, so $\rho = +2$. This requires that $x = -\sqrt{3}$. Sketching the vector as shown in Fig. 11-15(b), two different vectors can be drawn with $\rho = +2$ and $x = -\sqrt{3}$. This permits two solutions:

$$\theta_1 = 180° - 30° = 150°$$

and

$$\theta_2 = 180° + 30° = 210°.$$

It is worth noting here that if we had been given $\tan \theta = -1$ in part (a) of Example 6, we would have been obliged to show two solutions there, namely $\theta = 135°, 315°$. The reason is that the signs of the components are not specified.

Exercises

1. Give all six of the trigonometric functions of each of the following angles: 30°, 45°, 60°, 120°, 135°, 150°, 210°, 225°, 240°, 300°, 315°, 330°. Since there will be 72 answers, it may be helpful to arrange them in a chart.

Determine whether the expressions given in Exercises 2–15 are true or false. It is suggested that this be done by sketching vectors representing each member of the expression, where the magnitudes are identical and a general value of θ is assumed.

2. Cos θ = cos $(-\theta)$.   *Ans.* True.

3. Sin θ = sin $(-\theta)$.

4. Tan θ = tan $(\theta + 180°)$.   *Ans.* True.

5. Tan θ = $-$tan $(\theta + 90°)$.

6. Sec θ = sec $(\theta + 90°)$.   *Ans.* False.

7. Sin θ = sin $(180° - \theta)$.

8. Csc θ = csc $(180° - \theta)$.   *Ans.* True.

9. Ctn θ = $-$ctn $(180° - \theta)$.

10. Cos θ = cos $(180° - \theta)$.   *Ans.* False.

11. Cos θ = cos $(360° - \theta)$.

12. Sin θ = sin $(360° - \theta)$.   *Ans.* False.

13. Sin $(180° + \theta)$ = sin $(180° - \theta)$.

14. Tan $(180° + \theta)$ = $-$tan $(180° - \theta)$.   *Ans.* True.

15. Cos $(180° + \theta)$ = cos $(180° - \theta)$.

16. Complete the accompanying chart where the entries indicate the sign of a trigonometric function for reference angles in the quadrant indicated.

quadrant	sin	cos	tan	csc	sec	ctn
I		+				+
II	+		−			
III				−		
IV					+	

Give values of θ (there may be more than one solution) for 0° < θ < 360° that are solutions of the expressions given in Exercises 17–26.

17. Tan $\theta = \sqrt{3}$.   *Ans.* 60°, 240°.

18. Sec $\theta = -\sqrt{2}$.

19. Csc $\theta = -\sqrt{2}$.   *Ans.* 225°, 315°.

20. Sin $\theta = \frac{1}{2}$.

21. Cos $\theta = -\frac{1}{2}$.   *Ans.* 120°, 240°.

22. Tan $\theta = -\sqrt{3} / + 1$.

23. Ctn $\theta = -1/-1$.   *Ans.* 225°.

24. Sec $\theta = 2/\sqrt{3}$.

25. Sin $\theta = -\frac{1}{2}$.   *Ans.* 210°, 330°.

26. Sin $\theta = \cos \theta$.

Find the value of each of the given expressions.

27. Sin 930°.   *Ans.* $-\frac{1}{2}$.

28. Cos 1470°.

29. Tan 1125°.   *Ans.* $+1$.

30. Csc $(-330°)$.

31. Sec $(-390°)$.   *Ans.* $2/\sqrt{3}$.

32. Ctn $(-675°)$.

11-4   Trigonometric Functions of 0°, 90°, 180°, 270°

In preceding sections we have carefully avoided reference to trigonometric functions of angles coincident with the axes of the Cartesian coordinate plane, that is, angles of magnitude 0°, 90°, 180°, and 270°. A reason for this is the requirement of division by zero, which we will discuss here. Let us consider division by zero, or more exactly, division of a nonzero quantity by a number approaching zero.

Given $10/k$, let us assign values to k, where successive values of k approach zero:

$$\text{let } k = 1, \qquad \text{then} \quad \frac{10}{k} = 10;$$

$$k = 0.01, \qquad \frac{10}{k} = \frac{10}{0.01} = 1000;$$

$$k = 0.0001, \qquad \frac{10}{k} = \frac{10}{0.0001} = 100,000;$$

$$k = 1 \times 10^{-10}, \qquad \frac{10}{1 \times 10^{-10}} = 1 \times 10^{11}.$$

We see that as k goes to zero ($k \longrightarrow 0$), $10/k$ becomes very large. If k is zero, then $10/k$ is immense beyond the imagination; this immense quantity is symbolized as ∞ and we call it infinitely large. Caution is observed here calling attention to the fact that ∞ is no real number; it cannot be manipulated by the usual laws of algebra. We note, too, that if k had been negative and approaching zero, we would eventually arrive at the same division by zero, suggesting that then there is no real distinction between ∞ and $-\infty$.

Let us consider the functions of 90°. Here we sketch the vector **OP** in several positions with reference angles approaching 90° as in Fig. 11-16(a) Observe the behavior of the magnitude and the components. First, the magnitude of the vector is assumed to remain fixed. In Fig. 11-16(a) the magni-

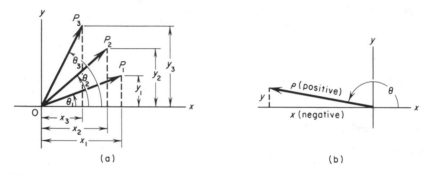

(a)   (b)

FIGURE 11–16

tude is the radius of an origin-centered circle. Next, as P passes through P_1, P_2, and P_3; that is, as θ increases toward 90°, the y-component increases as at y_1, y_2, and y_3. Similarly, the x-component diminishes. By inspection, we agree that as $\theta \longrightarrow 90°$, the y-component approaches as its limit the length OP, which is the magnitude ρ; also, the x-component approaches zero. In mathematical symbols we have:

$$\text{as } \theta \longrightarrow 90°, \quad \text{then } y \longrightarrow \rho \text{ and } x \longrightarrow 0.$$

Now consider the functions of 90°.

$$\sin 90° = \frac{y}{\rho} = \frac{\rho}{\rho} = 1, \qquad \csc 90° = \frac{\rho}{y} = \frac{\rho}{\rho} = 1,$$

$$\cos 90° = \frac{x}{\rho} = \frac{0}{\rho} = 0, \qquad \sec 90° = \frac{\rho}{x} = \frac{\rho}{0} = \infty,$$

$$\tan 90° = \frac{y}{x} = \frac{y}{0} = \infty, \qquad \operatorname{ctn} 90° = \frac{x}{y} = \frac{0}{y} = 0.$$

The functions of 0°, 180°, and 270° can be determined as in the preceding paragraphs. First determine what happens to the components as the reference angle approaches the angle desired, then apply the definitions. There is one point of caution interjected here; consider Fig. 11-16(b). As $\theta \rightarrow 180°$, the x-component approaches a length equal to the magnitude ρ; at least, it seems to. However, we have accepted the convention that the magnitude ρ is always positive. As $\theta \rightarrow 180°$, the x-component, being negative, approaches $-\rho$. Ratios involving the magnitude and the x-component at 180° will therefore be negative. Similarly, as $\theta \rightarrow 270°$, the y-component approaches $-\rho$, and functions of 270° involving the magnitude and the y-component will be negative.

Exercises

1. Give all six of the trigonometric functions of each of the angles 0°, 90°, 180°, and 270°. Since 24 answers are involved, it is suggested that they be arranged in a chart.

2. In view of the results in Exercise 1 and the discussion in Sec. 11-4,

(*a*) What is the range of value of $\sin \theta$? That is, as θ increases from 0° to 360°, $\sin \theta$ passes through a set of values. All of these values lie between two certain numbers; what are these two numbers?

Ans. Sin θ assumes all values between -1 and $+1$, including -1 and $+1$. Symbolically, $-1 \leq \sin \theta \leq +1$.

(*b*) What is the range of values of $\cos \theta$?

(*c*) What is the range or values of $\tan \theta$?   *Ans.* $-\infty < \tan \theta < +\infty$.

(*d*) What is the range of values of $\sec \theta$? $\csc \theta$? $\operatorname{ctn} \theta$?

3. Using sketches of vectors, their ratios of components to magnitudes, and the definitions of the functions, explain why $\sec \theta$ and $\csc \theta$ can never have values between -1 and $+1$.

4. If a vector has a horizontal component of zero and a vertical component equal to $-\rho$, what is the reference angle?

5. If a vector has a vertical component of zero and a horizontal component equal to ρ, what is the reference angle?

6. Consider a reference angle between 0° and 90°. Which trigonometric function always has the larger value, $\sin \theta$ or $\tan \theta$? [*Suggestion:* Sketch a vector in various positions between 0° and 90°, determine the components, set up appropriate ratios from the definitions and compare.]

11-5 Cofunctions and Reciprocal Functions

From definitions (1) through (6), it is readily apparent that certain of the trigonometric functions are reciprocals of others. Restating those definitions with reference to Fig. 11-17, we have

$$\sin \theta = \frac{y}{\rho}, \tag{16}$$

$$\cos \theta = \frac{x}{\rho}, \tag{17}$$

$$\tan \theta = \frac{y}{x}, \tag{18}$$

$$\csc \theta = \frac{\rho}{y}, \tag{19}$$

$$\sec \theta = \frac{\rho}{x}, \tag{20}$$

$$\operatorname{ctn} \theta = \frac{x}{y}. \tag{21}$$

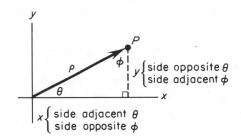

FIGURE 11–17

Observing definitions (16) and (19), we see that $\sin \theta = y/\rho$ and $\csc \theta = \rho/y$. Considering that $y/\rho = 1/(\rho/y)$, then

$$\sin \theta = \frac{1}{\csc \theta} \quad \text{or} \quad \csc \theta = \frac{1}{\sin \theta}. \tag{22}$$

Similarly, from (17) and (20),

$$\cos \theta = \frac{1}{\sec \theta} \quad \text{or} \quad \sec \theta = \frac{1}{\cos \theta}, \tag{23}$$

and from (18) and (21),

$$\tan \theta = \frac{1}{\operatorname{ctn} \theta} \quad \text{or} \quad \operatorname{ctn} \theta = \frac{1}{\tan \theta}. \tag{24}$$

Expressions (22), (23), and (24) are called the *reciprocal relationships* between the trigonometric functions. They are particularly useful in simplifying trigonometric expressions, in computations where they will permit multiplication instead of division, and in slide rule operations. All of these will be discussed later.

Referring again to Fig. 11-17, we can determine another group of relationships between trigonometric functions. First, observe that three of the six trigonometric functions possess the prefix "co-," namely the cosine, cosecant, and cotangent. This suggests that there might be some relationship between the sine and cosine, the secant and cosecant, and the tangent and cotangent.

In Fig. 11-17, we see two angles θ and ϕ; the triangle shown is a right triangle, so that $\theta + \phi = 90°$. In other words, θ and ϕ are *complementary* angles. Now observe any function of θ, say $\sin \theta$. From previous definitions,

$$\sin \theta = \frac{y}{\rho} = \frac{\text{side opposite } \theta}{\rho}. \tag{25}$$

Now observe the same ratio, y/ρ, as a function of the angle ϕ. We see that the side opposite θ is the side adjacent ϕ and

$$\cos \phi = \frac{\text{side adjacent } \phi}{\rho}. \tag{26}$$

From (25) and (26), we have

$$\text{sine } \theta = \text{cosine } \phi \quad (\theta + \phi = 90°). \tag{27}$$

Now, since θ and ϕ are complementary angles, we see from (27) that the *sine of an angle equals the cosine of the complementary angle, or the cosine of an angle equals the sine of the complementary angle.* Apparently the prefix "co-" is associated with the *co*mplementary angle.

By reference to Fig. 11-17, we can discover that

$$\tan \theta = \text{ctn } \phi \tag{28}$$

and

$$\sec \theta = \csc \phi, \tag{29}$$

where θ and ϕ are complementary angles and (27), (28), and (29) are the *cofunction relationships*. These are useful in many of the same ways that the reciprocal relationships are useful.

EXAMPLE 7. Find θ for $\theta \leq 90°$ if (*a*) $\tan \theta = \text{ctn } 30°$, (*b*) $\csc \theta = 1/\sin 22°$, (*c*) $\sec \theta = 1/\sin 15°$.

Solutions. (*a*) Given $\tan \theta = \operatorname{ctn} 30°$. By (28), the tangent of an angle equals the cotangent of the complementary angle. Therefore,

$$\tan 60° = \operatorname{ctn} 30° \quad \text{and} \quad \theta = 60°.$$

(*b*) Given $\csc \theta = 1/\sin 22°$. By (22), $\csc \theta = 1/\sin \theta$, so that

$$\csc 22° = \frac{1}{\sin 22°} \quad \text{and} \quad \theta = 22°.$$

(*c*) Given $\sec \theta = 1/\sin 15°$. By (23), $\sec \theta = 1/\cos \theta$. Also, by (27), $\sin \theta = \cos (90° - \theta)$. Now

$$\frac{1}{\sin 15°} = \frac{1}{\cos 75°} = \sec 75°$$

and we have the solution $\theta = 75°$.

Exercises

In Exercises 1–12, find the first quadrant value of θ for the given expressions.

1. Sin $47° = \cos \theta$.   *Ans.* $\theta = 43°$.

2. Sin $62° = 1/\csc \theta$.

3. Tan $\theta = \operatorname{ctn} 14°$.   *Ans.* $\theta = 76°$.

4. Tan $\theta = 1/\operatorname{ctn} 25°$.

5. Cos $\theta = 1/\sec 12°$.   *Ans.* $\theta = 12°$.

6. Cos $\theta = \sin 82°$.

7. Cos $\theta = 1/\csc 32°$.   *Ans.* $\theta = 58°$.

8. Ctn $\theta = \tan 85°$.

9. Sin $\theta \csc \theta = 1$.   *Ans.* $\theta = $ any value.

10. Sec $\theta \cos \theta = 1$.

11. Sin $\theta \sec \theta = 1/\csc \theta$.   *Ans.* $\theta = 0°$

12. Csc $72° = 1/\sin \theta$.

13. In Fig. 11-18 we are given a right triangle with acute angle θ and a unity hypotenuse. Using the definitions of the trigonometric functions, show that (*a*) $y = \sin \theta$, (*b*) $x = \cos \theta$, (*c*) $\sin \theta/\cos \theta = \tan \theta$. Using the Pythagorean theorem and the conclusions in parts (*a*) and (*b*), show that

$$(\sin \theta)^2 + (\cos \theta)^2 = 1.$$

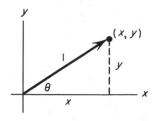

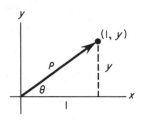

FIGURE 11–18   FIGURE 11–19

14. Using reciprocal and cofunction relationships, show that any trigonometric function of an acute angle can be expressed in terms of the sine or tangent of the angle or its complement. The conclusion here is useful in slide rule operations.

15. In Fig. 11-19 we are given a right triangle with acute angle θ and a unity x-component. Using the definitions of the trigonometric functions, show that (a) $y = \tan \theta$, (b) $\rho = \sec \theta$, (c) $\tan \theta / \sec \theta = \sin \theta$. Using the Pythagorean theorem and the conclusions in parts (a) and (b), show that

$$1 + (\tan \theta)^2 = (\sec \theta)^2.$$

16. Using a triangle as in Fig. 11-19 with an acute angle θ and a unity x-component, show that
(a) y-component $= \tan \theta$.
(b) $\rho = \sec \theta$.
(c) $\text{Cos } \theta = \dfrac{\text{ctn } \theta}{\text{csc } \theta}$.
(d) $1 + (\text{ctn } \theta)^2 = (\text{csc } \theta)^2$.

17. Using methods similar to those in Exercises 13, 15, and 16, show in Fig. 11-20 that $u = \sec \theta$, $v = \tan \theta$, $z = \sec \theta \tan \phi$, and $w = \sec \theta \sec \phi$.

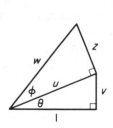

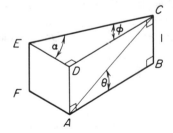

FIGURE 11–20   FIGURE 11–21

18. Given Fig. 11-21 with $ABCD$ a rectangle with diagonal AC forming an acute angle θ with side AB. Angle $EDC = 90°$. $EFAD$ is a square. Edge $CB = 1$. Show that

(a) $ED = \tan \phi \operatorname{ctn} \theta$.

(b) $ED = \operatorname{ctn} \alpha \operatorname{ctn} \theta$.

19. Given Fig. 11-22 with $AB = 1$. Show that $EC = (\cos \alpha)(\sin \beta \tan \theta + \cos \beta)$.

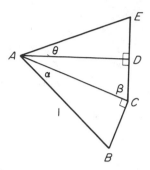

FIGURE 11-22

11-6   Vector Quantities

In many applications, quantities such as force, velocity, acceleration, and so forth come under consideration. These quantities have magnitude, direction, and sense, and are called *vector quantities*. We have previously defined the vector quantity and the scalar quantity. We did not clearly identify the third property of the vector, namely *sense*. A vehicle traveling at 30 mph in a specified direction is said to have a velocity of 30 mph; velocity here is a vector quantity. At times we may assume that the direction was totally specified when in fact it was not. Suppose we state that a vehicle is traveling at 30 mph in a direction parallel to the equator of the earth. In this case, magnitude is described fully, direction is described, but we do not know whether the vehicle is eastbound or westbound; this consideration embraces *sense*. The barb at the end of a vector gives sense to the vector.

In the following paragraphs there will be a limited amount of repetition of material from Sec. 11-1. This material is directed toward the solution of vector problems.

EXAMPLE 8. Three forces are applied to a body. Force F_1 is 6 lb. in a 40° direction; force F_2 is 8 lb. in a 180° direction, and force F_3 is 4 lb. in a 300° direction. Sketch the system in a Cartesian coordinate plane.

Solution. Using methods discussed in Sec. 11-1, we sketch the system as shown in Fig. 11-23.

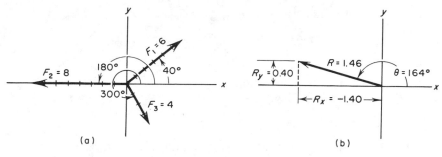

FIGURE 11-23

Components of Vectors

Operations with vectors (adding and subtracting) are often performed by determining the rectangular components of the vectors. These components are most wisely chosen as the horizontal and vertical components of the vectors. Thus, in Fig. 11-24(a), the horizontal component of OP is

$$OM = OP \cos \theta \tag{30}$$

and the vertical component of OP is

$$ON = PM = OP \sin \theta. \tag{31}$$

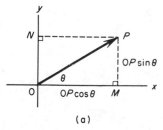

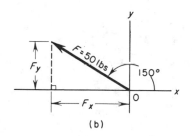

FIGURE 11-24

These rectangular components are the horizontal and vertical projections of the magnitude of the vector upon the coordinate axes. The process of breaking down a vector into its components is called *resolution* or *resolution of components*.

EXAMPLE 9. A force $F = 50$ lb. is applied to a body in a direction of 150°. Find the horizontal component F_x and the vertical component F_y of this force.

Solution. By (30) and (31) and Fig. 11-24(b),

$$F_x = 50 \cos 150° = -43.3 \text{ lb.}$$

and

$$F_y = 50 \sin 150° = +25 \text{ lb.}$$

Resultant Vectors

If two forces are applied to a body from different directions or the same direction, then there is a single force (with its own direction) which could be applied to obtain the same result upon the body. This single force is called the *resultant force* and, in the more general case of vectors, a single vector which can provide the displacement of two or more vectors is called the *resultant vector.* From Example 9 and Fig. 11-24(b), two forces (25 lb. at 90° and 43.3 lb. at 180°) have a resultant of 50 lb. at 150°.

A method commonly used to find the resultant of several vectors is to resolve the vectors into their rectangular components; the resultant vector will have as its horizontal component the sum of the horizontal components of the several vectors and will have as its vertical component the sum of the vertical components of the several vectors. Thus, the resultant **R** of vectors **A**, **B**, and **C** has

$$R_x = A_x + B_x + C_x,$$
$$R_y = A_y + B_y + C_y.$$

EXAMPLE 10. Find the resultant of the forces described in Example 8 and pictured in Fig. 11-23(a).

Solution. For force $\mathbf{F}_1$,

$$F_{1x} = 6 \cos 40° = 4.60,$$
$$F_{1y} = 6 \sin 40° = 3.86,$$

meaning that the horizontal component of $\mathbf{F}_1$ is of magnitude 4.6 lb. and the vertical component is 3.86 lb.

Now, for $\mathbf{F}_2$ none of the force is applied in the vertical direction and all of it is applied to the left in the horizontal direction so that

$$F_{2x} = 8 \cos 180° = -8.00,$$
$$F_{2y} = 8 \sin 180° = 0.$$

For $\mathbf{F}_3$,

$$F_{3x} = 4 \cos 300° = 2.00,$$
$$F_{3y} = 4 \sin 300° = -3.46.$$

The horizontal component R_x of the resultant **R** is

$$R_x = F_{1x} + F_{2x} + F_{3x} = 4.60 - 8.00 + 2.00 = -1.40$$

and the vertical component R_y of the resultant **R** is

$$R_y = F_{1y} + F_{2y} + F_{3y} = 3.86 + 0 - 3.46 = +0.40.$$

Figure 11-23(b) shows the resultant vector **R** drawn to a larger scale for clarity. There

$$\mathbf{R} = \sqrt{R_x^2 + R_y^2} = \sqrt{(-1.40)^2 + (0.40)^2} = 1.46$$

and

$$\tan \theta = \frac{R_y}{R_x} = \frac{0.40}{-1.40} = -0.286,$$

from which $\theta = 164°$. We conclude that the resultant of the system shown in Fig. 11-23(a) is a force of magnitude 1.46 and direction $\theta = 164°$.

It is commented here that in Example 10 the student may not yet be prepared to find θ by use of tables or the slide rule where $\tan \theta = 0.40/-1.40$. In this case θ may be found by use of a protractor where a vector with components 0.40 and -1.40 is laid off as in Fig. 11-23(b) and θ is found by measurement. The same applies to Example 8 where a 40° angle is given and the components of a vector of magnitude 6 are needed.

The *equilibrant* of a force system is the single force which would balance the system; i.e., the force which would exactly nullify the resultant. In Example 10, the resultant is of magnitude 1.46 at an angle of 164°. The equilibrant is of equal magnitude but oppositely directed, or of magnitude 1.46 at 344°.

Parallelogram Method Applied to Vector Problems

In previous examples, vector problems were considered where all of the vectors originated in a common point. Often, however, we wish to consider a group of vectors in series; i.e., the first vector may originate at the origin in a Cartesian coordinate plane, the second vector may originate where the first terminates, the third originates where the second terminates, and so forth. The method of solution of such a series system can be similar to that shown in Example 10. We may also use the parallelogram method which is described in Example 11.

EXAMPLE 11. The progress of an aircraft is plotted on a Cartesian coordinate plane. It flies at a heading of 45° at a velocity of 200 mph. A crosswind of 40 mph blows steadily on a heading of 300°. How many ground miles does the aircraft fly in one hour and what is its resultant direction?

Solution. In Fig. 11-25, we have pictured the vectors involved. Note that vector **OA** represents the progress of the aircraft, neglecting the crosswind. Its direction, 45°, is measured from the right-hand horizontal in a counter-clockwise direction. Vector **AB** represents the crosswind; its direction is measured in the same manner. Vector **OB** represents the resultant with magnitude OB and direction θ.

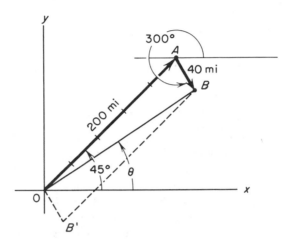

Figure 11-25

A parallelogram $OABB'$ can be sketched; from the properties of the parallelogram, **OB′** = **AB** and **OB′** is in the same direction as **AB**; therefore, **OB** may be considered as the resultant of **OA** and **OB′**. Now the system is the same as described in previous sections, where all of the vectors originate from a common point. Solving, we have the horizontal component of **OB** as

$$(OB)_x = 200 \cos 45° + 40 \cos 300° = 161.4$$

and the vertical component of **OB** as

$$(OB)_y = 200 \sin 45° + 40 \sin 300° = 106.8.$$

Now,

$$\mathbf{OB} = \sqrt{(OB)_x^2 + (OB)_y^2} = \sqrt{(161.4)^2 + (106.8)^2} = 193.4$$

and

$$\tan \theta = \frac{(OB)_y}{(OB)_x} = \frac{106.8}{161.4} = 0.661,$$

from which $\theta = 33.4°$. Once again the student may not be prepared to evaluate θ where $\tan \theta = 0.661$ is known. However, by carefully sketching the
vector with components 106.8 and 161.4 and measuring the reference angle
with a protractor, θ can be determined.

We conclude that the actual distance traveled by the aircraft is $\mathbf{OB} =$
193.4 ground miles and the direction is $\theta = 33.4°$.

Exercises

*In the following exercises, provide solutions as directed. In cases where the reference
angle is not a multiple of 30° or 45°, draw the vector to scale using a straight edge
and protractor. Where the components are known, find the angle with a protractor.*

1. An automobile travels at 45 mph in a direction 30° east of north. What are
its northerly and easterly components of velocity?   *Ans.* 38.95; 22.5.

2. A projectile fired from the ground at a distant target is traveling, at a certain
instant, at 1800 fps and is falling toward the earth such that the angle between
its path and the horizontal is 15°. What are its horizontal and vertical components
of velocity?

3. An object on a Cartesian coordinate plane starts at a point A. It moves from
A to B where the direction is 225° and the straight-line distance from A to B is
12 inches. Next it proceeds from B to C where the direction is 300° and the
distance is 15 inches. Find the straight-line distance AC and the direction from
A to C.   *Ans.* $AC = 21.52;\ \theta = 267.4°$.

4. Find the magnitude and direction of the system of forces shown in Fig. 11–26 if

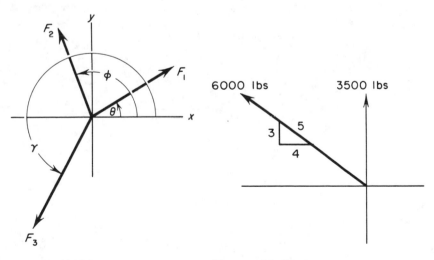

FIGURE 11–26   FIGURE 11–27

(a) $F_1 = 95$ lb., $F_2 = 210$ lb., $F_3 = 0$; $\theta = 25°$, $\phi = 130°$.

(b) $F_1 = 95$ lb., $F_2 = 210$ lb., $F_3 = 95$ lb.; $\theta = 25°$, $\phi = 130°$, $\gamma = 235°$.

Ans. 168. lb.0 at 130°.

(c) $F_1 = F_2 = F_3$; $\phi = \theta + 120°$, $\gamma = \phi + 120°$.   *Ans.* System is balanced.

5. Find the magnitude and direction of the equilibrant of the forces in Fig. 11-27.

Ans. 8590 lb. at 304.1°.

In the preceding chapter we defined the trigonometric functions and discussed co-functions and reciprocal functions. Very little attention was given to computations involving trigonometric functions. Since such computations are an important part of technical mathematics, they will be introduced here.

One use of trigonometry is in indirect measurements; that is, some known quantities are used to compute another magnitude or distance or force which may not be readily measurable because of obstructions, inaccessibility, and so forth. Another use is in resolution or composition of forces. We will concentrate on these applications.

Since computation is a primary goal, use of the table of natural trigonometric functions, use of the slide rule, interpolation, and angular measurements will be discussed.

COMPUTATIONS INVOLVING RIGHT-TRIANGLE TRIGONOMETRY 12

12-1 Angular Measurements, Degree System

The most commonly used unit for measuring angles is the *degree*. We will define a degree by referring to Fig. 12-1. A circle O has a circumference which is the length of the circular line measured along the arc $A_0, A_1, A_2, \ldots,$

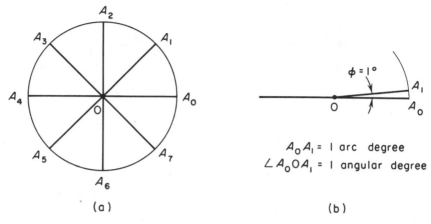

FIGURE 12-1

starting at any point on the arc and terminating at that point and passing through all points on the arc once and only once. Figure 12-1(a) shows a circle O with the circumference divided into eight equal parts; this creates eight equal angles like $\angle A_0 O A_1$ with vertices at O, called *central angles*. If the circumference of O were divided into 360 equal arcs, there would be 360 equal central angles like $\angle A_0 O A_1$ in Fig. 12-1(b). These 360 equal central angles are of magnitude $1°$ by definition. Figure 12-1 (b) is drawn out of scale, owing to the difficulty in representing a $1°$ angle.

The term *degree* is not restricted to angles. Instead, we refer to $\angle A_0 O A$ in Fig. 12-1(b) as being of magnitude *one angular degree*. The arc $A_0 A_1$ is called *one arc degree*. Hence, in a circle there are 360 arc degrees and 360 angular degrees.

For purposes of accuracy in many technical considerations the degree, despite its small magnitude, must be subdivided. The subdivisions are either tenths, hundredths, thousandths, etc. (decimal) or one-sixtieth and one-sixtieth of one-sixtieth. Let us clarify the last statement. One-tenth of one degree is called simply "one-tenth of one degree" and is symbolized as $0.1°$ One-hundredth of one degree is $0.01°$, etc. In contrast, one-sixtieth of one degree is called a *minute* and is symbolized

$$1' = \left(\frac{1}{60}\right)°,$$

Likewise, one-sixtieth of one minute is called a *second* and is symbolized

$$1'' = \left(\frac{1}{60}\right)' = \left(\frac{1}{60}\right)\left(\frac{1}{60}\right)^\circ = \left(\frac{1}{3600}\right)^\circ \tag{1}$$

and

$$60' = 1^\circ, \quad 60'' = 1', \quad \text{and} \quad 3600'' = 1^\circ. \tag{2}$$

Conversions between decimal degrees and minutes and seconds is reasonably simple. Let us consider some examples.

EXAMPLE 1. Convert 22.384° to degrees, minutes, and seconds.
Solution. We have here 22° and 0.384 of another degree. Two options are available now. Under option 1 we can convert 0.384° to seconds, then determine minutes. Under option 2 we can find minutes, then seconds. Observe the options.

Option 1. By (2), 1° = 3600″, therefore

$$0.384^\circ = (0.384 \text{ deg.})(3600 \text{ sec./deg.}) = 1382.4''.$$

Now, since 60″ = 1′, then by (1),

$$1382.4'' = (1382.4 \text{ sec.})(1/60 \text{ min./sec.}) = 23'$$

with remainder 2.4″ and we have the solution 22.384° = 22°23′02.4″.
Option 2. By (2), 1° = 60′. Therefore,

$$0.384^\circ = (0.384 \text{ deg.})(60 \text{ min./deg.}) = 23.04'.$$

Now by (2),

$$0.04' = (0.04 \text{ min.})(60 \text{ sec./ min.}) = 2.4'',$$

and we have 22.384° = 22°23′02.4″.

In the preceding example we converted from decimal notation to notation in minutes and degrees. In our next example the conversion will be in the opposite direction.

EXAMPLE 2. Convert 12°14′26″ to decimal notation accurate to thousandths.
Solution. If we convert 14′26″ to seconds and divide by 3600, we will have the decimal equivalent. Now

$$14'26'' = (14 \text{ min.})(60 \text{ sec./min.}) + 26 \text{ sec.} = 866''.$$

From (1),

$$866'' = (866 \text{ sec.})(1 \text{ deg.}/3600 \text{ sec.}) = 0.240°$$

and we have the solution $12°14'26'' = 12.240°$.

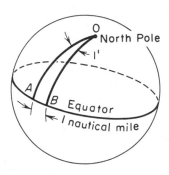

FIGURE 12–2

An idea of the magnitude of a minute or a second of angle is easily developed and is useful in considerations of accuracy. The nautical mile is a length defined by an interception of the equator of the earth by the sides of an angle of 1' with its vertex at the North Pole. Thus, the arc length $\overset{\frown}{AB}$ in Fig. 12-2 is a nautical mile. Since there are 360° along the equator and 60' per degree, then $\overset{\frown}{AB}$ is $\frac{1}{21600}$ of the length of the equator and is 6080 feet approximately. In other words, in the distance OA, which is a quarter of the way around the earth, an angle of 1' intercepts an arc of 6080 ft. Similarly, an angle of 1'' with vertex at the North Pole would intercept an equatorial arc of approximately $\frac{1}{60}(6080) = 101.3$ ft.

Exercises

In Exercises 1–8 convert the given decimal expressions to expressions in degrees, minutes, and seconds, correct to the nearest second.

1. 43.287°.   *Ans. 43°17′13″.*

2. 16.006°.

3. 12.009°.   *Ans. 12°00′32″.*

4. 97.842°.

5. 108.972°.   *Ans. 108°58′19″.*

6. 14.5°.

7. 13.6°.   *Ans. 13°36′00″.*

8. 185.35°.

In Exercises 9–16 convert the given expressions to decimal notation, correct to thousandths.

9. 12°26′45″.   *Ans. 12.446°.*

10. 82°15′15″.

11. 76°42′00″.   *Ans.* 76.700°.

12. 118°05′00″.

13. 327°00′40″.   *Ans.* 327.011°.

14. 225°09′25″.

15. 112°03′06″.   *Ans.* 112.052°.

16. 62°59′59″.

17. Referring to Fig. 12-2, find *AB* in statute miles (1 statute mile = 5280 ft.) if ∠ *AOB* = 1°.   *Ans.* 69.09 mi.

18. According to Fig. 12-2 and the accompanying discussion, a one-minute angle "runs out" 1 nautical mile in a distance of 6250 miles. How far would the same angle run out in a distance to the moon, given as 235,000 miles?
    Ans. Approx. 37.6 miles.

19. Express a conversion unit between one-thousandth of a degree and seconds. That is, find *x* if $0.001° = x''$.   *Ans.* $x = 3.6''$.

20. What is the decimal degree equivalent of one second of angle?
    Ans. $1'' = 0.000278°$.

21. We are given that the circumference of a circle is $C = 2\pi r$ or circumference $= 2\pi$ radii. This means that if the radius were bent into a curve to fit the arc, 2π such radii would be required to fit the entire circumference. How many degrees are in a central angle which intercepts an arc equal to the radius?   *Ans.* 57.3°.

12-2   Angular Measurement, Radian System

In Sec. 12-1 we discussed the degree system for measuring angles. Another system, commonly used in technical practice because of its properties, is the radian system. We refer to Fig. 12-3 to picture the radian, which is the basic unit in the radian system. Here we have a central angle θ intercepting an arc $\overset{\frown}{AB}$. The length of arc $\overset{\frown}{AB}$ is exactly the length of radius OA and we have $OA = r = \overset{\frown}{AB}$; under these restrictions, θ is defined as one radian. We have then the definition:

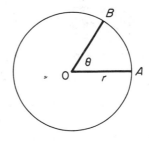

FIGURE 12-3

> *An angle of one radian is the central angle whose intercepted arc is equal in length to one radius.*

Let us now consider the relationship between radians and degrees. The circumference of a circle is given as

$$C = 2\pi r, \tag{3}$$

where we can read (3) as "the circumference is 2π radii." Now, according to the definition of a radian, one radian of angle intercepts an arc equal in length to one radius, so 2π radians of angle will intercept 2π radii of arc. Since 2π radii of arc constitute a circumference by (3), then 2π radians of angle constitute a complete circular angle of $360°$; hence, we have the conversion equation

$$2\pi \text{ radians } = 360° \tag{4}$$

from which

$$\pi \text{ radian } = 180° \tag{5}$$

and

$$1 \text{ radian } = 180°/\pi = 57.3°. \tag{6}$$

From (4), if we divide both sides by 360, we have

$$1° = 2\pi/360 = 0.01745 \text{ radians.}$$

An interesting property of the radian is worthy of discussion here. Since an *angle* of one radian intercepts an *arc* of length one radius, there is a one-to-one correspondence between radians and radii. We cannot strictly say that a radian equals a radius, for this would be an attempt to call an angular unit equal to a length unit. We can, however, correctly state that the *number* of radians of angle equals the *number* of radii of arc. This means that we can shift between linear and angular measurements at will if the angular measurements are in radians.

EXAMPLE 3. How many degrees are in (*a*) 3 radians, (*b*) $2\pi/3$ radians?

Solution. (*a*) Since, by (6) 1 radian $= 57.3°$, then

$$3 \text{ radians } = 3(57.3°) = 171.9°.$$

(*b*) Since, by (5), π radians $= 180°$, then

$$\frac{2\pi}{3} \text{ radians } = \frac{2}{3}(180)° = 120°.$$

EXAMPLE 4. A wheel of radius 12 inches rolls without slipping along a straight line. If it rolls through five revolutions (a) how many radians of angle does it rotate through, (b) how far does it travel?

Solution. (a) Since one revolution = 2π radians, then five revolutions = 10π radians.

(b) Since, by (a), 10π radians of angle are generated, then 10π radii of arc are traversed and, with one radius equal to 12 inches, then the distance is

$$10\pi \text{ radii} = 10\pi(12) \text{ inches} = 120\pi \text{ inches.}$$

Exercises

In Exercises 1–10 the angle given is in radians. Convert the angle to degrees.

1. $\theta = \pi/3$.   *Ans.* 60°.

2. $\theta = 3\pi$.

3. $\theta = 5\pi/12$.   *Ans.* 75°.

4. $\theta = 7\pi/18$.

5. $\theta = 37\pi/18$.   *Ans.* 370°.

6. $\theta = 2$.

7. $\theta = 51$.   *Ans.* 2922°.

8. $\theta = 6.7$.

9. $\theta = 0.02$.   *Ans.* 1.146°.

10. $\theta = 10.5$.

In Exercises 11–20 convert the given angle into radians.

11. $\theta = 90°$.   *Ans.* $\pi/2$.

12. $\theta = 45°$.

13. $\theta = 150°$.   *Ans.* $5\pi/6$.

14. $\theta = 198°$.

15. $\theta = 342°$.   *Ans.* 5.969.

16. $\theta = 27.6°$.

17. $\theta = 825°$.   *Ans.* 14.398.

18. $\theta = 125°12'26''$.

19. $\theta = 209°15'06''$.   *Ans.* 3.652.

20. $\theta = 925°47'12''$.

21. Given the angular velocity of a rotating body as 10 radians per second. Express this velocity in (a) degrees per minute, (b) revolutions per second.

Ans. (a) $(108/\pi) \times 10^3$ deg./min., (b) 5π rev./sec.

22. If a body is rotating at an angular velocity k revolutions per second, what is its angular velocity in degrees per minute?

23. A wheel of radius 28 inches is rolling along a flat surface in a straight line at 75 miles per hour. What is the angular velocity of a point on the wheel?

Ans. 330/7 rad./sec.

24. If a wheel of radius 12 inches rotates at 75 revolutions per minute, what is the linear velocity (a) of a point on the rim of the wheel, (b) of a point on a spoke of the wheel one-half of a radius from the center?

Ans. (a) 30π in./sec., (b) 15π in./sec.

25. If a vector **OP** of magnitude ρ is rotated with an angular velocity ω radians per second, what is the linear velocity of P?

12-3 Fundamental Operations on Angles in Degrees, Minutes, and Seconds

Adding and subtracting angles and multiplying or dividing an angle by an integer will, for our purposes, constitute the fundamental operations on angles. We will restrict our discussion to angles expressed in degrees, minutes, and seconds (as opposed to angles in decimal form); the reason given here is that operations on those angles in decimal form are like the fundamental operations on decimal quantities as studied in elementary mathematics.

Addition of angles is performed by columnizing like quantities and adding by normal procedures. If the sum of the seconds exceeds 60″, multiples of 60″ in the sum are converted to minutes and added to the minutes column. Excesses of 60′ are treated likewise in converting to degrees. Let us observe an example problem.

EXAMPLE 5. Given $A = 14°25'49''$, $B = 38°46'51''$, and $C = 42°37'46''$, find $A + B + C$.

Solution. Obeying the rules of algebra, which assert that only like quantities can be combined by addition, we regard all quantities in degree units alike, all quantities in minutes alike, and all in seconds alike. Hence, we columnize the quantities as

$$
\begin{array}{rl}
A = & 14° \ \ 25' \ \ 49'' \\
B = & 38° \ \ 46' \ \ 51'' \\
C = & 42° \ \ 37' \ \ 46'' \\
\hline
A + B + C = & 94°108'146''.
\end{array}
\tag{8}
$$

The sum (8) bears inspection. We have 146″, which exceeds 60″; our problem now is to determine the number of complete minutes which are contained in 146″ and transfer those minutes to the minute column. Now

$$146 \text{ sec} \div 60 \text{ sec./min.} = 2' + 26'' \text{ remainder}$$

or 146″ = 2′26″, so (8) becomes

$$94°108'146'' = 94°108' + 2' + 26'' = 94°110'26''.$$

Now 110′ are converted through division by 60 min./deg. to 110′ = 1° + 50′, so

$$94°110'26'' = 94° + 1° + 50' + 26'' = 95°50'26''.$$

In subtraction of angles, the usual procedure is to require the number of minutes of the minuend to exceed the number of minutes of the subtrahend; the same requirement applies to seconds. (This requirement assumes that negative minutes and seconds are not permitted.) We still obey the rule of algebra that only like quantities can be subtracted, hence we columnize again. Refer to Example 6.

EXAMPLE 6. Find $A - B$ if $A = 75°15'35''$ and $B = 36°45'42''$.

Solution. Columnizing, we have

$$A = 75°15'35'' \quad (\text{minuend})$$
$$B = 36°45'42'' \quad (\text{subtrahend}).$$

Referring to earlier comments, the number of seconds in the subtrahend here exceeds the number of seconds in the minuend. Subtraction would require a negative number of seconds in the difference. This can be remedied by borrowing 1′ = 60″ from the minutes column in A and applying the 60″ to the seconds column; hence

$$A = 75°15'35'' = 75°14'95''$$
$$B = 36°45'42'' = 36°45'42'' \tag{9}$$

Now (9) the number of minutes in A is less than the number of minutes in B. Borrowing 1° = 60′ from the degree column in A, we have

$$
\begin{aligned}
A &= 75°14'95'' = 74°74'95'' \\
B &= 36°45'42'' = 36°45'42'' \\
\hline
A - B & \qquad\quad = 38°29'53''.
\end{aligned}
\tag{10}
$$

Multiplication of an angle by an integer involves very little difficulty; the primary concern is that of aggregating more than 60″ or 60′ in the respective columns. Observe Example 7.

EXAMPLE 7. Multiply $15°35'42''$ by 5.

Solution. We have

$$(15°35'42'') \times 5 = 75°175'210'' \tag{11}$$
$$= 75°178'30'' \tag{12}$$
$$= 77°58'30'', \tag{13}$$

where (12) is obtained from (11) by transferring $180''$ of the $210''$ to the minutes column as $3'$ and (13) is obtained from (12) by transferring $120'$ of the $178'$ to the degree column as $2°$.

Division of an angle by a constant is complicated by the possibility of obtaining quotients which contain fractions of degrees, minutes, or seconds. This possibility can be remedied by manipulating the dividend in a manner which will require the degrees and minutes of the quotient to be integral and allowing the seconds part of the quotient to contain a fraction or decimal.

EXAMPLE 8. Perform the operation $(96°24'16'') \div 5$.

Solution. The procedure here will be to change the degrees to $95°$ (the largest multiple of 5 contained in $96°$). Next, transfer the excess degree to the minutes as $60'$, so that

$$96°24'16'' = 95°84'16''.$$

Now change the minutes to $80'$ (the largest multiple of 5 contained in $84'$). Next, transfer the excess $4' = 240''$ to the seconds and we have

$$96°24'16'' = 95°84'16'' = 95°80'256''.$$

Now we are prepared to divide:

$$(95°80'256'') \div 5 = 19°16'51.2''.$$

We could have divided the original expression by 5, such that

$$(96°24'16'') \div 5 = 19.2°4.8'3.2''.$$

Looking at the answer, $19.2° = 19°12''$ and

$$19.2°4.8'3.2'' = 19°16.8'3.2''.$$

Now, $16.8' = 16'48''$ and

$$19°16.8'3.2'' = 19°16'51.2''.$$

The latter solution converted fractional degrees to minutes and fractional minutes to seconds. This solution is preferred if the divisor is not integral.

Exercises

*In Exercises 1–15 we are given $A = 95°15'12''$, $B = 53°56'29''$, $C = 37°42'05''$,
$D = 18°03'58''$. Find:*

1. $A + B$.   *Ans.* 149°11'41''.

2. $B + D$.

3. $A - B$.   *Ans.* 41°18'43''.

4. $C - D$.

5. $A + C - D$.   *Ans.* 114°53'19''.

6. $B - (C + D)$.

7. $3B$.   *Ans.* 161°49'27''.

8. $4C$.

9. $3B - 4C$.   *Ans.* 11°01'07''.

10. $A - 5D$.

11. $\frac{1}{2}A$.   *Ans.* 47°37'36''.

12. $\frac{2}{3}B$.

13. $\frac{3}{4}C$.   *Ans.* 28°16'33.75''.

14. $\frac{1}{2}(A + B) - \frac{1}{2}(A - B)$.

15. $\frac{1}{2}(C + D) - \frac{1}{2}(C - D)$.   *Ans.* 18°03'58''.

Refer to Fig. 12-4 in Examples 16–20.

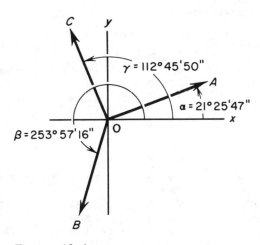

FIGURE 12-4

16. Find the reference angle of the bisector of $\angle AOC$.

17. Express the direction of OB as an angle measured in a clockwise direction from Ox.   *Ans.* $-(106°02'44'')$.

18. Find the direction of the vector bisecting $\angle BOC$.

19. The angle BOA is trisected. Find the directions of the trisectors. Note that there can be two answers in the fourth quadrant and two more in the second quadrant 180° removed from their fourth-quadrant companions. Accept the fourth-quadrant answers.   *Ans.* $296°26'46''$, $338°56'17''$.

20. What is the average angle represented?

12-4   Use of the Natural Trigonometric Tables

In Chap. 11 we defined the natural trigonometric functions and performed some elementary operations with them, including the solution of a restricted set of triangles. We used all six of the functions, but applied them only to those angles which are multiples of 30° or 45°. In restricting our usage to the angles mentioned, we avoided the use of a set of values of the trigonometric functions of many angles. It is our purpose here to broaden our use of the trigonometric functions to include the functions of angles described in accuracy to degrees, minutes, and seconds. We know, for instance, from Chap. 11, the functions of 30°, but what about the functions of 30°25′ or 30°25′16″? For an answer to this we must refer to the table of natural trigonometric functions in Appendix B. Let us examine a very small portion of that table by creating Table 12-1.

Table 12-1

NATURAL TRIGONOMETRIC FUNCTIONS

38°	(218°)			(321°)	141°
	sin	tan	ctn	cos	′
0	0.61566	0.78129	1.2799	0.78801	60
1	0.61589	0.78175	1.2792	0.78783	59
2	0.61612	0.78222	1.2784	0.78765	58
3	0.61635	0.78269	1.2776	0.78747	57
4	0.61658	0.78316	1.2769	0.78729	56
.					.
.					.
.					.
56	0.62842	0.80786	1.2378	0.77788	4
57	0.62864	0.80834	1.2371	0.77769	3
58	0.62887	0.80882	1.2364	0.77751	2
59	0.62909	0.80930	1.2356	0.77733	1
60	0.62932	0.80978	1.2349	0.77715	0
	cos	ctn	tan	sin	′
128°	(308°)			(231°)	51°

In Table 12-1 we have reproduced that portion of Appendix B from which we can read four of the trigonometric functions of angles between 38°00′ and 39°00′, also 51°00′ and 52°00′, at 1′ intervals. The functions of 38° and some minutes are read "down-left"; that is, sin 38°04′ = 0.61658 by reading 38° at the left and down to 4′. Also, ctn 38°58′ = 1.2364 reading the same way. The degree entry at the top left of the columns goes from 0° to 45°. For angles from 45° to 90°, the degree entry is at the bottom right and reading is done "up-right." Here, referring to Table 12-1, sin 51°00′ = 0.77715, tan 51°02′ = 1.2364, and cos 51°57′ = 0.61635.

Two of the entries noted in the preceding paragraph give an important key to the construction of Appendix B. We had

$$\tan 51°02′ = 1.2364 = \text{ctn } 38°58′.$$

Here 51°02′ and 38°58′ are complements and the tangent and cotangent are cofunctions. Hence, a single entry in the table is made for an angle less than 45° (by reading downward) and its complement, which is greater than 45° (by reading upward).

We also note degree entries other than 38° and 51° in Table 12-1. Note that 218° is given as a companion to 38°; the reason is that, from Fig. 12-5,

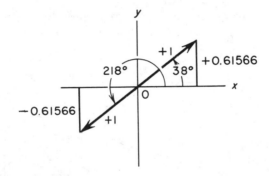

FIGURE 12-5

vectors at 38° and 218° are 180° apart. If their magnitudes are equal (= 1 in Fig. 12-5), the vertical components are equal but opposite in sign, making sin 38° = 0.61566 and sin 218° = −0.61566. When the angle is greater than 90°, the tabular entry is provided, but the reader must provide the *sign*.

Let us consider some problems involving use of the tables of natural trigonometric functions, where angles given are accurate to minutes.

EXAMPLE 9. From Fig. 12-6, find AC given $AB = 4.2$ inches and $\angle BAC = 17°28′$ with $\angle ACB = 90°$.

Solution. Since AC is to be found and AB and $\angle BAC$ are given, we have

an angle, the side adjacent, and the hypotenuse involved. This suggests use
of the cosine function or the secant function since

$$\cos\theta = \frac{\text{adjacent}}{\text{hypotenuse}} \quad \text{and} \quad \sec\theta = \frac{\text{hypotenuse}}{\text{adjacent}}. \quad (14)$$

Substituting given data in both expressions in (14),

$$\cos 17°28' = \frac{AC}{4.2} \quad \text{and} \quad \sec. 17°28' = \frac{4.2}{AC}.$$

Now

$$AC = 4.2 \cos 17°28' \quad \text{and} \quad AC = \frac{4.2}{\sec 17°28'}. \quad (15)$$

From (15) we see that we have the choice of either multiplying 4.2 by cos
17°28° or dividing 4.2 by sec 17°28'. The choice is easy to make since most of
us prefer to multiply by a five-digit number in preference to dividing by a
five-digit number. Also, Appendix B does not provide secants. Therefore,

$$AC = 4.2 \cos 17°28' = (4.2)(0.95389) = 4.00634 \text{ in.}, \quad (16)$$

where the product in (16) was obtained by longhand multiplication. It could,
instead, have been obtained by logarithms; this will be discussed in a later
chapter.

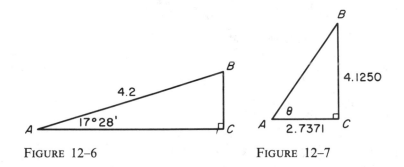

FIGURE 12–6   FIGURE 12–7

EXAMPLE 10. 'In Fig. 12-7, find θ to the nearest minute, given $AC = 2.7371$
in., $BC = 4.1250$ in., and $\angle ACB = 90°$.

Solution. As in Example 9, we have the choice of two functions, for either

$$\tan\theta = \frac{4.1250}{2.7371} \quad \text{or} \quad \operatorname{ctn}\theta = \frac{2.7371}{4.1250}. \quad (17)$$

Since long division is planned, neither expression in (17) has a great advantage over the other. We will use the first expression, so

$$\tan \theta = \frac{4.1250}{2.7371} = 1.5071. \tag{18}$$

From (18), since $\tan \theta$ is greater than unity, θ is greater than 45°, suggesting that we read from the bottom of the table in Appendix B. We search for the tangent entry closest to 1.5071 and we find 1.5070, so that to the nearest minute, $\theta = 56°26'$.

Exercises

Using the table of natural trigonometric functions, find the function of the angle given in Exercises 1–12. Also find the angle θ in Exercises 13–24 where $0° < \theta < 90°$.

1. Sin 12°25′.   *Ans.* 0.21502.

2. Cos 21°35′.

3. Sin 32°27′.   *Ans.* 0.53656.

4. Ctn 41°15′.

5. Sin 65°56′.   *Ans.* 0.91307.

6. Cos 81°12′.

7. Ctn 76°05′.   *Ans.* 0.24778.

8. Tan 49°59′.

9. Cos 127°15′.   *Ans.* −0.60529.

10. Sin 227°27′.

11. Tan 333°21′.   *Ans.* −0.50185.

12. Ctn 462°15′.

13. Sin θ = 0.34612.   *Ans.* 20°15′.

14. Cos θ = 0.97760.

15. Tan θ = 0.80020.   *Ans.* 38°40′.

16. Ctn θ = 1.0392.

17. Cos θ = 0.61107.   *Ans.* 52°20′.

18. Sin θ = 0.80902.

19. Ctn θ = 0.40098.   *Ans.* 68°09′.

20. Tan θ = 4.7046.

21. Sin θ = 0.99276.   *Ans.* 83°06′.

22. Ctn θ = 10.780.

23. Tan θ = 10.780.   *Ans.* 84°42′.

24. Ctn θ = 0.01600.

In Exercises 25–36 reference is to Fig. 12-8. Find the quantity indicated for the values of the other given quantities. When an angle is requested, find that angle to the closest minute.

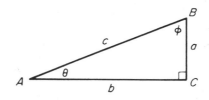

FIGURE 12-8

25. a = 3, b = 4, find θ.   *Ans.* 36°52′.

26. a = 3.2, b = 5.6, find ϕ.

27. c = 12.5, a = 7.29, find θ.   *Ans.* 35°40′.

28. c = 4.85, a = 2.16, find ϕ.

29. b = 8.18, c = 10.12, find ϕ.   *Ans.* 53°56′.

30. b = 13.11, c = 17.75, find θ.

31. A = 15°15′, a = 4, find b.   *Ans.* 14.672.

32. A = 32°15′, a = 3.15, find c.

33. A = 47°17′, b = 12.18, find a.   *Ans.* 13.192.

34. B = 62°36′, b = 6.5, find c.

35. B = 75°57′, c = 18.0, find a.   *Ans.* 4.3699.

36. B = 75°17′, c = 18.0, find b.

37. A surveyor proceeds from a point O to a point B in a direction θ measured off a base line Ox as in Fig. 12-9, then in a direction ϕ to D with BM parallel to Ox. If θ = 15°36′, OB = 308 ft., and ϕ = 47°27′ with BD = 427 ft.,

(*a*) How far is D from the line BM?   *Ans.* 314.56 ft.

(*b*) How far is D from the alternate line Ox?   *Ans.* 397.39 ft.

38. In Exercise 37, what is the direction of OD as measured from Ox?

39. A man starts at point A, walks due east 8 miles, turns due north for 6 miles, goes west for 2 miles, then south for 3 miles to a point B. What is the angle between AB and a north-south line through A correct to the nearest minute?   *Ans.* 63°26′.

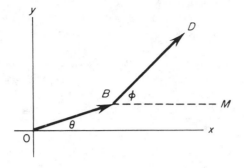

FIGURE 12-9

12-5 Interpolation

In Sec. 12-4 we discussed the use of the table of natural trigonometric functions, finding an angle when a function of that angle was given, or finding a function of a given angle. In each case, however, we restricted the refinement of the angle to the nearest minute, recognizing that the table of natural trigonometric functions listed in the appendix is given only to the minute, with no listings given for angles separated by a second. Good estimates are available for angles given accurate to the second, using the table in Appendix B, by a method called *interpolation* which will be discussed here. Interpolation is useful for finding values between entries in a table. Let us use an example problem to develop a general approach to interpolation.

EXAMPLE 11. Find the value of sin 35°45′17″ by interpolation.

Solution. For purposes of clarity and understanding we will show a graphical representation of our approach and will provide discussion. First, the angle in question lies between two angles in Appendix B whose sine functions are given; these are

$$\sin 35°45′00″ = 0.58425 \tag{19}$$

and

$$\sin 35°45′60″ = 0.58449 = \sin 35°46′. \tag{20}$$

A plot of (19) and (20) is given in Fig. 12-10, where we show the desired solution by geometrical means. Note many features of Fig. 12-10. We have an "angle"-axis and a "sine of angle"-axis. We locate 35°45′00″ at A and plot C where $AC = 0.53425 = \sin 35°45′00″$. At B we locate 35° 45′ 60″, making AB represent 60″ of angle. Also, above B we locate F where $BF = 0.58449 =$

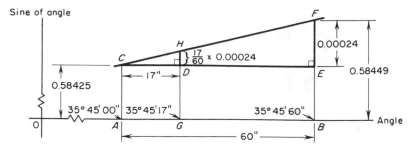

FIGURE 12-10

sin 35°45'60''. At G locate 35°45'17''; we assume that GH is a good approximation of sin 35°45'17'', where CHF is a straight line. (In the preceding sentence we assumed that the sine curve is linear for the 60'' interval under consideration. The sine curve is *not* linear between any two points on it, but can be assumed linear for brief intervals without major error.) Now we have two similar triangles; that is,

$$\triangle CDH \sim \triangle CEF,$$

and, since the corresponding parts of similar triangles are proportional,

$$\frac{DH}{CD} = \frac{EF}{CE}. \tag{21}$$

Now $CD = 17''$, $EF = 0.00024$, and $CE = 60''$, so (21) becomes

$$\frac{DH}{17''} = \frac{0.00024}{60''}, \tag{22}$$

and, from (22),

$$DH = \tfrac{17}{60} \times 0.00024 = 0.00007. \tag{23}$$

Now, GH is the interpolated value of sin 35°45'17'', and

$$GH = GD + DH,$$

but $GD = AC = 0.58425$ and $DH = 0.00007$, therefore

$$GH = \sin 35°45'17'' = 0.58425 + 0.00007 = 0.58432.$$

We note in (23) that the division is not is exact, for the computed $DH = 0.000068$. Since we have assumed linearity, we know already that our computations will not be exact. The sine value is given to five places after the decimal point. Using inexact methods to establish a sixth place is somewhat absurd, therefore we round (23) off to 0.00007.

Let us use the ideas advanced in Example 11 to create a general approach to interpolation. Given any function $y = f(x)$ which is free of unusual jumps and rapid curvature and has a single value of y for each value of x. We are also given two values of x, say $x = x_0$ and $x = x_0 + k$, with the corresponding values for y, namely, $f(x_0)$ and $f(x_0 + k)$, where k is small. This given information is plotted in Fig. 12-11, where we observe similar triangles which

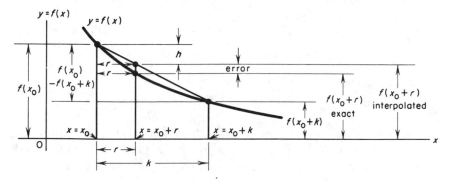

FIGURE 12-11

will give the proportion

$$\frac{h}{r} = \frac{f(x_0) - f(x_0 + k)}{k}$$

and

$$h = \frac{r}{k}[f(x_0) - f(x_0 + k)],$$

where the interpolated value of $f(x_0 + r)$ with $r < k$ is

$$f(x_0 + r) = f(x_0) - \frac{r}{k}[f(x_0) - f(x_0 + k)]. \tag{24}$$

Expression (24) is highly symbolic and somewhat diflcult to read; however, it is a general expression applicable to interpolation operations.

Note that in Fig. 12-11 the curve $y = f(x)$ was falling as x increased and in Fig. 12-10 the curve rose as x moved to the right. These two possibilities of increasing and decreasing functions introduce a possibility of error in interpolation. Let us show another example of interpolation; this time we will choose a decreasing function and will proceed arithmetically as opposed to geometrically.

EXAMPLE 12. Find the value of ctn 23°12′35″.

Solution. Let us list the cotangent of the two angles which are tabulated in Appendix B and which bracket the angle in question. We have the quantities

$$
\begin{array}{l}
\text{ctn } 23°12′00″ = 2.3332 \\
\text{difference} \qquad\qquad\qquad\qquad \text{difference} \\
= 35″ \qquad\qquad\qquad\qquad\qquad = r \\
\text{ctn } 23°12′25″ = \underline{\qquad\qquad} \qquad \text{difference} \\
\qquad\qquad\qquad\qquad\qquad\qquad\qquad = -0.0019 \\
\text{difference} \\
= 60″ \\
\text{ctn } 23°12′60″ = 2.3313
\end{array}
$$

where certain observations are in order. First, angle-wise we wish to pass through 35″ of a 60″ interval, or we wish to pass $\frac{35}{60}$ of the way through the tabular interval. Function-wise, we will pass $\frac{35}{60}$ of the way through the interval which is −0.0019 units in width. This suggests the proportion

$$
\frac{35}{60} = \frac{r}{-0.0019},
$$

from which the deviation from 2.332 is $r = -0.0011$ such that

$$
\text{ctn } 23°12′35″ = 2.3332 - 0.0011 = 2.3321.
$$

We note a few observations that are helpful. Since the angle in question is bracketed by two other angles drawn from the table, the function in question must be bracketed by the tabular functions used. Second, since 23°12′35″ is closer to 23°12′60″ than to 23°12′00″, then ctn 23°12′35″ is nearer 2.3313 than to 2.3332, but *is still between* 2.3313 and 2.3332.

In Examples 11 and 12 we were given an angle accurate to the second and were asked to find a certain function of that angle by interpolation. The reverse is often required; that is, we have a function of an angle and wish to determine the angle to seconds by interpolation. Methods are similar to those in Examples 11 and 12. Let us observe an example.

EXAMPLE 13. Find θ correct to seconds by interpolation if cos θ = 0.36600.

Solution: Proceeding as in Example 12, we bracket the given quantity with tabular entries:

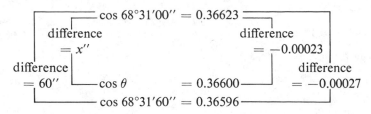

Since, function-wise, we are passing through $\frac{23}{27}$ of an interval and, angle-wise, we are passing through $x/60$ of the same interval, we have the proportion

$$\frac{x}{60} = \frac{-0.00023}{-0.00027} = \frac{23}{27} \quad \text{and} \quad x = 51'',$$

from which $\theta = 68°31'51''$.

Exercises

In Exercises 1–12, find the function indicated. Use interpolation.

1. Sin 8°40′30″.   *Ans.* 0.15083.

2. Cos 17°23′45″.

3. Tan 23°15′15″.   *Ans.* 0.42972.

4. Ctn 35°25′20″.

5. Cos 40°29′18″.   *Ans.* 0.76054.

6. Sin 39°27′07″.

7. Ctn 18°43′09″.   *Ans.* 2.9504.

8. Tan 7°14′21″.

9. Cos 56°32′12″.   *Ans.* 0.55140.

10. Tan 80°08′55″.

11. Ctn 65°22′03″.   *Ans.* 0.45852.

12. Sin 85°58′36″.

In Exercises 13–24, find the angle whose function is given. Use interpolation. In all cases, $\theta < 90°$.

13. Sin θ = 0.33334.   *Ans.* $\theta = 19°28'18''$.

14. Cos θ = 0.69293.

15. Tan θ = 0.46562.   *Ans.* θ = 24°58′03″.

16. Ctn θ = 1.4525.

17. Cos θ = 0.82832.   *Ans.* θ = 34°04′25″.

18. Tan θ = 1.3742.

19. Ctn θ = 0.25961.   *Ans.* θ = 75°26′48″.

20. Tan θ = 0.05941.

21. Cos θ = 0.03292.   *Ans.* θ = 88°06′52″.

22. Tan θ = 12.256.

23. Ctn θ = 6.4852.   *Ans.* θ = 8°45′58″.

24. Sin θ = 0.99914.

In Exercises 25–28 refer to Fig. 12-12 where we are given θ = 18°25′16″, *CB* = 4.2161 in., *and OB* = 6.8154 in.

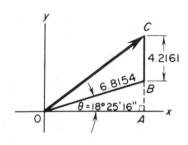

25. Find *AB*.   *Ans.* 2.1536 in.

26. Find *OA*.   *Ans.* 6.4662 in.

27. Find $\angle AOC$.   *Ans.* 44°34′10″.

28. Find *OC*.   *Ans.* 9.0768 in.

29. According to the cosine law, which will be introduced in a later chapter, angle *A* in Fig. 12-13(a) can be found by the equation

$$a^2 = b^2 + c^2 - 2bc \cos A.$$

FIGURE 12–12

Find *A* accurate to seconds if a = 4.0000 in., b = 6.0000 in., and c = 5.0000 in.
    Ans. *A* = 41°24′35″.

30. Referring to Fig. 12-13(a), angle *B* can be found by the equation

$$b^2 = a^2 + c^2 - 2ac \cos B.$$

Using the dimensions a = 3, b = 6, and c = 5, find angle *B* accurate to seconds. Observe that $B > 90°$, hence $\cos B < 0$.

12-6 Functions of Small Angles

For angles near zero, certain of the functions are good approximations of the magnitude of the angle in radians. In Fig. 12-13(b) we are given a unit vector **OP**. If θ is near zero, then *AP* is approximately equal to $\overparen{PB}$, that is,

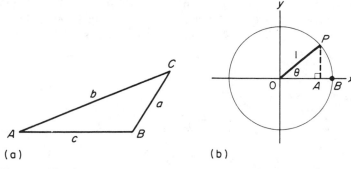

(a)   (b)

FIGURE 12-13

if θ is small, $AP \cong \overset{\frown}{PB}$. Now, by the definition of the radian, the number of radii in arc length PB equals the number of radians in θ. Again by definition,

$$\sin \theta = \frac{AP}{1} = AP.$$

Since $AP \cong \overset{\frown}{PB}$ for θ small, then

$$\sin \theta \cong \overset{\frown}{PB},$$

but since $\overset{\frown}{PB}$ equals the number of radians in θ, then

$$\sin \theta \cong \theta, \tag{25}$$

where θ is in radians and is small. Relationship (25) can be seen more clearly from Table 12-2 which shows some values of θ in degrees, θ in radians, and $\sin \theta$. Values of $\tan \theta$ are also shown, because for θ small, $\tan \theta \cong \theta \cong \sin \theta$; proof of this is an exercise which is left to the student.

Table 12-2

VALUES OF SIN θ, TAN θ, AND θ

θ (degrees)	θ (radians)	$\sin \theta$	$\tan \theta$
6	0.10472	0.10453	0.10510
5	0.08727	0.08716	0.08749
4	0.06981	0.06976	0.06993
3	0.05236	0.05234	0.05241
2	0.03491	0.03490	0.03492
1	0.01745	0.01745	0.01746

Upon inspecting Table 12-2, we see that

$$\sin \theta \cong \theta \cong \tan \theta \tag{26}$$

for θ near zero. This approximation is so good for $\theta \leq 0.1$ radians that the standard slide rule is constructed using it as a truth. More discussion on relationship (26) will follow in subsequent sections on the trigonometric scales of the slide rule.

Exercises

In the following exercises, use with slide rule accuracy the approximation concerning small angles.

1. Sin $\theta = 0.0400$. Find θ in degrees.   *Ans.* $\theta = 2.29°$.

2. Sin $\theta = 0.0300$. Find θ in degrees.

3. Tan $\theta = 0.0800$. Find θ in degrees.   *Ans.* $\theta = 4.58°$.

4. Tan $\theta = 0.0525$. Find θ in degrees.

5. $\theta = 4.50°$. Find sin θ, tan θ.   *Ans.* 0.0785.

6. $\theta = 5.25°$. Find sin θ, tan θ.

7. $\theta = 1.80°$. Find sin θ, tan θ.   *Ans.* 0.0314.

8. $\theta = 3.80°$. Find sin θ, tan θ.

9. $\theta = 2°20'$. Find sin θ, tan θ.   *Ans.* 0.0407.

10. $\theta = 5°48'$. Find sin θ, tan θ.

12-7   Trigonometric Scales on the Slide Rule

The standard slide rule contains an S (sine) and a T (tangent) scale. These scales are adequate to serve all six trigonometric functions, because through reciprocation and/or cofunctional relationships, the cosine, secant, cosecant, and cotangent can be expressed in terms of the sine or tangent. On most standard slide rules the trigonometric scales are placed on the sliding bar; in our discussion we will assume them to be there. Many slide rules also contain an ST-scale which serves for both the sine and tangent of angles between zero and 5.73°. We will discuss the scales by treating the S-scale first, T-scale next, and ST-scale last.

The S-scale

The S-scale is an arc sin scale. Note from Fig. 12-14 that the S-scale has angles marked off on it from 5.73° at the left end to 90° at the right end. This states that the S-scale is useful for θ if $5.73° \leq \theta \leq 90°$. The C-scale is usually

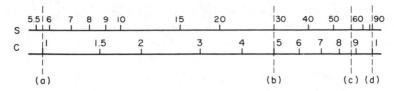

FIGURE 12–14

exactly aligned with the S-scale. If the hairline is placed over an angle θ on the S-scale, it is also over $\sin \theta$ on the C-scale; likewise, if the hairline is placed over $\sin \theta$ on the C-scale, it is also over θ on the S-scale ($5.73° \leq \theta \leq 90°$). In Fig. 12-14 we see the hairline (dotted) in four positions. At (d), $\sin 90° = 1$; at (c), $\sin 60° = 0.866$; at (b), $\sin 30° = 0.500$, and at (a), $\sin 5.73° = 0.100$. In Fig. 12-14 we can also assume that x has been hairlined on the C-scale and arc $\sin x$ (angle whose sine is x) is also hairlined on the S-scale. Thus if $x = 0.500$ as at (b), then arc $\sin x = 30°$ is read from the S-scale. Accordingly, the S-scale can be called the arc sine scale.

On many slide rules the S-scale is calibrated in tenths and hundredths of degrees as opposed to minutes and seconds, thereby taking the name "decimal-trig."

Both sine and cosine functions can be evaluated on the (C, S) combination of scales. Let us use an example problem to verify this.

EXAMPLE 14. Evaluate (a) $\sin 27.2°$ and (b) $\cos 36.5°$ on the slide rule.

Solution. (a) Place the hairline over 27.2° on the S-scale. (Many slide rules show two positions indicated as 27.2°, one by increasing as we read to the right, the other increasing as we read to the left. For sine functions we use the position obtained by increasing as we read to the right.) Now read $\sin 27.2° = 0.457$ as at (a) in Fig. 12-15.

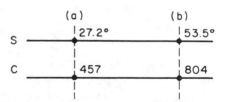

FIGURE 12–15

(b) Let us regard the S-scale as useful for sine functions only, increasing as we read to the right. We must find $\cos 36.5°$. Through cofunctional relationships $\cos 36.5° = \sin 35.5°$. Therefore, we place the hairline over 53.5° on the S-scale as at (b) in Fig. 12-15, where $\sin 53.5° = 0.804$.

Decimal points must be provided by the operator in finding the sine or cosine of an angle.

As seen from Example 14, the S-scale is useful for finding sines and cosines through the combination of the C and S scales. The secant and cosecant functions are reciprocals of the cosine and sine functions, respectively; the

C1 (or D1) scale reciprocates by direct transfer numbers on the C (or D) scale. Through these relationships, we can use the S-scale to obtain values of secant and cosecant relationships. Let us observe an example problem.

EXAMPLE 15. Evaluate (*a*) csc 16°, (*b*) sec 65°.

Solution: (*a*) Again, let us consider the S-scale as useful only for sine functions; therefore, we must convert csc 16° to an expression in the sine. Through reciprocal relationships, csc 16° = 1/sin 16°. Now place the hairline over 16° on the S-scale as at (*a*) in Fig. 12-16. Under the hairline on the C-scale

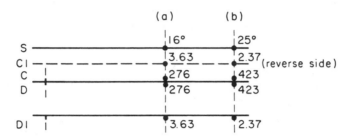

FIGURE 12-16

we read sin 16° = 0.276. Since we wish 1/sin 16°, and 276 on the C-scale can be reciprocated by direct transfer to the C1 scale, we read

$$\csc 16° = \frac{1}{\sin 16°} = \frac{1}{0.276} = 3.63$$

from the C1-scale under the hairline. (This assumes that the slide rule has a C1-scale and that the S, C, and C1 scales are all on the same bar.) In Fig. 12-16 we also have shown the slide rule zeroed (unities on the C and D scales are adjacent); now the same numbers on the C and D scales are under the hairline and the same reciprocals are on the C1 and D1 scales under the hairline. This means that those slide rules lacking the C1-scale can find csc 16° on the D1-scale.

(*b*) To find sec 65°, we use both the reciprocal and cofunctional relationships to relate sec 65° to a sine function. Hence,

$$\sec 65° = \frac{1}{\cos 65°} = \frac{1}{\sin 25°}.$$

Now place the hairline over 25° on the S-scale and read sec 65° = 2.37 from the C1-scale, or from the D1-scale if the rule is zeroed.

Let us now use the S-scale in the solution of a problem.

EXAMPLE 16. Solve the right triangle in Fig. 12-17(a) if $A = 37.5°$ and $c = 1.250$.

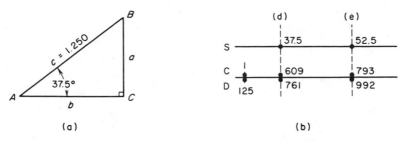

FIGURE 12–17

Solution. We must find A, b, and B. First, since the triangle is a right triangle, $B = 90° - 37.5° = 52.5°$. Now $\sin A = a/c$ and $a = c \sin A$; from the given information,

$$a = 1.250 \sin 37.5°. \tag{26}$$

Also, $\sin B = b/c$ and

$$b = 1.250 \sin 52.5°. \tag{27}$$

Solutions of (26) and (27) are shown in Fig. 12-17(b). Place the C-index opposite 1250 on the D-scale. Place the hairline over 37.5° on the S-scale at at (d). Note that the hairline is also over $0.609 = \sin 37.5°$ on the C-scale. We are set up for the multiplication of 1.250×0.609 or $1.250 \times \sin 37.5°$ and we read the product

$$a = 1.250 \sin 37.5° = 0.761$$

from the D-scale under the hairline.

The solution for side b from (27) is found exactly as the solution for side a. Without changing the position of the slide, move the hairline over 52.5° on the S-scale as at (e) in Fig. 12-17. The solution

$$b = 1.250 \sin 52.5° = 1.250 \times 0.793 = 0.992$$

is obtained from the D-scale under the hairline.

In brief summary, we can state that the S-scale is useful for computations involving the sine, cosine, secant, or cosecant functions. Its use is restricted to angles between 5.73° and 90°. For angles less than 5.73° we refer to a different (ST) scale.

The T-scale

The T-scale is an arc tangent scale. If the hairline is placed over an angle θ on the T-scale, then $\tan \theta$ is read under the hairline from the C-scale (within certain restrictions). In Fig. 12-18 we have a typical arrangement involving

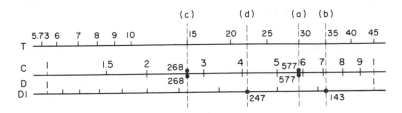

FIGURE 12-18

the T, C, D, and D1 scales (the C1 could be used as an alternate to the D1-scale). Note that the T-scale (reading from left to right) gives angles from $5.73°$ to $45°$. These are sufficient for finding $\tan \theta$ and $\operatorname{ctn} \theta$ for $5.73° < \theta < 84.27°$. If $5.73° < \theta < 45°$, $\tan \theta$ can be found by direct transfer from the T-scale to the C-scale. If $45° < \theta < 84.27°$, then $45° < 90 - \theta < 5.73°$ and

$$\tan \theta = \operatorname{ctn}(90° - \theta) = \frac{1}{\tan(90° - \theta)}. \tag{28}$$

With $\theta > 45°$ the last expression in (28) shows that we can find $\tan \theta$ by reciprocating $\tan(90° - \theta)$ where $90° - \theta$ is less than $45°$. Similarly, $\operatorname{ctn} \theta$ is found by reciprocating $\tan \theta$; if $\theta < 45°$, use a T-scale to D1-scale transfer. If $\theta > 45°$, convert $\operatorname{ctn} \theta$ to $\tan(90° - \theta)$ and use a direct transfer from the T-scale to the D-scale. Consider an example.

EXAMPLE 17. Find (a) $\tan 30°$, (b) $\tan 55°$, (c) $\operatorname{ctn} 75°$, (d) $\operatorname{ctn} 22°$.

Solution. Refer to Fig. 12-18 for all parts.
(a) To find $\tan 30°$, place the hairline over $30°$ on the T-scale. Read $\tan 30° = 0.577$ from the D-scale as at (a).
(b) To find $\tan 55°$, consider that

$$\tan 55° = \operatorname{ctn} 35° = \frac{1}{\tan 35°}.$$

Place the hairline over $35°$ on the T-scale and read $\tan 55° = 1.43$ from the D1-scale as at (b).

(*c*) To find ctn 75°, we have

$$\text{ctn } 75° = \tan 15°.$$

Place the hairline over 15° on the T-scale. Read ctn 75° = 0.268 from the D-scale as at (*c*).

(*d*) To find ctn 22°, we have

$$\text{ctn } 22° = \frac{1}{\tan 22°}.$$

Place the hairline over 22° on the T-scale. Read ctn 22° = 2.47 under the hairline from the D1-scale as at (*d*).

Some observations concerning the range of values of the cotangent and tangent are in order:

For 5.73° < θ < 45°, 0.1 < tan θ < 1.0 and 10 > ctn θ > 1.0.
For 45° < θ < 84.27°, 1.0 < tan θ < 10.0 and 1.0 > ctn θ > 0.1
For 0° < θ < 5.73° and 84.27° < θ < 90°, the T-scale is not used to find tan θ and ctn θ; instead, the ST-scale is used.

EXAMPLE 18. Solve for *b* in Fig. 12-19(a) using the slide rule.

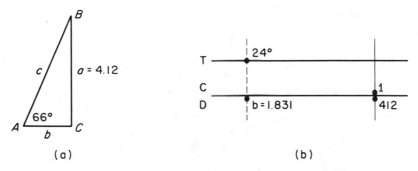

(a)

(b)

FIGURE 12–19

Solution. From the definition of the tangents,

$$\tan 66° = \frac{4.12}{b}$$

and

$$b = \frac{4.12}{\tan 66°} = \frac{4.12}{\text{ctn } 24°} = 4.12 \tan 24°.$$

Now multiply 4.12 by tan 24° as shown in Fig. 12-19(b). Oppose the C-index and 412 on the D-scale. Place the hairline over 24° on the T-scale. Read $b = 1.831$ under the hairline from the D-scale. The decimal point location is determined by the operator: knowledge of the fact that tan 24° lies between 0.1 and 1.0 is useful.

The ST-scale

In Sec. 12-6 functions of small angles were discussed. It was displayed in Table 12-2 that $\sin \theta \cong \tan \theta \cong \theta$ for $\theta < 5.73°$, where θ is given in radians. This suggests two important facts about the structure of the ST-scale. First, since $\sin \theta \cong \tan \theta$, then one scale can serve for both $\sin \theta$ and $\tan \theta$. Second, since θ is given in degrees on the ST-scale, construction of the ST-scale to be a duplicate of the C-scale with the ST-scale shifted laterally by a factor of 573 would enable a vertical tranfer from the ST-scale to the C-scale which would accomplish a division by 573. This division by 573 converts degrees to radians; also, since $\sin \theta \cong \tan \theta \cong \theta$ for θ small, this division also finds $\sin \theta$. The two facts just mentioned are incorporated into the usual ST-scale, suggesting these rules:

1. To find $\sin \theta$ or $\tan \theta$ for $0.573° < \theta < 5.73°$, place the hairline over θ on the ST-scale and read $\sin \theta$ or $\tan \theta$ from the C-scale under the hairline. Here $0.01 < \sin \theta < 0.1$ and $0.01 < \tan \theta < 0.1$.

2. To find $\tan \theta$ for $84.27° < \theta < 89.427°$, place the hairline over θ in the ST-scale and read $\tan \theta$ from the C1-scale under the hairline. Here $10 < \tan \theta < 100$.

3. To find $\sec \theta$, $\csc \theta$, $\operatorname{ctn} \theta$, or $\cos \theta$, convert to a sine or tangent function as previously done and apply rule (1) or (2).

EXAMPLE 19. Find (a) csc 2.8°, (b) ctn 1.6°, (c) ctn 86.8°.

Solution: In all cases refer to Fig. 12-20.

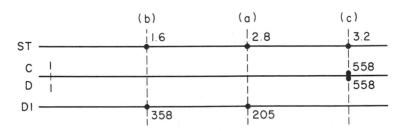

FIGURE 12–20

(a) To find csc 2.8°, we have

$$\csc 2.8° = \frac{1}{\sin 2.8°}.$$

Place the hairline over 2.8 on the ST-scale as at (a). Read

$$\csc 2.8° = \frac{1}{\sin 2.8°} = 20.5$$

from the D1 or C1 scale under the hairline.

(b) To find ctn 1.6°, we have

$$\text{ctn } 1.6° = \frac{1}{\tan 1.6°}.$$

Place the hairline over 1.6 on the ST-scale as at (b). Read

$$\text{ctn } 1.6° = \frac{1}{\tan 1.6°} = 35.8$$

from the C1 or D1 scale under the hairline.

(c) To find ctn 86.8°, we have

$$\text{ctn } 86.8° = \tan 3.2°.$$

Place the hairline over 3.2 on the ST-scale as at (c). Read

$$\text{ctn } 86.8° = \tan 3.2° = 0.0558$$

from the C or D scale under the hairline.

Exercises

In Exercises 1–36, use the slide rule to find N *or* θ.

1. Sin 36° = N.   *Ans.* 0.588.

2. Cos 43°45′ = N.

3. Sec 71.8° = N.   *Ans.* 3.20.

4. Csc 12°15′ = N.

5. Cos 36° = N.   *Ans.* 0.809.

6. Sec 36° = N.

7. Csc 36° = N.   *Ans.* 1.70.

8. Tan 27° = N.

9. Tan 35°15′ = N.   *Ans.* 0.707.

10. Ctn 14° = N.

11. Tan 68° = N.   *Ans.* 2.475.

12. Ctn 71° = N.

13. Sin 3.50° = N.   *Ans.* 0.0611.

14. Ctn 3.5° = N.

15. Cos 86.5° = N.   *Ans.* 0.0611.

16. Tan 1.375° = N.

17. Csc 2.9° = N.   *Ans.* 19.77.

18. Sec 86.9° = N.

19. Sin θ = 0.228.   *Ans.* 13.18°.

20. Cos θ = 0.726.

21. Sec θ = 1.422.   *Ans.* 45.4°.

22. Csc θ = 3.56.

23. Cos θ = 0.455.   *Ans.* 62.9°

24. Tan θ = 0.444.

25. Tan θ = 1.835.   *Ans.* 61.4°.

26. Tan θ = 7.30.

27. Ctn θ = 0.652.   *Ans.* 56.9°.

28. Ctn θ = 4.23.

29. Ctn θ = 0.104.   *Ans.* 84.07°.

30. Tan θ = 37.6.

31. Sin θ = 0.0821.   *Ans.* 4.71°.

32. Ctn θ = 0.0775.

33. Sec θ = 36.14.   *Ans.* 88.41°.

34. Csc θ = 11.16.

35. Cos θ = 0.0109.   *Ans.* 89.375°.

36. Tan θ = 0.0925.

In Exercises 37–43, reference is made to Fig. 12-21. Solve for the unknowns requested. Use a slide rule for computations.

37. Given $a = 14.4$, $c = 26.7$. Find A, b.   *Ans.* $A = 32.7°$, $b = 22.5$.

38. Given $c = 0.0486$, $A = 23.5°$. Find a, b.

39. Given $b = 16.85$, $c = 38.6$. Find A, a.   *Ans.* $A = 64.1°$, $a = 34.7$.

40. Given $a = 3.65$, $b = 8.82$. Find A.

41. Given $a = 4.72$, $b = 4.07$. Find A.   *Ans.* $A = 49.3°$.

42. Given $A = 17.4°$, $a = 12.25$. Find b.

43. Given $B = 64.5°$, $a = 0.746$. Find b.   *Ans.* $b = 1.565$.

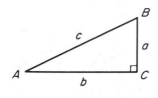

FIGURE 12–21

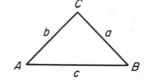

FIGURE 12–22

In Exercises 44–46, use the oblique triangle shown and apply the law

$$\frac{a}{\sin A} = \frac{b}{\sin B} = \frac{c}{\sin C}.$$

From the given information find the requested parts in Fig. 12-22.

44. Given $a = 4.25$, $A = 36.5°$, $B = 21.5°$. Find b.   *Ans.* $b = 2.62$.

45. Given $a = 82.6$, $A = 61°$, $b = 75.5$. Find c.

46. Given $C = 106°$, $B = 45°$, $a = 12.25$. Find c.   *Ans.* $c = 24.3$.

In Exercises 47–53, solve for the unknown indicated using the given information. Use the slide rule for computations.

47. Solve for θ in Fig. 12-23.   *Ans.* $13.5°$.

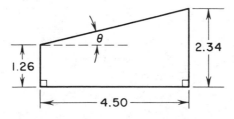

FIGURE 12–23

48. Solve for θ in Fig. 12-24.

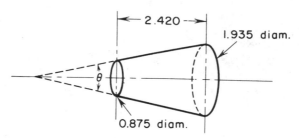

FIGURE 12–24

49. Solve for θ in Fig. 12-25. *Ans.* 47.2°.

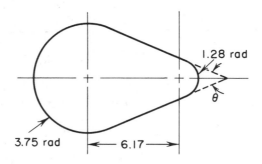

FIGURE 12–25

50. Solve for θ in Fig. 12-26.

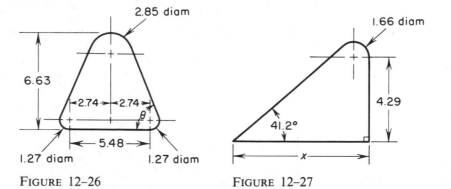

FIGURE 12–26   FIGURE 12–27

51. Solve for x in Fig. 12-27. *Ans.* 6.99.

52. Solve for x in Fig. 12-28.

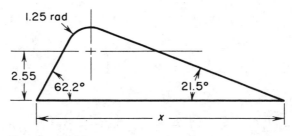

1.25 rad

2.55

62.2°

21.5°

x

FIGURE 12–28

In the preceding two chapters we introduced the solutions of right triangles by trigonometry and discussed computations as they involved the slide rule and the tables of natural trigonometric functions.

In this chapter we will introduce the solution of oblique triangles by deriving and employing the sine law and cosine law. Since computations with trigonometric functions involve numbers with many significant figures, we will also introduce the use of logarithms as they apply to the trigonometric functions.

We will also enlarge upon the applications of trigonometry by discussing more problems involving vectors, where these problems consider mechanics, solid geometry, force, acceleration, and the composition and resolution of forces.

13 SOLUTION OF OBLIQUE TRIANGLES

13-1   The Sine Law

An *oblique triangle* is defined here as a triangle which does not contain a right angle. It may be isosceles or equilateral or have no two sides equal to each other. It has many properties which may be expressed mathematically including those expressed by the sine law; the sine law asserts that the sides of a triangle are in the same ratio as the sines of the angles opposite those sides. Let us prove this assertion.

In Fig. 13-1 we show a general oblique triangle ABC. In this triangle we introduce a convention which will be used throughout this chapter. Capital letters are used to designate angles and the corresponding lower-case letters designate the sides opposite. Thus, side a is opposite angle A, side b is opposite angle B, and side c is opposite angle C.

If, in Fig. 13-1, we drop a perpendicular to AB from C, the length of the perpendicular is the altitude h. Now from the right triangle ADC we have

$$\frac{h}{b} = \sin A \quad \text{or} \quad h = b \sin A. \tag{1}$$

Also, from the right triangle BDC,

$$\frac{h}{a} = \sin B \quad \text{or} \quad h = a \sin B. \tag{2}$$

Equating the right-hand expressions in (1) and (2), we have

$$b \sin A = a \sin B,$$

from which

$$\frac{a}{\sin A} = \frac{b}{\sin B}. \tag{3}$$

To establish expression (3), an altitude was drawn from C to c. Another similar expression may be established by drawing another altitude from a

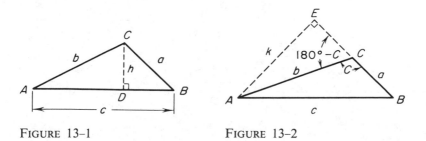

FIGURE 13–1   FIGURE 13–2

different vertex. In Fig. 13-2 we have chosen the same triangle, but have drawn an altitude from A to side a extended; this altitude has the length k and its foot is at E. Now, from the right triangle ABE, we have

$$\frac{k}{c} = \sin B \quad \text{or} \quad k = c \sin B. \tag{4}$$

Also, from the right triangle ACE,

$$\frac{k}{b} = \sin (180° - C) \quad \text{or} \quad k = b \sin (180° - C). \tag{5}$$

From (4) and (5),

$$c \sin B = b \sin (180° - C)$$

or

$$\frac{b}{\sin B} = \frac{c}{\sin (180° - C)}. \tag{6}$$

If we construct two vectors of magnitude b and reference angles $180° - C$ and C as shown in Fig. 13-3, we can observe that

$$\sin C = \sin (180° - C)$$

and (6) becomes, by substitution,

$$\frac{b}{\sin B} = \frac{c}{\sin C}. \tag{7}$$

Now (3) and (7) combine to the *sine law*

$$\frac{a}{\sin A} = \frac{b}{\sin B} = \frac{c}{\sin C}, \tag{8}$$

where (8) asserts that *the sides of an oblique triangle are in the same ratio as the sines of the angles opposite those sides.*

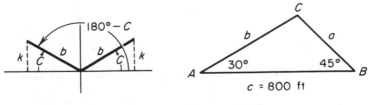

FIGURE 13–3   FIGURE 13–4

EXAMPLE 1. From the information shown in Fig. 13-4, find the lengths of sides a and b.

Solution. From the given triangle, $A = 30°$ and $B = 45°$, from which

$$C = 180° - (30° + 45°) = 105°.$$

Employing a part of (8), we have

$$\frac{a}{\sin A} = \frac{c}{\sin C}. \tag{9}$$

Substituting the known information into (9), we have

$$\frac{a}{\sin 30°} = \frac{800}{\sin 105°},$$

from which

$$a = \frac{800 \sin 30°}{\sin 105°} = \frac{800(0.5)}{0.96593} = 414.11 \text{ ft.}$$

To find b, we have

$$\frac{b}{\sin B} = \frac{c}{\sin C} \tag{10}$$

but $B = 45°$, $c = 800$, and $C = 105°$ so that we now have, from (10)

$$b = \frac{800 \sin 45°}{\sin 105°} = \frac{800(0.70711)}{0.96593} = 585.65 \text{ ft.} \tag{11}$$

Upon inspection of the computations involved in Example 1, the question quite naturally arises as to whether or not logarithms can be used. The answer is affirmative. In the absence of a table of logarithms of trigonometric functions, expression (11) can be computed by using the table of natural trigonometric functions to obtain $\sin 45° = 0.70711$ and $\sin 105° = 0.96593$ and then regarding (11) as

$$\log b = \log 800 + \log (0.70711) - \log (0.96593).$$

If, however, a table of logarithms of trigonometric functions is available, (11) may be written in the form

$$\log b = \log 800 + \log \sin 45° - \log \sin 105°.$$

More on the use of logarithms will follow in Sec. 13-2.

Another question which may arise is: "When can the sine law be applied?" Inspecting

$$\frac{a}{\sin A} = \frac{b}{\sin B} \tag{12}$$

we observe that if three parts of (12) are known, the fourth part can be found. Thus, the sine law can be used when we have known:

1. *Two angles and a side opposite one of them.* This can be modified because, if we know two angles, we can find the third angle where now the known side will lie opposite one of the three known angles. Thus, we can use the sine law when we are given two angles and any side of a triangle.

2. *Two sides and the angle opposite one of them.* This introduces the possibility of the *ambiguous case* which will be discussed in Sec. 13-3.

Exercises

In Exercises 1–12 find the quantity in parentheses where the given information refers to the general triangle ABC.

1. $A = 45°$, $B = 60°$, $b = 25$ (a).   *Ans.* $a = 20.417$.

2. $A = 60°$, $B = 75°$, $a = 14$ (b).

3. $B = 120°$, $C = 15°$, $a = 10$ (b).   *Ans.* $b = 12.247$.

4. $B = 150°$, $A = 10°$, $c = 6$ (b).

5. $C = 60°$, $B = 60°$, $a = 8$ (b).   *Ans.* $b = 8$.

6. $C = 35°$, $B = 2C$, $b = 10$ (c).

7. $A = 110°$, $C = 40°$, $a = 20$ (b).   *Ans.* $b = 10.642$.

8. $B = 60°$, $C = 70°$, $c = 12$ (a).

9. $A = 50°$, $B = 30°$, $b = 15$ (c).   *Ans.* $c = 29.544$.

10. $A = 45°$, $C = 105°$, $b = 10$ (c).

11. $A = 110°$, $C = 30°$, $c = 5$ (b).   *Ans.* $b = 6.4279$.

12. $B = 65°$, $C = 50°$, $a = 8$ (c).

In Exercises 13–24 we are given two sides and the angle opposite one of them. Find the angle in parentheses; give only those solutions where the angle requested is less than 90°.

13. $a = 3$, $c = 6$, $C = 30°$ (A).   *Ans.* $14°28'38''$.

14. $a = 3$, $c = 6$, $C = 60°$ (A).

15. $b = 7$, $a = 10$, $A = 45°$ (B).   *Ans.* 29°40'07".

16. $b = 25$, $a = 37.5$, $A = 30°$ (B).

17. $c = 18$, $b = 3$, $B = 20°$ (C).   *Ans.* No answer.

18. $c = 3$, $b = 18$, $B = 20°$ (C).

19. $a = 12$, $c = 6$, $A = 60°$ (C).   *Ans.* 25°39'33".

20. $a = 10$, $c = 7$, $A = 40°$ (C).

21. $a = 8$, $b = 4$, $A = 30°$ (B).   *Ans.* 14°28'39".

22. $b = 15$, $c = 3$, $B = 70°$ (C).

23. $a = 18$, $c = 9$, $C = 20°$ (A).   *Ans.* 43°9'37".

24. $a = 10$, $b = 6$, $B = 15°$ (A).

13-2   Use of the Table of Logarithms of Trigonometric Functions

In the computations involved in Sec. 13-1 it was apparent that the application of logarithms to the sine law would be helpful; in Chap. 12 the use of logarithms would have been useful also. We will discuss here the use of the logarithms of the trigonometric functions. Let us start with an example problem.

EXAMPLE 2. Evaluate N if $N = 14.276 \sin 25°16'25''$.

Solution. One method which could be used here would be to find the value of $\sin 25°16'25''$ by use of the table of natural trigonometric functions, then apply logarithms. This method requires the use of two tables and therefore consumes extra time as well as introducing the greater possibility of error. One table may be used to find the logarithm of the sine of $25°16'25''$. This is the table of logarithms of trigonometric functions (log-trig table) in Appendix D. Let us write the given expression in the logarithmic form:

$$\log N = \log 14.276 + \log \sin 25°16'25''. \tag{13}$$

Now in (13), $\log 14.276$ can be found from the table of common logarithms in Appendix C. To find $\log \sin 25°16'25''$, we refer to Appendix D where we find

$$\log \sin 25°16'00'' = 9.63026 - 10, \tag{14}$$

$$\log \sin 25°17'00'' = 9.63052 - 10. \tag{15}$$

Interpolation procedures to find log sin 25°16'25'' are similar to those in previous logarithm work, except that Appendix D provides some extra assistance. The d column in Appendix D shows that there are $d = 26$ logarithmic parts between (14) and (15). This can also be found by subtracting (14) from (15). We require 25'' worth of these 26 logarithmic parts, or $\frac{25}{60}$ of the difference $d = 26$. Rather than compute $\frac{25}{60}$ of 26, refer to the proportional parts column headed by 26. There is no entry in the '' column for 25'', so we create 25'' by adding any two entries there, say 20'' and 5'', which will total the required 25''. Now

$$
\begin{array}{l}
20'' \text{ shows } 8.7 \text{ log parts,} \\
\underline{5'' \text{ shows } 2.2 \text{ log parts.}} \\
25'' \text{ take } 10.9 \text{ log parts.}
\end{array}
$$

Rounding off these 10.9 log parts to 11 log parts, we say that the extra 25'' require 11 log parts, hence,

$$
\begin{array}{l}
\log \sin 25°16'00'' = 9.63026 - 10 \\
\underline{\text{for 25'' add } \quad 0.00011} \\
\log \sin 25°16'25'' = 9.63037 - 10
\end{array}
$$

Now, referring back to (13) and using a format, we continue with the requested solution:

$$
\begin{array}{r}
\log 14.276 = 11.15461 - 10 \\
+ \log \sin 25°16'25'' = \quad 9.63037 - 10 \\
\hline
\log N = 20.78498 - 20 \\
N = \quad 6.0951.
\end{array}
$$

In Example 2 we found the log sin of an angle. Often a situation arises requiring us to find the angle, given the log-trig value. Consider Example 3.

EXAMPLE 3. Find ϕ if log tan $\phi = 10.76008 - 10$.

Solution. Referring to Appendix D,

$$
\log \tan 80°08'00'' = 10.75963 - 10 \qquad (16)
$$
$$
{}_{45}
$$
$$
\log \tan \phi \qquad = 10.76008 - 10 \quad d = 75
$$
$$
\log \tan 80°09'00'' = 10.76038 - 10 \qquad (17)
$$

Now we see that ϕ lies between 80°08' and 80°09'. From Appendix D, the d column shows $d = 75$ log parts difference between (16) and (17). We wish to pass through the logarithmic interval from 10.75963 to 10.76008, or 45 log parts. Now we refer to the proportional parts column headed by 75 and attempt to find an entry of 45 parts. Finding no entry which is 45, we choose to find any two which add to 45, or as close to 45 as we can get. Let us use

$$\begin{array}{ll} 37.5 \text{ log parts give } 30'', \\ \underline{7.5 \text{ log parts give } 06''.} \\ 45 \quad \text{log parts give } 36''. \end{array}$$

With this we see that ϕ is $36''$ greater than (16) or

$$\log \tan 80°08'36'' = 10.76008 - 10.$$

EXAMPLE 4. Find log sec $37°12'48''$.

Solution. Since sec $\phi = 1/\cos \phi$, then

$$\log \sec \phi = \log 1 - \log \cos \phi = -\log \cos \phi.$$

Now, from Appendix D and previous methods,

$$\log \cos 37°12'48'' = 9.90113 - 10 = -0.09887$$

and

$$\log \sec 37°12'48'' = +0.09887.$$

Exercises

In Exercises 1–10 find the indicated function.

1. Log sin $31°26'45''$.　　　　　　　　　　*Ans.* $9.71742 - 10$.

2. Log sin $65°12'09''$.

3. Log cos $18°47'21''$.　　　　　　　　　　*Ans.* $9.97621 - 10$.

4. Log cos $49°07'37''$.

5. Log tan $35°35'52''$.　　　　　　　　　　*Ans.* $9.85483 - 10$.

6. Log ctn $35°35'52''$.

7. Log sec $18°52'12''$.　　　　　　　　　　　*Ans.* 0.02399.

8. Log tan $72°16'15''$.

9. Log csc $6°15'49''$.　　　　　　　　　　　*Ans.* 0.96216.

10. Log cos $85°08'29''$.

In Exercises 11–20, find ϕ to the nearest second if

11. Log sin $\phi = 9.98721 - 10$.　　　　　　*Ans.* $76°09'40''$.

12. Log sin $\phi = 9.01422 - 10$.

13. Log cos $\phi = 9.11232 - 10$.   *Ans.* 82°33′30″.

14. Log cos $\phi = 9.85727 - 10$.

15. Log tan $\phi = 0.14457$.   *Ans.* 54°21′53″.

16. Log tan $\phi = 9.11457 - 10$.

17. Log sec $\phi = 10.08875 - 10$.   *Ans.* 35°23′47″.

18. Log sec $\phi = 10.46651 - 10$.

19. Log csc $\phi = 10.01279 - 10$.   *Ans.* 76°09′40″.

20. Log ctn $\phi = 11.22445 - 10$.

21. Refer to the exercises following Sec. 12-7. Solve Exercises 47–53 using logarithms. Express the answers to accuracy as extensive as can be obtained from the tables of logarithms.

22. Use the sine law to find a from the general triangle ABC if $A = 34°12′24″$, $C = 102°29′15″$, and $b = 3.6525$.

23. Find DC in Fig. 13-5.   *Ans.* Impossible.

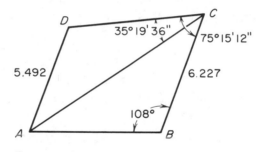

FIGURE 13–5

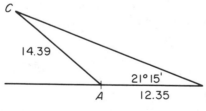

FIGURE 13–6

24. Find BC in Fig. 13-6.

25. A traveler proceeds from point O along a path OB as shown in Fig. 13-7. When he arrives at B, 12.5 miles from O, he changes course by 30°25′ to proceed to point C. If C is 18.3 miles from O in the direction shown, find angle α, his original direction.

Ans. $\alpha = 55°11′05″$.

26. Two forces act on a body at O as pictured in Fig. 13-8. Force F_1 is of magnitude 48.5 lb. and direction 62°20′; F_2 is 69.4 lb. at 235°15′. It is assumed that the resultant R is in a direction 160°. Check the validity of that assumption.

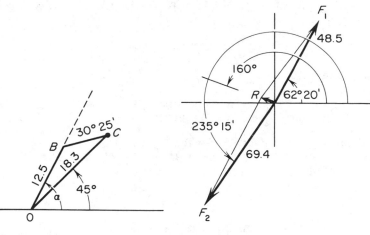

FIGURE 13–7   FIGURE 13–8

27. A vehicle pulls a 675-lb. load by exerting 275 lb. of force on a tow-chain slanting at 18° from the horizontal. What is the pulling force on the load? What vertical force does the load exert on the ground while being pulled?

Ans. 261.54 lb.; 590.02 lb.

28. In Fig. 13-9 the lines $Ox, Oy,$ and Oz are mutually perpendicular at O. A line is drawn from point A in the "floor" to point B in the "wall." Find the length of AB if $BB_z = 8.462$, $BB_y = 5.965$, $AA_x = 1.072$, and $AA_y = 6.337$.

Ans. 11.417.

29. In the general triangle ABC, angle A may be found by the equation

$$\sin \frac{A}{2} = \sqrt{\frac{(s-b)(s-c)}{bc}}$$

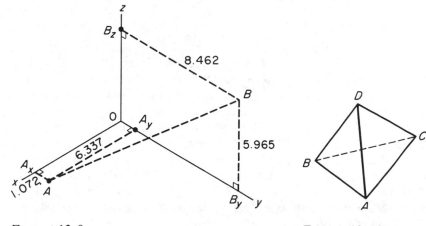

FIGURE 13–9   FIGURE 13–10

where $s = (a + b + c)/2$. Given a triangle ABC with $a = 3.286$, $b = 4.367$, and $c = 4.955$, find A by the given equation.   *Ans.* $A = 40°39'53''$.

30. Find the area of the triangle in Exercise 29 using the formula

$$\text{area} = \tfrac{1}{2}bc \sin A.$$

31. The angles of a triangle are in the ratio $2:3:4$. Find the longest side of the triangle if the shortest side is of length 14.275.   *Ans.* 22.902.

32. Given the pyramid in Fig. 13-10 with equilateral base ABC where $BC = 12.96$. Given also angle $ADC = 38°12'$, angle $BDA = 33°16'$, and angle $BDC = 41°56'$, and $AD = 15.05$. Find angle DBC.

13-3   Sine Law—the Ambiguous Case

In the preceding section we mentioned that the sine law was used to solve triangles when two angles and one side are known, or when two sides and an angle opposite one of those two sides are known. It was mentioned further that the latter case presented an ambiguity. Let us inspect this ambiguity with reference to Fig. 13-11.

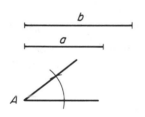

FIGURE 13-11

Assume that we know b, A, and a of a triangle as shown in Fig. 13-11. Note that these known parts constitute two sides and the angle opposite one of them. If we attempt to construct the proposed triangle from the information provided, we start by laying off line AC, indicating the distance from A to C as the given length b. Next, at A reproduce the given angle A, establishing base line AD. Now, side a is opposite angle A. We may complete the construction by swinging an arc of length a from C, with the intention of intersecting base line AD. This arc can intersect AD twice, as shown in Fig. 13-11. Note that two triangles $\triangle ABC$ and $\triangle AB'C$ both have the given properties; that is, they both have a side of length b, an angle of magnitude A, and a side of length a.

The implication in the preceding paragraph is clear. The given data do not necessarily describe a single triangle. Since two triangles are possible, we call this an *ambiguous case* and, in the absence of further information that would restrict us to only one of the triangles, we must accept that either triangle could be the desired triangle and we must therefore solve both of the triangles.

EXAMPLE 5. Solve the general triangle ABC if $b = 2$, $B = 30°$, and $c = 3$.

Solution. First, construct the triangle as shown in Fig. 13-12. The construction results in $\triangle BCA$ and $\triangle BC'A$, each of which has $b = 2$, $c = 3$ and $B = 30°$. Each triangle is solved separately employing the sine law.

For either triangle,

$$\frac{b}{\sin B} = \frac{c}{\sin C}$$

or $\quad \dfrac{b}{\sin B} = \dfrac{c}{\sin C'} \quad$ (18)

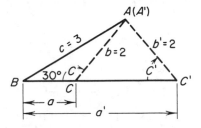

FIGURE 13–12

and, substituting $b = 2$, $c = 3$, and $B = 30°$ into (18), we have either

$$\sin C = 0.75 \quad \text{or} \quad \sin C' = 0.75. \tag{19}$$

Referring now to Fig. 13-12, since $\triangle ACC'$ is isosceles, angles C and C' are supplements, with C obtuse and C' acute. Therefore, from (19),

$$C = 131°24'35'' \quad \text{and} \quad C' = 48°35'25''. \tag{20}$$

Now, since the sum of the angles of a triangle equals 180°,

$$A' = \angle BAC' = 180° - (B + C') = 101°24'35'',$$
$$A = \angle BAC = 180° - (B + C) = 18°35'25''.$$

To find the remaining side, we have

$$\frac{a}{\sin \angle BAC} = \frac{2}{\sin 30°}, \quad \text{from which} \quad a = 1.2752,$$

and

$$\frac{a'}{\sin \angle BAC'} = \frac{2}{\sin 30°}, \quad \text{from which} \quad a' = 3.92096.$$

The organized solution shows

$$a = 1.27520, \quad C = 131°24'35'', \quad A = 18°35'25'',$$
$$a' = 3.92096, \quad C' = 48°35'25'', \quad A' = 101°24'35''.$$

Exercises

In Exercises 1–16 the given values give rise to the ambiguous case. Solve for the quantity in parentheses; give both solutions. In each case refer to the general triangle ABC.

1. $A = 30°$, $a = 10$, $b = 15$ (C).   *Ans.* 18°35'25'', 101°24'35''.

2. $A = 40°$, $a = 8$, $b = 10$ (C).

3. $C = 50°$, $c = 8$, $b = 10$ (a).   *Ans.* 4.1218, 8.7341.

4. $C = 45°$, $c = 12$, $b = 15$ (a).

5. $B = 30°$, $b = 6$, $c = 9$ (a).   *Ans.* 3.8256, 11.7629.

6. $C = 40°$, $c = 15$, $a = 20$ (B).

7. $A = 45°$, $a = 9$, $c = 12$ (B).   *Ans.* 25°31'48'', 64°28'12''.

8. $B = 45°$, $b = 12$, $a = 15$ (C).

9. $C = 60°$, $c = 9$, $b = 10$ (a).   *Ans.* 2.5505, 7.4495.

10. $A = 60°$, $a = 14$, $b = 15$ (c).

11. $A = 12°15'$, $a = 7.5$, $b = 15$ (C).   *Ans.* 12°51'14'', 142°38'46''.

12. $B = 67°20'$, $b = 8.44$, $c = 8.52$ (a).

13. $C = 10°29'15''$, $b = 3c$ (B).   *Ans.* 33°05'50'', 146°54'10''.

14. $C = 10°29'15''$, $b = 2c$ (B).

15. $A = 30°$, $a = 3.8264$, $b = 7.6528$ (C).   *Ans.* 60°00'00''.

16. $B = 12°25'35''$, $b = 8.165$, $c = 9.004$ (A).

Referring to Fig. 13-11, assume that we are given a, b, and A. Discuss the solutions of the triangle in Exercises 17–22 if

17. $a = b$.   **18.** $a = b \sin A$.

19. $a < b \sin A$.   **20.** $a > b$.

21. $A = 90°$.   **22.** A is obtuse.

Using the material in Sec. 13-3 and the congruency theorems from plane geometry, indicate whether or not a unique triangle is formed when the parts in Exercises 23–28 are known:

23. Three sides.

24. Two sides and the angle opposite one of them.

25. Two sides and the included angle.

26. Two angles and the included side.

27. Two angles and the side opposite one of them.

28. Three angles.

29. Given the general triangle ABC where A, a, and b are known. Show that

$$c = b \cos A \pm a \cos B.$$

13-4   The Cosine Law

Another law of trigonometry useful in solving triangles is the cosine law. We will first show its derivation, then discuss when it may be applied, and finally show applications of it.

Given the general triangle ABC pictured in Fig. 13-13. Construct a perpendicular from C to AB at D. It can readily be shown that

$$AD = b \cos A$$

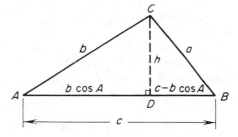

and that $DB = c - b \cos A$. Now, from the right triangle ADC,

$$h = \sqrt{b^2 - (b \cos A)^2}, \qquad \text{FIGURE } 13\text{--}13$$

$$(21)$$

and from the right triangle BDC,

$$h = \sqrt{a^2 - (c - b \cos A)^2}. \tag{22}$$

Equating (21) and (22) to eliminate h, we have

$$\sqrt{b^2 - (b \cos A)^2} = \sqrt{a^2 - (c - b \cos A)^2}. \tag{23}$$

Squaring both sides of (23) and solving for a^2, we have

$$a^2 = b^2 + c^2 - 2bc \cos A,$$

which is one form of the *cosine law.*

By using different perpendiculars in Fig. 13-13 and therefore involving angle B or angle C, we can obtain the three relationships

$$\begin{aligned} a^2 &= b^2 + c^2 - 2bc \cos A, \\ b^2 &= a^2 + c^2 - 2ac \cos B, \\ c^2 &= a^2 + b^2 - 2ab \cos C, \end{aligned} \tag{24}$$

where equations (24) are the three available forms of the cosine law.

Inspecting equations (24), we observe that the cosine law may be used to solve a triangle when the given parts are:

(a) *Three sides.* If a, b, and c are given, then angles A, B, or C can be found directly depending upon which of equations (24) is used.

(b) *Two sides and the included angle.* As an example, if b, c, and A are given, the first of equations (24) is readily solved for a.

(c) *Two sides and the angle opposite one of them.* As an example, if a, b, and A are given, the first of equations (24) becomes a quadratic in c. This quadratic can be difficult to solve, but it will give both of the values of c in the ambiguous case. This case is usually solved more easily by the sine law.

(d) *Two angles and a side.* This case, though possible by the cosine law, would produce simultaneous quadratics. The case is much more readily solved by the sine law.

The preceding discussion reveals that the cosine law can be used in all cases of solvable triangles. The last two cases listed are better solved by the sine law, however. The s.s.s. case and the s.a.s. case cannot be solved by the sine law; therefore the cosine law is recommended. Other trignometric laws such as the tangent law or certain laws involving functions of half-angles are also useful in solving triangles, but will not be discussed here.

EXAMPLE 6. Two forces $F_1 = 4$ lb. and $F_2 = 6$ lb. are applied upon a body, producing a resultant force of $R = 8$ lb. What is the angle between F_1 and R?

Solution. Sketching the forces as in Fig. 13-14(a), we produce the parallelogram $ABCD$ with sides F_1 and F_2 and diagonal R. The triangle ABC

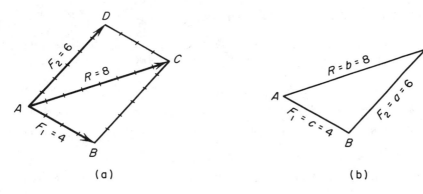

FIGURE 13-14

from Fig. 13-14(a) is reproduced in Fig. 13-14(b) where we observe that the angle A is the desired angle between F_1 and R. Applying $a = 6$, $b = 8$, and $c = 4$ to

$$a^2 = b^2 + c^2 - 2bc \cos A,$$

we have

$$(6)^2 = (8)^2 + (4)^2 - 2(8)(4) \cos A$$

from which

$$\cos A = \tfrac{44}{64} = 0.68750,$$

and

$$A = 46°34'03''.$$

EXAMPLE 7. Two aircraft leave the same point C at the same time, diverging at an angle of $60°$, each flying in a straight line. When aircraft A is 90 miles from C and aircraft B is 100 miles from C, how far are the aircraft apart?

Solution. Sketching the situation, we have Fig. 13-15. Here $a = 100$, $b = 90$, and $C = 60°$ and we wish to find c. Applying the last of equations (24),

$$c^2 = (100)^2 + (90)^2$$
$$- 2(100)(90) \cos 60°,$$

from which

$$c = \sqrt{9100} = 95.39 \text{ miles.}$$

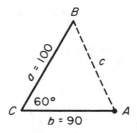

FIGURE 13-15

Exercises

*In Exercises 1–10 use the given information to solve for the quantity in parentheses.
In all cases reference is made to the general triangle ABC.*

1. $a = 3, b = 5, c = 6$ (B). *Ans.* 56°15′05″.

2. $a = 4, b = 5, c = 8$ (C).

3. $a = 8, b = 6, C = 45°$ (c). *Ans.* 5.6673.

4. $c = 5, b = 4, C = 60°$ (a).

5. $a = 4.073, b = 6.325, c = 5.923$ (C). *Ans.* 65°19′17″.

6. $a = 6.225, b = 7.140, c = 5.885$ (B).

7. $a = b = c$ (any angle). *Ans.* 60°00′00″.

8. $a = b, c = 2b$ (A).

9. $a = 3.2, c = 4.6, B = 150°$ (C). *Ans.* 17°45′09″.

10. $b = 5.6, c = 8.2, A = 150°$ (a).

11. Two forces $F_1 = 4.3$ lb. and $F_2 = 6.2$ lb. are applied to a body. The resultant force is 5.6 lb. What is the angle between F_1 and F_2?

12. Two forces $F_1 = 250$ lb. and F_2 are applied to a body with a resultant force $R = 310$ lb. If the directions of F_1 and F_2 differ by 60°, find F_2.

13. The cosine law fails for a triangle with sides $a = 2$, $b = 6$, and $c = 9$. Explain why.

14. Show by the cosine law that the angle opposite the largest side of the triangle with sides in a 5:12:13 ratio is a right angle.

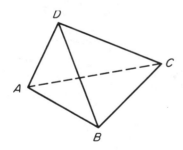

FIGURE 13–16

In Fig. 13-16 the tetrahedron pictured has $AB = 4.6$, $BC = 3.75$, $AD = 6.8$, $\angle ABD = 65.3°$, $\angle ABC = 59.2°$, and $\angle DBC = 68°$. Using a slide rule for the necessary computations, find

15. $\angle DAB$. *Ans.* 76.8°.

16. $\angle ADB$.

17. $\angle BCD$. *Ans.* 81.2°.

18. $\angle CDB$.

19. $\angle DAC$. *Ans.* 72.4°.

20. $\angle ACD$.

21. $\angle CDA$. *Ans.* 35.9°.

22. $\angle BAC.$

23. $\angle ACB.$ *Ans.* 70.6°.

24. $AC.$

25. $BD.$ *Ans.* 7.29.

26. $CD.$

27. Using the information given for the tetrahedron in Fig. 13–16, sketch a line from C perpendicular to AB at a point called E. Find angle ECD.   *Ans.* 74.4°.

28. Three forces F_1, F_2, and F_3 act on a body to produce a resultant R. If $F_1 = 20$ lb. at 30°, $F_2 = 40$ lb. at 270°, and $R = 50$ lb. at 120°, find the magnitude and direction of F_3. (*Note:* assume that all of the forces are acting in one plane.)
Ans. 85.2 lb. at 120.6°.

29. Simplify expression (23).

30. If n forces $F_1, F_2, F_3, \cdots, F_n$ act upon a body at angles $\phi_1, \phi_2, \phi_3, \cdots, \phi_n$, respectively, and all of the forces are in the same Cartesian coordinate plane, show that

$$R_x = F_1 \cos \phi_1 + F_2 \cos \phi_2 + F_3 \cos \phi_3 + \cdots + F_n \cos \phi_n$$

and

$$R_y = F_1 \sin \phi_1 + F_2 \sin \phi_2 + F_3 \sin \phi_3 + \cdots + F_n \sin \phi_n,$$

where R_x and R_y are the horizontal and vertical components of the resultant, respectively.

Each of the trigonometric functions can be plotted as a graph. The most commonly used function is the sine function. In this chapter we will show the graphs of the six elementary trigonometric functions, but will present a detailed study only of the sine wave.

Knowledge of the graphs of the trigonometric functions is especially useful in the study of alternating-current electricity, sound, vibrations, and many other phenomena which are periodic in nature. In addition to the graphs of the elementary trigonometric functions, we will also introduce a study of Lissajous figures which are often observed in oscilloscope work and which are useful in determining unknown frequencies.

14 GRAPHS OF THE TRIGONOMETRIC FUNCTIONS

14-1 Periodicity and Definitions

Let us assume that the pendulum pictured in Fig. 14-1 swings back and forth across a rest position. Assume further that each time it swings to the right it will exactly reach the position A and each time it swings to the left it will exactly reach the position B. Also, the time required to get from A to O to B to O and back to A is the same for each swing of the pendulum; call this time T. Now, if the timing is started when the pendulum is at any other position, say D, and the time required to traverse the D-O-B-O-D-A-D route is still T, then we have a case of *periodicity*.

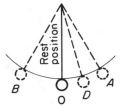

FIGURE 14-1

A body which is in periodic motion traverses a series of positions according to a fixed pattern. The series of positions which it assumes is called the *cycle*. The time required to complete one cycle—that is, to assume all of the positions and velocities—is called the *time period*. The number of cycles completed in a given time period is called the *frequency*.

The earth assumes positions periodically with reference to the sun. The time required to complete one cycle, i.e., one complete revolution about the sun, is approximately 365 days. This means that 365 days from today the earth will be in the same position relative to the sun that it is in today. It will be in the same position 2(365) days from today and 3(365) days and n(365) where n is an integer. The frequency of the earth's motion is then one cycle per 365 days, or one cycle per year. The time period is $T = 365$ days.

The position of the minute hand of a clock is periodic with time $T = 60$ minutes as the time period. The position of the hour hand of a clock is periodic with time period $T = 12$ hours. The frequencies are 24 cycles per day and 2 cycles per day for the minute hand and hour hand, respectively.

If the periodic motion is circular, the time period is the time required to make one full revolution. One full revolution is 360° or 2π radians, depending upon the system of angular measurement used. Let us consider the relationship between time period and frequency for circular motion, along with units.

Assume that a body is in circular motion with frequency f. This means (using time in seconds) that f is in cycles per second. Consider the motion to be effective and uniform for t seconds. The angle θ generated in t seconds is

$$\theta(\text{cycles}) = f\left(\frac{\text{cycles}}{\text{sec.}}\right) \times t \text{ (sec.)} = ft \text{ (cycles)}.$$

Now, since there are 2π radians per cycle, then

$$\theta \text{ (radians)} = f\left(\frac{\text{cycles}}{\text{sec.}}\right) \times 2\pi \left(\frac{\text{radians}}{\text{cycle}}\right) \times t \text{ (sec.)} = 2\pi ft \text{ (radians)}.$$

Also, since there are 360° per cycle, then

$$\theta \text{ (degrees)} = f\left(\frac{\text{cycles}}{\text{sec.}}\right) \times 360 \left(\frac{\text{degrees}}{\text{cycle}}\right) \times t \text{ (sec.)}$$

$$= 360ft \text{ (degrees)}.$$

As stated before, the time required to complete one cycle is T sec., or there are T sec./cycle. On the other hand, the frequency f is in cycles/sec. Since T and f have units which are reciprocals, then

$$T = \frac{1}{f} \quad \text{or} \quad f = \frac{1}{T}, \tag{1}$$

where (1) relates the time period and the frequency.

EXAMPLE 1. An airfield beacon sweeps in a uniform circular motion at the rate of 60° per second of time. (a) What is the time T required to complete one cycle? (b) What is its frequency in cycles per second?

Solution. (a) To find T, the time required to complete one cycle, we have

$$60 \frac{\text{degrees}}{\text{sec.}} \times T \frac{\text{sec.}}{\text{cycle}} = 360 \frac{\text{degrees}}{\text{cycle}} \tag{2}$$

or

$$60T = 360$$

from which,

$$T = 6 \frac{\text{sec.}}{\text{cycle}}.$$

To develop (2), we know that one cycle equals 360°. Since the beacon rotates at the rate of 60° for each second of time, then we see that it requires 6 seconds to complete one cycle.

(b) Since $T = 6$ sec./cycle, then by (1),

$$f = \frac{1}{T} = \frac{1}{6\dfrac{\text{sec.}}{\text{cycle}}} = \frac{1}{6} \frac{\text{cycles}}{\text{sec.}}.$$

Exercises

1. A satellite circles the globe exactly 12 times per day. What is its time period in minutes? What is its frequency in cycles/hour; cycles/min.?

Ans. 120 min.; $\frac{1}{2}$ cycle/hr.; $\frac{1}{120}$ cycle/min.

2. The earth spins on its axis one full revolution per 24 hours. What is its time period in days? What is its frequency in cycles/day; cycles/hr.; cycles/year?

3. A wheel rotates uniformly at the rate of 1000°/sec. A point on a spoke of the wheel passes through how many cycles/min.? What is the time period in seconds?

Ans. $\frac{500}{3}$ cycles/min.; $\frac{9}{25}$ sec.

4. An automobile is traveling at the rate of 40 mph. A point on a spoke of a wheel is in periodic motion with reference to the axle. The greatest radius of the tire is 16 inches. What is the time period for the point? What is the frequency in cycles/sec.?

5. Two points are on the same spoke of a wheel which is rotating at 10 cycles/sec. If point A is 12 inches from the axle and point B is 18 inches from the axle, what is the time period for A? For B?

Ans. For both A and B, $T = \frac{1}{10}$ sec.

6. Two wheels mounted on the same axis rotate at different angular velocities. Wheel A rotates at 80 cycles per sec and wheel B rotates at 60 cycles per sec. One and only one spoke on each wheel is painted red. Periodically the red spokes align into exactly the same position. What is the length of the time period between consecutive alignments if
(*a*) The wheels rotate in the same direction? *Ans.* $\frac{1}{20}$ sec.
(*b*) The wheels rotate in opposite directions? *Ans.* $\frac{1}{140}$ sec.

14-2 Rotating Vectors—the Sine Wave

A vector **OP** pictured in Fig. 14-2 can be considered to rotate. In the chapter on right triangles we considered a vector to be stationary, but certain conven-

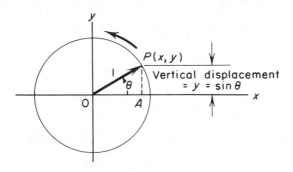

FIGURE 14–2

tions established there will be maintained here in our current discussion. Reviewing these, we will consider the positive direction of rotation to be counterclockwise. Also, the direction of **OP** is indicated by θ which initiates at the positive x-axis.

Referring again to Fig. 14-2, if **OP** rotates uniformly, it will assume the same position and velocity periodically. This assumption of the same position and velocity can be independent of time, although in many of our considerations later we will make it dependent upon time. Here the position of the end point of the vector (point P) depends upon the magnitude of θ. If P is at P_0 when θ is of value θ_0, then P is again at P_0 when $\theta = \theta_0 + 2\pi$, $\theta = \theta_0 + 4\pi$, $\theta = \theta_0 + 6\pi$, $\cdots$, $\theta = \theta_0 + 2n\pi$ where n is an integer. In other words, the position of P is cyclical with respect to θ, and the angular period of θ is 2π.

Continuing to refer to Fig. 14-2, the vertical displacement of P (namely, the ordinate y) is also periodic with respect to θ. We note two facts about this vertical displacement. First, y never exceeds OP in magnitude and the range of y is $-OP \leqq y \leqq OP$. Second, by the definition of the sine function,

$$\sin \theta = \frac{AP}{OP} = \frac{\text{vertical displacement}}{\text{magnitude}}. \tag{3}$$

If, in Fig. 14-2, we consider the circle to be a unit circle (that is, the radius is 1), then $OP = 1$. Further,

$$AP = \text{vertical displacement} = y.$$

These facts revise (3) to read

$$y = \sin \theta, \tag{4}$$

where (4) asserts that the vertical displacement of a rotating unit vector equals the sine of the angle passed through.

We earlier asserted that the vertical displacement of the unit vector ranges

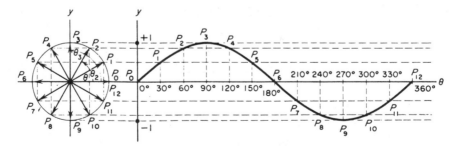

FIGURE 14–3

between -1 and $+1$, depending upon the size of θ. Let us portray this graphically as in Fig. 14-3. There we show the unit vector starting in the position OP_0 and subsequently assuming the positions OP_1, OP_2, etc. The vertical displacement of P_i (the general P) is, by (4), the sine of θ_i. In Fig. 14-3, the vectors are sketched 30° apart. These same 30° intervals are plotted on the θ-axis at the right. At each abscissa the proper vertical displacement is plotted, producing the curve shown, which is the graph of $y = \sin \theta$.

We will call the graph of $y = \sin \theta$ the graph of the *fundamental*. The equation $y = \sin \theta$ is not the general sine equation, but is highly restrictive. Several modifications can be made, each modifying the graph. For instance, we might be asked to graph

$$y = 3 \sin \theta,$$

$$y = 4 \sin 3\theta,$$

$$y = \tfrac{1}{2} \sin (2\theta - 45°),$$

$$y = a \sin (b\theta + c),$$

where the four listed equations introduce new properties such as amplitude, angular period, and phase angle, all of which will be discussed in subsequent sections.

EXAMPLE 2. Eliminating care for exactness, show a rapid way of producing a rough graph of $y = \sin x$.

Solution. Sketch an x-axis and a y-axis as shown in Fig. 14-4. Assign a positive and negative unity on the y-axis. Assign equally spaced positions along the x-axis, showing $x = 0°, 90°, 180°, 270°, 360°$. From knowledge of the sine function, we know that $\sin 0° = 0$, $\sin 90° = 1$, $\sin 180° = 0$, $\sin 270° = -1$, and $\sin 360° = 0$, establishing the five points shown in Fig. 14-4. Join these points with a smooth curve, duplicating the general shape of the curve shown in Fig. 14-3.

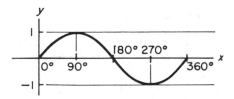

FIGURE 14-4

14-3   More on the Sine Wave

In Sec. 14-2 we showed how a rotating vector generates a sine wave. We were highly restrictive, however, showing only the graph of

$$y = a \sin (b\theta + c), \tag{5}$$

where both a and b were unity and c was zero, causing (5) to have the form of (4). We further suggested that we could call the graph of (4) the fundamental wave. The graph of the fundamental is useful for purposes of comparison when a or b of (5) is not unity and c is not zero. Let us now show how modifications of a, b, and c effect the sketch of the sine waves shown in Figs. 14-3 and 14-4.

EXAMPLE 3. Show the graph of

$$y = 2 \sin \theta. \tag{6}$$

Solution. First, for background and comparison purposes, sketch the fundamental

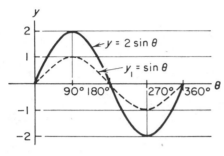

FIGURE 14–5

$$y_1 = \sin \theta \tag{7}$$

as shown in Fig. 14-5. Now compare the ordinates of (6) and (7). Since $y_1 = \sin \theta$ and $y = 2 \sin \theta$, then by comparison,

$$y = 2y_1, \tag{8}$$

where (8) means that the ordinate of (6) is twice the ordinate of (7) for any given value of θ. This suggests that all vertical displacements of the dotted curve in Fig. 14-5, when doubled, will be the appropriate vertical displacements of (6).

The preceding example suggests correctly that the only distinction between the graphs of $y_1 = \sin \theta$ and $y_2 = a \sin \theta$ is the factor a. Here

$$y_2 = ay_1,$$

and a is called the *amplitude factor*. It is often called the *amplitude*, corresponding to the greatest vertical displacement of $y = a \sin \theta$; we will use the latter terminology in subsequent discussions. Note that the introduction of the factor a merely elongates or shrinks the vertical displacements of the fundamental. If $a > 1$ we have elongation; if $a < 1$, we have shrinking. The value of a in no way effects the plots of the abscissas; i.e., it neither shrinks nor elongates the graph in the horizontal sense.

Now let us consider the introduction of a nonunity b in (5). We will show examples where $a = 1$ and $b \neq 1$. Consider Examples 4, 5, and 6.

EXAMPLE 4. Show the graph of

$$y = \sin 2\theta. \tag{9}$$

Solution. As before, we will first graph the fundamental equation

$$y_1 = \sin \theta \qquad (10)$$

shown as the dotted curve in Fig. 14-6. Comparing (9) and (10), we see that

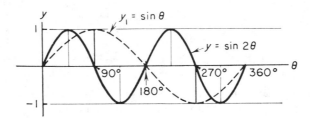

FIGURE 14-6

a given assignment for θ will not necessarily produce equal values for y and y_1 since $y = \sin 2\theta$ and $y_1 = \sin \theta$. We know that the critical values of y_1 occur 90° apart with respect to θ. That is, when $\theta = 90°$, $y_1 = 1 = $ maximum; when $\theta = 180°$, $y_1 = 0$; when $\theta = 270°$, $y_1 = -1 = $ minimum; when $\theta = 0°$ or 360°, $y_1 = 0$. The critical values will be called here the *zeroes, maxima,* and *minima* of the ordinate.

Inspecting (9), we assign to θ values which are multiples of 45°, then 2θ will assume values which are multiples of 90°, suggesting that the critical values of $y = \sin 2\theta$ are spaced 45° apart. Consider Table 14-1.

From the data in Table 14-1 and knowledge of the fact that critical values of y occur at intervals of 45°, we have the graph of $y = \sin 2\theta$ as shown by the solid line in Fig. 14-6.

Remarks. Inspection shows us that the *angular period* of $y = \sin \theta$ is 360°. This means that one full cycle of the sine wave is completed for each 360° increase in θ. Inspecting $y = \sin 2\theta$, an increase of 360° in θ increases 2θ

Table 14-1

$\theta°$	0	45	90	135	180	225	270	315	360
$2\theta°$	0	90	180	270	360	450	540	630	720
$y_1 = \sin \theta$	0	0.707	1	0.707	0	−0.707	−1	−0.707	0
$y = \sin 2\theta$	0	1	0	−1	0	1	0	−1	0

by 720°, meaning that we pass through *two* full cycles of the wave for each 360° increase in θ. This suggests that the angular period of $y = \sin 2\theta$ is

$360°/2 = 180°$. In practical applications, $y = \sin 2\theta$ is called the *second harmonic* of $y = \sin \theta$.

Extending the thinking in the preceding paragraph, let us compare the graphs of

$$y = \sin \theta, \tag{11}$$

$$y = \sin n\theta. \tag{12}$$

The angular period of (11) is 360°. If we increase θ by 360° in (12), $n\theta$ is increased by $n(360°)$, suggesting that a 360° increase in θ causes (12) to pass through n full cycles. Therefore the *angular period* of (12) is $360°/n$. If n is a positive integer, (12) is called the nth harmonic of (11).

EXAMPLE 5. Show the graph of $y = \sin 6\theta$.

Solution. The angular period of $y = \sin 6\theta$ is $360°/6 = 60°$. This means that one full cycle of $y = \sin 6\theta$ is completed for each 60° increase in θ. Further, the critical values occur $60°/4 = 15°$ apart. Figure 14-7 shows the graphs of $y = \sin 6\theta$ and the fundamental $y_1 = \sin \theta$. Here we call $y = \sin 6\theta$ the *sixth harmonic* of $y = \sin \theta$.

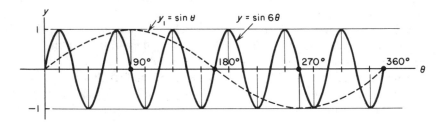

FIGURE 14–7

EXAMPLE 6. Show the graphs of

$$y = \sin x, \tag{13}$$

$$y = \sin\frac{\pi}{2}x, \tag{14}$$

laying off the horizontal axis in radians.

Solution. Regard (13) as the fundamental wave. An increase of 2π radians in x completes one full cycle of (13). Therefore 2π radians is the angular period of (13) and the critical values are $2\pi/4 = \pi/2$ radians apart. The graph of (13) is shown as the dotted line in Fig. 14-8.

Now the angular period of (14) is $2\pi \div \pi/2 = 4$ radians. The fussy part

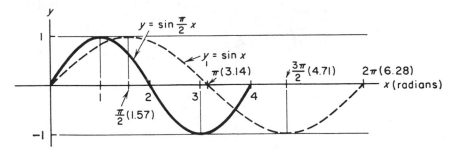

FIGURE 14–8

plotting (14) now is that of locating the positions $x = 1, 2, 3, 4$ radians along the horizontal axis. For convenience, the values $\pi/2$, π, $3\pi/2$, and 2π are shown as decimal values 1.57, 3.14, 4.71, and 6.28 in Fig. 14-8. Using these decimal values as guides, we plot the critical points for (14) and show the graph as the solid line.

In summary, the distinction between the graphs of $y = \sin \theta$ and $y = \sin b\theta$ is a matter of elongation along the θ-axis. The amplitude is not affected by the nonunity value of b; only the angular period of $y = \sin b\theta$ is affected. The angular period of $y = \sin b\theta$ is either $360°/b$ or $2\pi/b$, according to the system of angular measurement used.

Now let us consider the introduction of a nonzero value of c in (5). We show an example problem.

EXAMPLE 7. Show the graph of

$$y = \sin \theta, \tag{15}$$

$$y = \sin (\theta + 60°). \tag{16}$$

Solution. Once again, (15) is called the fundamental. Let us change our approach and show the generation of waves (15) and (16) by rotating vectors. First, observe that a 360° change in θ produces a 360° change in $\theta + 60°$, suggesting that the angular periods of (15) and (16) are both 360°. The dotted graph in Fig. 14-9 is the graph of (15) and is the result of rotating the vector **OP**, where it is important to observe that the initial direction of **OP** is 0°. The graph of (16) is shown as the result of rotating vector **OR** in Fig. 14-9 where we see that for $\theta = 0°$,

$$y = \sin (0° + 60°) = \sin 60°.$$

This asserts that **OR** is 60° ahead of **OP** for all assignments of θ; this is clear from the fact that $\theta + 60°$ is 60° greater than θ. It further asserts that the critical values of (16) are 60° *ahead* of the corresponding critical values of

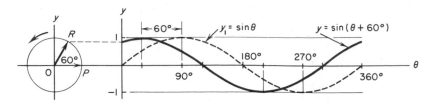

FIGURE 14–9

(15). (We say "ahead" here, despite the fact that the graphed critical values of (16) are 60° to the *left* of those of (15). If the θ-axis were a time axis with the time increasing to the right, the critical values of (16) would occur 60° *sooner* in time.)

Remarks. The distinction between the graphs of

$$y = \sin \theta, \tag{17}$$

$$y = \sin (\theta + c) \tag{18}$$

is a matter of horizontal shift. Accepting (17) as the reference curve, (18) is shifted left or right by an amount c according to the sign of c, and the curve is in no way distorted. If $c > 0$, the shift is to the left; if $c < 0$, the shift is to the right. Accordingly, c is called the *phase shift* or *phase angle*. We note that (17) and (18) are both first harmonics. If a phase shift is to be intelligently described, it must be with reference to an unshifted wave of the same harmonic. Consider Example 8.

EXAMPLE 8. Show the graphs of

$$y = \sin (3\theta + 60°), \tag{19}$$

$$y_1 = \sin 3\theta. \tag{20}$$

Solution. Inspecting (20), we have an unshifted third harmonic with angular period 120° and unity amplitude. This is shown as the dotted line in Fig. 14-10. To plot (20), we must be careful, for the phase shift is *not* 60°. Consider values of θ which will cause $3\theta + 60°$ to be the critical values 90°, 180°, 270°, 360°. If we wish the first maximum value of (19) then

$$3\theta + 60° = 90°,$$

from which $\theta = 10°$ and we plot a maximum at $\theta = 10°$. To obtain the 180° zero point,

$$3\theta + 60° = 180°,$$

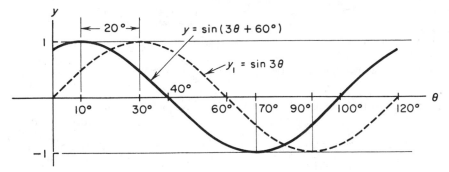

FIGURE 14–10

from which $\theta = 40°$. Continuing to plot the critical values of (19), we produce the graph shown in Fig. 14-10. Note that (19) leads (20) not by 60°, but by $60°/3 = 20°$.

Remarks. The distinction between the graphs of

$$y = \sin b\theta, \tag{21}$$

$$y = \sin (b\theta + c) \tag{22}$$

is a horizontal shift. The phase shift is of magnitude c/b. When $b > 0$, then (22) is shifted to the left of (21) if $c > 0$ and to the right of (21) if $c < 0$.

Summary. The general equation of the sine wave is given as

$$y = a \sin (bx + c)$$

where a is the *amplitude* or greatest vertical displacement, $360°/b$ or $2\pi/b$ is the *angular period*, and c/b is the *phase shift* with respect to the corresponding harmonic.

Exercises

Show graphs of the equations in Exercises 1–12. In all but Exercise 1 plot the fundamental wave for comparison purposes on the same set of axes.

1. $y = \sin x$.

2. $y = \frac{1}{2} \sin x$.

3. $y = 2.3 \sin x$.

4. $y = \sin 5\theta$.

5. $y = \sin (\theta/3)$.

6. $y = \sin 3\pi x$.

7. $y = \sin (\theta - 30°)$.

8. $y = 1.8 \sin (\theta + 90°)$.

9. $y = 3 \sin 4\theta$.

10. $y = 6 \sin (2\theta + 90°)$.

11. $y = 1.4 \sin (6\theta - 48°)$.

12. $y = 5 \sin \left(\dfrac{\pi}{2}x + \dfrac{\pi}{4} \right)$.

13. What are the amplitudes of the sine waves in Exercises 8, 9, and 10?

Ans. 1.8, 3, 6.

14. What are the angular periods of the sine waves in Exercises 4, 5, and 6?

Ans. 72°, 1080°, $\frac{2}{3}$ radian.

15. The sine wave in Exercise 10 is shifted how many degrees in which direction with reference to $y = \sin 2\theta$?

Ans. 45° left.

16. The sine waves in Exercises 11 and 12 are shifted how far in what direction with reference to $y = \sin 6\theta$ and $y = \sin (\pi/2)x$, respectively?

17. Refer to Fig. 14–11. From the given sketches determine the equations of curves A, B, and C.

Ans. (A) $y = 2 \sin 2\theta$, (B) $y = 2 \sin (\theta - 30°)$.

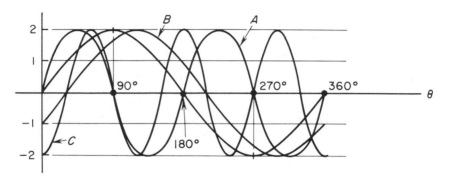

FIGURE 14–11

18. In Fig. 14–12 the graph of $y_1 = \sin \theta$ is shown as a solid line. Also shown is $y_2 = \sin (-\theta)$ as a dotted line. For any given θ, what relationship exists between y_1 and y_2? What relationship exists between the sine of an angle and the sine of the negative of the same angle?

Ans. $y_1 = -y_2$; $\sin \theta = -\sin (-\theta)$.

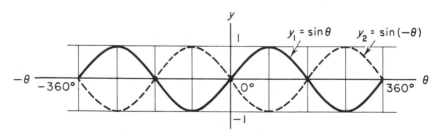

FIGURE 14–12

19. Given the equation $s = 100 \sin 3600\phi$. What is the angular period? What is the smallest positive value of ϕ for which s is a maximum?   *Ans.* $0.1°; 0.025°.$

20. Given the equation $s = 100 \sin (50\phi - 30°)$. What is the smallest positive value of ϕ for which s is a maximum?   *Ans.* $2.4°.$

14-4   The Angle as a Function of Time

In Sec. 14-1 we briefly discussed an angle as a function of time. If a vector rotates with a uniform velocity ω (omega), where ω is in units such as degrees/sec. or radians/sec., then the angle θ through which the vector passes is a function of time, namely

$$\theta = \omega t. \tag{23}$$

Now a typical sine function, usually written as

$$y = Y \sin (\theta \pm \psi) \tag{24}$$

may be written in the form

$$y = Y \sin (\omega t \pm \psi). \tag{25}$$

When the angular velocity is given as f cycles/sec., we can convert to radians/sec. by multiplying the number of cycles by 2π, or the angular velocity may be written as $2\pi f$ radians/sec. Now the angle θ through which the vector passes is

$$\theta = 2\pi ft, \tag{26}$$

where (26) is a revision of (23) and we can apply (23) or (26) to (24) which may be written as

$$y = Y \sin (2\pi ft \pm \psi). \tag{27}$$

Expressions (25) and (27) show y as a function of time t. In (27), Y is the amplitude, $2\pi f$ is the angular velocity, and ψ is the phase angle. It is emphasized here that the only variables in (27) are y and t. It is further emphasized that $2\pi ft$, ψ, and $2\pi ft \pm \psi$ are *angles*.

The student should know how to graph (27) and how to find any one of the five parts y, Y, f, t, ψ when the other four parts are given. This latter demand has some restrictions on it.

In the study of alternating current in electricity, (27) is revised commonly to the forms

$$i = I_{max} \sin 2\pi ft, \tag{28}$$

$$e = E_{max} \sin 2\pi ft, \tag{29}$$

where i and e are instantaneous current and voltage, I_{max} and E_{max} are maximum current and voltage, f is frequency, and t is time. Let us consider some applications of (28) and (29).

EXAMPLE 9. Referring to (28), at what least positive value of time will a 60 cycle/sec. generator with a maximum output of 100 amp. be instantaneously delivering 40 amp.?

Solution. We will show both a mathematical and a graphical solution. First, the mathematical solution. From the given data we have $i = 40$, $I_{max} = 100$, and $f = 60$ and we wish to find t. Substituting the given data into (28), we have

$$40 = 100 \sin (2)(\pi)(60)(t)$$

or

$$40 = 100 \sin 120\pi t. \tag{30}$$

In (30) it is emphasized that $120\pi t$ is an *angle* which is a function of time. Here 120π is angular velocity in radians/sec. and $120\pi t$ is in radians. Dividing both sides of (30) by 100, we have

$$\sin 120\pi t = 0.4 \tag{31}$$

Now $120\pi t$ is an angle whose sine is 0.4; the least such positive angle, by slide rule accuracy, is approximately 23.5° and, from (31),

$$120\pi t \text{(in radians)} = 23.5 \text{ (in degrees)}. \tag{32}$$

Now (32) is awkward because the left side is in radians and the right side is in degrees. For demonstration purposes we will show (32) converted entirely to degrees in (33) and entirely to radians in (34).

Since π radians equal 180°, then 120π radians equal 21,600° and (32) becomes

$$21,600t \text{ (degrees)} = 23.5 \text{ (degrees)}, \tag{33}$$

from which $t = 0.00109$ sec.

Since there are 180° in π radians, then

$$\frac{180°}{\pi} = \frac{23.5°}{x}$$

and $x = 0.1305\pi$ radians, meaning that there are 0.1305π radians in 23.5°. Substituting into (32), we have

$$120\pi t \text{ (radians)} = 0.1305\pi \text{ (radians)}, \tag{34}$$

from which $t = 0.00109$ sec.

Graphically, we obtain a fair approximation of the solution. The basic equation is

$$i = 100 \sin 120\pi t, \tag{35}$$

where 100 is the amplitude and the time period required to complete one cycle is 1/60 sec. since the frequency is 60 cycles/sec. These data produce the graph shown in Fig. 14-13. There we observe that the first 40-amp. output

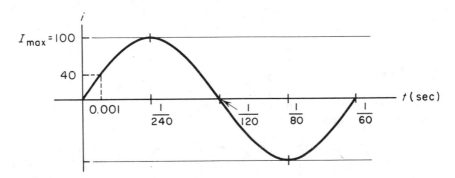

FIGURE 14–13

is reached at a time approximately one-quarter of $\frac{1}{240}$ sec. or about $\frac{1}{900}$ sec. This has a numerical value of slightly more than 0.001 sec., which agrees favorably with the more exact mathematical solution $t = 0.00109$ sec. The graphical approach is quick and is often useful in serving as a check against gross error.

EXAMPLE 10. Referring to (29), find $E_{\max}$ if $f = 100$ cycles/sec. and $e = 20$ volts when $t = 0.001$ sec.

Solution. Substituting the given data into (29) we have

$$20 = E_{\max} \sin (2\pi)(100)(0.001). \tag{36}$$

We emphasize that the quantity $(2\pi)(100)(0.001)$ in (36) is an *angle* and this angle is in radians. Simplifying (36), we have

$$E_{\max} \sin 0.2\pi = 20. \tag{37}$$

Now in (37) the angle is 0.2π radians, which are

$$(0.2)(180°) = 36°,$$

and (37) becomes

$$E_{\max} \sin 36° = 20,$$

but $\sin 36° = 0.588$, so that we now have

$$0.588 E_{\max} = 20,$$

from which

$$E_{\max} = \frac{20}{0.588} = 34 \text{ volts.}$$

Exercises

In Exercises 1–5 use the equation $i = I_{\max} \sin 2\pi ft$ *and the given information to find the value of the indicated unknown.*

1. Given $I_{\max} = 110$ amp., $f = 100$ cycles/sec., and $t = 0.0025$ sec., find i.
   Ans. $i = 110$ amp.

2. Given $I_{\max} = 100$ amp. and $f = 120$ cycles/sec., find the smallest positive value of t for which $i = 50$ amp. Find the second smallest positive value of t for which $i = 50$ amp. Give a general expression that identifies all values of t for which $i = 50$ amp.
   Ans. $1/1440$ sec.; $5/1440$ sec.; $(12n + 1)/1440$ sec.; $(12n + 5)/1440$ sec.

3. Given $i = I_{\max}$ when $f = 60$ cycles/sec. Find the least positive value of t.

4. In Exercise 1, what is the time interval between consecutive maximum values of i? Between consecutive zero values of i? Show the graph.

5. Given $i = I_{\max}$ when $t = 0.005$ sec. Give an expression for all frequencies under which this condition can be met.
   Ans. $f = (2n + 1)50$ cycles/sec. where n is an integer.

6. Given the equation $e = E_{\max} \sin (2\pi ft + c)$, find c if $E_{\max} = 12$ volts, $e = 4$ volts, and $f = 600$ cycles/sec. when $t = 0.0001$ sec. *Ans.* $c = -1.9°$.

7. Sketch the graphs of $y = -\sin \theta$ and $y = \sin (\theta - 180°)$. What seems to be the result of shifting the sine wave by $180°$?

8. A generator delivers current according to the equation

$$i = 50 \sin \left(240\pi t + \frac{\pi}{2}\right).$$

What is the maximum current that it can deliver? What is the frequency? What is the phase shift in terms of seconds?

In Exercises 9–16 use the equation $i = I_{max} \sin (2\pi ft + \gamma)$ *and the given information to find the value of the indicated unknown.*

9. If $f = 100$ cycles/sec., $\gamma = 18°$, and $i = 2$ amp. when $t = 0.001$ sec., find I_{max}.
Ans. $I_{max} = 2.47$ amp.

10. If $f = 200$ cycles/sec., $\gamma = 24°$, and $i = 12$ amp. when $t = 0.00075$ sec., find I_{max}.

11. What is the lowest frequency that will allow $i = 8.66$ amp. when $t = 0.001$ sec. if $I_{max} = 10$ amp. and $\gamma = 36°$?
Ans. $f = 66.5$ cycles/sec.

12. What is the lowest frequency that will allow $i = 10$ amp. when $t = 0.00015$ sec. if $I_{max} = 20$ amp. and $\gamma = 0.1 \pi$ radians?

13. Find the smallest positive value of t for which $i = 20$ amp. if $I_{max} = 50$ amp., $f = 400$ cycles/sec., and $\gamma = 30°$. Refer to Fig. 14–9 and note that both the first and second quadrants contain an angle whose sin $= 0.4$. *Ans.* $t = 0.000876$ sec.

14. Find the smallest positive value of t for which $i = 10$ amp. if $I_{max} = 20$ amp., $f = 100$ cycles/sec., and $\gamma = 40°$. See Exercise 13.

15. Find the phase angle γ if $i = 0$ amp. when $t = 0.0015$ sec., $I_{max} = 30$ amp., and $f = 60$ cycles/sec. Is the wave form ahead of or trailing (in time) the unshifted reference wave?
Ans. $\gamma = -32.4°$, trailing.

16. Find the phase angle γ if $i = 8.66$ amp. when $t = 0.002$ sec., $I_{max} = 10$ amp., and $f = 100$ cycles/sec.

14-5 Graphs of the Other Trigonometric Functions

In the preceding two sections we discussed the graph of the general sine function. We explored maximum and minimum points, amplitude, phase shift, and angular period, as they related to the sine function. The remaining five functions possess interesting graphs, but they are not as popular from the point of view of general usage as the sine function. It will be our purpose here to show the graphs of the other five functions and to discuss them briefly.

The Graph of y = cos θ

Consider that the cosine of an angle is the same as the sine of the complementary angle; this is by the definition of the cofunction. Therefore,

$$y = \cos \theta = \sin (90° - \theta). \tag{38}$$

We already have a firm picture of the graph of the sine function. Equation (38) suggests that the cosine wave is a shifted sine wave; this is precisely the case. Assigning values of θ to the sine function in (38), we note that (38) plots as shown in Fig. 14-14. The graph of $y = \sin \theta$ is shown for comparison purposes as the broken line in Fig. 14-14. We observe that the cosine wave

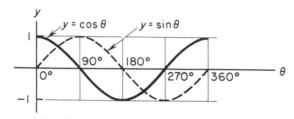

FIGURE 14–14

is merely a sine wave which has been shifted 90°. More precisely, the graph of $y = \cos \theta$ leads the graph of $y = \sin \theta$ by a 90° phase shift; otherwise, the graphs are identical. Discussions concerning angular period and amplitude that are appropriate for the sine wave are also appropriate for the cosine wave.

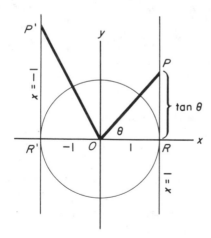

FIGURE 14–15

The Graph of y = tan θ

To consider the variation in y for $y = \tan \theta$, refer to Fig. 14-15. There we show the rotating vector **OP** where the vector is of changeable length, always terminating on either $x = 1$ or $x = -1$. From the triangle ORP, with $OR = 1$,

$$\tan \theta = \frac{PR}{OR} = \frac{PR}{1} = PR.$$

This asserts that PR equals the tangent of the reference angle. Observe that as $θ$ goes from 0° to

90°, tan θ goes from 0 to a very large positive number. If $90° < \theta < 180°$, then

$$\tan \theta = \frac{P'R'}{-1}$$

so that tan θ is negative, varying from a large negative value when θ is slightly greater than 90° to zero when $\theta = 180°$. This variation, extended through 360°, is shown in Fig. 14-16, where we observe that the angular

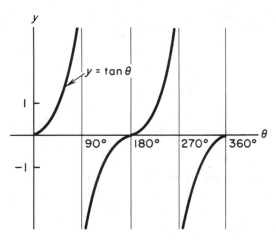

FIGURE 14-16

period of the function $y = \tan \theta$ is 180°, as opposed to 360° for $y = \sin \theta$ and $y = \cos \theta$. We note, too, that no effort is made to discuss amplitude because the greatest vertical displacement of $y = \tan \theta$ is not defined.

Graphs of $y = \sec \theta$, $y = \csc \theta$, and $y = \operatorname{ctn} \theta$ by Reciprocation of Ordinates

If we have two equations, $y_1 = \sin x$ and $y_2 = \csc x$, we know that the ordinates are related by the equation $y_1 = 1/y_2$ because sin x and csc x are reciprocals. This asserts that, for any assigned value of x, the value of y_2 is the reciprocal of the value of y_1, hence the notion of reciprocation of

$x°$	0	10	20	30	45	60	90	180	210	270
$y_1 = \sin x$	0	0.174	0.342	0.5	$\sqrt{2}/2$	$\sqrt{3}/2$	1	0	$-\frac{1}{2}$	-1
$y_2 = \csc x$	∞	5.75	2.92	2	$2/\sqrt{2}$	$2/\sqrt{3}$	1	∞	-2	-1

ordinates. To show this reciprocation, refer to the accompanying chart of values. These values plot a curve shown in Fig. 14-17 where $y_1 = \sin x$ is shown as a dotted line and the reciprocal function $y_2 = \csc x$ is shown as the solid line.

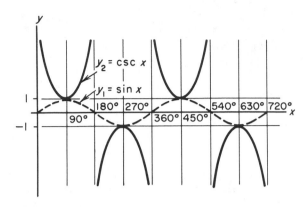

FIGURE 14-17

Some observations are in order. To graph $y = \csc \theta$, $y = \sec \theta$, and $y = \operatorname{ctn} \theta$, sketch first the graph of the reciprocal and then reciprocate ordinates. Reciprocation does not affect the angular period. Observe for Fig. 14-17 that y_2 has no finite value when $y_1 = 0$. Also, the reciprocal of a positive ordinate is positive and the reciprocal of a negative ordinate is negative.

Exercises

In Exercises 1–20 show the graphs of the given equations. Graph one full cycle of the function.

1. $y = \sin 2\theta$.

2. $y = \cos (\theta/3)$.

3. $z = \tan 3x$.

4. $z = \csc 5x$.

5. $s = \sec 120\pi t$.

6. $y = \operatorname{ctn} 5\phi$.

7. $x = 3 \tan \pi\phi$.

8. $x = 2 \csc 100\pi t$.

9. $y = 4.5 \sec 3\pi\theta$.

10. $y = 5/(\csc 12\theta)$.

11. $y = \sin (\theta + 40°)$.

12. $y = \sin (\theta - 40°)$.

13. $x = \sin (2\theta + 40°)$.

14. $x = \sin (2\theta - 40°)$.

15. $z = \cos (\theta + 30°)$.

16. $z = \cos (\theta - 30°)$.

17. $y = \cos (2\theta + 30°)$. **18.** $y = \cos (2\theta - 30°)$.

19. $x = \tan (\theta + 30°)$. **20.** $x = \tan (2\theta - 60°)$.

From the graphs of the appropriate trigonometric functions indicate whether the relationships given in Exercises 21–38 are true or false, considering any value of the angle.

21. $-\mathrm{Sin}\ \theta = \sin (-\theta)$. *Ans.* True.

22. $\mathrm{Cos}\ \theta = \cos (-\theta)$.

23. $\mathrm{Tan}\ \theta = -\tan (-\theta)$. *Ans.* True.

24. $\mathrm{Csc}\ \theta = \csc (-\theta)$.

25. $\mathrm{Sec}\ \theta = -\sec (-\theta)$. *Ans.* False.

26. $\mathrm{Sin}\ (90° + \phi) = \sin (90° - \phi)$.

27. $\mathrm{Tan}\ \phi = \tan (90° + \phi)$. *Ans.* False.

28. $\mathrm{Tan}\ (90° + \phi) = -\tan (90° - \phi)$.

29. $\mathrm{Tan}\ x = \tan (180° + x)$. *Ans.* True.

30. $\mathrm{Sin}\ \theta = \sin (\theta + 360°)$.

31. $\mathrm{Ctn}\ \phi = \mathrm{ctn} (-\phi)$. *Ans.* False.

32. $\mathrm{Tan}\ x = -\mathrm{ctn} (x + 90°)$.

33. $\mathrm{Sin}\ \phi = \cos (\phi + 90°)$. *Ans.* False.

34. $\mathrm{Sin}\ \phi = -\cos (\phi + 90°)$.

35. $\mathrm{Csc}\ \phi = \sec (\phi - 90°)$. *Ans.* True.

36. $\mathrm{Sin}\ 2\theta = \cos (2\theta - 90°)$.

37. $2 \sin \phi = 1/(2 \csc \phi)$. *Ans.* False.

38. $\mathrm{Cos}\ (90° - \phi) = \cos (90° + \phi)$.

39. For what values of x does $\tan x = \mathrm{ctn}\ x$?

40. For what values of x does $\sec x = \cos x$? *Ans.* $x = n(180°)$.

14-6 Graphing by Composition of Ordinates

In studies of such phenomena as vibration, resonance, and alternating current, equations of the form

$$y = f_1(x) + f_2(x) + f_3(x) + \cdots \tag{39}$$

arise where the total ordinate y is composed of contributions made by several functions. This is especially true in alternating-current studies where the contributing functions are trigonometric. The graph of an equation like (39) is usually difficult to construct by the elementary method of assigning arbitrary values to x, computing the corresponding y-values, then plotting the resulting (x, y) pairs. An alternate method will be discussed here which will provide a rapid way of showing what is often an adequate picture of the variation.

From (39) we may say that the composite ordinate y is of the form

$$y = y_1 + y_2 + y_3 + \cdots$$

where the components of the composite y are $y_1, y_2, y_3, \cdots$. We may say further that

$$y_1 = f_1(x), \qquad y_2 = f_2(x), \qquad y_3 = f_3(x), \qquad \cdots \tag{40}$$

The separate functions shown in (40) may be plotted and the ordinates $y_1, y_2, y_3, \cdots$ for arbitrarily chosen values of x can be added algebraically by use of dividers, a ruler, or a graph. The method described here is called *composition of ordinates*. Consider an example.

EXAMPLE 11. Show the graph of

$$y = \cos x + \tfrac{1}{2} \sin 2x \tag{41}$$

by the composition of ordinates.

Solution. If we express (41) in the form

$$y = y_1 + y_2,$$

we are assuming that

$$y_1 = \cos x \tag{42}$$

and

$$y_2 = \tfrac{1}{2} \sin 2x. \tag{43}$$

Now we graph (42) and (43) as shown in Fig. 14-18. At an arbitarily chosen abscissa, say $x = k$, (42) has the ordinate $y_1 = KN$ shown in Fig. 14-18. Note that KN is positive. Also at $x = k$, (43) has the ordinate $y_2 = KL$ where KL is negative, and is measured downward from the x-axis. To find

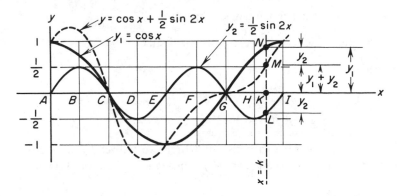

FIGURE 14–18

$y_1 + y_2$, we can measure y_2 downward from point N (here $y_2 = KL = NM$). Now $KM = y_1 + y_2$, where M is a point on the desired graph.

In Fig. 14-18 the specific locations A through I show maximum, minimum, and zero values of each y_1 and y_2. Some observations are in order. At A, $y_2 = 0$ and $y_1 = 1$ so that

$$y = y_1 + y_2 = 1.$$

At B, $y_2 = \frac{1}{2}$, so $y = y_1 + \frac{1}{2}$. At C, $y_1 = y_2 = 0$, so $y = 0$. Similar considerations of the ordinates provided by the components y_1 and y_2 at positions A through I give a reasonably complete description of (41) which is graphed as the dotted curve in Fig. 14-18.

In Example 11 we considered the graph of the sum of a sine and a cosine function where the amplitudes and the angular periods of the components differed. One particularly common and interesting form is

$$y = a \sin nx + b \cos nx, \tag{44}$$

where in (44) we have the sum of a sine and a cosine function and both functions are of the same angular period, with amplitudes which are not necessarily equal. To graph (44), we could employ the composition of ordinates; however, we can be more exact by expressing (44) as a shifted sine wave. Consider Example 12.

EXAMPLE 12. Show that

$$y = Y \sin (nx + \gamma) \tag{45}$$

can be expressed in the form of (44).

Solution. From the trigonometric identity

$$\sin (\theta + \phi) = \sin \theta \cos \phi + \cos \theta \sin \phi,$$

(45) becomes

$$y = Y(\sin nx \cos \gamma + \cos nx \sin \gamma)$$
$$= (Y \cos \gamma) \sin nx + (Y \sin \gamma) \cos nx. \qquad (46)$$

Now in (46), $Y \cos \gamma$ is a constant which we will call a and $Y \sin \gamma$ is a constant which we will call b, so (45) is now in the form of (44) where

$$a = Y \cos \gamma, \qquad (47)$$

$$b = Y \sin \gamma. \qquad (48)$$

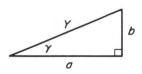

FIGURE 14–19

Expressions (47) and (48) can be fitted to the right triangle shown in Fig. 14-19 where we see the additional relationships

$$Y = \sqrt{a^2 + b^2}$$

and

$$\tan \gamma = \frac{b}{a} \quad \text{or} \quad \gamma = \text{arc tan} \frac{b}{a}.$$

Comparing (45) and (44), we now have

$$y = a \sin nx + b \cos nx = \sqrt{a^2 + b^2} \sin (nx + \gamma).$$

The graph of (44) is then a sine wave of angular period $2\pi/n$, of amplitude $\sqrt{a^2 + b^2}$, and of phase shift arc tan (b/a). Refer to Fig. 14-20.

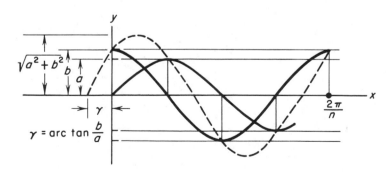

FIGURE 14–20

Exercises

In Exercises 1–16 show the graphs of the given equations, using the method of composition of ordinates. Plot the graphs in the interval shown.

1. $y = \sin x + \sin 2x, \quad 0 < x < 2\pi.$

2. $y = \sin x + \cos 2x, \quad -\pi < x < \pi.$

3. $y = \sin x + \dfrac{x}{2}, \quad 0 < x < 2\pi.$

4. $y = \sin x - \dfrac{x}{\pi}, \quad 0 < x < 2\pi.$

5. $y = \sin x + \frac{1}{3} \sin 3x, \quad 0 < x < 2\pi.$

6. $y = \cos x + \cos 2x, \quad -\pi < x < \pi.$

7. $y = \sin x + \frac{1}{2}\tan x, \quad 0 < x < 2\pi.$

8. $y = \cos x - \dfrac{x}{2\pi}, \quad -\pi < x < \pi.$

9. $y = \sin x + \dfrac{x^2}{4\pi}, \quad 0 < x < 2\pi.$

10. $y = 3\cos x - \dfrac{x^2}{2\pi}, \quad -\pi < x < \pi.$

11. $i = \sin 50\pi t + 25t, \quad 0 < t < 0.04.$

12. $i = 2\cos 200\,\pi t - 100t, \quad 0 < t < 0.01.$

13. $i = 2\sin 50\pi t + 2500t^2, \quad -0.02 < t < 0.02.$

14. $y = \sin 2x - \dfrac{x}{2\pi}, \quad 0 < x < 2\pi.$

15. $i = 3\sin 100\pi t + 4\sin 200\pi t, \quad 0 < t < 0.02.$

16. $i = 4\sin 100\pi t - 3\cos 200\pi t, \quad 0 < t < 0.02.$

17. Given the equation $s = 4\sin t + 3\cos t$. Express the equation in the form of (45). Show that it is a shifted sine wave of amplitude 5, phase shift 36.8°, and angular period 2π.

18. If the expression given in Example 7 were written as a shifted cosine wave, we would have the same amplitude 5, the same angular period 2π, but a different phase angle. What would that phase angle be?   *Ans.* $-53.2°$.

19. Show that the equation $y = a\sin x + b\sin(x + \theta)$ can be expressed in the form

$$y = \sqrt{a^2 + b^2 + 2ab\cos\theta}\,\sin(x + \phi),$$

where

$$\phi = \text{arc} \tan \frac{b \sin \theta}{a + b \cos \theta}.$$

14-7 Lissajous Figures—Parametric Equations

In most of the preceding work we have been able to express relationships in the form

$$y = f(x), \tag{49}$$

where the values assigned to the independent variáble x determined values of the dependent variable y. Many types of variation are difficult to express in the explicit form (49) and may be more simply expressed as

$$y = g(t), \tag{50}$$

$$x = h(t), \tag{51}$$

where t is the independent variable. Assignment of values to t imposes values upon the dependent variables y and x. Here t is called a *parameter* and (50) and (51) are called *parametric equations*.

A simple example of parametric equations can be shown with a circle. In Fig. 14-21 we show a circle of radius R with center on the origin. For any point (x, y) we have

$$x = R \cos \theta, \tag{52}$$

$$y = R \sin \theta, \tag{53}$$

where x and y are both determined when a value is assigned to the parameter θ.

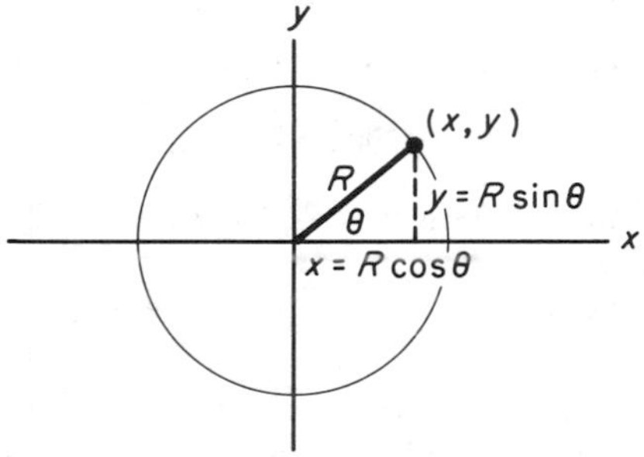

FIGURE 14–21

The parameter in (52) and (53) is readily eliminated by adding the squares, thus:

$$x^2 = R^2 \cos^2 \theta,$$

$$y^2 = R^2 \sin^2 \theta,$$

and

$$x^2 + y^2 = R^2(\sin^2 \theta + \cos^2 \theta) = R^2,$$

where $x^2 + y^2 = R^2$ is readily observed as the equation of the origin-centered circle shown in Fig. 14-21. Elimination of the parameter is generally more difficult.

If we inspect equations (50) and (51) we can make several observations. If we plot $y = g(t)$ on the (x, y) plane independent of $x = h(t)$, we see that modifications in t modify the *vertical position* of the point plotted. Introducing $x = h(t)$ and assigning values to t, we move the point *horizontally*. We may accept t as a time parameter, showing that modifications in time can cause both a horizontal and a vertical change in the position of the plotted point. If the equations (50) and (51) are periodic functions, the point moves horizontally according to some period and moves vertically according to some period. The result can be that the point will periodically traverse the same path. Let us use this last observation as a basis of discussion in Example 13.

EXAMPLE 13. Discuss the graph of the function represented by the parametric equations

$$x = 2 \sin 2\theta, \tag{54}$$

$$y = \cos 3\theta. \tag{55}$$

Solution. First we observe that both (54) and (55) are periodic. The angular period of (54) is 180°; the angular period of (55) is 120°. This asserts that a 360° change in θ will send x through two full cycles and will send y through three full cycles. A graphical interpretation of the preceding statement is this: as θ passes from 0° to 360°, the (x, y) point plotted passes through two full cycles in the horizontal sense and three full cycles in the vertical sense.

By inspection of (54) and (55), we observe that the value of x ranges from -2 to $+2$ and the value of y ranges from -1 to $+1$. Combining two of our observations, we see that x assumes a maximum value $(+2)$ *two* times and y assumes its maximum value $(+1)$ *three* times as θ ranges from 0° to 360°; the same is true for the number of minima involved. The graph will be inclosed in the rectangle of length 4 and height 2 shown in Fig. 14-22. It will contact both the right and left sides of the rectangle twice and the top and bottom of the rectangle three times as θ passes from 0° to 360°.

In plotting points we choose values of θ which will provide zeroes or maxima or minima for either x or y or both x and y. These points are shown in Table 14-2. The plot of the points results in the graph shown in Fig. 14-22, where the direction of movement along the curve is in the alphabetic sequence of points A through Q.

Note in Fig. 14-22 that the plotted curve tangents the right edge of the rectangle twice while it tangents the upper edge three times. In electricity this may have been shown on an oscilloscope where a known horizontal

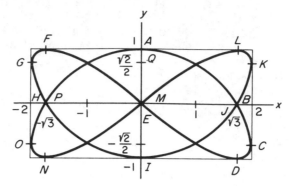

FIGURE 14–22

input signal of, say, 240 cycles is used to determine the frequency of an unknown vertical input. If the combined signals produce a trace which shows 3 vertical maxima for each 2 horizontal maxima, then the ratio of the frequencies is 3 to 2 and the unknown vertical input is $(\frac{3}{2})(240) = 360$ cycles.

Table 14-2

$\theta°$	0	30	45	60	90	120	135	150	180	210	225	240	270	300	315	330	360
x	0	$\sqrt{3}$	2	$\sqrt{3}$	0	$-\sqrt{3}$	-2	$-\sqrt{3}$	0	$\sqrt{3}$	2	$\sqrt{3}$	0	$-\sqrt{3}$	-2	$-\sqrt{3}$	0
y	1	0	$\frac{-\sqrt{2}}{2}$	-1	0	1	$\frac{\sqrt{2}}{2}$	0	-1	0	$\frac{\sqrt{2}}{2}$	1	0	-1	$\frac{-\sqrt{2}}{2}$	0	1
Point	A	B	C	D	E	F	G	H	I	J	K	L	M	N	O	P	Q

The group of figures characterized by the properties shown in Example 13 is known as the group of *Lissajous figures*. They are limited usually to two sine waves which vary about axes at right angles. The figures are used for phase and frequency measurements.

Exercises

In Exercises 1–20, prepare the graphs of the given sets of equations.

1. $x = \sin \theta$,
   $y = \cos \theta$.

2. $x = \sin \theta$,
   $y = \sin \theta$.

3. $x = \sin \theta$,
   $y = \sin 2\theta$.

4. $x = \sin \theta$,
   $y = \sin (\theta + 45°)$.

5. $x = 2 \sin \theta$,
   $y = 3 \sin \theta$.

6. $x = 4 \sin 2\theta$,
   $y = 3 \sin \theta$.

7. $x = 2 \sin \theta$,
   $y = 3 \sin (\theta + 90°)$.

8. $x = 2 \sin \theta$,
   $y = 3 \sin 2\theta$.

9. $x = 2 \cos 3\theta,$
   $y = 3 \sin 4\theta.$

10. $x = 3 \sin 120\pi t,$
    $y = 4 \cos 240\pi t.$

11. $x = \sin \theta,$
    $y = \sin (3\theta + 90°).$

12. $x = 4 \sin \theta,$
    $y = 4 \sin 4\theta.$

13. $x = 2 + \sin t,$
    $y = 2 \cos t.$

14. $x = \sin 5\theta,$
    $y = \cos 4\theta.$

15. $x = 5 \sin 120\pi t,$
    $y = 5 \sin (240\pi t + 30°).$

16. $x = 5 \sin \theta,$
    $y = 5 \sin (4\theta + 90°).$

17. $x = \sin (\theta + 45°),$
    $y = \cos 2\theta.$

18. $x = \tan \theta,$
    $y = \sin \theta.$

19. $x = 2 \sin 3\theta,$
    $y = \sin \left(3\theta + \dfrac{\pi}{3}\right).$

20. $x = 2 \sin 3\theta,$
    $y = \sin \left(3\theta - \dfrac{\pi}{3}\right).$

21. Compare the graph of Exercise 5 with the graph of

$$x = 2 \sin (\theta + 45°), \qquad y = 3 \cos \theta.$$

22. Determine the dimensions of the rectangle enclosing the Lissajous figure represented by the equations

$$x = 3 \sin 2t, \qquad y = 4 \cos 5t.$$

Ans. 6 units long, 8 units high.

23. A certain Lissajous figure is represented by the equations

$$x = a \sin kt, \qquad y = b \cos 20t.$$

If the graph of the figure contacts the vertical side of the containing rectangle 4 times for each 5 times that it contacts the horizontal side, determine k.

Ans. $k = 16$.

24. Eliminate the parameter in Exercises 1, 2, 5, 13.

Ans. Exercise 13: $4(x - 2)^2 + y^2 = 4$.

14-8 Definitions Involving Polar Coordinates

Polar coordinates probably have more common usage than rectangular coordinates. An example lies in the location of Boston with respect to New York City. The most probable description is that Boston is approximately 200 miles northeast of New York City, using distance (200 miles) and direction (northeast) instead of rectangular coordinates. In mathematics, distance ρ and direction θ are used, and a point in a plane is assigned the coordinates (ρ, θ) in a system of *polar coordinates*. The distance is measured from a reference point and the direction is measured as an angle from a reference line. The reference point is called a *pole* and the reference line a *polar axis*, hence the name *polar coordinates*. In standard usage, the reference point is the origin and is labeled O and the reference line is drawn through O to the right with the positive angle θ measured in a counterclockwise direction.

From Fig. 14-23(b) we locate P with respect to O by drawing OM to the right, indicating angle θ and distance ρ, and assigning the coordinates (ρ, θ) to P. Here, ρ is given the name *distance* or *magnitude* and OP is called the *radius vector*. Angle θ is called the *reference angle*. If P were to be located in rectangular coordinates as in Fig. 14-23(b), we see that by superimposing

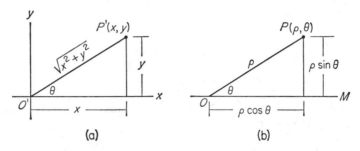

(a)   (b)

FIGURE 14–23

(a) upon (b) so that $O'x$ is imposed upon OM with O' and P' coinciding, respectively, with O and P, we have the following relationships between the rectangular and polar locations of P.

$$\rho = \sqrt{x^2 + y^2}, \quad x = \rho \cos \theta, \quad y = \rho \sin \theta,$$

$$\cos \theta = \frac{x}{\sqrt{x^2 + y^2}}, \quad \sin \theta = \frac{y}{\sqrt{x^2 + y^2}}, \quad \tan \theta = \frac{y}{x} \tag{56}$$

Consider two applications using the conversions in (56).

EXAMPLE 14. Convert $x^2 + y^2 = 25$ to polar form.

Solution. From (56),

$$\rho = \sqrt{x^2 + y^2} \quad \text{and} \quad \rho^2 = x^2 + y^2 = 25,$$

from which we have the solution $\rho = 5$.

Discussion. The equation $x^2 + y^2 = 25$ is recognized as an origin-centered circle of radius 5. Likewise, the equation $\rho = 5$ is a circle of radius 5; this is observed from the fact that $\rho = 5$ is an equation independent of θ. Therefore, the distance OP in Fig. 14-23(b) is 5 units regardless of the magnitude of θ.

EXAMPLE 15. Convert

$$\rho = \frac{5}{\sqrt{3 - 2 \cos 2\theta}}$$

into rectangular coordinates.

Solution. Given

$$\rho = \frac{5}{\sqrt{3 - 2 \cos 2\theta}}, \tag{57}$$

squaring both sides of (57) and clearing fractions, we have

$$\rho^2(3 - 2 \cos 2\theta) = 25. \tag{58}$$

Substituting the identity $\cos 2\theta = 1 - 2 \sin^2 \theta$ into (58) and collecting like terms, we have

$$\rho^2(1 + 4 \sin^2 \theta) = 25.$$

Now applying appropriate substitutions from (56), we have the solution,

$$x^2 + 5y^2 = 25,$$

which is recognized as an origin-centered ellipse. A more complete discussion of forms such as (57) will be made in a later section where the graphing of conics in the polar form is treated.

Exercises

Convert the equations in Exercises 1–10 into the polar form.

1. $x = 6.$
2. $x^2 + y^2 = 4.$

3. $x^2 - y^2 = 9.$
4. $y = 5.$

5. $xy = 8.$
6. $(x - 2)^2 + y^2 = 25.$

7. $y = 2x.$
8. $y^2 = 2x.$

9. $\sqrt{x^2 + y^2} = e^{\text{arc tan } (y/x)}.$
10. $x^2 + y^2 = \text{arc tan } \dfrac{y}{x}$

Convert the following in Exercises 11–20 into rectangular coordinates.

11. $\rho = 3.$
12. $\rho = 5 \sin \theta$

13. $\tan \theta = 2$.

14. $\rho \sin \theta = 5$.

15. $\rho = 3 + 2 \cos \theta$.

16. $\theta = 135°$.

17. $\rho = \sin 2\theta$.

18. $\rho = e^{\theta}$.

19. $\rho^2 = 9 \sin 2\theta$.

20. $\rho = \dfrac{\theta}{4}$

14-9　Graphs of Polar Equations

One approach to the problem of plotting curves in polar coordinates is that of expressing the equation in the explicit form $\rho = f(\theta)$, choosing arbitrary values of the independent variable θ and determining the corresponding values of the dependent variable. This creates a set of (ρ, θ) coordinates which can be plotted and joined with a smooth curve. This method is often tedious and does not necessarily reveal certain characteristics of the curve at critical portions.

The approach which we will apply here is that of expressing the equation in a mathematical form. We will type those equations which plot into straight lines, conics, and spirals; these three groups of curves are the curves most commonly studied in polar equations. First, let us discuss the plotting of a few selected points in polar. In Fig. 14-24 concentric circles with center

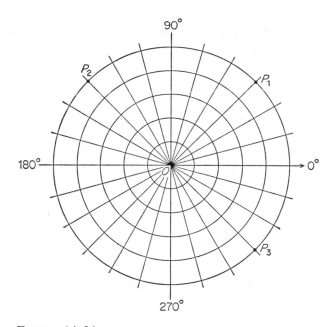

Figure 14–24

O are laid off to indicate lengths of the radius vector; we have also laid off angles in 15° increments. Further refinements for distance and angle could be established, depending upon the accuracy required. The point P_1 is given four different designations, the most common being $P_1(\rho, \theta) = (5, 45°)$ or $(5, \pi/4)$ depending upon the system of angular measurement requested. Alternate expressions for $P_1(\rho, \theta)$ are $(-5, 225°), (-5, -135°)$ and $(5, -315°)$. We note that if the angle is removed 180° from the proper smallest positive angle, the sense of ρ is changed.

Symmetry

In Fig. 14-24, point $P_1(5, 135°)$ is located symmetrically with P_1 across the terminal side of the line $\theta = 90°$. Similarly, $P_3(5, -45°)$ is symmetrical with P_1 across the line $\theta = 0°$. Expanding this discussion of symmetry to portions of curves rather than isolated points, we see that the equation $\rho = 5 + 2 \sin \theta$ is symmetrical about the line $\theta = 90°$ since $\sin(90° + \phi) = \sin(90° - \phi)$, where ϕ is any angle. In general, to check $\rho = f(\theta)$ for symmetry about an axis $\theta = k$, determine whether or not the expression $f(k + \phi) = f(k - \phi)$ is satisfied.

Equations Which Graph as Straight Lines

The general equation of a straight line in rectangular form is given as

$$Ax + By = C. \tag{59}$$

Substituting $x = \rho \cos \theta$ and $y = \rho \sin \theta$ into (59) and solving for ρ we have

$$\rho = \frac{C}{A \cos \theta + B \sin \theta} \tag{60}$$

as the equation of a straight line in polar coordinates. From (59) if $A = 0$, then $y = C/B$ and the line parallels the x-axis; if $A = 0$ is imposed upon (60), then $\rho = (C \csc \theta)/B$ is the equation of the line in polar form, symmetrical with the axis $\theta = 90°$ and C/B length units from the origin. Similar modifications regarding B in (59) and (60) produce $\rho = (C \sec \theta)/A$ as the equation of a line parallel with $\theta = 90°$.

From (59) again, if the line passes through the origin, then $C = 0$ and $Ax + By = 0$, or

$$\frac{y}{x} = -\frac{A}{B}.$$

But, from polars, $\tan \theta = y/x$; therefore, $\tan \theta = -A/B$ is the equation of a line passing through the origin in polar coordinates. We note that the equation $\tan \theta = -A/B$ is independent of ρ and that θ is a constant; further, the equation fails if $B = 0$.

Equations Which Graph as Conics

For our purposes here we will start with the assertion that in polar coordinates the equation of the general conic is

$$\rho = \frac{k}{a + b \cos \theta}, \tag{61}$$

where a, b, and k are non-zero constants.

If we use some of the substitutions (56) in (61) and simplify, we have

$$(a^2 - b^2)x^2 + b^2y^2 + 2kbx - k^2 = 0, \tag{62}$$

which is of the form

$$Ax^2 + By^2 + Cx + D = 0. \tag{63}$$

Note here that (63) is a conic which has been shifted off the origin along the x-axis (if $C \neq 0$). If we replaced $\cos \theta$ with $\sin \theta$ in (61), then (63) would have a first degree y-term in it and no first degree x-term in it, indicating a vertical shift off the origin. Some observations of (62) reveal the particular conic. Equation (62) is

a *parabola* if

$$a^2 - b^2 = 0,$$

an *ellipse* if

$$a^2 - b^2 > 0 \quad \text{and} \quad b \neq 0, \tag{64}$$

a *hyperbola* if

$$a^2 - b^2 < 0 \quad \text{and} \quad b \neq 0.$$

Equation (61) reveals that if $b = 0$, then $\rho = k/a$ and (61) is an origin-centered circle.

EXAMPLE 4. Graph the equation

$$\rho = \frac{2}{1 + \cos \theta}.$$

Solution. Comparing the given equation to (61), we have $a = 1$ and $b = 1$. From the observations (64), we see that the given equation is a parabola.

Further, since cos θ is symmetrical about $\theta = 0°$, we have symmetry about the line $\theta = 0°$, indicating that the parabola opens either to the right or the left. Referring now to the given equation, ρ is least when the denominator $|1 + \cos \theta|$ is greatest. This occurs when $\cos \theta = +1$, or when $\theta = 0°$. Similarly, ρ is greatest when $|1 + \cos \theta|$ is least, or when $\cos \theta = -1$. This shows that the parabola opens to the left. The graph, with a few extra points plotted, is shown in Fig. 14-25.

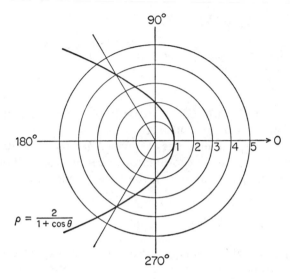

FIGURE 14-25

Spirals

Three equations of spirals will be discussed here.

The *spiral of Archimedes* has the equation $\rho = a\theta$, $a > 0$. We know from polar coordinates that two reference angles which differ by 2π radians produce the same direction for the radius vector; therefore, for

$$\theta = k, \quad \theta = k + 2\pi, \quad \theta = k + 4\pi, \quad \text{etc.},$$

ρ is similarly directed. Referring to $\rho = a\theta$, when

$$\theta = k, \quad k + 2\pi, \quad k + 4\pi, \quad \ldots ,$$
$$\rho = ak, \quad ak + 2a\pi, \quad ak + 4a\pi, \quad \ldots ,$$

respectively, where it is seen that each 2π change in θ produces a $2a\pi$ change in ρ. Phrased differently, this asserts that there is a fixed change in ρ accompanying a fixed change in θ.

The *reciprocal spiral* has the equation $\rho\theta = a$. Here it is apparent that each increase in θ is accompanied by a corresponding decrease in ρ and conversely, since the product of ρ and θ is constant. As θ increases to large values, ρ diminishes toward zero; as $\theta \rightarrow 0$, $\rho \rightarrow \infty$. The reciprocal spiral, unlike the spiral of Archimedes, does not pass through the origin.

The *logarithmic spiral* has the equation $\rho = e^{a\theta}$, $a \neq 0$. Here ρ is exponentially related to θ. We note, too, that for two values of θ which are 2π radians apart, say $\theta_1 = k$ and $\theta_2 = k + 2\pi$, then

$$\rho_1 = e^{ak} \quad \text{and} \quad \rho_2 = e^{ak+2a\pi}$$

and the relationship between ρ_1 and ρ_2 is such that

$$\rho_2 = \rho_1 e^{2a\pi}. \tag{65}$$

From (65) it is seen that for a 2π increase in the reference angle, the radius vector is multiplied by a constant factor $e^{2a\pi}$.

The logarithmic spiral illustrates convincingly the advantage of polar coordinates over rectangular coordinates in certain cases. If $\rho = e^{a\theta}$ were converted to rectangular coordinates, the result would be the very awkward expression

$$\sqrt{x^2 + y^2} = e^{a \arctan y/x}$$

illustrating the comparative simplicity of the polar expression.

Comparing two of the spirals mentioned above, note that for a 2π change in the reference angle, the magnitude of the radius vector of the Archimedes spiral is changed by an additive constant, while the magnitude of the radius vector of the logarithmic spiral is changed by a constant ratio.

Exercises

Plot Exercises 1–20 in polar coordinates.

1. $\theta = 45°$

2. $\rho = \dfrac{\sin \theta}{3}$

3. $\rho \cos \theta = 5$

4. $\rho(2 \sin \theta + \cos \theta) = 3$

5. $\rho(1 - \sin \theta) = 1$

6. $\rho(1 - 2 \sin \theta) = 1$

11. $\rho\theta = \dfrac{1}{2}$

12. $\rho\theta = -\pi$

13. $2\rho = e^{\theta}$

14. $3\rho = e^{-\theta}$

15. $2 + \cos \theta = \rho$

16. $2 + 3 \cos \theta = \rho$

7. $\rho(2 - \sin \theta) = 1$

8. $\rho = 5$

9. $\rho = \dfrac{\theta}{2}$

10. $\rho = 1 + \dfrac{\theta}{\pi}$

17. $3 + 2 \cos \theta = \rho$

18. $\rho = 5 \cos 2\theta$

19. $\rho = 4 \sin 3\theta$

20. $\rho = 3 \cos 5\theta$

21. Plot the graphs of the equation $\rho = a + b \cos \theta$ (a and b positive) if (a) $a > b$, (b) $a = b$, (c) $a < b$. If $a < b$, the figure is a limaçon. If $a > b$, the figure is a cardioid.

22. How many loops are on the graph of the equation $\rho = a \cos 2\theta$? of $\rho = a \sin 2\theta$? Why does the number of loops differ?

23. Show that $\rho = 2c \cos (\theta - \alpha)$ is the equation of a circle passing through $(0, 0)$ with center (c, α).

24. Plot the curve $\rho^2 = \cos 2\theta$. What is the domain of θ for which ρ is defined?

25. Convert $(x^2 + y^2)^2 = 4(x^2 - y^2)$ to polar coordinates.

It is often useful in engineering and science to express vectors in the form of a complex number. Manipulations with vectors, especially the fundamental operations (addition, subtraction, multiplication, and division), are often simplified when they are expressed in complex notation. In this chapter we will discuss the complex number, show its representation in the complex plane, and discuss the fundamental operations of the numbers and the vectors they represent. The number j which we shall use in this chapter is called i in pure mathematics. In technical mathematics the symbol i is reserved for electrical current; hence j is used here to avoid confusion.

The number j is often called the j-operator because its use facilitates the fundamental operations of vector quantities.

15 THE J-OPERATOR

15-1   The Number j

In Sec. 6-6 we defined the number j as

$$j = \sqrt{-1}, \tag{1}$$

where $\sqrt{-1}$ is one of the two equal factors of -1. The quantity j might be pictured geometrically as in Fig. 15-1 where we have a semicircle of radius unity with the center of the circle at the intersection of two perpendicular axes. Along one axis real numbers are laid out according to accepted convention, positive numbers to the right and negative numbers to the left.

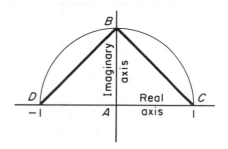

From plane geometry, angle DBC is a right angle because it is inscribed in a semicircle. Also, AB is the geometric mean between DA and AC; that is,

FIGURE 15-1

$$(AB)^2 = (DA)(AC) = (-1)(1) = -1. \tag{2}$$

Now, from (2),

$$AB = \sqrt{-1} = j,$$

and we see that AB may be interpreted in Fig. 15-1 as being of magnitude j where j is often called the imaginary unit or the j-operator.

Powers of j are cyclical in nature, as may be observed from the following:

$$j = \sqrt{-1},$$
$$j^2 = -1,$$
$$j^3 = j \cdot j^2 = j(-1) = -j,$$
$$j^4 = (j^2)^2 = (-1)^2 = +1,$$
$$j^5 = j \cdot j^4 = j(1) = j,$$
$$j^6 = j \cdot j^5 = j \cdot j = j^2 = -1.$$

Inspection shows that powers of j are cyclical in a four-element cycle, where the elements are j, -1, $-j$, and $+1$. In general, if n is any integer,

$$j^{4n+1} = j,$$
$$j^{4n+2} = -1,$$
$$j^{4n+3} = -j,$$
$$j^{4n+4} = +1.$$

Negative powers of j can also be expressed as one of the four elements previously mentioned:

$$j^{-1} = \frac{1}{j} = \frac{1}{j} \cdot \frac{j}{j} = \frac{j}{j^2} = \frac{j}{-1} = -j,$$

$$j^{-2} = \frac{1}{j^2} = \frac{1}{-1} = -1,$$

$$j^{-3} = \frac{1}{j^3} = \frac{1}{j^3} \cdot \frac{j}{j} = \frac{j}{j^4} = \frac{j}{1} = j,$$

$$j^{-4} = \frac{1}{j^4} = 1.$$

EXAMPLE 1. Simplify the expressions (a) j^{27}, (b) j^{41}, and (c) j^{-19}.

Solutions. We can solve these simply by removing the multiple of four which is nearest the value of the exponent. Thus, for j^{27}, we may call this $j^{24} \cdot j^3$ where $j^{24} = 1$, leaving the answer as $j^3 = -j$. We could also have called $j^{27} = j^{28} \cdot j^{-1}$ where $j^{28} = 1$ and $j^{-1} = -j$, so that once again, $j^{27} = -j$. We have, by using similar procedures,

(a) $j^{27} = j^{24} \cdot j^3 = -j$.

(b) $j^{41} = j^{40} \cdot j^1 = j$.

(c) $j^{-19} = j^{-20} \cdot j^1 = j$.

We note that any power of j where we have j^{4n} (n an integer) has the value $+1$.

15-2 The Argand Diagram—Various Forms of the Complex Number

Any number like $j5$, $-j5$, $j1.5$, $-j\frac{9}{2}$ or jb where b is a real number, is called a *pure imaginary number*, and can be represented as in Fig. 15-1. In the chapter on quadratics we encountered numbers like $3 + j5$, $\frac{3}{2} - j\frac{3}{2}$, or $a + jb$, where a and b are real numbers and $a + jb$ is called a *complex number*. Examining $a + jb$ carefully, we see that the complex number has two components; one is a real number a which could be measured along a horizontal axis (real axis), and the other is a pure imaginary number jb which is measured along the vertical axis (imaginary axis); these are shown in Fig. 15-2. Continuing to refer to Fig. 15-2, the vector **OP** can be represented by the complex number $a + jb$. The point P has the coordinates (a, b). The magnitude of the vector **OP** is, by the Pythagorean theorem,

$$\rho = \sqrt{a^2 + b^2}, \tag{3}$$

and the reference angle (the angle between the right-hand horizontal and the vector **OP** in the counterclockwise direction) is such that

$$\tan \theta = \frac{b}{a},$$

or

$$\theta = \arctan \frac{b}{a}. \tag{4}$$

The representation shown in Fig. 15-2 is a mathematical standard. The plane on which the axes are drawn is called the *complex plane* or *Gaussian plane* and the diagrammatic representation of the complex number is called the *Argand diagram*. The vector **OP** can be described by two different forms which are already established. In the *rectangular form* we have

$$\mathbf{OP} = a + jb$$

and in the polar form we have

$$\mathbf{OP} = \rho\underline{/\theta} = \sqrt{a^2 + b^2} \; \underline{/\arctan (b/a)}. \tag{5}$$

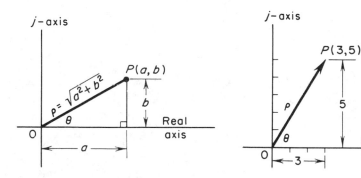

FIGURE 15–2   FIGURE 15–3

EXAMPLE 2. Represent the vector **OP** $= 3 + j5$ in the polar form.

Solution. First we sketch **OP** as in Fig. 15-3. Note that point P is 3 units to the right (3 real units) and 5 units upward (5 imaginary units). Now, by the Pythagorean theorem, we have

$$\rho = \sqrt{3^2 + 5^2} = \sqrt{9 + 25} = \sqrt{34}.$$

From the definition of the tangent function we have

$$\tan \theta = \tfrac{5}{3} \quad \text{or} \quad \arctan \tfrac{5}{3} = \theta = 59.1°$$

and

$$3 + j5 = \rho\underline{/\theta} = \sqrt{34}\ \underline{/59.1°},$$

where $3 + j5$ is the rectangular form of **OP** and $\sqrt{34}\ \underline{/59.1°}$ is the polar form of **OP**.

In the preceding example problem the rectangular form of a vector was given and we were asked to find the polar form. Frequently conversions from polar to rectangular are required. We refer to Fig. 15-4 to discuss the latter conversions. There we are given the vector **OP** in its polar form $\rho\underline{/\theta}$, where ρ and θ are known. The horizontal (real) component of **OP** is $\rho \cos \theta$ and the vertical component is $\rho \sin \theta$, where we can now express **OP** by the notations

$$\textbf{OP} = \rho\underline{/\theta} = \rho \cos \theta + j\rho \sin \theta = \rho(\cos \theta + j \sin \theta). \tag{6}$$

In (6), the factored form $\rho(\cos \theta + j \sin \theta)$ is called the *trigonometric form* of **OP**.

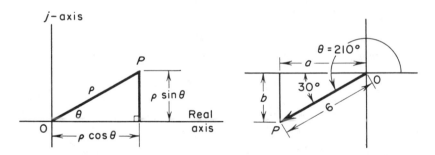

FIGURE 15–4   FIGURE 15–5

EXAMPLE 3. Express $6\underline{/210°}$ in rectangular and trigonometric forms.

Solution. Referring to Fig. 15-5 and (6), **OP** is in the third quadrant with $a = 6 \cos 210°$ and $b = 6 \sin 210°$ so that

$$a + jb = 6 \cos 210° + j6 \sin 210° = -6 \sin 30° - j6 \sin 30°$$
$$= -6(0.866) - j6(0.500) = -5.196 - j3.000, \tag{7}$$

where (7) is the rectangular form of **OP** and the trigonometric form is

$$6(\cos 210° + j \sin 210°).$$

An advantage of the trigonometric form over the rectangular form is that both the magnitude and direction of **OP** can be immediately seen by inspection of the trigonometric form. Also, the magnitude of the reference angle is exactly described, so that there is no doubt in the inquirer's mind as to which revolution the vector is in; that is, a vector **OP** $= 1 + j$ may have a reference angle of $45°$, $45° + 360°$, $45° + 2(360°)$, $45° + 3(360°)$, ..., $45° + n(360°)$, where n is an integer. The trigonometric form also is useful in discussion of DeMoivre's theorem which will be discussed later in this chapter.

Conversion betwen the trigonometric and polar forms is done by inspection since

$$\rho\underline{/\theta} = \rho(\cos\theta + j\sin\theta).$$

As examples, we have

$$3\underline{/330°} = 3(\cos 330° + j\sin 330°)$$

and

$$1.2(\cos 96° + j\sin 96°) = 1.2\underline{/96°}.$$

Exercises

In Exercises 1–10, express the given quantity as one of the elements in the four-element cycle of powers of j, *namely,* j, -1, $-j$, *or* $+1$.

1. j^{13}. *Ans. j.*

2. j^{11}.

3. j^{88}. *Ans. $+1$.*

4. j^{67}.

5. j^{-9}. *Ans. $-j$.*

6. j^{-14}.

7. $(j^2)^2(j^3)$. *Ans. $-j$.*

8. $(j^2)^3(j^3)^2$.

9. $(j^{-3})^{-2}$. *Ans. -1.*

10. $(j^6)(j^5)/j^{13}$.

In Exercises 11–20, convert the given expressions to the rectangular form.

11. $3\underline{/30°}$. *Ans. $2.6 + j1.5$.*

12. $4\underline{/45°}$.

13. $1.8\underline{/110°}$.   *Ans.* $-0.616 + j1.69$.

14. $2.7\underline{/152°}$.

15. $0.39\underline{/245°}$.   *Ans.* $-0.165 - j0.354$.

16. $260\underline{/188°}$.

17. $36\underline{/-30°}$.   *Ans.* $31.2 - j18$.

18. $120\underline{/-45°}$.

19. $480\underline{/-135°}$.   *Ans.* $-340 - j340$.

20. $210\underline{/-225°}$.

In Exercises 21–28, convert the given rectangular expressions to polar form.

21. $2 + j2$.   *Ans.* $2\sqrt{2}\underline{/45°}$.

22. $3 - j5$.

23. $4 - j4\sqrt{3}$.   *Ans.* $8\underline{/300°}$.

24. $3 + j4$.

25. $-0.635 + j0.727$.   *Ans.* $0.965\underline{/131.2°}$.

26. $-14 - j12$.

27. $-\sqrt{3} - j$.   *Ans.* $2\underline{/210°}$.

28. $3.62 + j8.27$.

15-3   Addition and Subtraction of Vectors

Two vectors $\mathbf{OP}_1 = a + jb$ and $\mathbf{OP}_2 = c + jd$ can be added in the rectangular form. To add

$$\mathbf{OP}_1 + \mathbf{OP}_2 = (a + jb) + (c + jd) = \mathbf{OP}_3,$$

we refer to Fig. 15-6. There we see that $\mathbf{OP}_1$ has a horizontal component a, $\mathbf{OP}_2$ has a horizontal component c, and the composite vector $\mathbf{OP}_3$ has a horizontal component $a + c$. Similarly, the vertical components add algebraically to $b + d$. Now, the sum may be shown as

$$\mathbf{OP}_1 + \mathbf{OP}_2 = (a + jb) + (c + jd) = (a + c) + j(b + d)$$
$$= \mathbf{OP}_3, \qquad (8)$$

where (8) asserts that the sum of two complex numbers has as its real part the algebraic sum of the real parts of the components and as its imaginary part the sum of the imaginary parts of its components.

We note here from Fig. 15-6 that the quadrilateral $OP_1P_3P_2$ is a parallelogarm; OP_2 is parallel to P_1P_3 and OP_1 is parallel to P_2P_3. In adding vectors, then, we are using the parallelogram method which is common to physics, mechanics, surveying, etc.

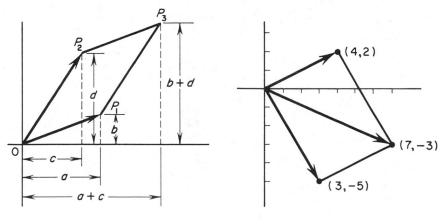

FIGURE 15-6   FIGURE 15-7

EXAMPLE 4. Add the vectors $3 - j5$ and $4 + j2$.

Solution. By (8), we have

$$(3 - j5) + (4 + j2) = (3 + 4) + j(-5 + 2) = 7 - j3.$$

Discussion. In effect we merely columnized the vertical and horizontal components as

$$\begin{array}{r} 3 - j5 \\ 4 + j2 \\ \hline 7 - j3 \end{array}$$

and proceeded as in the addition of algebraic polynomials. This is pictured in Fig. 15-7.

To subtract vectors in the complex plane, we proceed in a method similar to that for addition, except for the fact that we apply the rule of algebra: change the sign of the subtrahend and proceed as in addition. Thus, if $\mathbf{OP_1} = a + jb$ and $\mathbf{OP_2} = c + jd$, then

$$\mathbf{OP_1} - \mathbf{OP_2} = (a + jb) - (c + jd) = (a - c) + j(b - d).$$

The addition and subtraction of vectors in the polar form is somewhat more difficult in that the horizontal and vertical components must be determined before addition or subtraction is performed. Thus, if $\mathbf{OP}_1 = \rho_1/\theta$ and $\mathbf{OP}_2 = \rho_2/\phi$, then

$$\mathbf{OP}_1 = \rho_1 \cos \theta + j\rho_1 \sin \theta,$$
$$\mathbf{OP}_2 = \rho_2 \cos \phi + j\rho_2 \sin \phi,$$
$$\overline{\mathbf{OP}_1 + \mathbf{OP}_2 = (\rho_1 \cos \theta + \rho_2 \cos \phi) + j(\rho_1 \sin \theta + \rho_2 \sin \phi)}.$$

EXAMPLE 5. Add the vectors $\mathbf{OP}_1 = 3/35°$ and $\mathbf{OP}_2 = 5/308°$, expressing the sum in the polar form.

Solution. Converting to the rectangular form,

$$\mathbf{OP}_1 = 3 \cos 35° + j3 \sin 35° = 2.45 + j1.72,$$
$$\mathbf{OP}_2 = 5 \cos 308° + j5 \sin 308° = 3.08 - j3.94.$$

Now the sum $\mathbf{OP}_3$ is

$$\begin{array}{r} 2.45 - j1.72 \\ 3.08 - j3.94 \\ \hline 5.53 - j2.22 \end{array}$$

where $\mathbf{OP}_3$ is in the rectangular form. Since we were asked to express the sum in polar form, we must convert to polar, with

$$\mathbf{OP}_3 = 5.53 - j2.22 = 5.97/338.1°.$$

A rapid check for gross error in the addition or subtraction of vectors may be made by sketching the vectors on a complex plane and adding (or subtracting) them by the parallelogram method shown in Fig. 15-6.

Exercises

Add the expressions in Exercises 1–12, leaving the results in polar form.

1. $3 + j2, 4 - j3.$ *Ans.* $7.07/-8.1°.$

2. $4 + j5, 3 - j6.$

3. $4 + j2, 4 - j2.$ *Ans.* $8/0°.$

4. $6 + j, -6 + j.$

5. $3/30°, 4/120°.$ *Ans.* $5/83.1°.$

6. $1.5/45°, 3/-30°.$

7. $4/\underline{130°}$, $4/\underline{310°}$.   *Ans.* 0.

8. $6/\underline{72°}$, $6/\underline{-108°}$.

9. $12.6/\underline{308°}$, $14.2/\underline{75°}$.   *Ans.* $12.1/\underline{18.2°}$.

10. $3.5/\underline{12°}$, $4.2/\underline{102°}$.

11. $3/\underline{30°}$, $4/\underline{120°}$, $3/\underline{210°}$.   *Ans.* $4/\underline{120°}$.

12. $3 + j7$, $4.6/\underline{138°}$, $6.2/\underline{235°}$.

In Exercises 13–18, subtract the latter vector from the former. Express results in the polar form.

13. $3 + j6$, $5 - j2$.   *Ans.* $8.25/\underline{104.0°}$.

14. $2 - j5$, $6 + j8$.

15. $3/\underline{26°}$, $3/\underline{154°}$.   *Ans.* $5.39/\underline{0°}$.

16. $4/\underline{85°}$, $4/\underline{95°}$.

17. $3 + j4$, $4/\underline{53.1°}$.   *Ans.* $1/\underline{53.1°}$.

18. $120 + j8$, $45 + j8$.

19. If two vectors are equal in magnitude and have reference angles exactly $180°$ apart, what is their sum?

20. Given two vectors $\rho/\underline{\phi}$ and $\rho/\underline{-\phi}$, where the magnitudes are equal and one reference angle is the negative of the other, show that the sum of the vectors is $2\rho \cos \phi$.

21. Given the vector $3 + j6$, show that the vector $-6 + j3$ has the same magnitude, but has a reference angle $90°$ larger. In general, show that the vectors $a + jb$ and $-b + ja$ are of equal magnitudes but are $90°$ apart.

22. What are the rectangular forms of the vectors which are represented in the polar form by $1/\underline{0°}$, $1/\underline{90°}$, $1/\underline{180°}$, $1/\underline{270°}$?

15-4   Multiplication and Division of Vectors

We will discuss the multiplication and division of vectors first in the rectangular form, then in the polar form.

   Given two vectors $\mathbf{OP_1} = a + jb$ and $OP_2 = c + jd$, their product is found by the ordinary laws of algebraic multiplication of two binomials, thus:

$$(a + jb)(c + jd) = ac + jad + jbc + j^2bd.$$

Now, with $j^2 = -1$, we have

$$(a + jb)(c + jd) = (ac - bd) + j(ad + bc). \tag{9}$$

From (9) we observe that the product of two complex numbers is also a complex number.

The division of the vector $\mathbf{OP}_1 = a + jb$ by $\mathbf{OP}_2 = c + jd$ is accomplished by methods established in the chapter on radicals and exponents for the division of a quantity by a binomial where either or both terms of the divisor contain a square root. Thus,

$$\frac{\mathbf{OP}_1}{\mathbf{OP}_2} = \frac{a + jb}{c + jd} \cdot \frac{c - jd}{c - jd} = \frac{ac + jbc - jad - j^2bd}{c^2 - j^2d^2}$$

$$= \frac{(ac + bd) + j(bc - ad)}{c^2 + d^2} = \frac{ac + bd}{c^2 + d^2} + j\frac{bc - ad}{c^2 + d^2}, \tag{10}$$

where we rationalized the denominator by multiplying by its conjugate. From (10) we observe that the quotient of two complex numbers is also a complex number.

EXAMPLE 6. (a) Multiply $3 - j5$ by $4 + j2$. (b) Divide $6 - j3$ by $4 + j$.

Solution. (a) To multiply $3 - j5$ by $4 + j2$, we have

$$(3 - j5)(4 + j2) = 12 - j20 + j6 - j^2 10$$
$$= 12 + 10 - j20 + j6 = 22 - j14.$$

(b) To divide $6 - j3$ by $4 + j$, we have

$$\frac{6 - j3}{4 + j} \cdot \frac{4 - j}{4 - j} = \frac{24 - j12 - j6 + j^2 3}{16 - j^2} = \frac{21 - j18}{17}.$$

To multiply two vectors in polar form, we could choose the route of converting to the rectangular form and then multiplying as in (9). However, this method is usually tedious. Another method, somewhat cumbersome to prove, but easy to apply, is available. Let us derive the method.

Given two vectors $\rho_1/\underline{\phi_1}$ and $\rho_2/\underline{\phi_2}$, let us find their product $\rho_3/\underline{\phi_3}$. We will first express the given vectors in rectangular form, letting

$$\rho_1/\underline{\phi_1} = a + jb, \tag{11}$$

and

$$\rho_2/\underline{\phi_2} = c + jd. \tag{12}$$

By (9), the product of the two vectors is

$$\rho_3\underline{/\phi_3} = (\rho_1\underline{/\phi_1})(\rho_2\underline{/\phi_2}) = (ac - bd) + j(ad + bc). \qquad (13)$$

The vectors (11), (12), and (13) are pictured in Fig. 15-8 in parts (a), (b), and (c), respectively. Let us first show the relationship between ρ_1, ρ_2, and

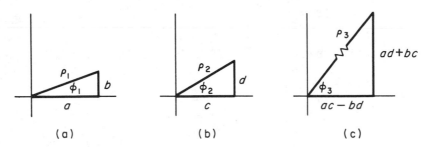

(a)   (b)   (c)

FIGURE 15-8

ρ_3. From Fig. 15-8(a),

$$\rho_1 = \sqrt{a^2 + b^2}; \qquad (14)$$

from Fig. 15-8(b),

$$\rho_2 = \sqrt{c^2 + d^2}; \qquad (15)$$

and from Fig. 15-8(c),

$$
\begin{aligned}
\rho_3 &= \sqrt{(ad + bc)^2 + (ac - bd)^2} \\
&= \sqrt{a^2d^2 + 2abcd + b^2c^2 + a^2c^2 - 2abcd + b^2d^2} \\
&= \sqrt{a^2d^2 + b^2c^2 + a^2c^2 + b^2d^2} \\
&= \sqrt{a^2(c^2 + d^2) + b^2(c^2 + d^2)} \\
&= \sqrt{(a^2 + b^2)(c^2 + d^2)} = \sqrt{a^2 + b^2} \cdot \sqrt{c^2 + d^2}. \qquad (16)
\end{aligned}
$$

Now, from (14), (15), and (16), we conclude that

$$\rho_3 = \rho_1 \cdot \rho_2. \qquad (17)$$

The conclusion in (17) is interpreted thus: *The magnitude of the product of two vectors is the product of the magnitudes of the two vectors.*

Next, we will show the relationship between ϕ_1, ϕ_2, and ϕ_3. From Fig. 15-8(a),

$$\tan \phi_1 = \frac{b}{a}; \qquad (18)$$

from Fig. 15-8(b),

$$\tan \phi_2 = \frac{d}{c}; \tag{19}$$

and from Fig. 15-8(c),

$$\tan \phi_3 = \frac{ad + bc}{ac - bd}. \tag{20}$$

If we divide the numerator and denominator of (20) by ac, we have

$$\tan \phi_3 = \frac{\dfrac{ad}{ac} + \dfrac{bc}{ac}}{\dfrac{ac}{ac} - \dfrac{bd}{ac}} = \frac{\dfrac{d}{c} + \dfrac{b}{a}}{1 - \left(\dfrac{b}{a}\right)\left(\dfrac{d}{c}\right)}. \tag{21}$$

Substituting (18) and (19) into (21), we have

$$\tan \phi_3 = \frac{\tan \phi_2 + \tan \phi_1}{1 - \tan \phi_2 \tan \phi_1}. \tag{22}$$

Now we refer to the trigonometric formula for the tangent of the sum of two angles:

$$\tan (A + B) = \frac{\tan A + \tan B}{1 - \tan A \tan B}. \tag{23}$$

Applying (23) to (22), we have

$$\tan \phi_3 = \tan (\phi_1 + \phi_2) = \frac{\tan \phi_2 + \tan \phi_1}{1 - \tan \phi_2 \tan \phi_1},$$

from which we reach the conclusion

$$\phi_3 = \phi_1 + \phi_2. \tag{24}$$

The conclusion in (24) is interpreted thus: *The reference angle of the product of two vectors is the sum of the reference angles of the two vectors.*

Now (13), (17), and (24) collect to the conclusion

$$\rho_1 \underline{/\phi_1} \cdot \rho_2 \underline{/\phi_2} = \rho_1 \rho_2 \underline{/\phi_1 + \phi_2}. \tag{25}$$

EXAMPLE 7. Here we show three examples of products of vectors in the polar form. In each case the product is obtained by multiplying the magnitudes and adding the reference angles according to (25).

(a) $3\underline{/30°} \cdot 4\underline{/45°} = (3)(4)\underline{/30° + 45°} = 12\underline{/75°}.$

(b) $6\underline{/-60°} \cdot 5\underline{/20} = (6)(5)\underline{/-60° + 20°} = 30\underline{/-40°}.$

(c) $2.5\underline{/330°} \cdot 10\underline{/285°} = (2.5)(10)\underline{/330° + 285°} = 25\underline{/615°} = 25\underline{/255°}.$

We will not show here the derivation of the appropriate equation for the division of vectors in the polar form, largely because it duplicates to a considerable extent the derivation of the product equation. We will, however, show the equation in mathematical symbolism and give a verbal statement of it. The student is asked to show the derivation.

Given the vectors $\rho_1\underline{/\phi_1}$ and $\rho_2\underline{/\phi_2}$, their quotient is given as

$$\frac{\rho_1\underline{/\phi_1}}{\rho_2\underline{/\phi_2}} = \frac{\rho_1}{\rho_2}\underline{/\phi_1 - \phi_2}. \tag{26}$$

The verbal statement of (26) is: *The magnitude of the quotient of two vectors is the quotient of the magnitudes of the two vectors. The reference angle of the quotient of two vectors is the difference of the reference angles of the two vectors.* The order of division and subtraction is as shown in (26).

EXAMPLE 8. Here we show three examples of the division of vectors in the polar form. Each division is in accordance with equation (26).

(a) $3\underline{/120°} \div 6\underline{/50°} = \frac{3}{6}\underline{/120° - 50°} = 0.5\underline{/70°}.$

(b) $110\underline{/90°} \div 4\underline{/200°} = \frac{110}{4}\underline{/90° - 200°} = 27.5\underline{/-110°}.$

(c) $4.5\underline{/-125°} \div 3.2\underline{/100°} = 4.5/3.2\underline{/-125° - 100°}$
$\qquad\qquad\qquad\qquad = 1.41\underline{/-225°} = 1.41\underline{/135°}.$

Exercises

For Exercises 1–24 we are given the vectors A *through* H.

$$A = 3 + j2, \qquad B = 3 - j2, \qquad C = -4 + j, \qquad D = -4 - j,$$
$$E = 6\underline{/30°}, \qquad F = 12\underline{/120°}, \qquad G = 3\underline{/225°}, \qquad H = 4\underline{/315°}.$$

Perform the indicated operations. Express the answers in the most convenient form.

1. *AB.*   *Ans.* 13.

2. *BC.*

3. *AD.*   *Ans.* $-10 - j11.$

4. *EF.*

5. *EG.*   *Ans.* $18\underline{/255°}.$

6. *FH*.

7. *AG*.   *Ans.* $10.8\underline{/258.7°}$.

8. *CF*.

9. *A/B*.   *Ans.* $(5 + j12)/13$.

10. *B/C*.

11. *A/D*.   *Ans.* $(-14 - j5)/17$.

12. *F/E*.

13. *G/H*.   *Ans.* $0.75\underline{/-90°}$.

14. *H/E*.

15. *F/C*.   *Ans.* $2.91\underline{/-45.9°}$.

16. *D/E*.

17. $(A + B)/AB$.   *Ans.* $\frac{6}{13}$.

18. $(C + B)/CB$.

19. $(E + G)/EG$.   *Ans.* $0.178\underline{/120.9°}$.

20. $(H + E)/HE$.

21. A^2.   *Ans.* $5 + j12$.

22. E^2.

23. G^3.   *Ans.* $27\underline{/-45°}$.

24. D^3.

25. Show the derivation of equation (26).

26. If a vector in the polar form is squared, how is the reference angle changed?

27. If a vector in the polar form is raised to the *n*th power, how is the reference angle changed?

28. What is the polar form of *j*? Multiplication by *j* advances the reference angle by how many degrees?

29. Show that the vector $1 + j$ may be represented in the polar form as

$$\sqrt{2}\,[\cos{(45° \pm n360°)} + j\sin{(45° \pm n360°)}].$$

15-5   Powers and Roots of Complex Numbers— DeMoivre's Theorem

According to (25), the product of two vectors is

$$\rho_1\underline{/\phi_1} \cdot \rho_2\underline{/\phi_2} = \rho_1\rho_2\underline{/\phi_1 + \phi_2}. \tag{27}$$

If, in (27), $\rho_1/\underline{\phi_1} = \rho_2/\underline{\phi_2}$, then we are squaring a vector and

$$(\rho_1/\underline{\phi_1})^2 = \rho_1^2/\underline{2\phi}, \tag{28}$$

where (28) asserts "to square a complex number, square the magnitude and double the reference angle." Repeated application of this notation shows that

$$(\rho/\underline{\phi})^n = \rho^n/\underline{n\phi}. \tag{29}$$

Converting to the trigonometric form, (29) may be written as

$$[\rho(\cos \phi + j \sin \phi)]^n = \rho^n(\cos n\phi + j \sin n\phi). \tag{30}$$

Expression (30) is a part of *DeMoivre's theorem* and is useful in finding powers of vectors in the complex plane.

EXAMPLE 9. Expand $(-2 + j2\sqrt{3})^6$.

Solution. First, let us convert the given expression $-2 + j2\sqrt{3}$ to the trigonometric form. Refer to Fig. 15-9, where we have a sketch of the vector and we may observe that $\rho = 4$ and the least positive value of ϕ is $\phi = 120°$ so that

$$-2 + j2\sqrt{3} = 4/\underline{120°} = 4(\cos 120° + j \sin 120°).$$

Now, according to DeMoivre's theorem (30),

$$4^6 (\cos 120° + j \sin 120°)^6 = 4^6(\cos 720° + j \sin 720°)$$
$$= 4^6(\cos 0° + j \sin 0°)$$
$$= 4^6 = 4096.$$

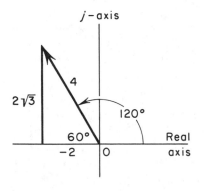

FIGURE 15–9

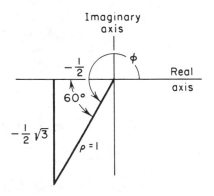

FIGURE 15–10

DeMoivre's theorem is also useful in finding roots of vectors in a complex plane. Let us observe an example problem, then establish a general expression for roots.

EXAMPLE 10. Evaluate the expression

$$(-\tfrac{1}{2} - j\tfrac{1}{2}\sqrt{3})^{1/3}.$$

Solution. First we sketch the vector as in Fig. 15-10. Inspecting Fig. 15-10, we might have a tendency to describe the reference angle ϕ as 240° only. Actually, ϕ has many values such as 240°, 240° + 360°, 240° + 2(360°), 240° + 3(360°), ..., where it is apparent that we need not restrict ourselves to the first-revolution value of ϕ. The general value of ϕ is given as

$$\phi = 240° + k(360°)$$

where k is an integer.

The magnitude of the desired vector, as seen in Fig. 15-10, is

$$\sqrt[3]{\rho} = \sqrt[3]{1} = 1.$$

Since we are taking the cube root, the reference angle(s) of the given vector will be divided by 3. Both of these facts may be seen to follow from the power form (30); if the three cube roots are each raised to the third power by (30), we should return to the given vector. Application of (30) necessitates cubing the magnitudes of the solution vectors and tripling their reference angles. The desired roots, then, are

$$r_1 = (1)^{1/3}\left(\cos\frac{240°}{3} + j\sin\frac{240°}{3}\right) = 1(\cos 80° + j\sin 80°)$$

$$= 0.174 + j0.985 = 1\underline{/80°},$$

$$r_2 = (1)^{1/3}\left(\cos\frac{600°}{3} + j\sin\frac{600°}{3}\right) = 1(\cos 200° + j\sin 200°)$$

$$= -0.940 - j0.342 = 1\underline{/200°},$$

$$r_3 = (1)^{1/3}\left(\cos\frac{960°}{3} + j\sin\frac{960°}{3}\right) = 1(\cos 320° + j\sin 320°)$$

$$= 0.766 - j0.643 = 1\underline{/320°}.$$

We observe that the first solution has a reference angle 80° = 240°/3 and each successive solution is advanced 360°/3 = 120° from the previous solution. Any attempt to go beyond three solutions (our was a *cube* root) would simply duplicate a previous solution. The solutions are shown in Fig. 15-11. In any root problem the solutions will be equally spaced; the angle between consecutive solutions will be 360°/n where we are interested in the nth roots.

In view of the preceding example problem and discussion, we will give here the general expression for the nth root of a vector in the complex plane:

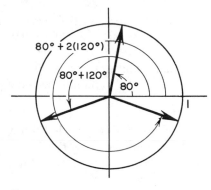

FIGURE 15–11

$$(a + jb)^{1/n} = (\rho/\phi)^{1/n}$$

$$= \rho^{1/n}\left[\cos\left(\frac{\phi + k\cdot360°}{n}\right)\right.$$

$$\left. + j\sin\left(\frac{\phi + k\cdot360°}{n}\right)\right]$$

(31)

where n is the order of the root and k is an integer. Expression (31) is also a a part of DeMoivre's theorem.

EXAMPLE 11. Find the three cube roots of -1.

Solution. Since -1 may be written in the polar form as $1/180°$, then by (31) and Fig. 15-12, we have $\rho = 1$, $n = 3$, $\phi = 180°$, and $k = 0, 1, 2$. Now we

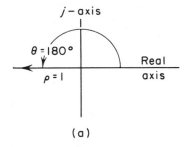

FIGURE 15–12

have the solutions

$$r_1 = (1)^{1/3}\left(\cos\frac{180°}{3} + j\sin\frac{180°}{3}\right)$$

$$= 1(\cos 60° + j\sin 60°) = \frac{1}{2} + j\frac{\sqrt{3}}{2},$$

$$r_2 = (1)^{1/3}\left(\cos\frac{540°}{3} + j\sin\frac{540°}{3}\right)$$

$$= 1(\cos 180° + j\sin 180°) = -1,$$

$$r_3 = (1)^{1/3}\left(\cos\frac{900°}{3} + j\sin\frac{900°}{3}\right)$$

$$= 1(\cos 300° + j\sin 300°) = \frac{1}{2} - j\frac{\sqrt{3}}{2}.$$

Figure 15-12(a) shows the given quantity, -1. Figure 15-12(b) shows the three solutions, spaced $120° = 360°/3$ apart, with the first solution having the reference angle $180°/3 = 60°$.

We can establish the correctness of the three solutions in Example 11 by cubing each and obtaining as the value of the cube the original number, -1.

It is worth noting here that through DeMoivre's theorem we observe that every real number has n nth roots. At most two of the roots are real. For instance, the number $+1$ has 4 fourth roots, namely $1, j, -1, -j$.

Exercises

Find the indicated roots and powers by using DeMoivre's theorem. Express results in the most convenient form. Wherever practical sketch the given vectors and solutions.

1. $\sqrt{-1}$. *Ans. j.*

2. $\sqrt[4]{-1}$.

3. $\sqrt{j}$. *Ans.* $\pm\sqrt{2}(1+j)/2$.

4. $\sqrt{1+j}$.

5. $(1+j)^3$. *Ans.* $-2+j2$.

6. $(1-j)^3$.

7. $\sqrt[4]{1}$. *Ans.* $\pm 1, \pm j$.

8. $(1-j\sqrt{3})^4$.

9. $(1+j\sqrt{3})^5$. *Ans.* $32\underline{/-60°}$.

10. $\left(-\dfrac{1}{2} + j\dfrac{\sqrt{3}}{2}\right)^4$.

11. $(-4+j4)^3$. *Ans.* $128\sqrt{2}\underline{/45°}$.

12. $(1+j2)^4$.

13. $(2+j)^4$. *Ans.* $-7+j24$.

14. $(3\underline{/0°})^3$.

15. $\sqrt{5\underline{/360°}}$. *Ans.* $\pm\sqrt{5}$.

16. $\sqrt[3]{-8}$.

17. $[2(\cos 72° + j\sin 72°)]^5$. *Ans.* 32.

18. $[3(\cos 30° + j \sin 30°)]^3$.

19. $\sqrt[3]{-j}$.   *Ans.* $j, (\pm\sqrt{3} - j)/2$.

20. $\sqrt[3]{1 - j}$.

15-6   Special Properties of Vectors in the Complex Plane

Reflections

Vectors can be reflected across either axis or through the origin by simple techniques. Such reflections find extensive application in a-c electricity. Refer to Fig. 15-13 where a given vector $a + jb$ is shown as a solid line and its reflection is shown as a dotted line.

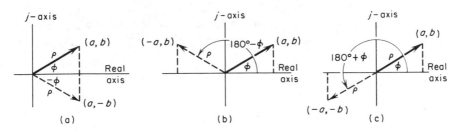

FIGURE 15–13

From Fig. 15-13(a), the reflection of $a + jb$ across the real axis is $a - jb$, accomplished by changing the sign of b. In the polar form, ρ/ϕ and $\rho/-\phi$ are reflections across the real axis; here we see that reflection across the real axis is accomplished by reversing the sign of the reference angle.

From Fig. 15-13(b), the reflection of $a + jb$ across the imaginary axis is $-a + jb$, accomplished by changing the sign of a. In polar form, ρ/ϕ and $\rho/180° - \phi$ are reflections of each other across the imaginary axis; here we see that reflection is accomplished by choosing the supplement of the reference angle.

From Fig. 15-13(c), the reflection of $a + jb$ through the origin is $-a - jb$, accomplished by changing the sign of both a and b. In polar form, ρ/ϕ and $\rho/180° + \phi$ are reflections of each other through the origin; this reflection is accomplished by increasing the reference angle 180°.

Advancing the Reference Angle

It is often useful to advance the reference angle 90°, 180°, or 270° (−90°). Referring to Fig. 15-14, let us observe how these advances may be made.

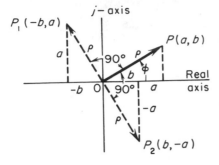

FIGURE 15-14

From Fig. 15-14, the vector $\mathbf{OP} = \rho/\underline{\phi} = a + jb$ is given. $\mathbf{OP_1}$ has reference angle $\phi + 90°$, therefore $\mathbf{OP}$ is perpendicular to $\mathbf{OP_1}$ and the slope of $\mathbf{OP_1}$ is the negative reciprocal of the slope of $\mathbf{OP}$ suggesting the choice of the vertical component a and horizontal component $-b$ for $\mathbf{OP_1}$ (as opposed to b and a respectively for $\mathbf{OP}$). Hence, if the vector $a + jb$ is advanced 90°, the resulting vector is $-b - ja$. We note that

$$j(a + jb) = -b + ja,$$

which suggests that an advance of 90° can be accomplished by multiplication by j. In polar form, $j = 1/\underline{90°}$; if the original vector $a + jb = \rho/\underline{\phi}$ is multiplied by j, we have

$$\rho/\underline{\phi} \cdot 1/\underline{90°} = \rho/\underline{\phi + 90°},$$

where it is observed that the magnitude of the vector is undisturbed, but the reference angle is advanced by 90°.

270° Advance

In Fig. 15-14, $\mathbf{OP_2}$ is advanced 270° (or moved backward 90°) from $\mathbf{OP}$. This is accomplished by choosing the new components b and $-a$, such that the new vector is $b - ja$. It is also accomplished by multiplying the given vector by $-j$ or by $1/\underline{-90°}$.

180° Advance

Referring to Fig. 15-13(c), we observe that an advance of 180° is accomplished by changing the signs of both a and b, such that $-a - jb$ is 180° removed from $a + jb$. We note that -1 is $1/\underline{180°}$ so that

$$\rho/\underline{\phi} \cdot 1/\underline{180°} = \rho/\underline{\phi + 180°}. \tag{32}$$

We also note that -1 is $-1/\underline{0°}$, so that

$$\rho/\underline{\phi} \cdot -1/\underline{0°} = -\rho/\underline{\phi}. \tag{33}$$

Comparing (32) and (33), we note that an advance of 180° is the equivalent of a change in sense of the vector.

Exercises

What is the polar form of the vectors in 1–4 ?

1. 1.   *Ans.* $1\underline{/0°}$.

2. j.

3. -1.   *Ans.* $1\underline{/180°}$ or $-1\underline{/0°}$.

4. $-j$.

What is the rectangular form of the vectors in 5–8 ?

5. $-2\underline{/180°}$.

6. $3\underline{/\phi + 180°}$.   *Ans.* $-3\cos\phi - j3\sin\phi$.

7. $(-2\underline{/180°})^2$.

8. $3 + j4$ advanced by $90°$.   *Ans.* $-4 + j3$.

In 9–11 show that multiplication of a vector by

9. j advances the reference angle by $90°$.

10. -1 reverses the sense of the vector.

11. $-j$ diminishes the reference angle by $90°$.

Given the vector OP $= -3 + j4$, *give the rectangular expression in 12–14 for the vector that is the reflection of* OP

12. across the real axis.

13. across the imaginary axis.   *Ans.* $3 + j4$.

14. through the origin.

In 15–17 given the vector OP $= \rho\underline{/\phi}$, *give the polar expression for the vector that is the reflection of* OP

15. across the real axis.   *Ans.* $\rho\underline{/-\phi}$.

16. across the imaginary axis.

17. through the origin.

Show the expression for the vector advanced $90°$ beyond the given vector in 18–22.

18. $3 - j5$.   *Ans.* $5 + j3$.

19. $-4 + j2$.

20. $3\underline{/120°}$.   *Ans.* $3\underline{/210°}$.

21. 3.

22. $-j5$. *Ans.* 5.

23. Show that division of a complex number by its reflection across the real axis doubles the reference angle.

24. Show that the product of a complex number by its reflection across the real axis results in a positive real number which is the square of the magnitude of the original number.

25. Show that the product of a complex number by its reflection across the imaginary axis results in a negative real number which is the negative of the square of the magnitude of the original vector.

26. Given two vectors with equal magnitudes and with reference angles 90° apart. Show that their product is a pure imaginary number if either of the original vectors was a pure imaginary number.

In preceding chapter we defined the trigonometric functions, applied trigonometry to right triangles and oblique triangles, graphed the trigonometric functions on the Cartesian coordinate plane, and discussed vectors in the complex plane.

In this chapter we will discuss certain miscellaneous topics in trigonometry including identities, trigonometric equations, inverse trigonometric functions, approximate solutions, and others. These topics are included to broaden our coverage of trigonometry and to show certain additional applications.

MISCELLANEOUS TOPICS IN TRIGONOMETRY 16

16-1   Square Relationships

An equation is called an *identity* if the two members of the equation are equal for all values assigned to the variables for which both members are defined. Thus,

$$x^2 - 1 = (x + 1)(x - 1)$$

is an identity because the left member and right member are equal regardless of the value assigned to x. The expression

$$x^2 - 2x = 3$$

is not an identity because the equality is true only for the values $x = 3$ and $x = -1$.

Identities are commonly used in trigonometry for two major reasons: (1) to reduce an expression which may contain two or more different functions of an angle to an expression containing only one trigonometric function, and (2) to interchange functions of multiple angles with powers of functions of single angles. More on this later.

We will consider four groups of identities in this chapter. They are the square relationships, functions of sums and differences of angles, multiple-angle formulas, and half-angle formulas. First, the square relationships.

In Fig. 16-1 we are given a point $P(x, y)$ on a circle of radius r. From the Pythagorean theorem we have

$$x^2 + y^2 = r^2. \tag{1}$$

Dividing (1) by r^2, we have

$$\frac{x^2}{r^2} + \frac{y^2}{r^2} = \frac{r^2}{r^2},$$

from which

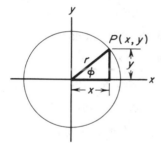

FIGURE 16-1

$$\left(\frac{y}{r}\right)^2 + \left(\frac{x}{r}\right)^2 = 1. \tag{2}$$

Now, from Fig. 16-1,

$$\frac{y}{r} = \sin \phi \quad \text{and} \quad \frac{x}{r} = \cos \phi,$$

so that (2) can now be written as

$$\sin^2 \phi + \cos^2 \phi = 1. \tag{3}$$

Equation (3) is an identity because it holds for any value assigned to ϕ. Two more square relationships are common. If we divide (1) by x^2, we have

$$\frac{x^2}{x^2} + \frac{y^2}{x^2} = \frac{r^2}{x^2}$$

or

$$1 + \left(\frac{y}{x}\right)^2 = \left(\frac{r}{x}\right)^2, \tag{4}$$

but, from Fig. 16-1,

$$\frac{y}{x} = \tan \phi \quad \text{and} \quad \frac{r}{x} = \sec \phi,$$

so that (4) becomes

$$1 + \tan^2 \phi = \sec^2 \phi. \tag{5}$$

If we divide (1) by y^2 and proceed as in the derivations of (3) and (5), we have a third square relationship:

$$1 + \text{ctn}^2 \phi = \csc^2 \phi. \tag{6}$$

We call expressions (3), (5), and (6) the *square relationships*. In conjunction with the reciprocal relationships they are useful in certain manipulations. Consider two examples.

EXAMPLE 1. Convert the expression

$$\cos^2 \phi - \text{ctn}^2 \phi = 5 \tag{7}$$

to an expression containing no trigonometric functions other than powers of $\sin \phi$.

Solution. From (3),

$$\cos^2 \phi = 1 - \sin^2 \phi, \tag{8}$$

and from (6),

$$\text{ctn}^2 \phi = \csc^2 \phi - 1 = \frac{1}{\sin^2 \phi} - 1. \tag{9}$$

Substituting (8) and (9) into (7), we have

$$1 - \sin^2 \phi - \left(\frac{1}{\sin^2 \phi} - 1\right) = 5,$$

from which

$$\sin^4 \phi + 3 \sin^2 \phi + 1 = 0, \tag{10}$$

where we note that (10) is a desired expression containing only powers of $\sin \phi$.

EXAMPLE 2. Using Fig. 16-1 as reference, show that

$$\tan \phi = \frac{\sin \phi}{\cos \phi}.$$

Solution. From Fig. 16-1,

$$\tan \phi = \frac{y}{x}; \tag{11}$$

dividing both the numerator and denominator of (11) by r, we have

$$\tan \phi = \frac{y/r}{x/r}.$$

But, from Fig. 16-1,

$$\frac{y}{r} = \sin \phi \quad \text{and} \quad \frac{x}{r} = \cos \phi$$

so that

$$\tan \phi = \frac{\sin \phi}{\cos \phi}.$$

A summary of certain square relationships and quotients is given in Table 16-1.

Table 16-1

IDENTITIES INVOLVING SQUARES AND QUOTIENTS

1. $\sin^2 \phi + \cos^2 \phi = 1$	**4.** $\tan \phi = \dfrac{\sin \phi}{\cos \phi}$
2. $1 + \tan^2 \phi = \sec^2 \phi$	
3. $1 + \text{ctn}^2 \phi = \csc^2 \phi$	**5.** $\text{ctn} \phi = \dfrac{\cos \phi}{\sin \phi}$

Exercises

Using the identities given in Table 16-1, in addition to the definitions and reciprocals of the trigonometric functions, perform the operations requested in Exercises 1–5.

1. Modify the expression

$$4 + \operatorname{ctn}^2 x = \sec^2 x$$

to an expression containing only powers of cos x.

Ans. $3 \cos^4 x - 5 \cos^2 x + 1 = 0$.

2. Modify the expression $\cos^2 x - \operatorname{ctn}^2 x = 3$ to an expression containing only powers of sin x.

3. Show that the expression

$$\frac{\sec \phi}{\tan \phi + \operatorname{ctn} \phi}$$

is equal to sin ϕ.

4. Modify the expression

$$\frac{\sec^2 \phi - \sin \phi \sec \phi - 1}{\tan \phi - 1}$$

to an expression containing the tangent function only.

5. Show that the expression

$$\frac{2 \tan x + \sec^2 x}{1 + \tan x}$$

is equal to $1 + \tan x$.

6. Show that the expression

$$\left(\tan \phi + \frac{\cos \phi}{\sin \phi} \right) (\cos \phi)$$

is equal to csc ϕ.

7. Show that the expression

$$\sec \phi = \cos \phi + \tan \phi$$

may be reduced to the expression sin $\phi = 1$.

8. Using Fig. 16-2 and the definitions of the trigonometric functions, express

$$\sec \phi = \cos \phi + \tan \phi$$

in terms of $x, y,$ and r only and simplify the resulting expression to $y/r = 1$. Compare this with the result in Exercise 7.

9. Given expression

$$\frac{x^2 + y^2}{x^2} - \frac{\sqrt{x^2 + y^2}}{y} = \frac{x^2}{r^2},$$

where $x, y,$ and r are obtained from Fig. 16-2, modify the given expression to another form containing only powers of $\sin \phi$.

10. Modify the expression

$$\sin^3 \phi - 3 \sin \phi + 1 = 0$$

to read

$$(1 + \tan^2 \phi)^{3/2} = 3 \tan \phi + 2 \tan^3 \phi.$$

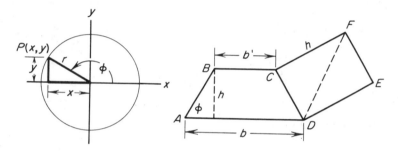

FIGURE 16–2   FIGURE 16–3

11. Given the isosceles trapezoid $ABCD$ in Fig. 16-3 with a rectangle $CDEF$ mounted on one of the equal sides. If $FC = h$, where h is the altitude of the trapezoid, show that $FD = h\sqrt{1 + \csc^2 \phi}$.

12. Show that the expression

$$\sin^4 \phi = \frac{1 - \sin^2 \phi}{-\csc^2 \phi} + \frac{1}{1 + \operatorname{ctn}^2 \phi}$$

is an identity by reducing it to one of the forms in Table 16-1.

13. Show that

$$9 \tan^2 \phi = 25(\sec^2 \phi - 1 - \sin^2 \phi)$$

is reducible to the expression $\csc \phi = \frac{5}{3}$.

16-2 Functions of Sums and Differences of Angles

It is often useful to express an angle as the sum or difference of two angles and to obtain a trigonometric function of this sum or difference in terms of functions of the separate angles. In Fig. 16-4 we have a unit circle with $OC = OG = OF = 1$, where $\angle COF = \theta + \phi$. Let us obtain expressions for $\sin(\theta + \phi)$ and $\cos(\theta + \phi)$.

From F construct $FA \perp OC$ and $FD \perp OG$. From D construct $DE \perp FA$. Now $\angle EFD = \angle COG = \theta$ because the sides of the angles are perpendicular left side to left side and right side to right side. It is also seen that $AE = BD$. Now,

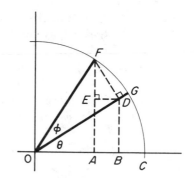

FIGURE 16–4

$$\sin(\theta + \phi) = AF$$

but

$$AF = BD + EF$$

so that

$$\sin(\theta + \phi) = BD + EF. \tag{12}$$

Now, from triangle EFD,

$$EF = FD \cos \theta,$$

and, from triangle OBD,

$$DB = OD \sin \theta,$$

so that (12) becomes

$$\sin(\theta + \phi) = OD \sin \theta + FD \cos \theta. \tag{13}$$

From triangle ODF,

$$FD = OF \sin \phi = \sin \phi$$

and

$$OD = OF \cos \phi = \cos \phi,$$

so that (13) now becomes

$$\sin(\theta + \phi) = \sin\theta\cos\phi + \cos\theta\sin\phi, \tag{14}$$

where (14) shows the sine of the sum of two angles in terms of the sine and cosine of the separate angles.

From Fig. 16-4 we may develop the equation

$$\cos(\theta + \phi) = \cos\theta\cos\phi - \sin\theta\sin\phi. \tag{15}$$

This will be left as an exercise for the student.

If we substitute $-\phi$ for ϕ in (14), we have

$$\sin(\theta - \phi) = \sin\theta\cos(-\phi) + \cos\theta\sin(-\phi),$$

but

$$\sin(-\phi) = -\sin\phi \quad \text{and} \quad \cos(-\phi) = \cos\phi,$$

so that we now have

$$\sin(\theta - \phi) = \sin\theta\cos\phi - \cos\theta\sin\phi. \tag{16}$$

If we substitute $-\phi$ for ϕ in (15), we obtain

$$\cos(\theta - \phi) = \cos\theta\cos\phi + \sin\theta\sin\phi. \tag{17}$$

Equations (14), (15), (16), and (17) give expressions for the sine and cosine functions of the sums and differences of two angles in terms of the sines and cosines of the separate angles.

Optional forms involving sines and cosines of the sums and differences of two angles are made available by combining pairs of equations (14)–(17). For example, by adding (15) and (17),

$$\cos(\theta + \phi) = \cos\theta\cos\phi - \sin\theta\sin\phi$$
$$\underline{\cos(\theta - \phi) = \cos\theta\cos\phi + \sin\theta\sin\phi}$$
$$\cos(\theta + \phi) + \cos(\theta - \phi) = 2\cos\theta\cos\phi$$

from which

$$\cos\theta\cos\phi = \tfrac{1}{2}[\cos(\theta + \phi) + \cos(\theta - \phi)]. \tag{18}$$

Other optional forms comparable to (18) are given in Table 16-2.

Table 16-2

TRIGONOMETRIC IDENTITIES

1. $\sin (\theta + \phi) = \sin \theta \cos \phi + \cos \theta \sin \phi$
2. $\sin (\theta - \phi) = \sin \theta \cos \phi - \cos \theta \sin \phi$
3. $\cos (\theta + \phi) = \cos \theta \cos \phi - \sin \theta \sin \phi$
4. $\cos (\theta - \phi) = \cos \theta \cos \phi + \sin \theta \sin \phi$
5. $\cos \theta \cos \phi = \frac{1}{2}[\cos (\theta + \phi) + \cos (\theta - \phi)]$
6. $\sin \theta \sin \phi = \frac{1}{2}[\cos (\theta - \phi) - \cos (\theta + \phi)]$
7. $\sin \theta \cos \phi = \frac{1}{2}[\sin (\theta + \phi) + \sin (\theta - \phi)]$
8. $\cos \theta \sin \phi = \frac{1}{2}[\sin (\theta + \phi) - \sin (\theta - \phi)]$
9. $\sin 2\theta = 2 \sin \theta \cos \theta$
10. $\cos 2\theta = \cos^2 \theta - \sin^2 \theta = 1 - 2 \sin^2 \theta = 2 \cos^2 \theta - 1$
11. $\cos^2 \theta = \frac{1}{2}(1 + \cos 2\theta)$
12. $\sin^2 \theta = \frac{1}{2}(1 - \cos 2\theta)$
13. $\cos \dfrac{\theta}{2} = \sqrt{\dfrac{1 + \cos \theta}{2}}$
14. $\sin \dfrac{\theta}{2} = \sqrt{\dfrac{1 - \cos \theta}{2}}$

Exercises

1. Referring to Fig. 16-4, derive form 3 of Table 16-2.

2. By substituting $-\phi$ for ϕ into form 3, derive form 4 of Table 16-2.

3. By adding or subtracting the proper pairs of forms 1–4 in Table 16-2, derive forms 6, 7, and 8.

In Exercises 4–11, assume knowledge of the functions

$$\sin 30° = \cos 60° = \frac{1}{2}, \qquad \cos 30° = \sin 60° = \frac{\sqrt{3}}{2},$$

$$\sin 45° = \cos 45° = \frac{\sqrt{2}}{2}, \qquad \sin 90° = 1, \qquad \cos 90° = 0.$$

Using this known information and appropriate forms from Table 16-2, obtain radical values of the given functions.

4. $\sin 15°$.

5. $\cos 15°$.   *Ans.* $(\sqrt{2}/4)(\sqrt{3} + 1)$.

6. $\cos 75°$.

7. $\sin 75°$.   *Ans.* $(\sqrt{2}/4)(\sqrt{3} + 1)$.

8. cos 105°.   *Ans.* ($\sqrt{2}/4)(1 - \sqrt{3}$).

9. cos 150°.

10. sin 120°.   *Ans.* ($\sqrt{3}/2$).

11. cos 135°.

12. A tapestry hung on a wall is viewed by an observer as shown in Fig. 16-5. The observer's eye is at *A*, 12 ft. from the wall *DB*. The tapestry *DC* is 7 ft. high and is hung so that its bottom is 9 ft. above the observer's eye. Find the magnitude of the angle ϕ without first finding θ.

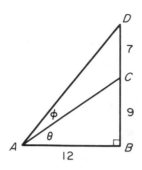

FIGURE 16–5

13. By using Form 2 in Table 16-2, show that

$$\sin(180° - \phi) = \sin\phi.$$

14. By using appropriate forms from Table 16-2, show that

$$\sin(90° \pm \phi) = \cos\phi.$$

15. Show that $\sin(\alpha + \beta + \gamma)$ may be written as

$$\sin\alpha\cos\beta\cos\gamma - \sin\alpha\sin\beta\sin\gamma + \cos\alpha\sin\beta\cos\gamma$$
$$+ \cos\alpha\cos\beta\sin\gamma.$$

16-3   Functions of Multiple and Partial Angles

It is often useful to refer to trigonometric functions of multiple angles such as 2θ or 3θ. The angle 2θ is called a *double angle*; sin 2θ and cos 2θ can be expressed in terms of sin θ and cos θ rather easily, provided that we have expressions for $\sin(\theta + \phi)$ and $\cos(\theta + \phi)$. Referring to Table 16-2, let us develop an expression (form 9) for sin 2θ in terms of functions of the single angle.

In form 1, where

$$\sin(\theta + \phi) = \sin\theta\cos\phi + \cos\theta\sin\phi,$$

let $\phi = \theta$, so that

$$\sin(\theta + \theta) = \sin\theta\cos\theta + \sin\theta\cos\theta,$$

from which

$$\sin 2\theta = 2 \sin \theta \cos \theta, \tag{19}$$

where (19) is form 9 of Table 16-2 and is an expression for the sine of the double angle in terms of functions of the single angle.

EXAMPLE 3. Express $\cos 3\theta$ in terms of $\cos \theta$ only.

Solution. Let us start with form 3 of Table 16-2 where

$$\cos (\theta + \phi) = \cos \theta \cos \phi - \sin \theta \sin \phi. \tag{20}$$

In (20), substitute 2θ for ϕ, obtaining

$$\cos 3\theta = \cos \theta \cos 2\theta - \sin \theta \sin 2\theta. \tag{21}$$

Now, substituting

$$\cos 2\theta = \cos^2 \theta - \sin^2 \theta$$

and

$$\sin 2\theta = 2 \sin \theta \cos \theta$$

into (21), we have

$$\cos 3\theta = \cos \theta(\cos^2 \theta - \sin^2 \theta) - \sin \theta(2 \sin \theta \cos \theta). \tag{22}$$

Simplifying (22), we have

$$\cos 3\theta = \cos^3 \theta - 3 \sin^2 \theta \cos \theta. \tag{23}$$

Substituting the identity $\sin^2 \theta = 1 - \cos^2 \theta$ into (23), we have

$$\cos 3\theta = 4 \cos^3 \theta - 3 \cos \theta.$$

Half-angle formulas follow from the double-angle formulas, which in turn follow from forms 5 and 6 of Table 16-2. Thus, from form 5,

$$\cos \theta \cos \phi = \tfrac{1}{2}[\cos (\theta + \phi) + \cos (\theta - \phi)].$$

Let $\phi = \theta$ and

$$\cos \theta \cos \theta = \tfrac{1}{2}[\cos (\theta + \theta) + \cos 0]$$

from which

$$\cos^2 \theta = \tfrac{1}{2}(1 + \cos 2\theta). \tag{24}$$

If we let $\phi = 2\theta$, or $\phi/2 = \theta$, in (24), then

$$\cos^2 \phi/2 = \tfrac{1}{2}(1 + \cos \phi),$$

which, when solved for $\cos \phi/2$ by taking the square root of both sides, becomes

$$\cos \frac{\phi}{2} = \sqrt{\frac{1 + \cos \phi}{2}},$$

which is comparable to form 13 of Table 16-2.

EXAMPLE 4. Express $\sin^4 \theta$ in terms of first powers of functions of multiples of θ.

Solution. From form 12 of Table 16-2,

$$\sin^4 \theta = (\sin^2 \theta)^2 = [\tfrac{1}{2}(1 - \cos 2\theta)]^2$$
$$= \tfrac{1}{4} - \tfrac{1}{2} \cos 2\theta + \tfrac{1}{4} \cos^2 2\theta. \qquad (25)$$

Since we wish to have $\sin^4 \theta$ expressed in terms of first powers of functions of multiple angles, we must convert $\cos^2 \theta$. Using form 13 and replacing $\theta/2$ by 2θ, we have

$$\cos^2 2\theta = \frac{1 + \cos 4\theta}{2}. \qquad (26)$$

Substituting (26) into (25) and simplifying, we have

$$\sin^4 \theta = \tfrac{1}{4} - \tfrac{1}{2} \cos 2\theta + \tfrac{1}{4}(1 + \cos 4\theta)/2$$
$$= \tfrac{3}{8} - \tfrac{1}{2} \cos 2\theta + \tfrac{1}{8} \cos 4\theta.$$

Exercises

1. Using form 3 of Table 16-2, derive form 10.

2. Using form 6 of Table 16-2, derive form 12.

3. Using form 6 of Table 16-2, derive form 14.

In Exercises 4–8, convert the forms $\cos n\theta$ and $\sin n\theta$ to forms involving only powers of functions of the single angle θ.

4. Sin 3θ.

5. Sin 5θ.   *Ans.* $16 \sin^5 \theta - 20 \sin^3 \theta + 5 \sin \theta.$

6. Cos 4θ.

7. Sin 4θ.   *Ans.* $4\sin\theta\cos\theta - 8\sin^3\theta\cos\theta$.

8. Cos 5θ.

9. In Fig. 16-6 we are given the graphs of

$$y_1 = a\sin\theta, \qquad y_2 = b\cos\theta,$$
$$y = y_1 + y_2 = a\sin\theta + b\cos\theta.$$

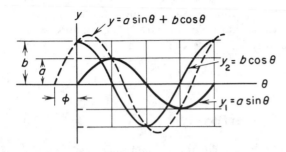

FIGURE 16-6   FIGURE 16-7

If y is written in the form

$$y = \sqrt{a^2 + b^2}\cos\phi\sin\theta + \sqrt{a^2 + b^2}\sin\phi\cos\theta,$$

where $a = \sqrt{a^2 + b^2}\cos\phi$ and $b = \sqrt{a^2 + b^2}\sin\phi$ as shown in Fig. 16-7, show that y can be expressed as

$$y = \sqrt{a^2 + b^2}\sin(\theta + \phi),$$

where $\phi =$ arc tan b/a. Also, interpret $\sqrt{a^2 + b^2}$ and ϕ as properties of the graph of y.

10. Referring to Exercise 9, a certain composite wave is made up of the components $y_1 = 3\sin\omega t$, $y_2 = 4\cos\omega t$. Determine the amplitude and the phase shift of the composite. What is the equation of the composite?
        Ans. Amp. $= 5$; phase shift $= 53.1°$; $y = 5\sin(\omega t + 53.1°)$.

11. Using form 13 of Table 16-2 and the fact that cos $30° = \sqrt{3}/2$, show that cos $15° = 0.965$.

12. Repeating the method used in Exercise 11, evaluate cos $3.75°$.

13. Referring to Exercise 9, we are given that a certain composite wave is of the form $y = 3\sin(x + 30°)$. Show that this wave is made up of the components $y_1 = a\sin x$, $y_2 = b\cos x$, where $a = 3\sqrt{3}/2$ and $b = \frac{3}{2}$.

14. Using appropriate forms from Table 16-2, show that

$$\sin\phi = \cos(90° - \phi).$$

In this section we will discuss two types of equations involving trigonometric functions. The first type will contain only trigonometric expressions and constants; the second type will contain trigonometric expressions and others that may be algebraic or logarithmic or exponential in nature.

For equations of the first type, we suggest this procedure of solution: Convert all of the trigonometric functions to the same function by way of identities, then solve the resulting equation by suitable means; that is, apply the quadratic formula for equations that are quadratic in the trigonometric function or use approximate methods where no formula is available. Observe Example 5.

EXAMPLE 5. Solve for ϕ if

$$3 \tan^2 \phi (1 - \sin \phi) + 1 - 3 \sin \phi = 0. \tag{27}$$

Solution. First, observe that (27) is an equation containing two trigonometric functions, namely $\tan \phi$ and $\sin \phi$. Let us rewrite (27) in terms of one trigonometric function only. It is often expedient to obtain the expression in terms of $\sin \phi$. Since

$$\tan \phi = \frac{\sin \phi}{\cos \phi},$$

then (27) may be written as

$$3\left(\frac{\sin^2 \phi}{\cos^2 \phi}\right)(1 - \sin \phi) + 1 - 3 \sin \phi = 0. \tag{28}$$

Clearing fractions in (28), we have

$$3 \sin^2 \phi - 3 \sin^3 \phi + \cos^2 \phi - 3 \sin \phi \cos^2 \phi = 0. \tag{29}$$

Substituting

$$\cos^2 \phi = 1 - \sin^2 \phi$$

into (29) and simplifying, we have

$$2 \sin^2 \phi - 3 \sin \phi + 1 = 0. \tag{30}$$

Inspecting (30), we observe that only one trigonometric function is present and that the equation is a quadratic in $\sin \phi$. We may factor (30) as

$$(2 \sin \phi - 1)(\sin \phi - 1) = 0,$$

from which

$$2 \sin \phi - 1 = 0 \quad \text{and} \quad \sin \phi = \tfrac{1}{2} \tag{31}$$

or

$$\sin \phi - 1 = 0 \quad \text{and} \quad \sin \phi = 1. \tag{32}$$

Inspecting (31) and (32), many solutions for ϕ are possible; we will choose here to accept only solutions for $0° \leqq \phi < 360°$, so that from (31),

$$\phi = 30°, 150°,$$

and from (32),

$$\phi = 90°.$$

A note of caution is interjected here. Not all of the answers found in Example 5 need be solutions of (27). We may check the validity of the answers by substituting $\phi = 30°$, $90°$, $150°$ into (27) to determine whether or not they satisfy (27). Upon substituting, we observe that only $\phi = 30°$, $150°$ are satisfactory, and that $\phi = 90°$ fails and is therefore not acceptable. This is a case of an extraneous root.

In equation (30), we might choose to substitute for $\sin \phi$ by making some choice such as $x = \sin \phi$, so that (30) may be written as

$$2x^2 - 3x + 1 = 0,$$

from which

$$x = \sin \phi = \tfrac{1}{2}, 1.$$

This substitution is useful if working with trigonometric functions is confusing or complicated.

EXAMPLE 6. Given the right triangle ABC in Fig. 16-8, find ϕ if

$$\sin \phi + \cos \phi = \frac{\sqrt{5}}{2}. \tag{33}$$

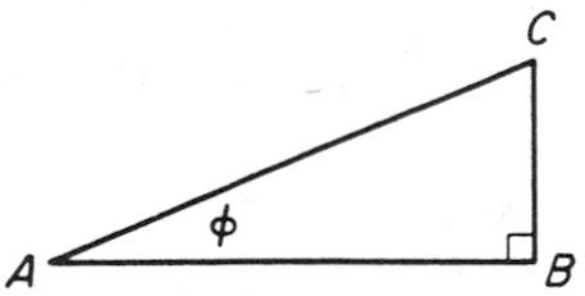

FIGURE 16–8

Solution 1. We cannot choose a single identity from our tables of identities that will enable us to convert directly to an expression in only one trigonometric function. However, if we square both sides of (33), we have

$$\sin^2 \phi + 2 \sin \phi \cos \phi + \cos^2 \phi = \tfrac{5}{4},$$

but

$$\sin^2 \phi + \cos^2 \phi = 1,$$

so that we now have

$$2 \sin \phi \cos \phi + 1 = \tfrac{5}{4}$$

or

$$2 \sin \phi \cos \phi = \tfrac{1}{4}. \tag{34}$$

From form 9, Table 16-2,

$$2 \sin \phi \cos \phi = \sin 2\phi,$$

and (34) becomes

$$\sin 2\phi = \tfrac{1}{4},$$

from which

$$2\phi = 14.5°, \ 165.5°$$

and

$$\phi = 7.25°, \ 82.75°.$$

Solution 2. From Exercise 9 following Sec. 16-3, we have

$$\sin \phi + \cos \phi = \sqrt{2} \sin (\phi + 45°). \tag{35}$$

Comparing (35) and (33),

$$\sqrt{2} \sin (\phi + 45°) = \frac{\sqrt{5}}{2},$$

from which

$$\sin (\phi + 45°) = \frac{\sqrt{5}}{2\sqrt{2}} = \frac{\sqrt{10}}{4} = 0.790$$

and

$$\phi + 45° = 52.25°, \ 127.75°$$

or

$$\phi = 7.25°, 82.75°.$$

Occasionally equations arise that present a mixture of trigonometric expressions with algebraic or logarithmic or exponential expressions. In these cases, solution of the equation usually depends upon graphical or approximate methods. Graphical methods provide accuracy to a degree dependent upon the care and scale used. Approximate methods that may be used are similar to those applied to polynomial equations in Chap. 8.

EXAMPLE 7. Solve for x if

$$x = \tan x \tag{36}$$

where x is given in radians.

Graphical Solution. We choose to graph on the same plane the equations

$$y_1 = x \qquad y_2 = \tan x,$$

where the graphs are shown in Fig. 16-9. Inspection of the graphs shows that where $y_1 = y_2$, there we have also $x = \tan x$ and we have a solution.

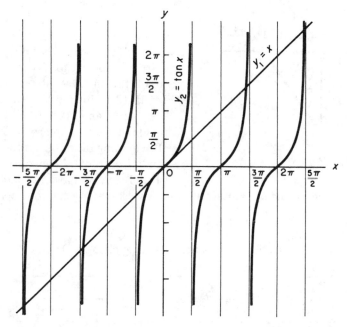

FIGURE 16–9

The graph suggests that there is an infinite number of solutions, where each intersection of the straight line and tangent curve constitutes a solution. Let us now refine one of the solutions to the nearest hundredth; we will choose the solution that is nearest $x = 3\pi/2 = 4.71$ radians.

Solution by the Method of Linear Interpolation. Restating the problem, we wish to find the solution, to the nearest hundredth, of

$$x = \tan x,$$

where the particular solution chosen is at approximately $x = 4.6$. First, we let

$$y = -x + \tan x,$$

from which $x = \tan x$ when $y = 0$. Consider a chart of values of y for values of x chosen near $x = 4.6$ radians; from this chart of values we observe that

x (radians)	4.7	4.6	4.5	4.4
$\tan x$	80.6	8.87	4.71	3.10
y	+75.9	+4.27	+0.21	−1.3

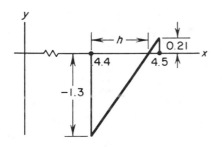

FIGURE 16–10

there seems to be a root for $4.4 < x < 4.5$ because of the change in the sign of y as x increases from 4.4 to 4.5. Further, it seems that the root in question appears to favor the 4.5 end of the interval. Refer now to Fig. 16-10, which plots the points (4.5, 0.21) and (4.4, −1.3) and provides a basis for interpolation.

By equating ratios of certain corresponding parts of the similar triangles in Fig. 16-10, we have $h \approx 0.08$. We now create a new chart of values, with the new estimate of the root being

$$4.4 + h = 4.4 + 0.08 = 4.48.$$

From the chart we see a sign change in y as x changes from $x = 4.49$ to

x (radians)	4.48	4.49	4.50
$\tan x$	4.225	4.425	4.637
y	−0.255	−0.065	+0.137

$x = 4.50$. Careful inspection shows that the root probably favors the 4.49 end of the interval, with the desired solution now $x = 4.49$.

In summary, we suggest that approximate solutions be obtained by first graphing the equation to get an approximation, then applying the method of linear interpolation.

Exercises

In Exercises 1–10 solve for the angle. In all cases an infinite number of solutions is possible; list only those for which the angle is between 0° and 360°.

1. $3 \cos^2 \phi - 2 \cos \phi - 1 = 0$.   *Ans.* $\phi = 0°$; $109.5°$; $250.5°$.

2. $2 \cos^2 \phi - 3 \cos \phi + 1 = 0$.

3. $2 \sin^2 \alpha + 5 \sin \alpha + 2 = 0$.   *Ans.* $\alpha = 210°$; $330°$.

4. $5 \sin^2 \alpha + 4 \sin \alpha - 1 = 0$.

5. $4 \tan^2 \tau + 4 \tan \tau + 1 = 0$.   *Ans.* $\tau = 153.4°$; $333.4°$.

6. $\tan^2 \tau - 3 \tan \tau - 4 = 0$.

7. $\sin^3 \beta + 2 \sin^2 \beta - \sin \beta = 2$.   *Ans.* $\beta = 90°$; $270°$.

8. $\cos^3 \beta + 3 \cos^2 \beta - \cos \beta - 3 = 0$.

9. $4 \sin^2 3\theta - 1 = 0$.   *Ans.* $\theta = 10°$; $50°$; $70°$; $110°$.

10. $\tan^2 5\theta - 1 = 0$.

11. Explain why the expressions given have no valid or real solutions.
(a) $\sin^2 \phi + 2 \sin \phi - 8 = 0$.   *Ans.* $|\sin \phi| \leq 1$ for a valid solution.
(b) $\sin^2 \phi + 2 \sin \phi + 8 = 0$.
(c) $\sin^3 \phi - 8 = 0$.

12. For what two values of α $(0° \leq \alpha \leq 180°)$ does $\sin \alpha$ exceed $\cos \alpha$ by unity?

13. For what range of values of k in

$$\sin \alpha = k + \cos \alpha$$

is $\sin \alpha$ or $\cos \alpha$ imaginary?   *Ans.* $k^2 > 2$.

In Exercises 14–19, obtain the solutions of the given equations graphically. Use the method of linear interpolation to obtain the root shown as an answer; where no answer is shown, find the least positive answer.

14. $\tan x = -x$.

15. $\sin x = 2x$.   *Ans.* $x = 0$.

16. $\cos x = -\frac{1}{3}x$.

17. $\sin x = e^{-x}$.   *Ans.* $x = 0.55$.

18. $\tan x = e^{x}$.

19. $\tan x = 1/x$.   *Ans.* $x = 0.86$.

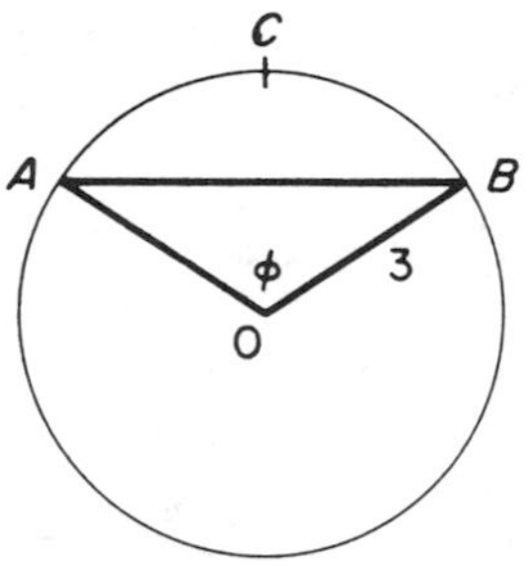

20. In Fig. 16-11 we are given a circle of radius 3 with a chord AB. What central angle ϕ will intercept an arc ACB such that the sum of the lengths of chord AB and arc ACB equals one radius?   *Ans.* $\phi = 0.51$ radians.

21. A cable that sags, owing to its own weight only, is in the shape of a catenary whose equation may be expressed as

$$y = \frac{e^{x} - e^{-x}}{2}.$$

FIGURE 16–11

For what value of x does $y = 2.1$?   *Ans.* $x = 1.49$.

22. The circular segment shown in Fig. 16-12(a) has a moment of inertia I_y about the y-axis expressed by the equation

$$I_y = \frac{r^4}{4}(\alpha + \sin \alpha \cos \alpha).$$

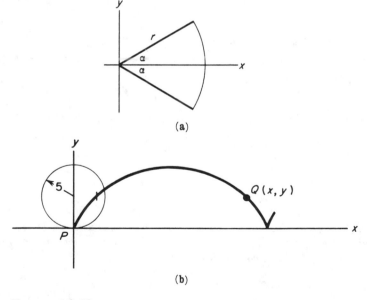

(a)

(b)

FIGURE 16–12

Find α for a sector that is such that $r = 4$ and $I_y = 101$.   *Ans.* $\alpha = 1.52$.

23. A curve traced by a point on the circumference of a circle that rolls along a fixed straight line without slipping is called a *cycloid*. The equation of the cycloid shown in Fig. 16-12(b) is given as

$$x = 5(\phi - \sin \phi), \qquad y = 5(1 - \cos \phi),$$

where x is the x-coordinate of the general point Q, y is the y-coordinate of Q, and ϕ is the angle through which the circle has turned. Find y and ϕ when $x = 2$.
    Ans. $\phi = 1\cdot38$; $y = 4.05$.

24. An equation describing an oscillating wave of decreasing amplitude may be given as

$$y = e^{-x} \sin x.$$

When $y = 0.274$, x has a value such that $0.25 < x < 0.50$. Find x to the nearest hundredth.   *Ans.* $x = 0.43$.

16-5   Inverse Trigonometric Functions

In previous chapters we have made reference to such expressions as $y = x^2$, $y = e^x$, and $y = \sin x$. Each of these expressions is explicit, with the dependent variable being y; each may be solved for x, giving $x = \sqrt{y}$, $x = \ln y$, and $x = \text{arc sin } y$, respectively. Our interest here is focused on the last expression; if $y = \sin x$, then $x = \text{arc sin } y$ where the latter is read "x is an angle whose sine is y."

Suppose we are asked the question: "Given $\sin x = \frac{1}{2}$, what is the value of x?" Our first impulse is to respond that $x = 30°$. It is granted that $x = 30°$ is *one* angle whose sine is $\frac{1}{2}$, but there are many others, such as $150°$, $30° \pm 360°$, $150° \pm 360°$, $30° \pm (2)(360°)$, $150° \pm (2)(360°)$, and any angle that differs from $30°$ or $150°$ by an integral multiple of $360°$. Hence, in more compact form, we may say that when $\sin x = \frac{1}{2}$, then

$$x = 30° \pm n(360°)$$

and

$$x = 150° \pm n(360°),$$

where n is an integer. This fact is shown graphically in Fig. 16-13 where $y = \sin x$ and $y = \frac{1}{2}$ are graphed; the intersections of $y = \frac{1}{2}$ and $y = \sin x$ show some of the values of x for which $\sin x = \frac{1}{2}$.

We call $x = \text{arc sin } y$ the *inverse function* of $y = \sin x$ within the framework of certain restrictions. Those restrictions are concerned with the fact

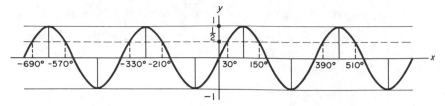

FIGURE 16–13

that $y = \sin x$ is a single-valued function for a given value of x, but $x = $ arc sin y is not single-valued for a given value of y. As a matter of practice here we will set aside these restrictions and accept as solutions of $x = $ arc sin y those values of x such that $0° \leqq x \leqq 360°$.

EXAMPLE 8. Find ϕ if $\phi = $ arc tan 1.

Solution. The given statement asks us to "find the angles (for $0° \leqq \phi \leqq 360°$) that are such that tan $\phi = 1$." From our knowledge of the tangent variation, we have the solutions $\phi = 45°, 225°$.

EXAMPLE 9. Find the value of cos (arc sin 1).

Solution. Starting inside the parentheses,

$$\text{arc sin } 1 = 90°,$$

so that

$$\cos (\text{arc sin } 1) = \cos (90°) = 0.$$

EXAMPLE 10. If $\theta = $ arc sec a/b, find tan θ in terms of a and b.

Solution. By definition,

$$\sec \theta = \frac{a}{b} = \frac{\text{hypotenuse}}{\text{horizontal component}}.$$

Now, from Fig. 16-14, we place a on the hypotenuse and b on the horizontal leg, requiring that the remaining leg be $\sqrt{a^2 - b^2}$. Resorting to the definition of the tangent function,

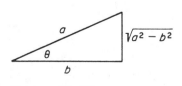

FIGURE 16–14

$$\tan \theta = \frac{\sqrt{a^2 - b^2}}{b}.$$

Exercises

In Exercises 1–10, find the values of the angle ϕ, where ϕ is between 0° and 360°, which are solutions of the given inverse functions.

1. $\phi = \text{arc sin } (\sqrt{3}/2)$. *Ans.* 60°, 120°.

2. $\phi = \text{arc cos } \frac{1}{2}$.

3. $\phi = \text{arc tan } (-1)$. *Ans.* 135°, 315°.

4. $\phi = \text{arc csc } (2/\sqrt{2})$.

5. $\phi = \text{arc sec } (-2/\sqrt{3})$. *Ans.* 150°, 210°.

6. $\phi = \text{arc ctn } 1$.

7. $3\phi = \text{arc cos } 0.93358$. *Ans.* 7°, 113°.

8. $5\phi = \text{arc ctn } (-3)$.

9. $\phi = 30° + 3 \text{ arc tan } 1$. *Ans.* 165°.

10. $\phi = 50° + \frac{i}{2} \text{ arc sin } (-1)$.

11. Find the value of x that satisfies the equation

$$\text{arc tan } x = \text{arc cos } 2x.$$

Ans. $x = 0.455$.

12. Find the value of

(*a*) $\sin (\text{arc sin } 1)$. *Ans.* 1.

(*b*) $\sec (\text{arc cos } 0.5)$.

(*c*) $\tan (\text{arc sin } 0.8660)$. *Ans.* ± 1.732.

(*d*) $\text{ctn} (\text{arc sec } 2)$.

13. Given that $y_1 = \text{arc sin } k$, $y_2 = \text{arc cos } 2k$, show that y_1 and y_2 are related by the equation

$$2 \sin y_1 = \cos y_2.$$

Additional Exercises

1. A vertical pole PE, shown in Fig. 16-15, is supported by four guy wires. The pole is sunk into terrain that slopes at 15°. Find the lengths of the wires PA, PB, PC, and PD if A, B, C, and D are located 20, 40, 20, and 30 feet respectively from E and the pole PE is 50 feet high.

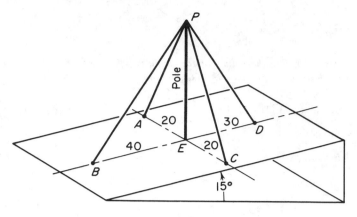

FIGURE 16–15

2. Figure 16-16 shows a rough sketch of a speedometer dial. Lay out calibrations along a 12-inch scale, *AB*, showing markings for 0, 10, 20, 30, $\cdots$, 120 mph. Assume that the speedometer needle will sweep through an angle *AOB* where $\angle AOB = 120°$.

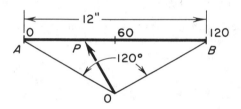

FIGURE 16–16

3. A piston rod *AB* is connected to the rim of a wheel of radius one foot as shown in Fig. 16-17. The wheel rotates at 60 rps and the rod is 4 feet long. Show that the displacement *x* of the piston (point *B*) from the center of the wheel at

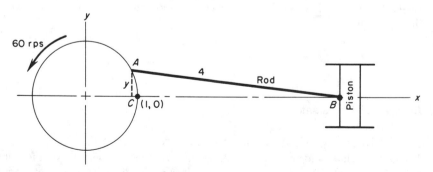

FIGURE 16–17

any time, t, is

$$x = \sqrt{16 - \sin^2 120\pi t} + \cos 120\pi t,$$

assuming that $t = 0$ when A is at $(1, 0)$. Find x when $t = \frac{1}{720}$ sec.

Ans. $x = (\sqrt{63} + \sqrt{3})/2.$

4. A one-inch ball is inserted into a V-shaped slot as shown in Fig. 16-18. What is the radius x of another ball which will touch the smaller ball and the sides of the slot if the slot angle is $30°$? *Ans.* $x = 1.70$ in.

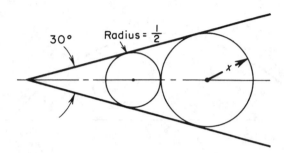

30°   Radius = $\frac{1}{2}$

FIGURE 16–18

5. A gunner at A in Fig. 16-19 fires at an aircraft moving at 500 ft./sec. which is 500 yards away at the closest point B. If the gunner has a weapon which fires at 2700 ft./sec. and he fires when the aircraft is at the closest point, by how far will he miss the point on the plane at which he aims? *Ans.* Approx. 33 in.

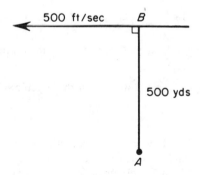

500 ft/sec B

500 yds

A

FIGURE 16–19

6. Given $i = I_{max} \sin (2\pi ft + \phi)$. Find t if $I_{max} = 120$, $i = 100$, $f = 60$, and $\phi = 30°$.

7. A ball thrown from the ground with initial velocity v_0 at an angle ϕ with the ground (see Fig. 16-20) travels a path according to the equation

$$y = x \tan \phi - \frac{16x^2}{v_0^2} \sec^2 \phi,$$

where y and x are the vertical and horizontal displacements, respectively, of the ball from the launch point. At what two angles can the ball be thrown if it is released at initial velocity 100 ft./sec. and strikes the earth 200 ft. from the point of launch? *Ans.* Approx. 20° and 70°.

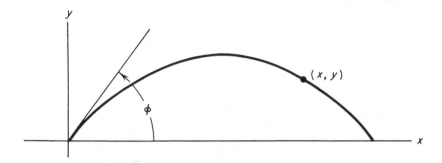

FIGURE 16-20

8. An automobile travels along a level surface at 60 mph. A point P is located on a wheel of the vehicle 10 in. from the center of the wheel. If P is directly below the axle when $t = 0$ sec., how fast is the point moving upward when $t = 3$ sec.?

9. Given the equation

$$45 \sin \phi = 4 + 180\left(\phi - \frac{\pi}{6}\right)$$

find, by approximate methods, the value of ϕ that satisfies the equation.
Ans. $\phi = 37.4°$.

10. From the expression $y = \sin \phi$ we obtain the differential

$$dy = \sin \phi \, d\phi,$$

where $d\phi$ is a change in ϕ and dy is an approximation of the corresponding change in y when $d\phi$ is small. Find dy when $\phi = 30°$ and $d\phi = 1°$. Compare the value of $y + dy$ to the value of $\sin 31°$ obtained in a table of values of trigonometric functions. *Ans.* $dy = 0.00872$; $y + dy = 0.50872$.

11. Give all of the real roots of the equation

$$\tan^3 \phi - 4 \tan^2 \phi - 3 \tan \phi + 1 = 0,$$

where $0° < \phi < 360°$. *Ans.* $\phi = 14°13'$; $77°45'$; $139°23'$.

In this chapter the binomial expansion and certain progressions are introduced. The binomial expansion is useful in such areas as statistics, probability, finance, and calculus. Progressions have a large variety of applications in finance, mechanics, number studies, and other areas. Considerations of progressions are readily expanded into series studies where series are important in approximate solutions, differential equations, wave analysis, and so forth.

BINOMIAL EXPANSION
AND PROGRESSIONS 17

17-1   Binomial Expansions—the General Term

Given the binomial $a + b$, we may choose to raise the binomial to a variety of powers. These powers may have integral, fractional, positive, or negative exponents in the more common applications of the binomial expansion. The first consideration here will involve positive integral (and zero) values of the exponents. A few expansions are listed here:

$$
\begin{aligned}
(a + b)^0 &= 1, \\
(a + b)^1 &= a + b, \\
(a + b)^2 &= a^2 + 2ab + b^2, \\
(a + b)^3 &= a^3 + 3a^2b + 3ab^2 + b^3, \\
(a + b)^4 &= a^4 + 4a^3b + 6a^2b^2 + 4ab^3 + b^4.
\end{aligned}
\tag{1}
$$

The coefficients of the expansions in (1) may be arranged in *Pascal's triangle* where any number in the triangle may be obtained by adding the nearest two numbers above it.

$$
\begin{array}{ccccccccccc}
 & & & & & 1 & & & & & \\
 & & & & 1 & & 1 & & & & \\
 & & & 1 & & 2 & & 1 & & & \\
 & & 1 & & 3 & & 3 & & 1 & & \\
 & 1 & & 4 & & 6 & & 4 & & 1 & \\
1 & & 5 & & 10 & & 10 & & 5 & & 1
\end{array}
$$

Pascal's triangle may be used as method of determining the coefficients of the expansion of a binomial. However, a superior method is through the general expansion of the binomial, which is given here without proof:

$$
(a + b)^n = a^n + na^{n-1}b + \frac{n(n - 1)a^{n-2}b^2}{2!}
$$
$$
+ \frac{n(n - 1)(n - 2)a^{n-3}b^3}{3!} + \cdots .
\tag{2}
$$

In (2), n can be a variety of number types, including negative and positive integers, fractions, and zero. The symbol (!) in (2) may be unfamiliar. We define $k!$ (k factorial) as the product of all of the positive integers from 1 through k, or

$$
k! = 1 \cdot 2 \cdot 3 \cdot 4 \cdot \,\cdots\, \cdot k.
$$

We also make the definition $0! = 1$.

EXAMPLE 1. Using (2), expand the expression

$$\left(x^2 - \frac{2}{x}\right)^4. \tag{3}$$

Solution. Comparing (3) to the left member of (2), we have $a = x^2$, $b = -2/x$, and $n = 4$. Substituting these into the right member of (2), we have

$$\left(x^2 - \frac{2}{x}\right)^4 = (x^2)^4 + 4(x^2)^3\left(-\frac{2}{x}\right) + \frac{(4)(3)(x^2)^2}{2!}\left(-\frac{2}{x}\right)^2$$

$$+ \frac{(4)(3)(2)(x^2)^1}{3!}\left(-\frac{2}{x}\right)^3 + \frac{(4)(3)(2)(1)(x^2)^0}{4!}\left(-\frac{2}{x}\right)^4,$$

which simplifies to the expression

$$x^8 - 8x^5 + 24x^2 - \frac{32}{x} + \frac{16}{x^4}.$$

Certain useful observations of the properties of (2) are in order. Some of these observations are seen more readily through expressions (1) and Pascal's triangle; all are made assuming that n is a positive integer:

(a) The expression contains $n + 1$ terms.

(b) The sum of the exponents of a and b in any term is n.

(c) The coefficients are symmetrical; i.e., the coefficients of the first and last terms are the same, the coefficients of the terms numbered 2 from the ends are the same, etc.

(d) The exponent of b agrees with the factorial indicated in the same term.

The general term of (2) may be derived intuitively by numbering the terms of (2) and comparing the term numbers with certain portions of the expression for that term. The observations of the properties of the expansion listed above are also useful in the derivation. Numbering the terms from left to right in (2) as term 1, term 2, term 3, etc., we note that

(a) Term $k + 1$ contains $k!$ in its denominator.

(b) Term $k + 1$ contains an exponent for b equal to k.

(c) Since the sum of the exponents in any term is n, then term $k + 1$ contains an exponent $n - k$, in view of the exponent of b shown in (b).

(d) The factors of the numerator of the coefficient are such that the least factor is one greater than the exponent of a.

From these observations, we may see that *the $(k + 1)$st term of the expansion*

(2) is

$$\frac{n(n-1)(n-2)\cdots(n-k+1)}{k!}a^{n-k}b^k.$$ (4)

EXAMPLE 2. Find the fourth term of the expansion

$$\left(\frac{y}{3}-\frac{6}{y^2}\right)^{13}.$$

Solution. Comparing the given expression to (2) and then referring to (4), we have $n = 13$, $k + 1 = 4$ or $k = 3$, $a = y/3$, and $b = -6/y^2$. Substituting into (4), we have the fourth term of the given expansion as

$$\frac{13\cdot12\cdot11}{3!}\left(\frac{y}{3}\right)^{10}\left(-\frac{6}{y^2}\right)^3 = -\frac{2288}{2187}y^4.$$

Exercises

In Exercises 1–5 show in simplified form all of the terms of the given expansion.

1. $(x^2 - y)^3$.   *Ans.* $x^6 - 3x^4y + 3x^2y^2 - y^3$.

2. $\left(m - \dfrac{1}{n}\right)^5$.

3. $\left(a^2 - \dfrac{2}{b}\right)^4$.   *Ans.* $a^8 - \dfrac{8a^6}{b} + \dfrac{24a^4}{b^2} - \dfrac{32a^2}{b^3} + \dfrac{16}{b^4}$.

4. $(x + \Delta x)^3$.

5. $\left(1 + \dfrac{1}{x}\right)^5$.   *Ans.* $1 + \dfrac{5}{x} + \dfrac{10}{x^2} + \dfrac{10}{x^3} + \dfrac{5}{x^4} + \dfrac{1}{x^5}$.

In Exercises 6–10, give the term requested.

6. Fifth term of $\left(\dfrac{3}{x} - y^2\right)^7$.

7. Fourth term of $\left(\dfrac{2}{y} + \dfrac{y}{4}\right)^8$.   *Ans.* $\dfrac{28}{y^2}$.

8. Seventh term of $\left(3 + \dfrac{m}{2}\right)^6$.

9. Third term of $(x + \Delta x)^5$ *Ans.* $10x^3(\Delta x)^2$.

10. Third term of $\left(m^2 - \dfrac{1}{m^4}\right)^6$.

11. Which term of $[x^2 - (1/x)]^{12}$ contains no x?   *Ans.* Ninth.

12. Which term of $[x^3 + (3/x^2)]^{15}$ contains no x?

13. Which term of $[m - (2/m^3)]^{11}$ contains m^{-9}? *Ans.* Sixth.

14. How many terms are in $(a^2 - b)^{23}$?

15. How many terms are in $(a^2 - b)^{14}$? *Ans.* 15.

16. Evaluate $(1 - \frac{1}{2})^4$ by the binomial expansion.

17. Expand $[(a - b) - (c - d)]^3$ by the binomial expansion.

18. How many terms of $(x + \Delta x)^n$ will contain a power of Δx?

19. Evaluate the expressions $(1 + 1/x)^x$ where $x = 2$, 5, 10. Use the binomial expansion. *Ans.* 2.25, 2.488, 2.594.

17-2   More on the Binomial Expansion—Roots

In Sec. 17-1, discussion of the binomial expansion was restricted to those expansions involving positive integral values of the exponent. In this section we will expand our discussion to include other values of the exponent.

Given expression (2), if n is either a negative integer or a fraction, we assert the following properties to be true:

    (*a*) The number of terms in the expansion is infinite.

    (*b*) The array of coefficients is not symmetrical.

    (*c*) Expression (4) is still valid for the $(k + 1)$ st term.

Let us show an expansion of (2) where n is not a positive integer.

EXAMPLE 3. Show the first four terms of the expansion of

$$\sqrt[3]{x^2 - 9}. \tag{4}$$

Solution. We may write (5) in the power form $(x^2 - 9)^{1/3}$ and compare it to the left member of (2), from which we have $a = x^2$, $b = -9$, and $n = \frac{1}{3}$. Substituting the quantities into the right member of (2), we have

$$(x^2 - 9)^{1/3} = (x^2)^{1/3} + \left(\frac{1}{3}\right)(x^2)^{-2/3}(-9) + \frac{(\frac{1}{3})(-\frac{2}{3})(x^2)^{-5/3}}{2!}(-9)^2$$

$$+ \frac{(\frac{1}{3})(-\frac{2}{3})(-\frac{5}{3})}{3!}(x^2)^{-8/3}(-9)^3 + \cdots,$$

where the right-hand member simplifies to

$$x^{2/3} - 3x^{-4/3} - 9x^{-10/3} - 45x^{-16/3} - \cdots. \tag{6}$$

It is observed that the binomial expansion may be used to compute roots.

In Example 3, with x assigned a numerical value, (6) may be used to obtain the cube root of $x^2 - 9$. Other roots can be obtained with any degree of accuracy imposed.

EXAMPLE 4. Evaluate $\sqrt{24}$ correct to thousandths, using the binomial expansion.

Solution. Note that the number 24 may be expressed as the sum or difference of many number pairs; this sum or difference would establish the number 24 as a binomial. Some such binomials include $13 + 11$, $30 - 6$, $25 - 1$, and $16 + 8$. We will select (for reasons that will become apparent when the expansion is displayed) a binomial consisting in part of the perfect square closest to 24, namely 25. (If the problem had requested the *cube* root of 24, we would select as a part of the binomial the perfect *cube* closest to 24.) Now we have

$$\sqrt{24} = (25 - 1)^{1/2} = (25)^{1/2} + \frac{1}{2}(25)^{-1/2}(-1)$$

$$+ \frac{\frac{1}{2}(-\frac{1}{2})}{2!}(25)^{-3/2}(-1)^2 + \frac{\frac{1}{2}(-\frac{1}{2})(-\frac{3}{2})}{3!}(25)^{-5/2}(-1)^3 + \cdots \tag{7}$$

$$= 5 - \frac{1}{10} - \frac{1}{1000} - \frac{1}{50,000} - \cdots$$

$$= 5.00000 - 0.10000 - 0.00100 - 0.00002 - \cdots$$

$$= 4.89898.$$

Since the problem requested accuracy to thousandths, we have the answer $\sqrt{24} = 4.899$. Remarks on the selection of the number of terms to which the binomial is expanded are important here; the number of terms depends upon the rate at which the successive terms are converging on a zero value. In (7), the fourth term is already too small to affect the answer as given to thousandths. The third term might affect the thousandths place through carrying operations or borrowing operations. Convergence, then, is the key to the choice; rate of convergence is determined by the choice of the binomial representing the number 24, namely $25 - 1$. Some other choice such as $49 - 25$ or $-11 + 36$ may converge painfully slowly or may even diverge.

Exercises

In Exercises 1–8 show the first four terms of the expansion of the given binomial.

1. $(x + 1)^{-1}$.   *Ans.* $\dfrac{1}{x} - \dfrac{1}{x^2} + \dfrac{1}{x^3} - \dfrac{1}{x^4} + \cdots$.

2. $(1 + x)^{-1}$.

3. $(4m - n)^{-1/2}$. $\quad\quad\quad$ *Ans.* $\dfrac{m^{-1/2}}{2} + \dfrac{m^{-3/2}n}{16} + \dfrac{3m^{-5/2}n^2}{256} + \dfrac{5m^{-7/2}n^2}{2048} + \cdots$

4. $\left(1 + \dfrac{i}{n}\right)^{nt}$.

5. $(x + \Delta x)^n$. $\quad\quad\quad$ *Ans.* $x^n + nx^{n-1}(\Delta x) + \dfrac{n(n-1)x^{n-2}}{2!}(\Delta x)^2$

$$+ \dfrac{n(n-1)(n-2)}{3!}x^{n-3}(\Delta x)^3 + \cdots$$

6. $(x^2 - \tfrac{1}{2})^{1/2}$.

7. $(4 + 3x)^{1/2}$. $\quad\quad\quad$ *Ans.* $2 + \dfrac{3x}{4} - \dfrac{9x^2}{64} + \dfrac{27x^3}{512}$

8. $(y^2 - 2)^{-1/2}$.

9. The number e is defined as

$$e = \lim_{x \to \infty} \left(1 + \frac{1}{x}\right)^x = 2.718\cdots.$$

Evaluate the binomial involved with $x = 100$ and $x = 1000$. Use only the first six terms of the expansions.

10. Evaluate $(1.05)^{-4}$ for the first five terms of the expansion. Next, evaluate $(1.05)^4$. Reciprocate the latter result and compare it to the former.

In Exercises 11–12 evaluate the given expression by the binomial expansion, correct to the nearest thousandth.

11. $\sqrt{37}$. $\quad\quad\quad\quad\quad\quad\quad\quad\quad\quad\quad\quad\quad$ *Ans.* 6.083.

12. $\sqrt{15}$.

13. $\sqrt{47}$. $\quad\quad\quad\quad\quad\quad\quad\quad\quad\quad\quad\quad\quad$ *Ans.* 6.856.

14. $\sqrt{80}$.

15. $\sqrt{120}$. $\quad\quad\quad\quad\quad\quad\quad\quad\quad\quad\quad\quad$ *Ans.* 10.955.

16. $\sqrt[3]{7}$.

17. $\sqrt{\tfrac{1}{10}}$. $\quad\quad\quad\quad\quad\quad\quad\quad\quad\quad\quad\quad\quad$ *Ans.* 0.316.

18. $\sqrt[3]{120}$.

19. $(10)^{3/2}$. $\quad\quad\quad\quad\quad\quad\quad\quad\quad\quad\quad\quad$ *Ans.* 31.623.

20. $(27)^{-3/2}$.

21. $(50)^{-3/2}$. $\quad\quad\quad\quad\quad\quad\quad\quad\quad\quad\quad\quad$ *Ans.* 0.003.

22. $(31)^{0.2}$.

17-3   Arithmetic Progressions

A *sequence* is a set of elements that may be arranged according to some order or property. An *arithmetic progression* is a sequence whose consecutive elements differ by a common quantity called the *common difference*. Accordingly, the sequences in (8), (9), and (10) are arithmetic progressions. In (8), (9), and (10), the common differences are

$$4, 6, 8, 10, 12, \cdots \tag{8}$$

$$121, 110, 99, 88, 77, \cdots \tag{9}$$

$$4a + 8b, 5a + 6b, 6a + 4b, 7a + 2b, \cdots \tag{10}$$

$+2$, -11, and $a - 2b$ respectively. The common difference may be obtained by subtracting any term (save the last) in the arithmetic progression from the succeeding term.

Table 17-1

Term Number	Value of Term from Expression (9)	Value of Term in General Arithmetic Progression
1	121	a
2	$121 + 1(-11)$	$a + d$
3	$121 + 2(-11)$	$a + 2d$
4	$121 + 3(-11)$	$a + 3d$
.	.	.
.	.	.
.	.	.
n	$121 + (n - 1)(-11)$	$a + (n - 1)d$

Arithmetic progressions provide excellent opportunities for formulation. In Table 17-1 we predict the value of the nth (general) term of expression (9). We see that the first term is 121, the second term is 121 plus *one* common difference, the third term is 121 plus *two* common differences, and so forth to the nth term which is 121 plus $n - 1$ common differences. In the right column of Table 17-1 we see the intuitive development of the formula for the nth term of the general arithmetic progression,

$$l = a + (n - 1)d, \tag{11}$$

where l is the value of the nth term, a is the value of the first term, and d is the common difference.

EXAMPLE 5. Give the value of the twenty-first term of the A.P.

$$91, 85, 79, 73, 67, \cdots.$$

Solution. By inspection, the common difference is -6 and the first term is 91. Referring to (11), we have $n = 21$, $a = 91$, and $d = -6$. Substituting,

$$l = a + (n - 1)d = 91 + (21 - 1)(-6) = 91 - 120 = -29.$$

If we indicate the sum of the separate terms of a sequence, we have a *series*. It is often useful to obtain the sum of n terms of an arithmetic progression. We may obtain the sum by inspection and, by the same inspection method, discover a means of formulating a general expression for the sum. Let us consider the sum of the first 24 terms of the A.P.

$$64, 59, 54, 49, 44, \cdots. \tag{12}$$

First, we obtain the twenty-fourth term of (12) by applying (11):

$$l = 64 + (23)(-5) = 64 - 115 = -51.$$

Listing the first three and the last three terms of (12), we have

$$64, 59, 54, \cdots, -41, -46, -51. \tag{13}$$

We now note from (13) that the sum of the first and last terms is $+13$. The sum of the terms numbered two from each end is $+13$, the sum of the terms numbered three from each end is $+13$, etc. Since there are 24 terms, there are 12 such pairs, each of value $+13$, or the sum of the first 24 terms of (12) is

$$S = 12(+13) = 156.$$

At this point we may generalize. The sum S of an arithmetic series is written here in two ways; in these two ways the terms are simply reversed. Adding expressions (14) and (15) produces the sum (16).

$$S = a + a + d + a + 2d + \cdots + l - 2d + l - d + l \tag{14}$$

$$S = l + l - d + l - 2d + \cdots + a + 2d + a + d + a \tag{15}$$

$$2S = (a + l) + (a + l) + (a + l) + \cdots + (a + l)$$

$$+ (a + l) + (a + l) \tag{16}$$

Assuming that there are n terms in each (14) and (15), then there are n terms in (16) each of value $a + l$, so that (16) may be written as

$$2S = n(a + l)$$

or

$$S = \frac{n}{2}(a + l) \tag{17}$$

where S is the sum of n terms of an A.P. whose first term is a and whose nth term is l. Here $n/2$ is the number of pairs of terms and $a + l$ is the value of the sum of the first and nth terms.

EXAMPLE 6. Find the sum of the first 33 terms of the A.P.

$$-105, -98, -91, -84, \cdots.$$

Solution. First, we find the value of the thirty-third term by (11):

$$l = -105 + (33 - 1)(+7) = -105 + 224 = +119.$$

Now apply (17) with $n = 33$, $a = -105$, and $l = 119$, so that

$$S = \tfrac{33}{2}(-105 + 119) = \tfrac{33}{2}(14) = 231.$$

In Example 6 some work could have been eliminated if expressions (11) and (17) had previously been combined in such a way that l was eliminated. If we substitute (11) into (17), we have another expression for the sum of n terms of an A.P., namely

$$S = \frac{n}{2}[a + a + (n - 1)d] = \frac{n}{2}[2a + (n - 1)d]. \tag{18}$$

EXAMPLE 7. A man takes a job at an annual salary of \$4800. At the end of each year he is given a raise of \$240. What will be his total earnings for his first 10 years on the job?

Solution. This will be an A.P. with terms

$$4800, 5040, 5280, 5520, \cdots,$$

where $a = 4800$, $n = 10$, and $d = 240$. Applying (18) to find the total earnings, we have

$$S = \tfrac{10}{2}[2(4800) + (10 - 1)(240)] = \$58,800.$$

Exercises

In Exercises 1–6 find the value of the term indicated.

1. Twentieth term of 3, 5, 7, 9, $\cdots$.   *Ans.* 41.

2. Fifty-fifth term of 4, 6, 8, 10, $\cdots$.

3. Seventeenth term of 68, 56, 44, 32, $\cdots$.   *Ans.* −124.

4. Twenty-fourth term of 82, 66, 50, 34, $\cdots$.

5. Fourteenth term of $5m + 8n$, $6m + 6n$, $7m + 4n$, $\cdots$,   *Ans.* $18m − 18n$.

6. Fifteenth term of $12a − 21b$, $9a − 18b$, $6a − 15b$, $\cdots$.

7. Thirty-third term of $−73$, $−66$, $−59$, $−52$.   *Ans.* 151.

8. Fifteenth term of $−17$, $−25$, $−33$, $−41$.

9. Twenty-first term of $−15a + 24$, $−17a + 19$, $−19a + 14$.

Ans. $−55a − 76$.

10. Thirteenth term of $−36 − 7x$, $−30 − 11x$, $−24 − 15x$.

11. Thirty-first term of $−12x^2 + 40$, $−9x^2 + 32$, $−6x^2 + 24$.

Ans. $78x^2 − 200$.

12. Twenty-sixth term of $\dfrac{24}{a} + 13a$, $\dfrac{19}{a} + 19a$, $\dfrac{14}{a} + 25a$.

In Exercises 13–18 provide values for the missing items. In each case assume that the given information is appropriate for an arithmetic progression.

	S	n	a	l	d	
13.		6	−12	13		*Ans.* $S = 3$, $d = 5$.
14.		13	27		−3	
15.	3612		50		32	*Ans.* $n = 14$, $l = 466$.
16.	6750	15		−900		
17.	0		360		9	*Ans.* $n = 81$, $a = −360$.
18.		46		91	5	

19. Show that the sum of the first n terms of an A.P. is zero if the first and last terms are equal but opposite in sign.

20. The initial taxable value of a machine is $8000. Each year the taxable value depreciates by $1200. A tax of 5 per cent of the current value of the machine is charged at the end of each year. What total taxes are paid in the first 5 years of the life of the machine?

21. An automobile steadily uses more gasoline per mile owing to wear, dirt, etc. During each 500 miles driven, the automobile uses one more pint of gasoline than it did during the previous 500 miles. The automobile averaged 20 miles per gallon during its first 500 miles. What is its gasoline consumption (in miles per gallon) during the period when its distance travelled is between 8500 and 9000 miles? *Ans.* 18.43 mpg.

22. A salaried employee earns $5200 during his first year of employment. At the end of each year he receives a raise of $250. What is his salary during his tenth year of employment? What are his total earnings during his first eight years of employment? During which year of his employment does he earn $7450 as his year's salary?

23. A spherical balloon is inflated. During each second its radius expands by an amount equal to 0.01 inches less than the radius expanded during the previous second. If the radius R expands at the rate of 0.35 in. per sec. when $R = 18$ in., what is R exactly 30 sec. later? *Ans.* 24.15 in.

24. Given the sequence

$$-24, -19, -21, -16, -18, -13, -15, -10, -12, \cdots,$$

which combines two arithmetic progressions. What is the fortieth term of the combined progression? What is the sum of the first 40 terms of the combined progression?

25. It is known that the terms a, ab, b form an A.P. Show that the fourth term may be $3ab - 2a$.

26. A free-falling body falls in such a way that its velocity increases by 32 ft./sec. each sec. Assume that a free-falling body has an initial velocity of 120 ft./sec. What is its velocity at the end of 9 sec.?

27. Show that the terms $a, a + b, b$ are in an A.P. only if $a = -b$.

17-4   Geometric Progressions

A *geometric progression* is a sequence in which successive terms are related by a common ratio. The common ratio is determined by dividing any term (after the first) by the preceding term. Examples of a G.P. are shown in (19), (20), and (21) where the ratios are $\frac{1}{2}$, -1, and $3m$ respectively.

$$16, 8, 4, 2, 1, \tfrac{1}{2}, \tfrac{1}{4}, \cdots \tag{19}$$

$$1, -1, 1, -1, 1, -1, \cdots \tag{20}$$

$$2m, 6m^2, 18m^3, 54m^4, 162m^5, \cdots \tag{21}$$

Table 17-2 shows an intuitive development of the value of the nth term of (19) and the general geometric progression. From the table we observe that

$$l = ar^{n-1}, \tag{22}$$

where l is the value of the nth term of the G.P., a is the first term, and r is the common ratio.

Table 17-2

Term Number	Value of Term From Expression (19)	Value of Term in General Geometric Progression
1	16	a
2	$16(\frac{1}{2})$	ar
3	$16(\frac{1}{2})^2$	ar^2
4	$16(\frac{1}{2})^3$	ar^3
.	.	.
.	.	.
.	.	.
n	$16(\frac{1}{2})^{n-1}$	ar^{n-1}

EXAMPLE 8. Give the value of the ninth term of the G.P.

$$243, -81, 27, -9, \cdots. \tag{23}$$

Solution. Observe that (23) is a G.P. with first term $a = 243$ and common ratio $r = -\frac{1}{3}$. Since we wish to find the value of the ninth term, then $n = 9$. Substituting these values into (22),

$$l = 243\left(-\tfrac{1}{3}\right)^{9-1} = 243\left(-\tfrac{1}{3}\right)^8 = \tfrac{1}{27}.$$

To find the sum of the first n terms of a G.P., we have

$$S = a + ar + ar^2 + ar^3 + \cdots + ar^{n-1}. \tag{24}$$

The right member of (24) is expressible as the quotient of two quantities, namely

$$\frac{a(1 - r^n)}{1 - r} = a + ar + ar^2 + ar^3 + \cdots + ar^{n-1}. \tag{25}$$

Now, from (24) and (25), we have

$$S = \frac{a(1 - r^n)}{1 - r} \quad (r \neq 1) \tag{26}$$

where S is the sum of the first n terms of a G.P. with common ratio r and first term a.

EXAMPLE 9. Find the sum of the first ten terms of the G.P.

$$20, 10, 5, \tfrac{5}{2}, \cdots. \tag{27}$$

Solution. By inspection we have first term $a = 20$, common ratio $r = \tfrac{1}{2}$ and $n = 10$. Substituting into (24), we have

$$S = \frac{20[1 - (\tfrac{1}{2})^{10}]}{1 - \tfrac{1}{2}} = \frac{20[1 - \tfrac{1}{1024}]}{\tfrac{1}{2}} = 40\left(\frac{1023}{1024}\right).$$

A graphical representation of (27) is interesting. It is shown in Fig. 17-1 where $S_1, S_2, S_3, \cdots$ are the sums of $1, 2, 3, \cdots$ terms of (27) respectively. The terms S_8, S_9, S_{10} appear to contribute very little to the value of S. It seems, too, that as n increases without bound, S approaches the value $S = 40$.

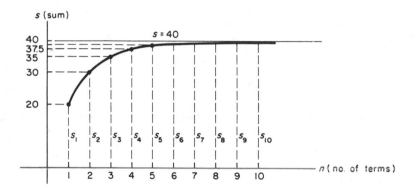

FIGURE 17-1

Example 9 might illustrate the case of a man leaping toward a wall which is 40 ft. away. With each leap he covers one-half ($r = \tfrac{1}{2}$) of the distance remaining between himself and the wall. His limit is 40 ft.; even with n becoming a very large number, he will never cover the entire 40 ft., but can cover as close to 40 ft. as he pleases.

The sum of all of the terms of a G.P. may be discussed with reference to (28). From

$$S = \frac{a(1 - r^n)}{1 - r}, \tag{28}$$

let n become very large ($n \longrightarrow \infty$). Three cases occur.

Case 1. If $|r| > 1$, then $|r^n| \to \infty$ and the numerator of (28) goes to negative infinity. Thus, we can assert that if $|r| > 1$, the sum of a G.P. cannot be determined.

Case 2. If $r = 1$, then $1 - r = 1 - r^n = 0$ and S is the ratio $0/0$ which cannot be determined. If $r = -1$, then $1 - r = 2$ and $= -r^n$ has either the value $+2$ or 0 with n odd or even, respectively; therefore, S can have the value $+a$ or zero.

Case 3. If $|r| < 1$, then $r^n \to 0$ as $n \to \infty$. Therefore, (28) becomes

$$S = \frac{a}{1 - r} \quad (|r| < 1). \tag{29}$$

where (29) gives the sum of *all* of the terms of a G.P.

EXAMPLE 10. Give the sum of all of the terms of

$$64, \ -16, \ 4, \ -1, \ + \tfrac{1}{4}, \ \cdots.$$

Solution. Here $r = -\tfrac{1}{4}$ and (29) is appropriate because $r < \infty$. Also, $a = 64$. Substituting into (29),

$$S = \frac{64}{1 - (-\tfrac{1}{4})} = \frac{64}{\tfrac{5}{4}} = \frac{256}{5}.$$

Exercises

In Exercises 1–12 find the value of the term indicated for the given geometric progression.

1. Eighth term of $\frac{1}{243}, \frac{1}{81}, \frac{1}{27}, \cdots$.   *Ans.* 9.

2. Tenth term of $128, -64, 32, \cdots$.

3. Fifty-fifth term of $1, -1, 1, -1, \cdots$.   *Ans.* 1.

4. Thirty-sixth term of $m^{44}, m^{42}, m^{40}, \cdots$.

5. Twenty-sixth term of $a^{12}/b^{15}, a^{11}/b^{16}, a^{10}/b^{17}, \cdots$.   *Ans.* a^{-13}/b^{40}.

6. Fifteenth term of $(1 + i)^6, (1 + i)^7, (1 + i)^8, \cdots$.

7. Eleventh term of $64x^5, 32x^4, 16x^3, \cdots$.   *Ans.* $\dfrac{x^{-5}}{16}$

8. Twenty-first term of $\dfrac{x^{10}}{128}, \dfrac{-x^9}{64}, \dfrac{x^8}{32}, \cdots$.

9. Twelfth term of $\dfrac{(1 + x)^{-8}}{128}, \dfrac{(1 + x)^{-7}}{64}, \dfrac{(1 + x)^{-6}}{32}, \cdots$.   *Ans.* $16(1 + x)^3$.

10. Tenth term of $\dfrac{y^{-4}}{243}, \dfrac{-y^{-7/2}}{81}, \dfrac{y^{-3}}{27}, \cdots$.

11. Fifteenth term of $\dfrac{y^7}{(2)^8}, \dfrac{y^{13/2}}{(2)^7}, \dfrac{y^6}{(2)^6}, \cdots$.   *Ans.* 64.

12. Twelfth term of $\dfrac{(1+y)^8}{729}, \dfrac{-(1+y)^7}{243}, \dfrac{(1+y)^6}{81}, \cdots$.

In Exercises 13–18, provide values for the missing terms, assuming that the given information is appropriate for a geometric progression.

	S	n	a	r	l	
13.		8	100	$\frac{1}{10}$		*Ans.* $S = 111.11111$, $l = 10^{-5}$.
14.	$\frac{181}{144}$			$-\frac{3}{4}$	$\frac{9}{16}$	
15.	-1	15	-1			*Ans.* $r = -1$, $l = -1$.
16.	2.222			0.1	0.002	
17.		5	m^{16}		m^8	*Ans.* $S = \dfrac{m^8 - m^{18}}{1 - m^2}$, $r = \dfrac{1}{m^2}$.
18.	$P(1+i)^n$		P	$1+i$		

19. A man earns $1000 during a certain year. In each successive year he doubles his income. What are his earnings during his seventh year? What is his total income during his first seven years?   *Ans.* $64,000; $127,000.

20. A ball bounces in such a way that it always gains a height that is three-fourths of the height gained on the previous bounce. Assume that the ball is dropped from a height of 40 ft. What will be the distance that the ball travels before coming to rest?

21. The assessed value of a machine in a factory declines, for tax purposes, at the rate of 20 per cent per year. A tax of 4 per cent is charged on the assessed value each year. If the machine is initially worth $10,000, how much taxes are paid during the first five years of the life of the machine?

22. A hot metallic body at a temperature of 350°F is placed outdoors to cool, where the temperature outdoors is 70°F. During each five-minute interval, the temperature of the body will fall 60 per cent of the difference between the temperature of the body and the outdoor temperature. Show that the body will cool to approximately 73°F after 25 minutes outdoors.

23. Two vehicles, A and B, are in motion. At a certain instant, $t = 0$, A is travelling at 100 mph and B at 20 mph. Thereafter, A decreases in speed by an amount of 10 per cent per minute of the speed at the beginning of the minute and B gains 15 per cent per minute. When will A and B be travelling at the same speed?
     Ans. After about 6.5 min.

24. Show a graphical solution of Exercise 23. Graph the progress of A and B on the same set of axes. The point where the graphs intersect is the desired solution.

25. A substance goes into solution at the rate of 25 per cent of the undissolved portion each minute. If the initial amount was $\frac{64}{27}$ lb., what amount is undissolved after 6 minutes? *Ans.* $\frac{27}{64}$ lb.

26. A man builds an annuity by depositing \$1000 at the beginning of each year into an account. The account collects interest at 3 per cent annually (compounded). Show that the amount of the annuity after 10 years is

$$A = 1000 \left[\frac{(1.03)^{11} - 1}{0.03} \right] = \$11,464.$$

27. Show that the series

$$\tfrac{1}{10} + (\tfrac{1}{10})^2 + (\tfrac{1}{10})^3 + (\tfrac{1}{10})^4 + \cdots$$

has the same value as the fraction $\frac{1}{9}$.

17-5 Arithmetic and Geometric Means

Assume that we are given two nonconsecutive terms of a progression. The terms that lie between the given terms are called *means*. Means are reasonably simple to find without the aid of a formula; on the other hand, a formula is easily developed. In Example 11 we will solve a specific case of arithmetic means and will develop a formula for the general case.

EXAMPLE 11. Find three arithmetic means between 46 and 18.

Solution. We may list five terms of the A.P. with 46 as the first term, 18 as the fifth term, and blanks provided for the three missing terms:

$$46, \quad , \quad , \quad , 18.$$

Now by inspection we see that, in order to proceed from the first term to the fifth term, we require four common differences, or

$$46 + 4d = 18,$$

from which the common difference is $d = -7$. Now the missing means are

$$46 + \ d = 46 - \ 7 = 39,$$

$$46 + 2d = 46 - 14 = 32,$$

$$46 + 3d = 46 - 21 = 25.$$

We may use Example 11 to generalize. Assume that we wish to find k

arithmetic means between a and b. There will be $k + 1$ common differences accumulated in proceeding from a to b, or

$$a + (k + 1)d = b,$$

from which

$$d = \frac{b - a}{k + 1}, \tag{30}$$

where d is the common difference, a is the first term, b is the last term, and k is the number of means to be provided. Expression (30) is useful for arithmetic progressions.

EXAMPLE 12. Find six arithmetic means between -12 and $+23$.

Solution. Employing (30), we have $k = 6$, $a = -12$, $b = 23$, and

$$d = \frac{23 - (-12)}{6 + 1} = \frac{35}{7} = 5.$$

The common difference is then 5 and the missing means are -7, -2, $+3$, $+8$, $+13$, and $+18$.

Geometric means may be found by a method similar to that used in the solution of Example 11. Consider Example 13.

EXAMPLE 13. Find two geometric means between -2 and $+54$.

Solution. We may list four terms of a G.P. with -2 as the first term, $+54$ as the fourth term, and blanks for the second and third terms:

$$-2, \quad , \quad , +54.$$

By inspection we see that -2 must be multiplied by the common ratio three times to proceed to $+54$, or

$$-2r^3 = 54,$$

from which the common ratio is

$$r = \sqrt[3]{-27} = -3.$$

Now the desired geometric means are

$$-2(-3) = +6, \qquad -2(-3)^2 = -18.$$

Assume that we wish to find k geometric means between a and b. This requires $k + 1$ common ratios, or

$$ar^{k+1} = b,$$

from which

$$r = \sqrt[k+1]{b/a}. \tag{31}$$

Note from (31) that if $k + 1$ is an even number, r may be positive or negative with a and b of the same sign and r is imaginary if a and b are of different signs. If $k + 1$ is odd, r will be of the same sign as the ratio of b/a.

EXAMPLE 14. Find three geometric means between $\frac{1}{16}$ and 16.

Solution. Applying (31), we have $k = 3$, $a = \frac{1}{16}$, and $b = 16$ with

$$r = \sqrt[4]{16/\tfrac{1}{16}} = \sqrt[4]{256} = \pm 4.$$

The means are then either $\frac{1}{4}$, 1, 4 or $-\frac{1}{4}$, 1, -4.

Exercises

Find the means indicated in Exercises 1–9.

1. One arithmetic mean between 4 and -4.   *Ans.* 0.

2. One arithmetic mean between 7 and 15.

3. Three arithmetic means between -6 and 14.   *Ans.* $-1, 4, 9$.

4. Five arithmetic means between 7 and 19.

5. One arithmetic mean between a^2 and a^3.   *Ans.* $(a^3 + a^2)/2$.

6. Two geometric means between 2 and 16.

7. Three geometric means between 6 and $\frac{3}{8}$.   *Ans.* $\pm 3, +\frac{3}{2}, \pm\frac{3}{4}$.

8. Four geometric means between 1 and -1.

9. Four geometric means between 10 and 0.0001.   *Ans.* 1, 0.1, 0.01, 0.001.

10. Show that the imaginary unit j may be defined as the geometric mean between 1 and -1.

11. A machine depreciates in value at the same amount each year. The initial value of the machine is V_0 and the value after n years is V_n. What is its value during the third year? Fifth year? kth year?   *Ans.* $V_k = (k/n)(V_0 - V_n)$.

12. A bouncing ball rebounds on each bounce to a height which is a fixed fractional part of the height achieved on the previous bounce. On the first bounce it reaches

a height of 24 ft.; on the fourth bounce it reaches 9 ft. What heights does it reach on the second and third bounces?

13. A simple interest account grows in the form of an A.P. The account is worth $1300 after 5 years and is worth $1780 after 13 years. What was its original value? What is its value after 9 years?   *Ans.* $1000; $1540.

14. An altitude drawn from the vertex of a right triangle to the hypotenuse is the geometric mean of the segments of the hypotenuse. How long are the segments of the hypotenuse of a right triangle if the altitude is 3 inches and the hypotenuse is 12 inches?

15. Show that the vectors $1/90°$, $1/180°$, and $1/270°$ may be regarded as the three geometric means between $1/0°$ and $1/360°$.

16. Show that the value of the one arithmetic mean between two numbers is the arithmetic average of the two numbers.

17. The geometric mean of a group of n numbers is the nth root of the product of the n numbers. What is the geometric mean of the group of numbers 1, 2, 1, 4, -1, 8, -2? Of 3, 6, 9, 0, 4?   *Ans.* 2; 0.

18. Give a general formula for the geometric mean G in Exercise 17 if the n numbers are $a_1, a_2, a_3, \cdots, a_n$.

19. Using the definition of the geometric mean given in Exercise 17, show that $G = ar^2$ for the numbers a, ar, ar^2, ar^3, ar^4.

20. The arithmetic mean, $\bar{x}$, of the numbers $x_1, x_2, x_3, \cdots, x_n$ is defined as

$$\bar{x} = \frac{x_1 + x_2 + x_3 + \cdots + x_n}{n} = \frac{1}{n} \sum_{i=1}^{n} x_i.$$

Find the arithmetic mean of the numbers 6, 12, 3, 4, -12, -9, -15, 6, 2, 6.

APPENDICES

A PROPERTIES OF GEOMETRIC FUNCTIONS

For the figures shown,

$$A = \text{plane area}$$
$$V = \text{volume}$$
$$C = \text{circumference}$$
$$S = \text{surface area}$$
$$p = \text{perimeter}$$

square
$A = s^2$

rectangle
$A = bh$

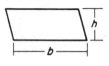

parallelogram
$A = bh$

trapezoid
$A = \frac{1}{2}(b + b')h$

triangle
$A = \frac{1}{2}bh$

cube
$V = s^3$
$S = 6s^2$

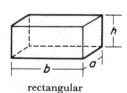

rectangular
parallelepiped
$V = abh$
$S = 2ab + 2ah + 2bh$

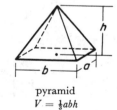

pyramid
$V = \frac{1}{3}abh$

right
circular
cylinder
$V = \pi r^2 h$
$S = 2\pi r^2 + 2\pi rh$

right
circular
cone
$V = \frac{1}{3}\pi r^2 h$

circle
$C = 2\pi r$

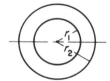

annulus
$A = \pi(r_2^2 - r_1^2)$

circular
sector
$A = \frac{1}{2}r^2\theta$

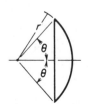

circular
segment

$A = r^2\left(\theta - \dfrac{\sin 2\theta}{2}\right)$

sphere
$V = \frac{4}{3}\pi r^3$
$S = 4\pi r^2$

NATURAL
TRIGONOMETRIC FUNCTIONS
B

′	Sin	Tan	Ctn	Cos	′		′	Sin	Tan	Ctn	Cos	′
0	.00000	.00000	∞	1.0000	60		0	.01745	.01746	57.290	.99985	60
1	.00029	.00029	3437.7	1.0000	59		1	.01774	.01775	56.351	.99984	59
2	.00058	.00058	1718.9	1.0000	58		2	.01803	.01804	55.442	.99984	58
3	.00087	.00087	1145.9	1.0000	57		3	.01832	.01833	54.561	.99983	57
4	.00116	.00116	859.44	1.0000	56		4	.01862	.01862	53.709	.99983	56
5	.00145	.00145	687.55	1.0000	55		5	.01891	.01891	52.882	.99982	55
6	.00175	.00175	572.96	1.0000	54		6	.01920	.01920	52.081	.99982	54
7	.00204	.00204	491.11	1.0000	53		7	.01949	.01949	51.303	.99981	53
8	.00233	.00233	429.72	1.0000	52		8	.01978	.01978	50.549	.99980	52
9	.00262	.00262	381.97	1.0000	51		9	.02007	.02007	49.816	.99980	51
10	.00291	.00291	343.77	1.0000	50		10	.02036	.02036	49.104	.99979	50
11	.00320	.00320	312.52	.99999	49		11	.02065	.02066	48.412	.99979	49
12	.00349	.00349	286.48	.99999	48		12	.02094	.02095	47.740	.99978	48
13	.00378	.00378	264.44	.99999	47		13	.02123	.02124	47.085	.99977	47
14	.00407	.00407	245.55	.99999	46		14	.02152	.02153	46.449	.99977	46
15	.00436	.00436	229.18	.99999	45		15	.02181	.02182	45.829	.99976	45
16	.00465	.00465	214.86	.99999	44		16	.02211	.02211	45.226	.99976	44
17	.00495	.00495	202.22	.99999	43		17	.02240	.02240	44.639	.99975	43
18	.00524	.00524	190.98	.99999	42		18	.02269	.02269	44.066	.99974	42
19	.00553	.00553	180.93	.99998	41		19	.02298	.02298	43.508	.99974	41
20	.00582	.00582	171.89	.99998	40		20	.02327	.02328	42.964	.99973	40
21	.00611	.00611	163.70	.99998	39		21	.02356	.02357	42.433	.99972	39
22	.00640	.00640	156.26	.99998	38		22	.02385	.02386	41.916	.99972	38
23	.00669	.00669	149.47	.99998	37		23	.02414	.02415	41.411	.99971	37
24	.00698	.00698	143.24	.99998	36		24	.02443	.02444	40.917	.99970	36
25	.00727	.00727	137.51	.99997	35		25	.02472	.02473	40.436	.99969	35
26	.00756	.00756	132.22	.99997	34		26	.02501	.02502	39.965	.99969	34
27	.00785	.00785	127.32	.99997	33		27	.02530	.02531	39.506	.99968	33
28	.00814	.00815	122.77	.99997	32		28	.02560	.02560	39.057	.99967	32
29	.00844	.00844	118.54	.99996	31		29	.02589	.02589	38.618	.99966	31
30	.00873	.00873	114.59	.99996	30		30	.02618	.02619	38.188	.99966	30
31	.00902	.00902	110.89	.99996	29		31	.02647	.02648	37.769	.99965	29
32	.00931	.00931	107.43	.99996	28		32	.02676	.02677	37.358	.99964	28
33	.00960	.00960	104.17	.99995	27		33	.02705	.02706	36.956	.99963	27
34	.00989	.00989	101.11	.99995	26		34	.02734	.02735	36.563	.99963	26
35	.01018	.01018	98.218	.99995	25		35	.02763	.02764	36.178	.99962	25
36	.01047	.01047	95.489	.99995	24		36	.02792	.02793	35.801	.99961	24
37	.01076	.01076	92.908	.99994	23		37	.02821	.02822	35.431	.99960	23
38	.01105	.01105	90.463	.99994	22		38	.02850	.02851	35.070	.99959	22
39	.01134	.01135	88.144	.99994	21		39	.02879	.02881	34.715	.99959	21
40	.01164	.01164	85.940	.99993	20		40	.02908	.02910	34.368	.99958	20
41	.01193	.01193	83.844	.99993	19		41	.02938	.02939	34.027	.99957	19
42	.01222	.01222	81.847	.99993	18		42	.02967	.02968	33.694	.99956	18
43	.01251	.01251	79.943	.99992	17		43	.02996	.02997	33.366	.99955	17
44	.01280	.01280	78.126	.99992	16		44	.03025	.03026	33.045	.99954	16
45	.01309	.01309	76.390	.99991	15		45	.03054	.03055	32.730	.99953	15
46	.01338	.01338	74.729	.99991	14		46	.03083	.03084	32.421	.99952	14
47	.01367	.01367	73.139	.99991	13		47	.03112	.03114	32.118	.99952	13
48	.01396	.01396	71.615	.99990	12		48	.03141	.03143	31.821	.99951	12
49	.01425	.01425	70.153	.99990	11		49	.03170	.03172	31.528	.99950	11
50	.01454	.01455	68.750	.99989	10		50	.03199	.03201	31.242	.99949	10
51	.01483	.01484	67.402	.99989	9		51	.03228	.03230	30.960	.99948	9
52	.01513	.01513	66.105	.99989	8		52	.03257	.03259	30.683	.99947	8
53	.01542	.01542	64.858	.99988	7		53	.03286	.03288	30.412	.99946	7
54	.01571	.01571	63.657	.99988	6		54	.03316	.03317	30.145	.99945	6
55	.01600	.01600	62.499	.99987	5		55	.03345	.03346	29.882	.99944	5
56	.01629	.01629	61.383	.99987	4		56	.03374	.03376	29.624	.99943	4
57	.01658	.01658	60.306	.99986	3		57	.03403	.03405	29.371	.99942	3
58	.01687	.01687	59.266	.99986	2		58	.03432	.03434	29.122	.99941	2
59	.01716	.01716	58.261	.99985	1		59	.03461	.03463	28.877	.99940	1
60	.01745	.01746	57.290	.99985	0		60	.03490	.03492	28.636	.99939	0
′	Cos	Ctn	Tan	Sin	′		′	Cos	Ctn	Tan	Sin	′

′	Sin	Tan	Ctn	Cos	′		′	Sin	Tan	Ctn	Cos	′
0	.03490	.03492	28.636	.99939	60		0	.05234	.05241	19.081	.99863	60
1	.03519	.03521	28.399	.99938	59		1	.05263	.05270	18.976	.99861	59
2	.03548	.03550	28.166	.99937	58		2	.05292	.05299	18.871	.99860	58
3	.03577	.03579	27.937	.99936	57		3	.05321	.05328	18.768	.99858	57
4	.03606	.03609	27.712	.99935	56		4	.05350	.05357	18.666	.99857	56
5	.03635	.03638	27.490	.99934	55		5	.05379	.05387	18.564	.99855	55
6	.03664	.03667	27.271	.99933	54		6	.05408	.05416	18.464	.99854	54
7	.03693	.03696	27.057	.99932	53		7	.05437	.05445	18.366	.99852	53
8	.03723	.03725	26.845	.99931	52		8	.05466	.05474	18.268	.99851	52
9	.03752	.03754	26.637	.99930	51		9	.05495	.05503	18.171	.99849	51
10	.03781	.03783	26.432	.99929	50		10	.05524	.05533	18.075	.99847	50
11	.03810	.03812	26.230	.99927	49		11	.05553	.05562	17.980	.99846	49
12	.03839	.03842	26.031	.99926	48		12	.05582	.05591	17.886	.99844	48
13	.03868	.03871	25.835	.99925	47		13	.05611	.05620	17.793	.99842	47
14	.03897	.03900	25.642	.99924	46		14	.05640	.05649	17.702	.99841	46
15	.03926	.03929	25.452	.99923	45		15	.05669	.05678	17.611	.99839	45
16	.03955	.03958	25.264	.99922	44		16	.05698	.05708	17.521	.99838	44
17	.03984	.03987	25.080	.99921	43		17	.05727	.05737	17.431	.99836	43
18	.04013	.04016	24.898	.99919	42		18	.05756	.05766	17.343	.99834	42
19	.04042	.04046	24.719	.99918	41		19	.05785	.05795	17.256	.99833	41
20	.04071	.04075	24.542	.99917	40		20	.05814	.05824	17.169	.99831	40
21	.04100	.04104	24.368	.99916	39		21	.05844	.05854	17.084	.99829	39
22	.04129	.04133	24.196	.99915	38		22	.05873	.05883	16.999	.99827	38
23	.04159	.04162	24.026	.99913	37		23	.05902	.05912	16.915	.99826	37
24	.04188	.04191	23.859	.99912	36		24	.05931	.05941	16.832	.99824	36
25	.04217	.04220	23.695	.99911	35		25	.05960	.05970	16.750	.99822	35
26	.04246	.04250	23.532	.99910	34		26	.05989	.05999	16.668	.99821	34
27	.04275	.04279	23.372	.99909	33		27	.06018	.06029	16.587	.99819	33
28	.04304	.04308	23.214	.99907	32		28	.06047	.06058	16.507	.99817	32
29	.04333	.04337	23.058	.99906	31		29	.06076	.06087	16.428	.99815	31
30	.04362	.04366	22.904	.99905	30		30	.06105	.06116	16.350	.99813	30
31	.04391	.04395	22.752	.99904	29		31	.06134	.06145	16.272	.99812	29
32	.04420	.04424	22.602	.99902	28		32	.06163	.06175	16.195	.99810	28
33	.04449	.04454	22.454	.99901	27		33	.06192	.06204	16.119	.99808	27
34	.04478	.04483	22.308	.99900	26		34	.06221	.06233	16.043	.99806	26
35	.04507	.04512	22.164	.99898	25		35	.06250	.06262	15.969	.99804	25
36	.04536	.04541	22.022	.99897	24		36	.06279	.06291	15.895	.99803	24
37	.04565	.04570	21.881	.99896	23		37	.06308	.06321	15.821	.99801	23
38	.04594	.04599	21.743	.99894	22		38	.06337	.06350	15.748	.99799	22
39	.04623	.04628	21.606	.99893	21		39	.06366	.06379	15.676	.99797	21
40	.04653	.04658	21.470	.99892	20		40	.06395	.06408	15.605	.99795	20
41	.04682	.04687	21.337	.99890	19		41	.06424	.06438	15.534	.99793	19
42	.04711	.04716	21.205	.99889	18		42	.06453	.06467	15.464	.99792	18
43	.04740	.04745	21.075	.99888	17		43	.06482	.06496	15.394	.99790	17
44	.04769	.04774	20.946	.99886	16		44	.06511	.06525	15.325	.99788	16
45	.04798	.04803	20.819	.99885	15		45	.06540	.06554	15.257	.99786	15
46	.04827	.04833	20.693	.99883	14		46	.06569	.06584	15.189	.99784	14
47	.04856	.04862	20.569	.99882	13		47	.06598	.06613	15.122	.99782	13
48	.04885	.04891	20.446	.99881	12		48	.06627	.06642	15.056	.99780	12
49	.04914	.04920	20.325	.99879	11		49	.06656	.06671	14.990	.99778	11
50	.04943	.04949	20.206	.99878	10		50	.06685	.06700	14.924	.99776	10
51	.04972	.04978	20.087	.99876	9		51	.06714	.06730	14.860	.99774	9
52	.05001	.05007	19.970	.99875	8		52	.06743	.06759	14.795	.99772	8
53	.05030	.05037	19.855	.99873	7		53	.06773	.06788	14.732	.99770	7
54	.05059	.05066	19.740	.99872	6		54	.06802	.06817	14.669	.99768	6
55	.05088	.05095	19.627	.99870	5		55	.06831	.06847	14.606	.99766	5
56	.05117	.05124	19.516	.99869	4		56	.06860	.06876	14.544	.99764	4
57	.05146	.05153	19.405	.99867	3		57	.06889	.06905	14.482	.99762	3
58	.05175	.05182	19.296	.99866	2		58	.06918	.06934	14.421	.99760	2
59	.05205	.05212	19.188	.99864	1		59	.06947	.06963	14.361	.99758	1
60	.05234	.05241	19.081	.99863	0		60	.06976	.06993	14.301	.99756	0
′	Cos	Ctn	Tan	Sin	′		′	Cos	Ctn	Tan	Sin	′

′	Sin	Tan	Ctn	Cos	′		′	Sin	Tan	Ctn	Cos	′
0	.06976	.06993	14.301	.99756	60		0	.08716	.08749	11.430	.99619	60
1	.07005	.07022	14.241	.99754	59		1	.08745	.08778	11.392	.99617	59
2	.07034	.07051	14.182	.99752	58		2	.08774	.08807	11.354	.99614	58
3	.07063	.07080	14.124	.99750	57		3	.08803	.08837	11.316	.99612	57
4	.07092	.07110	14.065	.99748	56		4	.08831	.08866	11.279	.99609	56
5	.07121	.07139	14.008	.99746	55		5	.08860	.08895	11.242	.99607	55
6	.07150	.07168	13.951	.99744	54		6	.08889	.08925	11.205	.99604	54
7	.07179	.07197	13.894	.99742	53		7	.08918	.08954	11.168	.99602	53
8	.07208	.07227	13.838	.99740	52		8	.08947	.08983	11.132	.99599	52
9	.07237	.07256	13.782	.99738	51		9	.08976	.09013	11.095	.99596	51
10	.07266	.07285	13.727	.99736	50		10	.09005	.09042	11.059	.99594	50
11	.07295	.07314	13.672	.99734	49		11	.09034	.00971	11.024	.99591	49
12	.07324	.07344	13.617	.99731	48		12	.09063	.09101	10.988	.99588	48
13	.07353	.07373	13.563	.99729	47		13	.09092	.09130	10.953	.99586	47
14	.07382	.07402	13.510	.99727	46		14	.09121	.09159	10.918	.99583	46
15	.07411	.07431	13.457	.99725	45		15	.09150	.09189	10.883	.99580	45
16	.07440	.07461	13.404	.99723	44		16	.09179	.09218	10.848	.99578	44
17	.07469	.07490	13.352	.99721	43		17	.09208	.09247	10.814	.99575	43
18	.07498	.07519	13.300	.99719	42		18	.09237	.09277	10.780	.99572	42
19	.07527	.07548	13.248	.99716	41		19	.09266	.09306	10.746	.99570	41
20	.07556	.07578	13.197	.99714	40		20	.09295	.09335	10.712	.99567	40
21	.07585	.07607	13.146	.99712	39		21	.09324	.09365	10.678	.99564	39
22	.07614	.07636	13.096	.99710	38		22	.09353	.09394	10.645	.99562	38
23	.07643	.07665	13.046	.99708	37		23	.09382	.09423	10.612	.99559	37
24	.07672	.07695	12.996	.99705	36		24	.09411	.09453	10.579	.99556	36
25	.07701	.07724	12.947	.99703	35		25	.09440	.09482	10.546	.99553	35
26	.07730	.07753	12.898	.99701	34		26	.09469	.09511	10.514	.99551	34
27	.07759	.07782	12.850	.99699	33		27	.09498	.09541	10.481	.99548	33
28	.07788	.07812	12.801	.99696	32		28	.09527	.09570	10.449	.99545	32
29	.07817	.07841	12.754	.99694	31		29	.09556	.09600	10.417	.99542	31
30	.07846	.07870	12.706	.99692	30		30	.09585	.09629	10.385	.99540	30
31	.07875	.07899	12.659	.99689	29		31	.09614	.09658	10.354	.99537	29
32	.07904	.07929	12.612	.99687	28		32	.09642	.09688	10.322	.99534	28
33	.07933	.07958	12.566	.99685	27		33	.09671	.09717	10.291	.99531	27
34	.07962	.07987	12.520	.99683	26		34	.09700	.09746	10.260	.99528	26
35	.07991	.08017	12.474	.99680	25		35	.09729	.09776	10.229	.99526	25
36	.08020	.08046	12.429	.99678	24		36	.09758	.09805	10.199	.99523	24
37	.08049	.08075	12.384	.99676	23		37	.09787	.09834	10.168	.99520	23
38	.08078	.08104	12.339	.99673	22		38	.09816	.09864	10.138	.99517	22
39	.08107	.08134	12.295	.99671	21		39	.09845	.09893	10.108	.99514	21
40	.08136	.08163	12.251	.99668	20		40	.09874	.09923	10.078	.99511	20
41	.08165	.08192	12.207	.99666	19		41	.09903	.09952	10.048	.99508	19
42	.08194	.08221	12.163	.99664	18		42	.09932	.09981	10.019	.99506	18
43	.08223	.08251	12.120	.99661	17		43	.09961	.10011	9.9893	.99503	17
44	.08252	.08280	12.077	.99659	16		44	.09990	.10040	9.9601	.99500	16
45	.08281	.08309	12.035	.99657	15		45	.10019	.10069	9.9310	.99497	15
46	.08310	.08339	11.992	.99654	14		46	.10048	.10099	9.9021	.99494	14
47	.08339	.08368	11.950	.99652	13		47	.10077	.10128	9.8734	.99491	13
48	.08368	.08397	11.909	.99649	12		48	.10106	.10158	9.8448	.99488	12
49	.08397	.08427	11.867	.99647	11		49	.10135	.10187	9.8164	.99485	11
50	.08426	.08456	11.826	.99644	10		50	.10164	.10216	9.7882	.99482	10
51	.08455	.08485	11.785	.99642	9		51	.10192	.10246	9.7601	.99479	9
52	.08484	.08514	11.745	.99639	8		52	.10221	.10275	9.7322	.99476	8
53	.08513	.08544	11.705	.99637	7		53	.10250	.10305	9.7044	.99473	7
54	.08542	.08573	11.664	.99635	6		54	.10279	.10334	9.6768	.99470	6
55	.08571	.08602	11.625	.99632	5		55	.10308	.10363	9.6493	.99467	5
56	.08600	.08632	11.585	.99630	4		56	.10337	.10393	9.6220	.99464	4
57	.08629	.08661	11.546	.99627	3		57	.10366	.10422	9.5949	.99461	3
58	.08658	.08690	11.507	.99625	2		58	.10395	.10452	9.5679	.99458	2
59	.08687	.08720	11.468	.99622	1		59	.10424	.10481	9.5411	.99455	1
60	.08716	.08749	11.430	.99619	0		60	.10453	.10510	9.5144	.99452	0
′	Cos	Ctn	Tan	Sin	′		′	Cos	Ctn	Tan	Sin	′

′	Sin	Tan	Ctn	Cos	′		′	Sin	Tan	Ctn	Cos	′
0	.10453	.10510	9.5144	.99452	60		0	.12187	.12278	8.1443	.99255	60
1	.10482	.10540	9.4878	.99449	59		1	.12216	.12308	8.1248	.99251	59
2	.10511	.10569	9.4614	.99446	58		2	.12245	.12338	8.1054	.99248	58
3	.10540	.10599	9.4352	.99443	57		3	.12274	.12367	8.0860	.99244	57
4	.10569	.10628	9.4090	.99440	56		4	.12302	.12397	8.0667	.99240	56
5	.10597	.10657	9.3831	.99437	55		5	.12331	.12426	8.0476	.99237	55
6	.10626	.10687	9.3572	.99434	54		6	.12360	.12456	8.0285	.99233	54
7	.10655	.10716	9.3315	.99431	53		7	.12389	.12485	8.0095	.99230	53
8	.10684	.10746	9.3060	.99428	52		8	.12418	.12515	7.9906	.99226	52
9	.10713	.10775	9.2806	.99424	51		9	.12447	.12544	7.9718	.99222	51
10	.10742	.10805	9.2553	.99421	50		10	.12476	.12574	7.9530	.99219	50
11	.10771	.10834	9.2302	.99418	49		11	.12504	.12603	7.9344	.99215	49
12	.10800	.10863	9.2052	.99415	48		12	.12533	.12633	7.9158	.99211	48
13	.10829	.10893	9.1803	.99412	47		13	.12562	.12662	7.8973	.99208	47
14	.10858	.10922	9.1555	.99409	46		14	.12591	.12692	7.8789	.99204	46
15	.10887	.10952	9.1309	.99406	45		15	.12620	.12722	7.8606	.99200	45
16	.10916	.10981	9.1065	.99402	44		16	.12649	.12751	7.8424	.99197	44
17	.10945	.11011	9.0821	.99399	43		17	.12678	.12781	7.8243	.99193	43
18	.10973	.11040	9.0579	.99396	42		18	.12706	.12810	7.8062	.99189	42
19	.11002	.11070	9.0338	.99393	41		19	.12735	.12840	7.7882	.99186	41
20	.11031	.11099	9.0098	.99390	40		20	.12764	.12869	7.7704	.99182	40
21	.11060	.11128	8.9860	.99386	39		21	.12793	.12899	7.7525	.99178	39
22	.11089	.11158	8.9623	.99383	38		22	.12822	.12929	7.7348	.99175	38
23	.11118	.11187	8.9387	.99380	37		23	.12851	.12958	7.7171	.99171	37
24	.11147	.11217	8.9152	.99377	36		24	.12880	.12988	7.6996	.99167	36
25	.11176	.11246	8.8919	.99374	35		25	.12908	.13017	7.6821	.99163	35
26	.11205	.11276	8.8686	.99370	34		26	.12937	.13047	7.6647	.99160	34
27	.11234	.11305	8.8455	.99367	33		27	.12966	.13076	7.6473	.99156	33
28	.11263	.11335	8.8225	.99364	32		28	.12995	.13106	7.6301	.99152	32
29	.11291	.11364	8.7996	.99360	31		29	.13024	.13136	7.6129	.99148	31
30	.11320	.11394	8.7769	.99357	30		30	.13053	.13165	7.5958	.99144	30
31	.11349	.11423	8.7542	.99354	29		31	.13081	.13195	7.5787	.99141	29
32	.11378	.11452	8.7317	.99351	28		32	.13110	.13224	7.5618	.99137	28
33	.11407	.11482	8.7093	.99347	27		33	.13139	.13254	7.5449	.99133	27
34	.11436	.11511	8.6870	.99344	26		34	.13168	.13284	7.5281	.99129	26
35	.11465	.11541	8.6648	.99341	25		35	.13197	.13313	7.5113	.99125	25
36	.11494	.11570	8.6427	.99337	24		36	.13226	.13343	7.4947	.99122	24
37	.11523	.11600	8.6208	.99334	23		37	.13254	.13372	7.4781	.99118	23
38	.11552	.11629	8.5989	.99331	22		38	.13283	.13402	7.4615	.99114	22
39	.11580	.11659	8.5772	.99327	21		39	.13312	.13432	7.4451	.99110	21
40	.11609	.11688	8.5555	.99324	20		40	.13341	.13461	7.4287	.99106	20
41	.11638	.11718	8.5340	.99320	19		41	.13370	.13491	7.4124	.99102	19
42	.11667	.11747	8.5126	.99317	18		42	.13399	.13521	7.3962	.99098	18
43	.11696	.11777	8.4913	.99314	17		43	.13427	.13550	7.3800	.99094	17
44	.11725	.11806	8.4701	.99310	16		44	.13456	.13580	7.3639	.99091	16
45	.11754	.11836	8.4490	.99307	15		45	.13485	.13609	7.3479	.99087	15
46	.11783	.11865	8.4280	.99303	14		46	.13514	.13639	7.3319	.99083	14
47	.11812	.11895	8.4071	.99300	13		47	.13543	.13669	7.3160	.99079	13
48	.11840	.11924	8.3863	.99297	12		48	.13572	.13698	7.3002	.99075	12
49	.11869	.11954	8.3656	.99293	11		49	.13600	.13728	7.2844	.99071	11
50	.11898	.11983	8.3450	.99290	10		50	.13629	.13758	7.2687	.99067	10
51	.11927	.12013	8.3245	.99286	9		51	.13658	.13787	7.2531	.99063	9
52	.11956	.12042	8.3041	.99283	8		52	.13687	.13817	7.2375	.99059	8
53	.11985	.12072	8.2838	.99279	7		53	.13716	.13846	7.2220	.99055	7
54	.12014	.12101	8.2636	.99276	6		54	.13744	.13876	7.2066	.99051	6
55	.12043	.12131	8.2434	.99272	5		55	.13773	.13906	7.1912	.99047	5
56	.12071	.12160	8.2234	.99269	4		56	.13802	.13935	1759	.99043	4
57	.12100	.12190	8.2035	.99265	3		57	.13831	.13965	7.1607	.99039	3
58	.12129	.12219	8.1837	.99262	2		58	.13860	.13995	7.1455	.99035	2
59	.12158	.12249	8.1640	.99258	1		59	.13889	.14024	7.1304	.99031	1
60	.12187	.12278	8.1443	.99255	0		60	.13917	.14054	7.1154	.99027	0
′	Cos	Ctn	Tan	Sin	′		′	Cos	Ctn	Tan	Sin	′

′	Sin	Tan	Ctn	Cos	′		′	Sin	Tan	Ctn	Cos	′
0	.13917	.14054	7.1154	.99027	60		0	.15643	.15838	6.3138	.98769	60
1	.13946	.14084	7.1004	.99023	59		1	.15672	.15868	6.3019	.98764	59
2	.13975	.14113	7.0855	.99019	58		2	.15701	.15898	6.2901	.98760	58
3	.14004	.14143	7.0706	.99015	57		3	.15730	.15928	6.2783	.98755	57
4	.14033	.14173	7.0558	.99011	56		4	.15758	.15958	6.2666	.98751	56
5	.14061	.14202	7.0410	.99006	55		5	.15787	.15988	6.2549	.98746	55
6	.14090	.14232	7.0264	.99002	54		6	.15816	.16017	6.2432	.98741	54
7	.14119	.14262	7.0117	.98998	53		7	.15845	.16047	6.2316	.98737	53
8	.14148	.14291	6.9972	.98994	52		8	.15873	.16077	6.2200	.98732	52
9	.14177	.14321	6.9827	.98990	51		9	.15902	.16107	6.2085	.98728	51
10	.14205	.14351	6.9682	.98986	50		10	.15931	.16137	6.1970	.98723	50
11	.14234	.14381	6.9538	.98982	49		11	.15959	.16167	6.1856	.98718	49
12	.14263	.14410	6.9395	.98978	48		12	.15988	.16196	6.1742	.98714	48
13	.14292	.14440	6.9252	.98973	47		13	.16017	.16226	6.1628	.98709	47
14	.14320	.14470	6.9110	.98969	46		14	.16046	.16256	6.1515	.98704	46
15	.14349	.14499	6.8969	.98965	45		15	.16074	.16286	6.1402	.98700	45
16	.14378	.14529	6.8828	.98961	44		16	.16103	.16316	6.1290	.98695	44
17	.14407	.14559	6.8687	.98957	43		17	.16132	.16346	6.1178	.98690	43
18	.14436	.14588	6.8548	.98953	42		18	.16160	.16376	6.1066	.98686	42
19	.14464	.14618	6.8408	.98948	41		19	.16189	.16405	6.0955	.98681	41
20	.14493	.14648	6.8269	.98944	40		20	.16218	.16435	6.0844	.98676	40
21	.14522	.14678	6.8131	.98940	39		21	.16246	.16465	6.0734	.98671	39
22	.14551	.14707	6.7994	.98936	38		22	.16275	.16495	6.0624	.98667	38
23	.14580	.14737	6.7856	.98931	37		23	.16304	.16525	6.0514	.98662	37
24	.14608	.14767	6.7720	.98927	36		24	.16333	.16555	6.0405	.98657	36
25	.14637	.14796	6.7584	.98923	35		25	.16361	.16585	6.0296	.98652	35
26	.14666	.14826	6.7448	.98919	34		26	.16390	.16615	6.0188	.98648	34
27	.14695	.14856	6.7313	.98914	33		27	.16419	.16645	6.0080	.98643	33
28	.14723	.14886	6.7179	.98910	32		28	.16447	.16674	5.9972	.98638	32
29	.14752	.14915	6.7045	.98906	31		29	.16476	.16704	5.9865	.98633	31
30	.14781	.14945	6.6912	.98902	30		30	.16505	.16734	5.9758	.98629	30
31	.14810	.14975	6.6779	.98897	29		31	.16533	.16764	5.9651	.98624	29
32	.14838	.15005	6.6646	.98893	28		32	.16562	.16794	5.9545	.98619	28
33	.14867	.15034	6.6514	.98889	27		33	.16591	.16824	5.9439	.98614	27
34	.14896	.15064	6.6383	.98884	26		34	.16620	.16854	5.9333	.98609	26
35	.14925	.15094	6.6252	.98880	25		35	.16648	.16884	5.9228	.98604	25
36	.14954	.15124	6.6122	.98876	24		36	.16677	.16914	5.9124	.98600	24
37	.14982	.15153	6.5992	.98871	23		37	.16706	.16944	5.9019	.98595	23
38	.15011	.15183	6.5863	.98867	22		38	.16734	.16974	5.8915	.98590	22
39	.15040	.15213	6.5734	.98863	21		39	.16763	.17004	5.8811	.98585	21
40	.15069	.15243	6.5606	.98858	20		40	.16792	.17033	5.8708	.98580	20
41	.15097	.15272	6.5478	.98854	19		41	.16820	.17063	5.8605	.98575	19
42	.15126	.15302	6.5350	.98849	18		42	.16849	.17093	5.8502	.98570	18
43	.15155	.15332	6.5223	.98845	17		43	.16878	.17123	5.8400	.98565	17
44	.15184	.15362	6.5097	.98841	16		44	.16906	.17153	5.8298	.98561	16
45	.15212	.15391	6.4971	.98836	15		45	.16935	.17183	5.8197	.98556	15
46	.15241	.15421	6.4846	.98832	14		46	.16964	.17213	5.8095	.98551	14
47	.15270	.15451	6.4721	.98827	13		47	.16992	.17243	5.7994	.98546	13
48	.15299	.15481	6.4596	.98823	12		48	.17021	.17273	5.7894	.98541	12
49	.15327	.15511	6.4472	.98818	11		49	.17050	.17303	5.7794	.98536	11
50	.15356	.15540	6.4348	.98814	10		50	.17078	.17333	5.7694	.98531	10
51	.15385	.15570	6.4225	.98809	9		51	.17107	.17363	5.7594	.98526	9
52	.15414	.15600	6.4103	.98805	8		52	.17136	.17393	5.7495	.98521	8
53	.15442	.15630	6.3980	.98800	7		53	.17164	.17423	5.7396	.98516	7
54	.15471	.15660	6.3859	.98796	6		54	.17193	.17453	5.7297	.98511	6
55	.15500	.15689	6.3737	.98791	5		55	.17222	.17483	5.7199	.98506	5
56	.15529	.15719	6.3617	.98787	4		56	.17250	.17513	5.7101	.98501	4
57	.15557	.15749	6.3496	.98782	3		57	.17279	.17543	5.7004	.98496	3
58	.15586	.15779	6.3376	.98778	2		58	.17308	.17573	5.6906	.98491	2
59	.15615	.15809	6.3257	.98773	1		59	.17336	.17603	5.6809	.98486	1
60	.15643	.15838	6.3138	.98769	0		60	.17365	.17633	5.6713	.98481	0
′	Cos	Ctn	Tan	Sin	′		′	Cos	Ctn	Tan	Sin	′

′	Sin	Tan	Ctn	Cos	′		′	Sin	Tan	Ctn	Cos	′
0	.17365	.17633	5.6713	.98481	60		0	.19081	.19438	5.1446	.98163	60
1	.17393	.17663	5.6617	.98476	59		1	.19109	.19468	5.1366	.98157	59
2	.17422	.17693	5.6521	.98471	58		2	.19138	.19498	5.1286	.98152	58
3	.17451	.17723	5.6425	.98466	57		3	.19167	.19529	5.1207	.98146	57
4	.17479	.17753	5.6329	.98461	56		4	.19195	.19559	5.1128	.98140	56
5	.17508	.17783	5.6234	.98455	55		5	.19224	.19589	5.1049	.98135	55
6	.17537	.17813	5.6140	.98450	54		6	.19252	.19619	5.0970	.98129	54
7	.17565	.17843	5.6045	.98445	53		7	.19281	.19649	5.0892	.98124	53
8	.17594	.17873	5.5951	.98440	52		8	.19309	.19680	5.0814	.98118	52
9	.17623	.17903	5.5857	.98435	51		9	.19338	.19710	5.0736	.98112	51
10	.17651	.17933	5.5764	.98430	50		10	.19366	.19740	5.0658	.98107	50
11	.17680	.17963	5.5671	.98425	49		11	.19395	.19770	5.0581	.98101	49
12	.17708	.17993	5.5578	.98420	48		12	.19423	.19801	5.0504	.98096	48
13	.17737	.18023	5.5485	.98414	47		13	.19452	.19831	5.0427	.98090	47
14	.17766	.18053	5.5393	.98409	46		14	.19481	.19861	5.0350	.98084	46
15	.17794	.18083	5.5301	.98404	45		15	.19509	.19891	5.0273	.98079	45
16	.17823	.18113	5.5209	.98399	44		16	.19538	.19921	5.0197	.98073	44
17	.17852	.18143	5.5118	.98394	43		17	.19566	.19952	5.0121	.98067	43
18	.17880	.18173	5.5026	.98389	42		18	.19595	.19982	5.0045	.98061	42
19	.17909	.18203	5.4936	.98383	41		19	.19623	.20012	4.9969	.98056	41
20	.17937	.18233	5.4845	.98378	40		20	.19652	.20042	4.9894	.98050	40
21	.17966	.18263	5.4755	.98373	39		21	.19680	.20073	4.9819	.98044	39
22	.17995	.18293	5.4665	.98368	38		22	.19709	.20103	4.9744	.98039	38
23	.18023	.18323	5.4575	.98362	37		23	.19737	.20133	4.9669	.98033	37
24	.18052	.18353	5.4486	.98357	36		24	.19766	.20164	4.9594	.98027	36
25	.18081	.18384	5.4397	.98352	35		25	.19794	.20194	4.9520	.98021	35
26	.18109	.18414	5.4308	.98347	34		26	.19823	.20224	4.9446	.98016	34
27	.18138	.18444	5.4219	.98341	33		27	.19851	.20254	4.9372	.98010	33
28	.18166	.18474	5.4131	.98336	32		28	.19880	.20285	4.9298	.98004	32
29	.18195	.18504	5.4043	.98331	31		29	.19908	.20315	4.9225	.97998	31
30	.18224	.18534	5.3955	.98325	30		30	.19937	.20345	4.9152	.97992	30
31	.18252	.18564	5.3868	.98320	29		31	.19965	.20376	4.9078	.97987	29
32	.18281	.18594	5.3781	.98315	28		32	.19994	.20406	4.9006	.97931	28
33	.18309	.18624	5.3694	.98310	27		33	.20022	.20436	4.8933	.97975	27
34	.18338	.18654	5.3607	.98304	26		34	.20051	.20466	4.8860	.97969	26
35	.18367	.18684	5.3521	.98299	25		35	.20079	.20497	4.8788	.97963	25
36	.18395	.18714	5.3435	.98294	24		36	.20108	.20527	4.8716	.97958	24
37	.18424	.18745	5.3349	.98288	23		37	.20136	.20557	4.8644	.97952	23
38	.18452	.18775	5.3263	.98283	22		38	.20165	.20588	4.8573	.97946	22
39	.18481	.18805	5.3178	.98277	21		39	.20193	.20618	4.8501	.97940	21
40	.18509	.18835	5.3093	.98272	20		40	.20222	.20648	4.8430	.97934	20
41	.18538	.18865	5.3008	.98267	19		41	.20250	.20679	4.8359	.97928	19
42	.18567	.18895	5.2924	.98261	18		42	.20279	.20709	4.8288	.97922	18
43	.18595	.18925	5.2839	.98256	17		43	.20307	.20739	4.8218	.97916	17
44	.18624	.18955	5.2755	.98250	16		44	.20336	.20770	4.8147	.97910	16
45	.18652	.18986	5.2672	.98245	15		45	.20364	.20800	4.8077	.97905	15
46	.18681	.19016	5.2588	.98240	14		46	.20393	.20830	4.8007	.97899	14
47	.18710	.19046	5.2505	.98234	13		47	.20421	.20861	4.7937	.97893	13
48	.18738	.19076	5.2422	.98229	12		48	.20450	.20891	4.7867	.97887	12
49	.18767	.19106	5.2339	.98223	11		49	.20478	.20921	4.7798	.97881	11
50	.18795	.19136	5.2257	.98218	10		50	.20507	.20952	4.7729	.97875	10
51	.18824	.19166	5.2174	.98212	9		51	.20535	.20982	4.7659	.97869	9
52	.18852	.19197	5.2092	.98207	8		52	.20563	.21013	4.7591	.97863	8
53	.18881	.19227	5.2011	.98201	7		53	.20592	.21043	4.7522	.97857	7
54	.18910	.19257	5.1929	.98196	6		54	.20620	.21073	4.7453	.97851	6
55	.18938	.19287	5.1848	.98190	5		55	.20649	.21104	4.7385	.97845	5
56	.18967	.19317	5.1767	.98185	4		56	.20677	.21134	4.7317	.97839	4
57	.18995	.19347	5.1686	.98179	3		57	.20706	.21164	4.7249	.97833	3
58	.19024	.19378	5.1606	.98174	2		58	.20734	.21195	4.7181	.97827	2
59	.19052	.19408	5.1526	.98168	1		59	.20763	.21225	4.7114	.97821	1
60	.19081	.19438	5.1446	.98163	0		60	.20791	.21256	4.7046	.97815	0
′	Cos	Ctn	Tan	Sin	′		′	Cos	Ctn	Tan	Sin	′

′	Sin	Tan	Ctn	Cos	′	′	Sin	Tan	Ctn	Cos	′
0	.20791	.21256	4.7046	.97815	60	0	.22495	.23087	4.3315	.97437	60
1	.20820	.21286	4.6979	.97809	59	1	.22523	.23117	4.3257	.97430	59
2	.20848	.21316	4.6912	.97803	58	2	.22552	.23148	4.3200	.97424	58
3	.20877	.21347	4.6845	.97797	57	3	.22580	.23179	4.3143	.97417	57
4	.20905	.21377	4.6779	.97791	56	4	.22608	.23209	4.3086	.97411	56
5	.20933	.21408	4.6712	.97784	55	5	.22637	.23240	4.3029	.97404	55
6	.20962	.21438	4.6646	.97778	54	6	.22665	.23271	4.2972	.97398	54
7	.20990	.21469	4.6580	.97772	53	7	.22693	.23301	4.2916	.97391	53
8	.21019	.21499	4.6514	.97766	52	8	.22722	.23332	4.2859	.97384	52
9	.21047	.21529	4.6448	.97760	51	9	.22750	.23363	4.2803	.97378	51
10	.21076	.21560	4.6382	.97754	50	10	.22778	.23393	4.2747	.97371	50
11	.21104	.21590	4.6317	.97748	49	11	.22807	.23424	4.2691	.97365	49
12	.21132	.21621	4.6252	.97742	48	12	.22835	.23455	4.2635	.97358	48
13	.21161	.21651	4.6187	.97735	47	13	.22863	.23485	4.2580	.97351	47
14	.21189	.21682	4.6122	.97729	46	14	.22892	.23516	4.2524	.97345	46
15	.21218	.21712	4.6057	.97723	45	15	.22920	.23547	4.2468	.97338	45
16	.21246	.21743	4.5993	.97717	44	16	.22948	.23578	4.2413	.97331	44
17	.21275	.21773	4.5928	.97711	43	17	.22977	.23608	4.2358	.97325	43
18	.21303	.21804	4.5864	.97705	42	18	.23005	.23639	4.2303	.97318	42
19	.21331	.21834	4.5800	.97698	41	19	.23033	.23670	4.2248	.97311	41
20	.21360	.21864	4.5736	.97692	40	20	.23062	.23700	4.2193	.97304	40
21	.21388	.21895	4.5673	.97686	39	21	.23090	.23731	4.2139	.97298	39
22	.21417	.21925	4.5609	.97680	38	22	.23118	.23762	4.2084	.97291	38
23	.21445	.21956	4.5546	.97673	37	23	.23146	.23793	4.2030	.97284	37
24	.21474	.21986	4.5483	.97667	36	24	.23175	.23823	4.1976	.97278	36
25	.21502	.22017	4.5420	.97661	35	25	.23203	.23854	4.1922	.97271	35
26	.21530	.22047	4.5357	.97655	34	26	.23231	.23885	4.1868	.97264	34
27	.21559	.22078	4.5294	.97648	33	27	.23260	.23916	4.1814	.97257	33
28	.21587	.22108	4.5232	.97642	32	28	.23288	.23946	4.1760	.97251	32
29	.21616	.22139	4.5169	.97636	31	29	.23316	.23977	4.1706	.97244	31
30	.21644	.22169	4.5107	.97630	30	30	.23345	.24008	4.1653	.97237	30
31	.21672	.22200	4.5045	.97623	29	31	.23373	.24039	4.1600	.97230	29
32	.21701	.22231	4.4983	.97617	28	32	.23401	.24069	4.1547	.97223	28
33	.21729	.22261	4.4922	.97611	27	33	.23429	.24100	4.1493	.97217	27
34	.21758	.22292	4.4860	.97604	26	34	.23458	.24131	4.1441	.97210	26
35	.21786	.22322	4.4799	.97598	25	35	.23486	.24162	4.1388	.97203	25
36	.21814	.22353	4.4737	.97592	24	36	.23514	.24193	4.1335	.97196	24
37	.21843	.22383	4.4676	.97585	23	37	.23542	.24223	4.1282	.97189	23
38	.21871	.22414	4.4615	.97579	22	38	.23571	.24254	4.1230	.97182	22
39	.21899	.22444	4.4555	.97573	21	39	.23599	.24285	4.1178	.97176	21
40	.21928	.22475	4.4494	.97566	20	40	.23627	.24316	4.1126	.97169	20
41	.21956	.22505	4.4434	.97560	19	41	.23656	.24347	4.1074	.97162	19
42	.21985	.22536	4.4373	.97553	18	42	.23684	.24377	4.1022	.97155	18
43	.22013	.22567	4.4313	.97547	17	43	.23712	.24408	4.0970	.97148	17
44	.22041	.22597	4.4253	.97541	16	44	.23740	.24439	4.0918	.97141	16
45	.22070	.22628	4.4194	.97534	15	45	.23769	.24470	4.0867	.97134	15
46	.22098	.22658	4.4134	.97528	14	46	.23797	.24501	4.0815	.97127	14
47	.22126	.22689	4.4075	.97521	13	47	.23825	.24532	4.0764	.97120	13
48	.22155	.22719	4.4015	.97515	12	48	.23853	.24562	4.0713	.97113	12
49	.22183	.22750	4.3956	.97508	11	49	.23882	.24593	4.0662	.97106	11
50	.22212	.22781	4.3897	.97502	10	50	.23910	.24624	4.0611	.97100	10
51	.22240	.22811	4.3838	.97496	9	51	.23938	.24655	4.0560	.97093	9
52	.22268	.22842	4.3779	.97489	8	52	.23966	.24686	4.0509	.97086	8
53	.22297	.22872	4.3721	.97483	7	53	.23995	.24717	4.0459	.97079	7
54	.22325	.22903	4.3662	.97476	6	54	.24023	.24747	4.0408	.97072	6
55	.22353	.22934	4.3604	.97470	5	55	.24051	.24778	4.0358	.97065	5
56	.22382	.22964	4.3546	.97463	4	56	.24079	.24809	4.0308	.97058	4
57	.22410	.22995	4.3488	.97457	3	57	.24108	.24840	4.0257	.97051	3
58	.22438	.23026	4.3430	.97450	2	58	.24136	.24871	4.0207	.97044	2
59	.22467	.23056	4.3372	.97444	1	59	.24164	.24902	4.0158	.97037	1
60	.22495	.23087	4.3315	.97437	0	60	.24192	.24933	4.0108	.97030	0
′	Cos	Ctn	Tan	Sin	′	′	Cos	Ctn	Tan	Sin	′

′	Sin	Tan	Ctn	Cos	′		′	Sin	Tan	Ctn	Cos	′
0	.24192	.24933	4.0108	.97030	60		0	.25882	.26795	3.7321	.96593	60
1	.24220	.24964	4.0058	.97023	59		1	.25910	.26826	3.7277	.96585	59
2	.24249	.24995	4.0009	.97015	58		2	.25938	.26857	3.7234	.96578	58
3	.24277	.25026	3.9959	.97008	57		3	.25966	.26888	3.7191	.96570	57
4	.24305	.25056	3.9910	.97001	56		4	.25994	.26920	3.7148	.96562	56
5	.24333	.25087	3.9861	.96994	55		5	.26022	.26951	3.7105	.96555	55
6	.24362	.25118	3.9812	.96987	54		6	.26050	.26982	3.7062	.96547	54
7	.24390	.25149	3.9763	.96980	53		7	.26079	.27013	3.7019	.96540	53
8	.24418	.25180	3.9714	.96973	52		8	.26107	.27044	3.6976	.96532	52
9	.24446	.25211	3.9665	.96966	51		9	.26135	.27076	3.6933	.96524	51
10	.24474	.25242	3.9617	.96959	50		10	.26163	.27107	3.6891	.96517	50
11	.24503	.25273	3.9568	.96952	49		11	.26191	.27138	3.6848	.96509	49
12	.24531	.25304	3.9520	.96945	48		12	.26219	.27169	3.6806	.96502	48
13	.24559	.25335	3.9471	.96937	47		13	.26247	.27201	3.6764	.96494	47
14	.24587	.25366	3.9423	.96930	46		14	.26275	.27232	3.6722	.96486	46
15	.24615	.25397	3.9375	.96923	45		15	.26303	.27263	3.6680	.96479	45
16	.24644	.25428	3.9327	.96916	44		16	.26331	.27294	3.6638	.96471	44
17	.24672	.25459	3.9279	.96909	43		17	.26359	.27326	3.6596	.96463	43
18	.24700	.25490	3.9232	.96902	42		18	.26387	.27357	3.6554	.96456	42
19	.24728	.25521	3.9184	.96894	41		19	.26415	.27388	3.6512	.96448	41
20	.24756	.25552	3.9136	.96887	40		20	.26443	.27419	3.6470	.96440	40
21	.24784	.25583	3.9089	.96880	39		21	.26471	.27451	3.6429	.96433	39
22	.24813	.25614	3.9042	.96873	38		22	.26500	.27482	3.6387	.96425	38
23	.24841	.25645	3.8995	.96866	37		23	.26528	.27513	3.6346	.96417	37
24	.24869	.25676	3.8947	.96858	36		24	.26556	.27545	3.6305	.96410	36
25	.24897	.25707	3.8900	.96851	35		25	.26584	.27576	3.6264	.96402	35
26	.24925	.25738	3.8854	.96844	34		26	.26612	.27607	3.6222	.96394	34
27	.24954	.25769	3.8807	.96837	33		27	.26640	.27638	3.6181	.96386	33
28	.24982	.25800	3.8760	.96829	32		28	.26668	.27670	3.6140	.96379	32
29	.25010	.25831	3.8714	.96822	31		29	.26696	.27701	3.6100	.96371	31
30	.25038	.25862	3.8667	.96815	30		30	.26724	.27732	3.6059	.96363	30
31	.25066	.25893	3.8621	.96807	29		31	.26752	.27764	3.6018	.96355	29
32	.25094	.25924	3.8575	.96800	28		32	.26780	.27795	3.5978	.96347	28
33	.25122	.25955	3.8528	.96793	27		33	.26808	.27826	3.5937	.96340	27
34	.25151	.25986	3.8482	.96786	26		34	.26836	.27858	3.5897	.96332	26
35	.25179	.26017	3.8436	.96778	25		35	.26864	.27889	3.5856	.96324	25
36	.25207	.26048	3.8391	.96771	24		36	.26892	.27921	3.5816	.96316	24
37	.25235	.26079	3.8345	.96764	23		37	.26920	.27952	3.5776	96308	23
38	.25263	.26110	3.8299	.96756	22		38	.26948	.27983	3.5736	.96301	22
39	.25291	.26141	3.8254	.96749	21		39	.26976	.28015	3.5696	.96293	21
40	.25320	.26172	3.8208	.96742	20		40	.27004	.28046	3.5656	.96285	20
41	.25348	.26203	3.8163	.96734	19		41	.27032	.28077	3.5616	.96269	19
42	.25376	.26235	3.8118	.96727	18		42	.27060	.28109	3.5576	.96269	18
43	.25404	.26266	3.8073	.96719	17		43	.27088	.28140	3.5536	.96261	17
44	.25432	.26297	3.8028	.96712	16		44	.27116	.28172	3.5497	.96253	16
45	.25460	.26328	3.7983	.96705	15		45	.27144	.28203	3.5457	.96246	15
46	.25488	.26359	3.7938	.96697	14		46	.27172	.28234	3.5418	.96238	14
47	.25516	.26390	3.7893	.96690	13		47	.27200	.28266	3.5379	.96230	13
48	.25545	.26421	3.7848	.96682	12		48	.27228	.28297	3.5339	.96222	12
49	.25573	.26452	3.7804	.96675	11		49	.27256	.28329	3.5300	.96214	11
50	.25601	.26483	3.7760	.96667	10		50	.27284	.28360	3.5261	.96206	10
51	.25629	.26515	3.7715	.96660	9		51	.27312	.28391	3.5222	.96198	9
52	.25657	.26546	3.7671	.96653	8		52	.27340	.28423	3.5183	.96190	8
53	.25685	.26577	3.7627	.96645	7		53	.27368	.28454	3.5144	.96182	7
54	.25713	.26608	3.7583	.96638	6		54	.27396	.28486	3.5105	.96174	6
55	.25741	.26639	3.7539	.96630	5		55	.27424	.28517	3.5067	.96166	5
56	.25769	.26670	3.7495	.96623	4		56	.27452	.28549	3.5028	.96158	4
57	.25798	.26701	3.7451	.96615	3		57	.27480	.28580	3.4989	.96150	3
58	.25826	.26733	3.7408	.96608	2		58	.27508	.28612	3.4951	.96142	2
59	.25854	.26764	3.7364	.96600	1		59	.27536	.28643	3.4912	.96134	1
60	.25882	.26795	3.7321	.96593	0		60	.27564	.28675	3.4874	.96126	0
′	Cos	Ctn	Tan	Sin	′		′	Cos	Ctn	Tan	Sin	′

′	Sin	Tan	Ctn	Cos	′
0	.27564	.28675	3.4874	.96126	60
1	.27592	.28706	3.4836	.96118	59
2	.27620	.28738	3.4798	.96110	58
3	.27648	.28769	3.4760	.96102	57
4	.27676	.28801	3.4722	.96094	56
5	.27704	.28832	3.4684	.96086	55
6	.27731	.28864	3.4646	.96078	54
7	.27759	.28895	3.4608	.96070	53
8	.27787	.28927	3.4570	.96062	52
9	.27815	.28958	3.4533	.96054	51
10	.27843	.28990	3.4495	.96046	50
11	.27871	.29021	3.4458	.96037	49
12	.27899	.29053	3.4420	.96029	48
13	.27927	.29084	3.4383	.96021	47
14	.27955	.29116	3.4346	.96013	46
15	.27983	.29147	3.4308	.96005	45
16	.28011	.29179	3.4271	.95997	44
17	.28039	.29210	3.4234	.95989	43
18	.28067	.29242	3.4197	.95981	42
19	.28095	.29274	3.4160	.95972	41
20	.28123	.29305	3.4124	.95964	40
21	.28150	.29337	3.4087	.95956	39
22	.28178	.29368	3.4050	.95948	38
23	.28206	.29400	3.4014	.95940	37
24	.28234	.29432	3.3977	.95931	36
25	.28262	.29463	3.3941	.95923	35
26	.28290	.29495	3.3904	.95915	34
27	.28318	.29526	3.3868	.95907	33
28	.28346	.29558	3.3832	.95898	32
29	.28374	.29590	3.3796	.95890	31
30	.28402	.29621	3.3759	.95882	30
31	.28429	.29653	3.3723	.95874	29
32	.28457	.29685	3.3687	.95865	28
33	.28485	.29716	3.3652	.95857	27
34	.28513	.29748	3.3616	.95849	26
35	.28541	.29780	3.3580	.95841	25
36	.28569	.29811	3.3544	.95832	24
37	.28597	.29843	3.3509	.95824	23
38	.28625	.29875	3.3473	.95816	22
39	.28652	.29906	3.3438	.95807	21
40	.28680	.29938	3.3402	.95799	20
41	.28708	.29970	3.3367	.95791	19
42	.28736	.30001	3.3332	.95782	18
43	.28764	.30033	3.3297	.95774	17
44	.28792	.30065	3.3261	.95766	16
45	.28820	.30097	3.3226	.95757	15
46	.28847	.30128	3.3191	.95749	14
47	.28875	.30160	3.3156	.95740	13
48	.28903	.30192	3.3122	.95732	12
49	.28931	.30224	3.3087	.95724	11
50	.28959	.30255	3.3052	.95715	10
51	.28987	.30287	3.3017	.95707	9
52	.29015	.30319	3.2983	.95698	8
53	.29042	.30351	3.2948	.95690	7
54	.29070	.30382	3.2914	.95681	6
55	.29098	.30414	3.2879	.95673	5
56	.29126	.30446	3.2845	.95664	4
57	.29154	.30478	3.2811	.95656	3
58	.29182	.30509	3.2777	.95647	2
59	.29209	.30541	3.2743	.95639	1
60	.29237	.30573	3.2709	.95630	0
′	Cos	Ctn	Tan	Sin	′

′	Sin	Tan	Ctn	Cos	′
0	.29237	.30573	3.2709	.95630	60
1	.29265	.30605	3.2675	.95622	59
2	.29293	.30637	3.2641	.95613	58
3	.29321	.30669	3.2607	.95605	57
4	.29348	.30700	3.2573	.95596	56
5	.29376	.30732	3.2539	.95588	55
6	.29404	.30764	3.2506	.95579	54
7	.29432	.30796	3.2472	.95571	53
8	.29460	.30828	3.2438	.95562	52
9	.29487	.30860	3.2405	.95554	51
10	.29515	.30891	3.2371	.95545	50
11	.29543	.30923	3.2338	.95536	49
12	.29571	.30955	3.2305	.95528	48
13	.29599	.30987	3.2272	.95519	47
14	.29626	.31019	3.2238	.95511	46
15	.29654	.31051	3.2205	.95502	45
16	.29682	.31083	3.2172	.95493	44
17	.29710	.31115	3.2139	.95485	43
18	.29737	.31147	3.2106	.95476	42
19	.29765	.31178	3.2073	.95467	41
20	.29793	.31210	3.2041	.95459	40
21	.29821	.31242	3.2008	.95450	39
22	.29849	.31274	3.1975	.95441	38
23	.29876	.31306	3.1943	.95433	37
24	.29904	.31338	3.1910	.95424	36
25	.29932	.31370	3.1878	.95415	35
26	.29960	.31402	3.1845	.95407	34
27	.29987	.31434	3.1813	.95398	33
28	.30015	.31466	3.1780	.95389	32
29	.30043	.31498	3.1748	.95380	31
30	.30071	.31530	3.1716	.95372	30
31	.30098	.31562	3.1684	.95363	29
32	.30126	.31594	3.1652	.95354	28
33	.30154	.31626	3.1620	.95345	27
34	.30182	.31658	3.1588	.95337	26
35	.30209	.31690	3.1556	.95328	25
36	.30237	.31722	3.1524	.95319	24
37	.30265	.31754	3.1492	.95310	23
38	.30292	.31786	3.1460	.95301	22
39	.30320	.31818	3.1429	.95293	21
40	.30348	.31850	3.1397	.95284	20
41	.30376	.31882	3.1366	.95275	19
42	.30403	.31914	3.1334	.95266	18
43	.30431	.31946	3.1303	.95257	17
44	.30459	.31978	3.1271	.95248	16
45	.30486	.32010	3.1240	.95240	15
46	.30514	.32042	3.1209	.95231	14
47	.30542	.32074	3.1178	.95222	13
48	.30570	.32106	3.1146	.95213	12
49	.30597	.32139	3.1115	.95204	11
50	.30625	.32171	3.1084	.95195	10
51	.30653	.32203	3.1053	.95186	9
52	.30680	.32235	3.1022	.95177	8
53	.30708	.32267	3.0991	.95168	7
54	.30736	.32299	3.0961	.95159	6
55	.30763	.32331	3.0930	.95150	5
56	.30791	.32363	3.0899	.95142	4
57	.30819	.32396	3.0868	.95133	3
58	.30846	.32428	3.0838	.95124	2
59	.30874	.32460	3.0807	.95115	1
60	.30902	.32492	3.0777	.95106	0
′	Cos	Ctn	Tan	Sin	′

′	Sin	Tan	Ctn	Cos	′		′	Sin	Tan	Ctn	Cos	′
0	.30902	.32492	3.0777	.95106	60		0	.32557	.34433	2.9042	.94552	60
1	.30929	.32524	3.0746	.95097	59		1	.32584	.34465	2.9015	.94542	59
2	.30957	.32556	3.0716	.95088	58		2	.32612	.34498	2.8987	.94533	58
3	.30985	.32588	3.0686	.95079	57		3	.32639	.34530	2.8960	.94523	57
4	.31012	.32621	3.0655	.95070	56		4	.32667	.34563	2.8933	.94514	56
5	.31040	.32653	3.0625	.95061	55		5	.32694	.34596	2.8905	.94504	55
6	.31068	.32685	3.0595	.95052	54		6	.32722	.34628	2.8878	.94495	54
7	.31095	.32717	3.0565	.95043	53		7	.32749	.34661	2.8851	.94485	53
8	.31123	.32749	3.0535	.95033	52		8	.32777	.34693	2.8824	.94476	52
9	.31151	.32782	3.0505	.95024	51		9	.32804	.34726	2.8797	.94466	51
10	.31178	.32814	3.0475	.95015	50		10	.32832	.34758	2.8770	.94457	50
11	.31206	.32846	3.0445	.95006	49		11	.32859	.34791	2.8743	.94447	49
12	.31233	.32878	3.0415	.94997	48		12	.32887	.34824	2.8716	.94438	48
13	.31261	.32911	3.0385	.94988	47		13	.32914	.34856	2.8689	.94428	47
14	.31289	.32943	3.0356	.94979	46		14	.32942	.34889	2.8662	.94418	46
15	.31316	.32975	3.0326	.94970	45		15	.32969	.34922	2.8636	.94409	45
16	.31344	.33007	3.0296	.94961	44		16	.32997	.34954	2.8609	.94399	44
17	.31372	.33040	3.0267	.94952	43		17	.33024	.34987	2.8582	.94390	43
18	.31399	.33072	3.0237	.94943	42		18	.33051	.35020	2.8556	.94380	42
19	.31427	.33104	3.0208	.94933	41		19	.33079	.35052	2.8529	.94370	41
20	.31454	.33136	3.0178	.94924	40		20	.33106	.35085	2.8502	.94361	40
21	.31482	.33169	3.0149	.94915	39		21	.33134	.35118	2.8476	.94351	39
22	.31510	.33201	3.0120	.94906	38		22	.33161	.35150	2.8449	.94342	38
23	.31537	.33233	3.0090	.94897	37		23	.33189	.35183	2.8423	.94332	37
24	.31565	.33266	3.0061	.94888	36		24	.33216	.35216	2.8397	.94322	36
25	.31593	.33298	3.0032	.94878	35		25	.33244	.35248	2.8370	.94313	35
26	.31620	.33330	3.0003	.94869	34		26	.33271	.35281	2.8344	.94303	34
27	.31648	.33363	2.9974	.94860	33		27	.33298	.35314	2.8318	.94293	33
28	.31675	.33395	2.9945	.94851	32		28	.33326	.35346	2.8291	.94284	32
29	.31703	.33427	2.9916	.94842	31		29	.33353	.35379	2.8265	.94274	31
30	.31730	.33460	2.9887	.94832	30		30	.33381	.35412	2.8239	.94264	30
31	.31758	.33492	2.9858	.94823	29		31	.33408	.35445	2.8213	.94254	29
32	.31786	.33524	2.9829	.94814	28		32	.33436	.35477	2.8187	.94245	28
33	.31813	.33557	2.9800	.94805	27		33	.33463	.35510	2.8161	.94235	27
34	.31841	.33589	2.9772	.94795	26		34	.33490	.35543	2.8135	.94225	26
35	.31868	.33621	2.9743	.94786	25		35	.33518	.35576	2.8109	.94215	25
36	.31896	.33654	2.9714	.94777	24		36	.33545	.35608	2.8083	.94206	24
37	.31923	.33686	2.9686	.94768	23		37	.33573	.35641	2.8057	.94196	23
38	.31951	.33718	2.9657	.94758	22		38	.33600	.35674	2.8032	.94186	22
39	.31979	.33751	2.9629	.94749	21		39	.33627	.35707	2.8006	.94176	21
40	.32006	.33783	2.9600	.94740	20		40	.33655	.35740	2.7980	.94167	20
41	.32034	.33816	2.9572	.94730	19		41	.33682	.35772	2.7955	.94157	19
42	.32061	.33848	2.9544	.94721	18		42	.33710	.35805	2.7929	.94147	18
43	.32089	.33881	2.9515	.94712	17		43	.33737	.35838	2.7903	.94137	17
44	.32116	.33913	2.9487	.94702	16		44	.33764	.35871	2.7878	.94127	16
45	.32144	.33945	2.9459	.94693	15		45	.33792	.35904	2.7852	.94118	15
46	.32171	.33978	2.9431	.94684	14		46	.33819	.35937	2.7827	.94108	14
47	.32199	.34010	2.9403	.94674	13		47	.33846	.35969	2.7801	.94098	13
48	.32227	.34043	2.9375	.94665	12		48	.33874	.36002	2.7776	.94088	12
49	.32254	.34075	2.9347	.94656	11		49	.33901	.36035	2.7751	.94078	11
50	.32282	.34108	2.9319	.94646	10		50	.33929	.36068	2.7725	.94068	10
51	.32309	.34140	2.9291	.94637	9		51	.33956	.36101	2.7700	.94058	9
52	.32337	.34173	2.9263	.94627	8		52	.33983	.36134	2.7675	.94049	8
53	.32364	.34205	2.9235	.94618	7		53	.34011	.36167	2.7650	.94039	7
54	.32392	.34238	2.9208	.94609	6		54	.34038	.36199	2.7625	.94029	6
55	.32419	.34270	2.9180	.94599	5		55	.34065	.36232	2.7600	.94019	5
56	.32447	.34303	2.9152	.94590	4		56	.34093	.36265	2.7575	.94009	4
57	.32474	.34335	2.9125	.94580	3		57	.34120	.36298	2.7550	.93999	3
58	.32502	.34368	2.9097	.94571	2		58	.34147	.36331	2.7525	.93989	2
59	.32529	.34400	2.9070	.94561	1		59	.34175	.36364	2.7500	.93979	1
60	.32557	.34433	2.9042	.94552	0		60	.34202	.36397	2.7475	.93969	0
′	Cos	Ctn	Tan	Sin	′		′	Cos	Ctn	Tan	Sin	′

′	Sin	Tan	Ctn	Cos	′	′	Sin	Tan	Ctn	Cos	′
0	.34202	.36397	2.7475	.93969	60	0	.35837	.38386	2.6051	.93358	60
1	.34229	.36430	2.7450	.93959	59	1	.35864	.38420	2.6028	.93348	59
2	.34257	.36463	2.7425	.93949	58	2	.35891	.38453	2.6006	.93337	58
3	.34284	.36496	2.7400	.93939	57	3	.35918	.38487	2.5983	.93327	57
4	.34311	.36529	2.7376	.93929	56	4	.35945	.38520	2.5961	.93316	56
5	.34339	.36562	2.7351	.93919	55	5	.35973	.38553	2.5938	.93306	55
6	.34366	.36595	2.7326	.93909	54	6	.36000	.38587	2.5916	.93295	54
7	.34393	.36628	2.7302	.93899	53	7	.36027	.38620	2.5893	.93285	53
8	.34421	.36661	2.7277	.93889	52	8	.36054	.38654	2.5871	.93274	52
9	.34448	.36694	2.7253	.93879	51	9	.36081	.38687	2.5848	.93264	51
10	.34475	.36727	2.7228	.93869	50	10	.36108	.38721	2.5826	.93253	50
11	.34503	.36760	2.7204	.93859	49	11	.36135	.38754	2.5804	.93243	49
12	.34530	.36793	2.7179	.93849	48	12	.36162	.38787	2.5782	.93232	48
13	.34557	.36826	2.7155	.93839	47	13	.36190	.38821	2.5759	.93222	47
14	.34584	.36859	2.7130	.93829	46	14	.36217	.38854	2.5737	.93211	46
15	.34612	.36892	2.7106	.93819	45	15	.36244	.38888	2.5715	.93201	45
16	.34639	.36925	2.7082	.93809	44	16	.36271	.38921	2.5693	.93190	44
17	.34666	.36958	2.7058	.93799	43	17	.36298	.38955	2.5671	.93180	43
18	.34694	.36991	2.7034	.93789	42	18	.36325	.38988	2.5649	.93169	42
19	.34721	.37024	2.7009	.93779	41	19	.36352	.39022	2.5627	.93159	41
20	.34748	.37057	2.6985	.93769	40	20	.36379	.39055	2.5605	.93148	40
21	.34775	.37090	2.6961	.93759	39	21	.36406	.39089	2.5583	.93137	39
22	.34803	.37123	2.6937	.93748	38	22	.36434	.39122	2.5561	.93127	38
23	.34830	.37157	2.6913	.93738	37	23	.36461	.39156	2.5539	.93116	37
24	.34857	.37190	2.6889	.93728	36	24	.36488	.39190	2.5517	.93106	36
25	.34884	.37223	2.6865	.93718	35	25	.36515	.39223	2.5495	.93095	35
26	.34912	.37256	2.6841	.93708	34	26	.36542	.39257	2.5473	.93084	34
27	.34939	.37289	2.6818	.93698	33	27	.36569	.39290	2.5452	.93074	33
28	.34966	.37322	2.6794	.93688	32	28	.36596	.39324	2.5430	.93063	32
29	.34993	.37355	2.6770	.93677	31	29	.36623	.39357	2.5408	.93052	31
30	.35021	.37388	2.6746	.93667	30	30	.36650	.39391	2.5386	.93042	30
31	.35048	.37422	2.6723	.93657	29	31	.36677	.39425	2.5365	.93031	29
32	.35075	.37455	2.6699	.93647	28	32	.36704	.39458	2.5343	.93020	28
33	.35102	.37488	2.6675	.93637	27	33	.36731	.39492	2.5322	.93010	27
34	.35130	.37521	2.6652	.93626	26	34	.36758	.39526	2.5300	.92999	26
35	.35157	.37554	2.6628	.93616	25	35	.36785	.39559	2.5279	.92988	25
36	.35184	.37588	2.6605	.93606	24	36	.36812	.39593	2.5257	.92978	24
37	.35211	.37621	2.6581	.93596	23	37	.36839	.39626	2.5236	.92967	23
38	.35239	.37654	2.6558	.93585	22	38	.36867	.39660	2.5214	.92956	22
39	.35266	.37687	2.6534	.93575	21	39	.36894	.39694	2.5193	.92945	21
40	.35293	.37720	2.6511	.93565	20	40	.36921	.39727	2.5172	.92935	20
41	.35320	.37754	2.6488	.93555	19	41	.36948	.39761	2.5150	.92924	19
42	.35347	.37787	2.6464	.93544	18	42	.36975	.39795	2.5129	.92913	18
43	.35375	.37820	2.6441	.93534	17	43	.37002	.39829	2.5108	.92902	17
44	.35402	.37853	2.6418	.93524	16	44	.37029	.39862	2.5086	.92892	16
45	.35429	.37887	2.6395	.93514	15	45	.37056	.39896	2.5065	.92881	15
46	.35456	.37920	2.6371	.93503	14	46	.37083	.39930	2.5044	.92870	14
47	.35484	.37953	2.6348	.93493	13	47	.37110	.39963	2.5023	.92859	13
48	.35511	.37986	2.6325	.93483	12	48	.37137	.39997	2.5002	.92849	12
49	.35538	.38020	2.6302	.93472	11	49	.37164	.40031	2.4981	.92838	11
50	.35565	.38053	2.6279	.93462	10	50	.37191	.40065	2.4960	.92827	10
51	.35592	.38086	2.6256	.93452	9	51	.37218	.40098	2.4939	.92816	9
52	.35619	.38120	2.6233	.93441	8	52	.37245	.40132	2.4918	.92805	8
53	.35647	.38153	2.6210	.93431	7	53	.37272	.40166	2.4897	.92794	7
54	.35674	.38186	2.6187	.93420	6	54	.37299	.40200	2.4876	.92784	6
55	.35701	.38220	2.6165	.93410	5	55	.37326	.40234	2.4855	.92773	5
56	.35728	.38253	2.6142	.93400	4	56	.37353	.40267	2.4834	.92762	4
57	.35755	.38286	2.6119	.93389	3	57	.37380	.40301	2.4813	.92751	3
58	.35782	.38320	2.6096	.93379	2	58	.37407	.40335	2.4792	.92740	2
59	.35810	.38353	2.6074	.93368	1	59	.37434	.40369	2.4772	.92729	1
60	.35837	.38386	2.6051	.93358	0	60	.37461	.40403	2.4751	.92718	0
′	Cos	Ctn	Tan	Sin	′	′	Cos	Ctn	Tan	Sin	′

′	Sin	Tan	Ctn	Cos	′	′	Sin	Tan	Ctn	Cos	′
0	.37461	.40403	2.4751	.92718	60	0	.39073	.42447	2.3559	.92050	60
1	.37488	.40436	2.4730	.92707	59	1	.39100	.42482	2.3539	.92039	59
2	.37515	.40470	2.4709	.92697	58	2	.39127	.42516	2.3520	.92028	58
3	.37542	.40504	2.4689	.92686	57	3	.39153	.42551	2.3501	.92016	57
4	.37569	.40538	2.4668	.92675	56	4	.39180	.42585	2.3483	.92005	56
5	.37595	.40572	2.4648	.92664	55	5	.39207	.42619	2.3464	.91994	55
6	.37622	.40606	2.4627	.92653	54	6	.39234	.42654	2.3445	.91982	54
7	.37649	.40640	2.4606	.92642	53	7	.39260	.42688	2.3426	.91971	53
8	.37676	.40674	2.4586	.92631	52	8	.39287	.42722	2.3407	.91959	52
9	.37703	.40707	2.4566	.92620	51	9	.39314	.42757	2.3388	.91948	51
10	.37730	.40741	2.4545	.92609	50	10	.39341	.42791	2.3369	.91936	50
11	.37757	.40775	2.4525	.92598	49	11	.39367	.42826	2.3351	.91925	49
12	.37784	.40809	2.4504	.92587	48	12	.39394	.42860	2.3332	.91914	48
13	.37811	.40843	2.4484	.92576	47	13	.39421	.42894	2.3313	.91902	47
14	.37838	.40877	2.4464	.92565	46	14	.39448	.42929	2.3294	.91891	46
15	.37865	.40911	2.4443	.92554	45	15	.39474	.42963	2.3276	.91879	45
16	.37892	.40945	2.4423	.92543	44	16	.39501	.42998	2.3257	.91868	44
17	.37919	.40979	2.4403	.92532	43	17	.39528	.43032	2.3238	.91856	43
18	.37946	.41013	2.4383	.92521	42	18	.39555	.43067	2.3220	.91845	42
19	.37973	.41047	2.4362	.92510	41	19	.39581	.43101	2.3201	.91833	41
20	.37999	.41081	2.4342	.92499	40	20	.39608	.43136	2.3183	.91822	40
21	.38026	.41115	2.4322	.92488	39	21	.39635	.43170	2.3164	.91810	39
22	.38053	.41149	2.4302	.92477	38	22	.39661	.43205	2.3146	.91799	38
23	.38080	.41183	2.4282	.92466	37	23	.39688	.43239	2.3127	.91787	37
24	.38107	.41217	2.4262	.92455	36	24	.39715	.43274	2.3109	.91775	36
25	.38134	.41251	2.4242	.92444	35	25	.39741	.43308	2.3090	.91764	35
26	.38161	.41285	2.4222	.92432	34	26	.39768	.43343	2.3072	.91752	34
27	.38188	.41319	2.4202	.92421	33	27	.39795	.43378	2.3053	.91741	33
28	.38215	.41353	2.4182	.92410	32	28	.39822	.43412	2.3035	.91729	32
29	.38241	.41387	2.4162	.92399	31	29	.39848	.43447	2.3017	.91718	31
30	.38268	.41421	2.4142	.92388	30	30	.39875	.43481	2.2998	.91706	30
31	.38295	.41455	2.4122	.92377	29	31	.39902	.43516	2.2980	.91694	29
32	.38322	.41490	2.4102	.92366	28	32	.39928	.43550	2.2962	.91683	28
33	.38349	.41524	2.4083	.92355	27	33	.39955	.43585	2.2944	.91671	27
34	.38376	.41558	2.4063	.92343	26	34	.39982	.43620	2.2925	.91660	26
35	.38403	.41592	2.4043	.92332	25	35	.40008	.43654	2.2907	.91648	25
36	.38430	.41626	2.4023	.92321	24	36	.40035	.43689	2.2889	.91636	24
37	.38456	.41660	2.4004	.92310	23	37	.40062	.43724	2.2871	.91625	23
38	.38483	.41694	2.3984	.92299	22	38	.40088	.43758	2.2853	.91613	22
39	.38510	.41728	2.3964	.92287	21	39	.40115	.43793	2.2835	.91601	21
40	.38537	.41763	2.3945	.92276	20	40	.40141	.43828	2.2817	.91590	20
41	.38564	.41797	2.3925	.92265	19	41	.40168	.43862	2.2799	.91578	19
42	.38591	.41831	2.3906	.92254	18	42	.40195	.43897	2.2781	.91566	18
43	.38617	.41865	2.3886	.92243	17	43	.40221	.43932	2.2763	.91555	17
44	.38644	.41899	2.3867	.92231	16	44	.40248	.43966	2.2745	.91543	16
45	.38671	.41933	2.3847	.92220	15	45	.40275	.44001	2.2727	.91531	15
46	.38698	.41968	2.3828	.92209	14	46	.40301	.44036	2.2709	.91519	14
47	.38725	.42002	2.3808	.92198	13	47	.40328	.44071	2.2691	.91508	13
48	.38752	.42036	2.3789	.92186	12	48	.40355	.44105	2.2673	.91496	12
49	.38778	.42070	2.3770	.92175	11	49	.40381	.44140	2.2655	.91484	11
50	.38805	.42105	2.3750	.92164	10	50	.40408	.44175	2.2637	.91472	10
51	.38832	.42139	2.3731	.92152	9	51	.40434	.44210	2.2620	.91461	9
52	.38859	.42173	2.3712	.92141	8	52	.40461	.44244	2.2602	.91449	8
53	.38886	.42207	2.3693	.92130	7	53	.40488	.44279	2.2584	.91437	7
54	.38912	.42242	2.3673	.92119	6	54	.40514	.44314	2.2566	.91425	6
55	.38939	.42276	2.3654	.92107	5	55	.40541	.44349	2.2549	.91414	5
56	.38966	.42310	2.3635	.92096	4	56	.40567	.44384	2.2531	.91402	4
57	.38993	.42345	2.3616	.92085	3	57	.40594	.44418	2.2513	.91390	3
58	.39020	.42379	2.3597	.92073	2	58	.40621	.44453	2.2496	.91378	2
59	.39046	.42413	2.3578	.92062	1	59	.40647	.44488	2.2478	.91366	1
60	.39073	.42447	2.3559	.92050	0	60	.40674	.44523	2.2460	.91355	0
′	Cos	Ctn	Tan	Sin	′	′	Cos	Ctn	Tan	Sin	′

′	Sin	Tan	Ctn	Cos	′	′	Sin	Tan	Ctn	Cos	′
0	.40674	.44523	2.2460	.91355	60	0	.42262	.46631	2.1445	.90631	60
1	.40700	.44558	2.2443	.91343	59	1	.42288	.46666	2.1429	.90618	59
2	.40727	.44593	2.2425	.91331	58	2	.42315	.46702	2.1413	.90606	58
3	.40753	.44627	2.2408	.91319	57	3	.42341	.46737	2.1396	.90594	57
4	.40780	.44662	2.2390	.91307	56	4	.42367	.46772	2.1380	.90582	56
5	.40806	.44697	2.2373	.91295	55	5	.42394	.46808	2.1364	.90569	55
6	.40833	.44732	2.2355	.91283	54	6	.42420	.46843	2.1348	.90557	54
7	.40860	.44767	2.2338	.91272	53	7	.42446	.46879	2.1332	.90545	53
8	.40886	.44802	2.2320	.91260	52	8	.42473	.46914	2.1315	.90532	52
9	.40913	.44837	2.2303	.91248	51	9	.42499	.46950	2.1299	.90520	51
10	.40939	.44872	2.2286	.91236	50	10	.42525	.46985	2.1283	.90507	50
11	.40966	.44907	2.2268	.91224	49	11	.42552	.47021	2.1267	.90495	49
12	.40992	.44942	2.2251	.91212	48	12	.42578	.47056	2.1251	.90483	48
13	.41019	.44977	2.2234	.91200	47	13	.42604	.47092	2.1235	.90470	47
14	.41045	.45012	2.2216	.91188	46	14	.42631	.47128	2.1219	.90458	46
15	.41072	.45047	2.2199	.91176	45	15	.42657	.47163	2.1203	.90446	45
16	.41098	.45082	2.2182	.91164	44	16	.42683	.47199	2.1187	.90433	44
17	.41125	.45117	2.2165	.91152	43	17	.42709	.47234	2.1171	.90421	43
18	.41151	.45152	2.2148	.91140	42	18	.42736	.47270	2.1155	.90408	42
19	.41178	.45187	2.2130	.91128	41	19	.42762	.47305	2.1139	.90396	41
20	.41204	.45222	2.2113	.91116	40	20	.42788	.47341	2.1123	.90383	40
21	.41231	.45257	2.2096	.91104	39	21	.42815	.47377	2.1107	.90371	39
22	.41257	.45292	2.2079	.91092	38	22	.42841	.47412	2.1092	.90358	38
23	.41284	.45327	2.2062	.91080	37	23	.42867	.47448	2.1076	.90346	37
24	.41310	.45362	2.2045	.91068	36	24	.42894	.47483	2.1060	.90334	36
25	.41337	.45397	2.2028	.91056	35	25	.42920	.47519	2.1044	.90321	35
26	.41363	.45432	2.2011	.91044	34	26	.42946	.47555	2.1028	.90309	34
27	.41390	.45467	2.1994	.91032	33	27	.42972	.47590	2.1013	.90296	33
28	.41416	.45502	2.1977	.91020	32	28	.42999	.47626	2.0997	.90284	32
29	.41443	.45538	2.1960	.91008	31	29	.43025	.47662	2.0981	.90271	31
30	.41469	.45573	2.1943	.90996	30	30	.43051	.47698	2.0965	.90259	30
31	.41496	.45608	2.1926	.90984	29	31	.43077	.47733	2.0950	.90246	29
32	.41522	.45643	2.1909	.90972	28	32	.43104	.47769	2.0934	.90233	28
33	.41549	.45678	2.1892	.90960	27	33	.43130	.47805	2.0918	.90221	27
34	.41575	.45713	2.1876	.90948	26	34	.43156	.47840	2.0903	.90208	26
35	.41602	.45748	2.1859	.90936	25	35	.43182	.47876	2.0887	.90196	25
36	.41628	.45784	2.1842	.90924	24	36	.43209	.47912	2.0872	.90183	24
37	.41655	.45819	2.1825	.90911	23	37	.43235	.47948	2.0856	.90171	23
38	.41681	.45854	2.1808	.90899	22	38	.43261	.47984	2.0840	.90158	22
39	.41707	.45889	2.1792	.90887	21	39	.43287	.48019	2.0825	.90146	21
40	.41734	.45924	2.1775	.90875	20	40	.43313	.48055	2.0809	.90133	20
41	.41760	.45960	2.1758	.90863	19	41	.43340	.48091	2.0794	.90120	19
42	.41787	.45995	2.1742	.90851	18	42	.43366	.48127	2.0778	.90108	18
43	.41813	.46030	2.1725	.90839	17	43	.43392	.48163	2.0763	.90095	17
44	.41840	.46065	2.1708	.90826	16	44	.43418	.48198	2.0748	.90082	16
45	.41866	.46101	2.1692	.90814	15	45	.43445	.48234	2.0732	.90070	15
46	.41892	.46136	2.1675	.90802	14	46	.43471	.48270	2.0717	.90057	14
47	.41919	.46171	2.1659	.90790	13	47	.43497	.48306	2.0701	.90045	13
48	.41945	.46206	2.1642	.90778	12	48	.43523	.48342	2.0686	.90032	12
49	.41972	.46242	2.1625	.90766	11	49	.43549	.48378	2.0671	.90019	11
50	.41998	.46277	2.1609	.90753	10	50	.43575	.48414	2.0655	.90007	10
51	.42024	.46312	2.1592	.90741	9	51	.43602	.48450	2.0640	.89994	9
52	.42051	.46348	2.1576	.90729	8	52	.43628	.48486	2.0625	.89981	8
53	.42077	.46383	2.1560	.90717	7	53	.43654	.48521	2.0609	.89968	7
54	.42104	.46418	2.1543	.90704	6	54	.43680	.48557	2.0594	.89956	6
55	.42130	.46454	2.1527	.90692	5	55	.43706	.48593	2.0579	.89943	5
56	.42156	.46489	2.1510	.90680	4	56	.43733	.48629	2.0564	.89930	4
57	.42183	.46525	2.1494	.90668	3	57	.43759	.48665	2.0549	.89918	3
58	.42209	.46560	2.1478	.90655	2	58	.43785	.48701	2.0533	.89905	2
59	.42235	.46595	2.1461	.90643	1	59	.43811	.48737	2.0518	.89892	1
60	.42262	.46631	2.1445	.90631	0	60	.43837	.48773	2.0503	.89879	0
′	Cos	Ctn	Tan	Sin	′	′	Cos	Ctn	Tan	Sin	′

′	Sin	Tan	Ctn	Cos	′
0	.43837	.48773	2.0503	.89879	60
1	.43863	.48809	2.0488	.89867	59
2	.43889	.48845	2.0473	.89854	58
3	.43916	.48881	2.0458	.89841	57
4	.43942	.48917	2.0443	.89828	56
5	.43968	.48953	2.0428	.89816	55
6	.43994	.48989	2.0413	.89803	54
7	.44020	.49026	2.0398	.89790	53
8	.44046	.49062	2.0383	.89777	52
9	.44072	.49098	2.0368	.89764	51
10	.44098	.49134	2.0353	.89752	50
11	.44124	.49170	2.0338	.89739	49
12	.44151	.49206	2.0323	.89726	48
13	.44177	.49242	2.0308	.89713	47
14	.44203	.49278	2.0293	.89700	46
15	.44229	.49315	2.0278	.89687	45
16	.44255	.49351	2.0263	.89674	44
17	.44281	.49387	2.0248	.89662	43
18	.44307	.49423	2.0233	.89649	42
19	.44333	.49459	2.0219	.89636	41
20	.44359	.49495	2.0204	.89623	40
21	.44385	.49532	2.0189	.89610	39
22	.44411	.49568	2.0174	.89597	38
23	.44437	.49604	2.0160	.89584	37
24	.44464	.49640	2.0145	.89571	36
25	.44490	.49677	2.0130	.89558	35
26	.44516	.49713	2.0115	.89545	34
27	.44542	.49749	2.0101	.89532	33
28	.44568	.49786	2.0086	.89519	32
29	.44594	.49822	2.0072	.89506	31
30	.44620	.49858	2.0057	.89493	30
31	.44646	.49694	2.0042	.89480	29
32	.44672	.49931	2.0028	.89467	28
33	.44698	.49967	2.0013	.89454	27
34	.44724	.50004	1.9999	.89441	26
35	.44750	.50040	1.9984	.89428	25
36	.44776	.50076	1.9970	.89415	24
37	.44802	.50113	1.9955	.89402	23
38	.44828	.50149	1.9941	.89389	22
39	.44854	.50185	1.9926	.89376	21
40	.44880	.50222	1.9912	.89363	20
41	.44906	.50258	1.9897	.89350	19
42	.44932	.50295	1.9883	.89337	18
43	.44958	.50331	1.9868	.89324	17
44	.44984	.50368	1.9854	.89311	16
45	.45010	.50404	1.9840	.89298	15
46	.45036	.50441	1.9825	.89285	14
47	.45062	.50477	1.9811	.89272	13
48	.45088	.50514	1.9797	.89259	12
49	.45114	.50550	1.9782	.89245	11
50	.45140	.50587	1.9768	.89232	10
51	.45166	.50623	1.9754	.89219	9
52	.45192	.50660	1.9740	.89206	8
53	.45218	.50696	1.9725	.89193	7
54	.45243	.50733	1.9711	.89180	6
55	.45269	.50769	1.9697	.89167	5
56	.45295	.50806	1.9683	.89153	4
57	.45321	.50843	1.9669	.89140	3
58	.45347	.50879	1.9654	.89127	2
59	.45373	.50916	1.9640	.89114	1
60	.45399	.50953	1.9626	.89101	0
′	Cos	Ctn	Tan	Sin	′

′	Sin	Tan	Ctn	Cos	′
0	.45399	.50953	1.9626	.89101	60
1	.45425	.50989	1.9612	.89087	59
2	.45451	.51026	1.9598	.89074	58
3	.45477	.51063	1.9584	.89061	57
4	.45503	.51099	1.9570	.89048	56
5	.45529	.51136	1.9556	.89035	55
6	.45554	.51173	1.9542	.89021	54
7	.45580	.51209	1.9528	.89008	53
8	.45606	.51246	1.9514	.68995	52
9	.45632	.51283	1.9500	.88981	51
10	.45658	.51319	1.9486	.88968	50
11	.45684	.51356	1.9472	.88955	49
12	.45710	.51393	1.9458	.88942	48
13	.45736	.51430	1.9444	.88928	47
14	.45762	.51467	1.9430	.88915	46
15	.45787	.51503	1.9416	.88902	45
16	.45813	.51540	1.9402	.88888	44
17	.45839	.51577	1.9388	.88875	43
18	.45865	.51614	1.9375	.88862	42
19	.45891	.51651	1.9361	.88848	41
20	.45917	.51688	1.9347	.88835	40
21	.45942	.51724	1.9333	.88822	39
22	.45968	.51761	1.9319	.88808	38
23	.45994	.51798	1.9306	.88795	37
24	.46020	.51835	1.9292	.88782	36
25	.46046	.51872	1.9278	.88768	35
26	.46072	.51909	1.9265	.88755	34
27	.46097	.51946	1.9251	.88741	33
28	.46123	.51983	1.9237	.88728	32
29	.46149	.52020	1.9223	.88715	31
30	.46175	.52057	1.9210	.88701	30
31	.46201	.52094	1.9196	.88688	29
32	.46226	.52131	1.9183	.88674	28
33	.46252	.52168	1.9169	.88661	27
34	.46278	.52205	1.9155	.88647	26
35	.46304	.52242	1.9142	.88634	25
36	.46330	.52279	1.9128	.88620	24
37	.46355	.52316	1.9115	.88607	23
38	.46381	.52353	1.9101	.88593	22
39	.46407	.52390	1.9088	.88580	21
40	.46433	.52427	1.9074	.88566	20
41	.46458	.52464	1.9061	.88553	19
42	.46484	.52501	1.9047	.88539	18
43	.46510	.52538	1.9034	.88526	17
44	.46536	.52575	1.9020	.88512	16
45	.46561	.52613	1.9007	.88499	15
46	.46587	.52650	1.8993	.88485	14
47	.46613	.52687	1.8980	.88472	13
48	.46639	.52724	1.8967	.88458	12
49	.46664	.52761	1.8953	.88445	11
50	.46690	.52798	1.8940	.88431	10
51	.46716	.52836	1.8927	.88417	9
52	.46742	.52873	1.8913	.88404	8
53	.46767	.52910	1.8900	.88390	7
54	.46793	.52947	1.8887	.88377	6
55	.46819	.52985	1.8873	.88363	5
56	.46844	.53022	1.8860	.88349	4
57	.46870	.53059	1.8847	.88336	3
58	.46896	.53096	1.8834	.88322	2
59	.46921	.53134	1.8820	.88308	1
60	.46947	.53171	1.8807	.88295	0
′	Cos	Ctn	Tan	Sin	′

′	Sin	Tan	Ctn	Cos	′	′	Sin	Tan	Ctn	Cos	′
0	.46947	.53171	1.8807	.88295	60	0	.48481	.55431	1.8040	.87462	60
1	.46973	.53208	1.8794	.88281	59	1	.48506	.55469	1.8028	.87448	59
2	.46999	.53246	1.8781	.88267	58	2	.48532	.55507	1.8016	.87434	58
3	.47024	.53283	1.8768	.88254	57	3	.48557	.55545	1.8003	.87420	57
4	.47050	.53320	1.8755	.88240	56	4	.48583	.55583	1.7991	.87406	56
5	.47076	.53358	1.8741	.88226	55	5	.48608	.55621	1.7979	.87391	55
6	.47101	.53395	1.8728	.88213	54	6	.48634	.55659	1.7966	.87377	54
7	.47127	.53432	1.8715	.88199	53	7	.48659	.55697	1.7954	.87363	53
8	.47153	.53470	1.8702	.88185	52	8	.48684	.55736	1.7942	.87349	52
9	.47178	.53507	1.8689	.88172	51	9	.48710	.55774	1.7930	.87335	51
10	.47204	.53545	1.8676	.88158	50	10	.48735	.55812	1.7917	.87321	50
11	.47229	.53582	1.8663	.88144	49	11	.48761	.55850	1.7905	.87306	49
12	.47255	.53620	1.8650	.88130	48	12	.48786	.55888	1.7893	.87292	48
13	.47281	.53657	1.8637	.88117	47	13	.48811	.55926	1.7881	.87278	47
14	.47306	.53694	1.8624	.88103	46	14	.48837	.55964	1.7868	.87264	46
15	.47332	.53732	1.8611	.88089	45	15	.48862	.56003	1.7856	.87250	45
16	.47358	.53769	1.8598	.88075	44	16	.48888	.56041	1.7844	.87235	44
17	.47383	.53807	1.8585	.88062	43	17	.48913	.56079	1.7832	.87221	43
18	.47409	.53844	1.8572	.88048	42	18	.48938	.56117	1.7820	.87207	42
19	.47434	.53882	1.8559	.88034	41	19	.48964	.56156	1.7808	.87193	41
20	.47460	.53920	1.8546	.88020	40	20	.48989	.56194	1.7796	.87178	40
21	.47486	.53957	1.8533	.88006	39	21	.49014	.56232	1.7783	.87164	39
22	.47511	.53995	1.8520	.87993	38	22	.49040	.56270	1.7771	.87150	38
23	.47537	.54032	1.8507	.87979	37	23	.49065	.56309	1.7759	.87136	37
24	.47562	.54070	1.8495	.87965	36	24	.49090	.56347	1.7747	.87121	36
25	.47588	.54107	1.8482	.87951	35	25	.49116	.56385	1.7735	.87107	35
26	.47614	.54145	1.8469	.87937	34	26	.49141	.56424	1.7723	.87093	34
27	.47639	.54183	1.8456	.87923	33	27	.49166	.56462	1.7711	.87079	33
28	.47665	.54220	1.8443	.87909	32	28	.49192	.56501	1.7699	.87064	32
29	.47690	.54258	1.8430	.87896	31	29	.49217	.56539	1.7687	.87050	31
30	.47716	.54296	1.8418	.87882	30	30	.49242	.56577	1.7675	.87036	30
31	.47741	.54333	1.8405	.87868	29	31	.49268	.56616	1.7663	.87021	29
32	.47767	.54371	1.8392	.87854	28	32	.49293	.56654	1.7651	.87007	28
33	.47793	.54409	1.8379	.87840	27	33	.49318	.56693	1.7639	.86993	27
34	.47818	.54446	1.8367	.87826	26	34	.49344	.56731	1.7627	.86978	26
35	.47844	.54484	1.8354	.87812	25	35	.49369	.56769	1.7615	.86964	25
36	.47869	.54522	1.8341	.87798	24	36	.49394	.56808	1.7603	.86949	24
37	.47895	.54560	1.8329	.87784	23	37	.49419	.56846	1.7591	.86935	23
38	.47920	.54597	1.8316	.87770	22	38	.49445	.56885	1.7579	.86921	22
39	.47946	.54635	1.8303	.87756	21	39	.49470	.56923	1.7567	.86906	21
40	.47971	.54673	1.8291	.87743	20	40	.49495	.56962	1.7556	.86892	20
41	.47997	.54711	1.8278	.87729	19	41	.49521	.57000	1.7544	.86878	19
42	.48022	.54748	1.8265	.87715	18	42	.49546	.57039	1.7532	.86863	18
43	.48048	.54786	1.8253	.87701	17	43	.49571	.57078	1.7520	.86849	17
44	.48073	.54824	1.8240	.87687	16	44	.49596	.57116	1.7508	.86834	16
45	.48099	.54862	1.8228	.87673	15	45	.49622	.57155	1.7496	.86820	15
46	.48124	.54900	1.8215	.87659	14	46	.49647	.57193	1.7485	.86805	14
47	.48150	.54938	1.8202	.87645	13	47	.49672	.57232	1.7473	.86791	13
48	.48175	.54975	1.8190	.87631	12	48	.49697	.57271	1.7461	.86777	12
49	.48201	.55013	1.8177	.87617	11	49	.49723	.57309	1.7449	.86762	11
50	.48226	.55051	1.8165	.87603	10	50	.49748	.57348	1.7437	.86748	10
51	.48252	.55089	1.8152	.87589	9	51	.49773	.57386	1.7426	.86733	9
52	.48277	.55127	1.8140	.87575	8	52	.49798	.57425	1.7414	.86719	8
53	.48303	.55165	1.8127	.87561	7	53	.49824	.57464	1.7402	.86704	7
54	.48328	.55203	1.8115	.87546	6	54	.49849	.57503	1.7391	.86690	6
55	48354	55241	1 8103	87532	5	55	49874	57541	1 7379	86675	5
56	.48379	.55279	1.8090	.87518	4	56	.49899	57580	1 7367	86661	4
57	.48405	.55317	1.8078	.87504	3	57	.49924	.57619	1.7355	.86646	3
58	.48430	.55355	1.8065	.87490	2	58	.49950	.57657	1.7344	.86632	2
59	.48456	.55393	1.8053	.87476	1	59	.49975	.57696	1.7332	.86617	1
60	.48481	.55431	1.8040	.87462	0	60	.50000	.57735	1.7321	.86603	0
′	Cos	Ctn	Tan	Sin	′	′	Cos	Ctn	Tan	Sin	′

′	Sin	Tan	Ctn	Cos	′	′	Sin	Tan	Ctn	Cos	′
0	.50000	.57735	1.7321	.86603	60	0	.51504	.60086	1.6643	.85717	60
1	.50025	.57774	1.7309	.86588	59	1	.51529	.60126	1.6632	.85702	59
2	.50050	.57813	1.7297	.86573	58	2	.51554	.60165	1.6621	.85687	58
3	.50076	.57851	1.7286	.86559	57	3	.51579	.60205	1.6610	.85672	57
4	.50101	.57890	1.7274	.86544	56	4	.51604	.60245	1.6599	.85657	56
5	.50126	.57929	1.7262	.86530	55	5	.51628	.60284	1.6588	.85642	55
6	.50151	.57968	1.7251	.86515	54	6	.51653	.60324	1.6577	.85627	54
7	.50176	.58007	1.7239	.86501	53	7	.51678	.60364	1.6566	.85612	53
8	.50201	.58046	1.7228	.86486	52	8	.51703	.60403	1.6555	.85597	52
9	.50227	.58085	1.7216	.86471	51	9	.51728	.60443	1.6545	.85582	51
10	.50252	.58124	1.7205	.86457	50	10	.51753	.60483	1.6534	.85567	50
11	.50277	.58162	1.7193	.86442	49	11	.51778	.60522	1.6523	.85551	49
12	.50302	.48201	1.7182	.86427	48	12	.51803	.60562	1.6512	.85536	48
13	.50327	.58240	1.7170	.86413	47	13	.51828	.60602	1.6501	.85521	47
14	.50352	.58279	1.7159	.86398	46	14	.51852	.60642	1.6490	.85506	46
15	.50377	.58318	1.7147	.86384	45	15	.51877	.60681	1.6479	.85491	45
16	.50403	.58357	1.7136	.86369	44	16	.51902	.60721	1.6469	.85476	44
17	.50428	.58396	1.7124	.86354	43	17	.51927	.60761	1.6458	.85461	43
18	.50453	.58435	1.7113	.86340	42	18	.51952	.60801	1.6447	.85446	42
19	.50478	.58474	1.7102	.86325	41	19	.51977	.60841	1.6436	.85431	41
20	.50503	.58513	1.7090	.86310	40	20	.52002	.60881	1.6426	.85416	40
21	.50528	.58552	1.7079	.86295	39	21	.52026	.60921	1.6415	.85401	39
22	.50553	.58591	1.7067	.86281	38	22	.52051	.60960	1.6404	.85385	38
23	.50578	.58631	1.7056	.86266	37	23	.52076	.61000	1.6393	.85370	37
24	.50603	.58670	1.7045	.86251	36	24	.52101	.61040	1.6383	.85355	36
25	.50628	.58709	1.7033	.86237	35	25	.52126	.61080	1.6372	.85340	35
26	.50654	.58748	1.7022	.86222	34	26	.52151	.61120	1.6361	.85325	34
27	.50679	.58787	1.7011	.86207	33	27	.52175	.61160	1.6351	.85310	33
28	.50704	.58826	1.6999	.86192	32	28	.52200	.61200	1.6340	.85294	32
29	.50729	.58865	1.6988	.86178	31	29	.52225	.61240	1.6329	.85279	31
30	.50754	.58905	1.6977	.86163	30	30	.52250	.61280	1.6319	.85264	30
31	.50779	.58944	1.6965	.86148	29	31	.52275	.61320	1.6308	.85249	29
32	.50804	.58983	1.6954	.86133	28	32	.52299	.61360	1.6297	.85234	28
33	.50829	.59022	1.6943	.86119	27	33	.52324	.61400	1.6287	.85218	27
34	.50854	.59061	1.6932	.86104	26	34	.52349	.61440	1.6276	.85203	26
35	.50879	.59101	1.6920	.86089	25	35	.52374	.61480	1.6265	.85188	25
36	.50904	.59140	1.6909	.86074	24	36	.52399	.61520	1.6255	.85173	24
37	.50929	.59179	1.6898	.86059	23	37	.52423	.61561	1.6244	.85157	23
38	.50954	.59218	1.6887	.86045	22	38	.52448	.61601	1.6234	.85142	22
39	.50979	.59258	1.6875	.86030	21	39	.52473	.61641	1.6223	.85127	21
40	.51004	.59297	1.6864	.86015	20	40	.52498	.61681	1.6212	.85112	20
41	.51029	.59336	1.6853	.86000	19	41	.52522	.61721	1.6202	.85096	19
42	.51054	.59376	1.6842	.85985	18	42	.52547	.61761	1.6191	.85081	18
43	.51079	.59415	1.6831	.85970	17	43	.52572	.61801	1.6181	.85066	17
44	.51104	.59454	1.6820	.85956	16	44	.52597	.61842	1.6170	.85051	16
45	.51129	.59494	1.6808	.85941	15	45	.52621	.61882	1.6160	.85035	15
46	.51154	.59533	1.6797	.85926	14	46	.52646	.61922	1.6149	.85020	14
47	.51179	.59573	1.6786	.85911	13	47	.52671	.61962	1.6139	.85005	13
48	.51204	.59612	1.6775	.85896	12	48	.52696	.62003	1.6128	.84989	12
49	.51229	.59651	1.6764	.85881	11	49	.52720	.62043	1.6118	.84974	11
50	.51254	.59691	1.6753	.85866	10	50	.52745	.62083	1.6107	.84959	10
51	.51279	.59730	1.6742	.85851	9	51	.52770	.62124	1.6097	.84943	9
52	.51304	.59770	1.6731	.85836	8	52	.52794	.62164	1.6087	.84928	8
53	.51329	.59809	1.6720	.85821	7	53	.52819	.62204	1.6076	.84913	7
54	.51354	.59849	1.6709	.85806	6	54	.52844	.62245	1.6066	.84897	6
55	.51379	.59888	1.6698	.85792	5	55	.52869	.62285	1.6055	.84882	5
56	.51404	.59928	1.6687	.85777	4	56	.52893	.62325	1.6045	.84866	4
57	.51429	.59967	1.6676	.85762	3	57	.52918	.62366	1.6034	.84851	3
58	.51454	.60007	1.6665	.85747	2	58	.52943	.62406	1.6024	.84836	2
59	.51479	.60046	1.6654	.85732	1	59	.52967	.62446	1.6014	.84820	1
60	.51504	.60086	1.6643	.85717	0	60	.52992	.62487	1.6003	.84805	0
′	Cos	Ctn	Tan	Sin	′	′	Cos	Ctn	Tan	Sin	′

′	Sin	Tan	Ctn	Cos	′	′	Sin	Tan	Ctn	Cos	′
0	.52992	.62487	1.6003	.84805	60	0	.54464	.64941	1.5399	.83867	60
1	.53017	.62527	1.5993	.84789	59	1	.54488	.64982	1.5389	.83851	59
2	.53041	.62568	1.5983	.84774	58	2	.54513	.65024	1.5379	.83835	58
3	.53066	.62608	1.5972	.84759	57	3	.54537	.65065	1.5369	.83819	57
4	.53091	.62649	1.5962	.84743	56	4	.54561	.65106	1.5359	.83804	56
5	.53115	.62689	1.5952	.84728	55	5	.54586	.65148	1.5350	.83788	55
6	.53140	.62730	1.5941	.84712	54	6	.54610	.65189	1.5340	.83772	54
7	.53164	.62770	1.5931	.84697	53	7	.54635	.65231	1.5330	.83756	53
8	.53189	.62811	1.5921	.84681	52	8	.54659	.65272	1.5320	.83740	52
9	.53214	.62852	1.5911	.84666	51	9	.54683	.65314	1.5311	.83724	51
10	.53238	.62892	1.5900	.84650	50	10	.54708	.65355	1.5301	.83708	50
11	.53263	.62933	1.5890	.84635	49	11	.54732	.65397	1.5291	.83692	49
12	.53288	.62973	1.5880	.84619	48	12	.54756	.65438	1.5282	.83676	48
13	.53312	.63014	1.5869	.84604	47	13	.54781	.65480	1.5272	.83660	47
14	.53337	.63055	1.5859	.84588	46	14	.54805	.65521	1.5262	.83645	46
15	.53361	.63095	1.5849	.84573	45	15	.54829	.65563	1.5253	.83629	45
16	.53386	.63136	1.5839	.84557	44	16	.54854	.65604	1.5243	.83613	44
17	.53411	.63177	1.5829	.84542	43	17	.54878	.65646	1.5233	.83597	43
18	.53435	.63217	1.5818	.84526	42	18	.54902	.65688	1.5224	.83581	42
19	.53460	.63258	1.5808	.84511	41	19	.54927	.65729	1.5214	.83565	41
20	.53484	.63299	1.5798	.84495	40	20	.54951	.65771	1.5204	.83549	40
21	.53509	.63340	1.5788	.84480	39	21	.54975	.65813	1.5195	.83533	39
22	.53534	.63380	1.5778	.84464	38	22	.54999	.65854	1.5185	.83517	38
23	.53558	.63421	1.5768	.84448	37	23	.55024	.65896	1.5175	.83501	37
24	.53583	.63462	1.5757	.84433	36	24	.55048	.65938	1.5166	.83485	36
25	.53607	.63503	1.5747	.84417	35	25	.55072	.65980	1.5156	.83469	35
26	.53632	.63544	1.5737	.84402	34	26	.55097	.66021	1.5147	.83453	34
27	.53656	.63584	1.5727	.84386	33	27	.55121	.66063	1.5137	.83437	33
28	.53681	.63625	1.5717	.84370	32	28	.55145	.66105	1.5127	.83421	32
29	.53705	.63666	1.5707	.84355	31	29	.55169	.66147	1.5118	.83405	31
30	.53730	.63707	1.5697	.84339	30	30	.55194	.66189	1.5108	.83389	30
31	.53754	.63748	1.5687	.84324	29	31	.55218	.66230	1.5099	.83373	29
32	.53779	.63789	1.5677	.84308	28	32	.55242	.66272	1.5089	.83356	28
33	.53804	.63830	1.5667	.84292	27	33	.55266	.66314	1.5080	.83340	27
34	.53828	.63871	1.5657	.84277	26	34	.55291	.66356	1.5070	.83324	26
35	.53853	.63912	1.5647	.84261	25	35	.55315	.66398	1.5061	.83308	25
36	.53877	.63953	1.5637	.84245	24	36	.55339	.66440	1.5051	.83292	24
37	.53902	.63994	1.5627	.84230	23	37	.55363	.66482	1.5042	.83276	23
38	.53926	.64035	1.5617	.84214	22	38	.55388	.66524	1.5032	.83260	22
39	.53951	.64076	1.5607	.84198	21	39	.55412	.66566	1.5023	.83244	21
40	.53975	.64117	1.5597	.84182	20	40	.55436	.66608	1.5013	.83228	20
41	.54000	.64158	1.5587	.84167	19	41	.55460	.66650	1.5004	.83212	19
42	.54024	.64199	1.5577	.84151	18	42	.55484	.66692	1.4994	.83195	18
43	.54049	.64240	1.5567	.84135	17	43	.55509	.66734	1.4985	.83179	17
44	.54073	.64281	1.5557	.84120	16	44	.55533	.66776	1.4975	.83163	16
45	.54097	.64322	1.5547	.84104	15	45	.55557	.66818	1.4966	.83147	15
46	.54122	.64363	1.5537	.84088	14	46	.55581	.66860	1.4957	.83131	14
47	.54146	.64404	1.5527	.84072	13	47	.55605	.66902	1.4947	.83115	13
48	.54171	.64446	1.5517	.84057	12	48	.55630	.66944	1.4938	.83098	12
49	.54195	.64487	1.5507	.84041	11	49	.55654	.66986	1.4928	.83082	11
50	.54220	.64528	1.5497	.84025	10	50	.55678	.67028	1.4919	.83066	10
51	.54244	.64569	1.5487	.84009	9	51	.55702	.67071	1.4910	.83050	9
52	.54269	.64610	1.5477	.83994	8	52	.55726	.67113	1.4900	.83034	8
53	.54293	.64652	1.5468	.83978	7	53	.55750	.67155	1.4891	.83017	7
54	.54317	.64693	1.5458	.83962	6	54	.55775	.67197	1.4882	.83001	6
55	.54342	.64734	1.5448	.83946	5	55	.55799	.67239	1.4872	.82985	5
56	.54366	.64775	1.5438	.83930	4	56	.55823	.67282	1.4863	.82969	4
57	.54391	.64817	1.5428	.83915	3	57	.55847	.67324	1.4854	.82953	3
58	.54415	.64858	1.5418	.83899	2	58	.55871	.67366	1.4844	.82936	2
59	.54440	.64899	1.5408	.83883	1	59	.55895	.67409	1.4835	.82920	1
60	.54464	.64941	1.5399	.83867	0	60	.55919	.67451	1.4826	.82904	0
′	Cos	Ctn	Tan	Sin	′	′	Cos	Ctn	Tan	Sin	′

′	Sin	Tan	Ctn	Cos	′		′	Sin	Tan	Ctn	Cos	′
0	.55919	.67451	1.4826	.82904	60		0	.57358	.70021	1.4281	.81915	60
1	.55943	.67493	1.4816	.82887	59		1	.57381	.70064	1.4273	.81899	59
2	.55968	.67536	1.4807	.82871	58		2	.57405	.70107	1.4264	.81882	58
3	.55992	.67578	1.4798	.82855	57		3	.57429	.70151	1.4255	.81865	57
4	.56016	.67620	1.4788	.82839	56		4	.57453	.70194	1.4246	.81848	56
5	.56040	.67663	1.4779	.82822	55		5	.57477	.70238	1.4237	.81832	55
6	.56064	.67705	1.4770	.82806	54		6	.57501	.70281	1.4229	.81815	54
7	.56088	.67748	1.4761	.82790	53		7	.57524	.70325	1.4220	.81798	53
8	.56112	.67790	1.4751	.82773	52		8	.57548	.70368	1.4211	.81782	52
9	.56136	.67832	1.4742	.82757	51		9	.57572	.70412	1.4202	.81765	51
10	.56160	.67875	1.4733	.82741	50		10	.57596	.70455	1.4193	.81748	50
11	.56184	.67917	1.4724	.82724	49		11	.57619	.70499	1.4185	.81731	49
12	.56208	.67960	1.4715	.82708	48		12	.57643	.70542	1.4176	.81714	48
13	.56232	.68002	1.4705	.82692	47		13	.57667	.70586	1.4167	.81698	47
14	.56256	.68045	1.4696	.82675	46		14	.57691	.70629	1.4158	.81681	46
15	.56280	.68088	1.4687	.82659	45		15	.57715	.70673	1.4150	.81664	45
16	.56305	.68130	1.4678	.82643	44		16	.57738	.70717	1.4141	.81647	44
17	.56329	.68173	1.4669	.82626	43		17	.57762	.70760	1.4132	.81631	43
18	.56353	.68215	1.4659	.82610	42		18	.57786	.70804	1.4124	.81614	42
19	.56377	.68258	1.4650	.82593	41		19	.57810	.70848	1.4115	.81597	41
20	.56401	.68301	1.4641	.82577	40		20	.57833	.70891	1.4106	.81580	40
21	.56425	.68343	1.4632	.82561	39		21	.57857	.70935	1.4097	.81563	39
22	.56449	.68386	1.4623	.82544	38		22	.57881	.70979	1.4089	.81546	38
23	.56473	.68429	1.4614	.82528	37		23	.57904	.71023	1.4080	.81530	37
24	.56497	.68471	1.4605	.82511	36		24	.57928	.71066	1.4071	.81513	36
25	.56521	.68514	1.4596	.82495	35		25	.57952	.71110	1.4063	.81496	35
26	.56545	.68557	1.4586	.82478	34		26	.57976	.71154	1.4054	.81479	34
27	.56569	.68600	1.4577	.82462	33		27	.57999	.71198	1.4045	.81462	33
28	.56593	.68642	1.4568	.82446	32		28	.58023	.71242	1.4037	.81445	32
29	.56617	.68685	1.4559	.82429	31		29	.58047	.71285	1.4028	.81428	31
30	.56641	.68728	1.4550	.82413	30		30	.58070	.71329	1.4019	.81412	30
31	.56665	.68771	1.4541	.82396	29		31	.58094	.71373	1.4011	.81395	29
32	.56689	.68814	1.4532	.82380	28		32	.58118	.71417	1.4002	.81378	28
33	.56713	.68857	1.4523	.82363	27		33	.58141	.71461	1.3994	.81361	27
34	.56736	.68900	1.4514	.82347	26		34	.58165	.71505	1.3985	.81344	26
35	.56760	.68942	1.4505	.82330	25		35	.58189	.71549	1.3976	.81327	25
36	.56784	.68985	1.4496	.82314	24		36	.58212	.71593	1.3968	.81310	24
37	.56808	.69028	1.4487	.82297	23		37	.58236	.71637	1.3959	.81293	23
38	.56832	.69071	1.4478	.82281	22		38	.58260	.71681	1.3951	.81276	22
39	.56856	.69114	1.4469	.82264	21		39	.58283	.71725	1.3942	.81259	21
40	.56880	.69157	1.4460	.82248	20		40	.58307	.71769	1.3934	.81242	20
41	.56904	.69200	1.4451	.82231	19		41	.58330	.71813	1.3925	.81225	19
42	.56928	.69243	1.4442	.82214	18		42	.58354	.71857	1.3916	.81208	18
43	.56952	.69286	1.4433	.82198	17		43	.58378	.71901	1.3908	.81191	17
44	.56976	.69329	1.4424	.82181	16		44	.58401	.71946	1.3899	.81174	16
45	.57000	.69372	1.4415	.82165	15		45	.58425	.71990	1.3891	.81157	15
46	.57024	.69416	1.4406	.82148	14		46	.58449	.72034	1.3882	.81140	14
47	.57047	.69459	1.4397	.82132	13		47	.58472	.72078	1.3874	.81123	13
48	.57071	.69502	1.4388	.82115	12		48	.58496	.72122	1.3865	.81106	12
49	.57095	.69545	1.4379	.82098	11		49	.58519	.72167	1.3857	.81089	11
50	.57119	.69588	1.4370	.82082	10		50	.58543	.72211	1.3848	.81072	10
51	.57143	.69631	1.4361	.82065	9		51	.58567	.72255	1.3840	.81055	9
52	.57167	.69675	1.4352	.82048	8		52	.58590	.72299	1.3831	.81038	8
53	.57191	.69718	1.4344	.82032	7		53	.58614	.72344	1.3823	.81021	7
54	.57215	.69761	1.4335	.82015	6		54	.58637	.72388	1.3814	.81004	6
55	.57238	.69804	1.4326	.81999	5		55	.58661	.72432	1.3806	.80987	5
56	.47262	.69847	1.4317	.81982	4		56	.58684	.72477	1.3798	.80970	4
57	.57286	.69891	1.4308	.81965	3		57	.58708	.72521	1.3789	.80953	3
58	.57310	.69934	1.4299	.81949	2		58	.58731	.72565	1.3781	.80936	2
59	.57334	.69977	1.4290	.81932	1		59	.58755	.72610	1.3772	.80919	1
60	.57358	.70021	1.4281	.81915	0		60	.58779	.72654	1.3764	.80902	0
′	Cos	Ctn	Tan	Sin	′		′	Cos	Ctn	Tan	Sin	′

′	Sin	Tan	Ctn	Cos	′	′	Sin	Tan	Ctn	Cos	′
0	.58779	.72654	1.3764	.80902	60	0	.60182	.75355	1.3270	.79864	60
1	.58802	.72699	1.3755	.80885	59	1	.60205	.75401	1.3262	.79846	59
2	.58826	.72743	1.3747	.80867	58	2	.60228	.75447	1.3254	.79829	58
3	.58849	.72788	1.3739	.80850	57	3	.60251	.75492	1.3246	.79811	57
4	.58873	.72832	1.3730	.80833	56	4	.60274	.75538	1.3238	.79793	56
5	.58896	.72877	1.3722	.80816	55	5	.60298	.75584	1.3230	.79776	55
6	.58920	.72921	1.3713	.80799	54	6	.60321	.75629	1.3222	.79758	54
7	.58943	.72966	1.3705	.80782	53	7	.60344	.75675	1.3214	.79741	53
8	.58967	.73010	1.3697	.80765	52	8	.60367	.75721	1.3206	.79723	52
9	.58990	.73055	1.3688	.80748	51	9	.60390	.75767	1.3198	.79706	51
10	.59014	.73100	1.3680	.80730	50	10	.60414	.75812	1.3190	.79688	50
11	.59037	.73144	1.3672	.80713	49	11	.60437	.75858	1.3182	.79671	49
12	.59061	.73189	1.3663	.80696	48	12	.60460	.75904	1.3175	.79653	48
13	.59084	.73234	1.3655	.80679	47	13	.60483	.75950	1.3167	.79635	47
14	.59108	.73278	1.3647	.80662	46	14	.60506	.75996	1.3159	.79618	46
15	.59131	.73323	1.3638	.80644	45	15	.60529	.76042	1.3151	.79600	45
16	.59154	.73368	1.3630	.80627	44	16	.60553	.76088	1.3143	.79583	44
17	.59178	.73413	1.3622	.80610	43	17	.60576	.76134	1.3135	.79565	43
18	.59201	.73457	1.3613	.80593	42	18	.60599	.76180	1.3127	.79547	42
19	.59225	.73502	1.3605	.80576	41	19	.60622	.76226	1.3119	.79530	41
20	.59248	.73547	1.3597	.80558	40	20	.60645	.76272	1.3111	.79512	40
21	.59272	.73592	1.3588	.80541	39	21	.60668	.76318	1.3103	.79494	39
22	.59295	.73637	1.3580	.80524	38	22	.60691	.76364	1.3095	.79477	38
23	.59318	.73681	1.3572	.80507	37	23	.60714	.76410	1.3087	.79459	37
24	.59342	.73726	1.3564	.80489	36	24	.60738	.76456	1.3079	.79441	36
25	.59365	.73771	1.3555	.80472	35	25	.60761	.76502	1.3072	.79424	35
26	.59389	.73816	1.3547	.80455	34	26	.60784	.76548	1.3064	.79406	34
27	.59412	.73861	1.3539	.80438	33	27	.60807	.76594	1.3056	.79388	33
28	.59436	.73906	1.3531	.80420	32	28	.60830	.76640	1.3048	.79371	32
29	.59459	.73951	1.3522	.80403	31	29	.60853	.76686	1.3040	.79353	31
30	.59482	.73996	1.3514	.80386	30	30	.60876	.76733	1.3032	.79335	30
31	.59506	.74041	1.3506	.80368	29	31	.60899	.76779	1.3024	.79318	29
32	.59529	.74086	1.3498	.80351	28	32	.60922	.76825	1.3017	.79300	28
33	.59552	.74131	1.3490	.80334	27	33	.60945	.76871	1.3009	.79282	27
34	.59576	.74176	1.3481	.80316	26	34	.60968	.76918	1.3001	.79264	26
35	.59599	.74221	1.3473	.80299	25	35	.60991	.76964	1.2993	.79247	25
36	.59622	.74267	1.3465	.80282	24	36	.61015	.77010	1.2985	.79229	24
37	.59646	.74312	1.3457	.80264	23	37	.61038	.77057	1.2977	.79211	23
38	.59669	.74357	1.3449	.80247	22	38	.61061	.77103	1.2970	.79193	22
39	.59693	.74402	1.3440	.80230	21	39	.61084	.77149	1.2962	.79176	21
40	.59716	.74447	1.3432	.80212	20	40	.61107	.77196	1.2954	.79158	20
41	.59739	.74492	1.3424	.80195	19	41	.61130	.77242	1.2946	.79140	19
42	.59763	.74538	1.3416	.80178	18	42	.61153	.77289	1.2938	.79122	18
43	.59786	.74583	1.3408	.80160	17	43	.61176	.77335	1.2931	.79105	17
44	.59809	.74628	1.3400	.80143	16	44	.61199	.77382	1.2923	.79087	16
45	.59832	.74674	1.3392	.80125	15	45	.61222	.77428	1.2915	.79069	15
46	.59856	.74719	1.3384	.80108	14	46	.61245	.77475	1.2907	.79051	14
47	.59879	.74764	1.3375	.80091	13	47	.61268	.77521	1.2900	.79033	13
48	.59902	.74810	1.3367	.80073	12	48	.61291	.77568	1.2892	.79016	12
49	.59926	.74855	1.3359	.80056	11	49	.61314	.77615	1.2884	.78998	11
50	.59949	.74900	1.3351	.80038	10	50	.61337	.77661	1.2876	.78980	10
51	.59972	.74946	1.3343	.80021	9	51	.61360	.77708	1.2869	.78962	9
52	.59995	.74991	1.3335	.80003	8	52	.61383	.77754	1.2861	.78944	8
53	.60019	.75037	1.3327	.79986	7	53	.61406	.77801	1.2853	.78926	7
54	.60042	.75082	1.3319	.79968	6	54	.61429	.77848	1.2846	.78908	6
55	.60065	.75128	1.3311	.79951	5	55	.61451	.77895	1.2838	.78891	5
56	.60089	.75173	1.3303	.79934	4	56	.61474	.77941	1.2830	.78873	4
57	.60112	.75219	1.3295	.79916	3	57	.61497	.77988	1.2822	.78855	3
58	.60135	.75264	1.3287	.79899	2	58	.61520	.78035	1.2815	.78837	2
59	.60158	.75310	1.3278	.79881	1	59	.61543	.78082	1.2807	.78819	1
60	.60182	.75355	1.3270	.79864	0	60	.61566	.78129	1.2799	.78801	0
′	Cos	Ctn	Tan	Sin	′	′	Cos	Ctn	Tan	Sin	′

′	Sin	Tan	Ctn	Cos	′	′	Sin	Tan	Ctn	Cos	′
0	.61566	.78129	1.2799	.78801	60	0	.62932	.80978	1.2349	.77715	60
1	.61589	.78175	1.2792	.78783	59	1	.62955	.81027	1.23+2	.77696	59
2	.61612	.78222	1.2784	.78765	58	2	.62977	.81075	1.2334	.77678	58
3	.61635	.78269	1.2776	.78747	57	3	.63000	.81123	1.2327	.77660	57
4	.61658	.78316	1.2769	.78729	56	4	.63022	.81171	1.2320	.77641	56
5	.61681	.78363	1.2761	.78711	55	5	.63045	.81220	1.2312	.77623	55
6	.61704	.78410	1.2753	.78694	54	6	.63068	.81268	1.2305	.77605	54
7	.61726	.78457	1.2746	.78676	53	7	.63090	.81316	1.2298	.77586	53
8	.61749	.78504	1.2738	.78658	52	8	.63113	.81364	1.2290	.77568	52
9	.61772	.78551	1.2731	.78640	51	9	.63135	.81413	1.2283	.77550	51
10	.61795	.78598	1.2723	.78622	50	10	.63158	.81461	1.2276	.77531	50
11	.61818	.78645	1.2715	.78604	49	11	.63180	.81510	1.2268	.77513	49
12	.61841	.78692	1.2708	.78586	48	12	.63203	.81558	1.2261	.77494	48
13	.61864	.78739	1.2700	.78568	47	13	.63225	.81606	1.2254	.77476	47
14	.61887	.78786	1.2693	.78550	46	14	.63248	.81655	1.2247	.77458	46
15	.61909	.78834	1.2685	.78532	45	15	.63271	.81703	1.2239	.77439	45
16	.61932	.78881	1.2677	.78514	44	16	.63293	.81752	1.2232	.77421	44
17	.61955	.78928	1.2670	.78496	43	17	.63316	.81800	1.2225	.77402	43
18	.61978	.78975	1.2662	.78478	42	18	.63338	.81849	1.2218	.77384	42
19	.62001	.79022	1.2655	.78460	41	19	.63361	.81898	1.2210	.77366	41
20	.62024	.79070	1.2647	.78442	40	20	.63383	.81946	1.2203	.77347	40
21	.62046	.79117	1.2640	.78424	39	21	.63406	.81995	1.2196	.77329	39
22	.62069	.79164	1.2632	.78405	38	22	.63428	.82044	1.2189	.77310	38
23	.62092	.79212	1.2624	.78387	37	23	.63451	.82092	1.2181	.77292	37
24	.62115	.79259	1.2617	.78369	36	24	.63473	.82141	1.2174	.77273	36
25	.62138	.79306	1.2609	.78351	35	25	.63496	.82190	1.2167	.77255	35
26	.62160	.79354	1.2602	.78333	34	26	.63518	.82238	1.2160	.77236	34
27	.62183	.79401	1.2594	.78315	33	27	.63540	.82287	1.2153	.77218	33
28	.62206	.79449	1.2587	.78297	32	28	.63563	.82336	1.2145	.77199	32
29	.62229	.79496	1.2579	.78279	31	29	.63585	.82385	1.2138	.77181	31
30	.62251	.79544	1.2572	.78261	30	30	.63608	.82434	1.2131	.77162	30
31	.62274	.79591	1.2564	.78243	29	31	.63630	.82483	1.2124	.77144	29
32	.62297	.79639	1.2557	.78225	28	32	.63653	.82531	1.2117	.77125	28
33	.62320	.79686	1.2549	.78206	27	33	.63675	.82580	1.2109	.77107	27
34	.62342	.79734	1.2542	.78188	26	34	.63698	.82629	1.2102	.77088	26
35	.62365	.79781	1.2534	.78170	25	35	.63720	.82678	1.2095	.77070	25
36	.62388	.79829	1.2527	.78152	24	36	.63742	.82727	1.2088	.77051	24
37	.62411	.79877	1.2519	.78134	23	37	.63765	.82776	1.2081	.77033	23
38	.62433	.79924	1.2512	.78116	22	38	.63787	.82825	1.2074	.77014	22
39	.62456	.79972	1.2504	.78098	21	39	.63810	.82874	1.2066	.76996	21
40	.62479	.80020	1.2497	.78079	20	40	.63832	.82923	1.2059	.76977	20
41	.62502	.80067	1.2489	.78061	19	41	.63854	.82972	1.2052	.76959	19
42	.62524	.80115	1.2482	.78043	18	42	.63877	.83022	1.2045	.76940	18
43	.62547	.80163	1.2475	.78025	17	43	.63899	.83071	1.2038	.76921	17
44	.62570	.80211	1.2467	.78007	16	44	.63922	.83120	1.2031	.76903	16
45	.62592	.80258	1.2460	.77988	15	45	.63944	.83169	1.2024	.76884	15
46	.62615	.80306	1.2452	.77970	14	46	.63966	.83218	1.2017	.76866	14
47	.62638	.80354	1.2445	.77952	13	47	.63989	.83268	1.2009	.76847	13
48	.62660	.80402	1.2437	.77934	12	48	.64011	.83317	1.2002	.76828	12
49	.62683	.80450	1.2430	.77916	11	49	.64033	.83366	1.1995	.76810	11
50	.62706	.80498	1.2423	.77897	10	50	.64056	.83415	1.1988	.76791	10
51	.62728	.80546	1.2415	.77879	9	51	.64078	.83465	1.1981	.76772	9
52	.62751	.80594	1.2408	.77861	8	52	.64100	.83514	1.1974	.76754	8
53	.62774	.80642	1.2401	.77843	7	53	.64123	.83564	1.1967	.76735	7
54	.62796	.80690	1.2393	.77824	6	54	.64145	.83613	1.1960	.76717	6
55	.62819	.80738	1.2386	.77806	5	55	.64167	.83662	1.1953	.76698	5
56	.62842	.80786	1.2378	.77788	4	56	.64190	.83712	1.1946	.76679	4
57	.62864	.80834	1.2371	.77769	3	57	.64212	.83761	1.1939	.76661	3
58	.62887	.80882	1.2364	.77751	2	58	.64234	.83811	1.1932	.76642	2
59	.62909	.80930	1.2356	.77733	1	59	.64256	.83860	1.1925	.76623	1
60	.62932	.80978	1.2349	.77715	0	60	.64279	.83910	1.1918	.76604	0
′	Cos	Ctn	Tan	Sin	′	′	Cos	Ctn	Tan	Sin	′

′	Sin	Tan	Ctn	Cos	′		′	Sin	Tan	Ctn	Cos	′
0	.64279	.83910	1.1918	.76604	60		0	.65606	.86929	1.1504	.75471	60
1	.64301	.83960	1.1910	.76586	59		1	.65628	.86980	1.1497	.75452	59
2	.64323	.84009	1.1903	.76567	58		2	.65650	.87031	1.1490	.75433	58
3	.64346	.84059	1.1896	.76548	57		3	.65672	.87082	1.1483	.75414	57
4	.64368	.84108	1.1889	.76530	56		4	.65694	.87133	1.1477	.75395	56
5	.64390	.84158	1.1882	.76511	55		5	.65716	.87184	1.1470	.75375	55
6	.64412	.84208	1.1875	.76492	54		6	.65738	.87236	1.1463	.75356	54
7	.64435	.84258	1.1868	.76473	53		7	.65759	.87287	1.1456	.75337	53
8	.64457	.84307	1.1861	.76455	52		8	.65781	.87338	1.1450	.75318	52
9	.64479	.84357	1.1854	.76436	51		9	.65803	.87389	1.1443	.75299	51
10	.64501	.84407	1.1847	.76417	50		10	.65825	.87441	1.1436	.75280	50
11	.64524	.84457	1.1840	.76398	49		11	.65847	.87492	1.1430	.75261	49
12	.64546	.84507	1.1833	.76380	48		12	.65869	.87543	1.1423	.75241	48
13	.64568	.84556	1.1826	.76361	47		13	.65891	.87595	1.1416	.75222	47
14	.64590	.84606	1.1819	.76342	46		14	.65913	.87646	1.1410	.75203	46
15	.64612	.84656	1.1812	.76323	45		15	.65935	.87698	1.1403	.75184	45
16	.64635	.84706	1.1806	.76304	44		16	.65956	.87749	1.1396	.75165	44
17	.64657	.84756	1.1799	.76286	43		17	.65978	.87801	1.1389	.75146	43
18	.64679	.84806	1.1792	.76267	42		18	.66000	.87852	1.1383	.75126	42
19	.64701	.84856	1.1785	.76248	41		19	.66022	.87904	1.1376	.75107	41
20	.64723	.84906	1.1778	.76229	40		20	.66044	.87955	1.1369	.75088	40
21	.64746	.84956	1.1771	.76210	39		21	.66066	.88007	1.1363	.75069	39
22	.64768	.85006	1.1764	.76192	38		22	.66088	.88059	1.1356	.75050	38
23	.64790	.85057	1.1757	.76173	37		23	.66109	.88110	1.1349	.75030	37
24	.64812	.85107	1.1750	.76154	36		24	.66131	.88162	1.1343	.75011	36
25	.64834	.85157	1.1743	.76135	35		25	.66153	.88214	1.1336	.74992	35
26	.64856	.85207	1.1736	.76116	34		26	.66175	.88265	1.1329	.74973	34
27	.64878	.85257	1.1729	.76097	33		27	.66197	.88317	1.1323	.74953	33
28	.64901	.85308	1.1722	.76078	32		28	.66218	.88369	1.1316	.74934	32
29	.64923	.85358	1.1715	.76059	31		29	.66240	.88421	1.1310	.74915	31
30	.64945	.85408	1.1708	.76041	30		30	.66262	.88473	1.1303	.74896	30
31	.64967	.85458	1.1702	.76022	29		31	.66284	.88524	1.1296	.74876	29
32	.64989	.85509	1.1695	.76003	28		32	.66306	.88576	1.1290	.74857	28
33	.65011	.85559	1.1688	.75984	27		33	.66327	.88628	1.1283	.74838	27
34	.65033	.85609	1.1681	.75965	26		34	.66349	.88680	1.1276	.74818	26
35	.65055	.85660	1.1674	.75946	25		35	.66371	.88732	1.1270	.74799	25
36	.65077	.85710	1.1667	.75927	24		36	.66393	.88784	1.1263	.74780	24
37	.65100	.85761	1.1660	.75908	23		37	.66414	.88836	1.1257	.74760	23
38	.65122	.85811	1.1653	.75889	22		38	.66436	.88888	1.1250	.74741	22
39	.65144	.85862	1.1647	.75870	21		39	.66458	.88940	1.1243	.74722	21
40	.65166	.85912	1.1640	.75851	20		40	.66480	.88992	1.1237	.74703	20
41	.65188	.85963	1.1633	.75832	19		41	.66501	.89045	1.1230	.74683	19
42	.65210	.86014	1.1626	.75813	18		42	.66523	.89097	1.1224	.74664	18
43	.65232	.86064	1.1619	.75794	17		43	.66545	.89149	1.1217	.74644	17
44	.65254	.86115	1.1612	.75775	16		44	.66566	.89201	1.1211	.74625	16
45	.65276	.86166	1.1606	.75756	15		45	.66588	.89253	1.1204	.74606	15
46	.65298	.86216	1.1599	.75738	14		46	.66610	.89306	1.1197	.74586	14
47	.65320	.86267	1.1592	.75719	13		47	.66632	.89358	1.1191	.74567	13
48	.65342	.86318	1.1585	.75700	12		48	.66653	.89410	1.1184	.74548	12
49	.65364	.86368	1.1578	.75680	11		49	.66675	.89463	1.1178	.74528	11
50	.65386	.86419	1.1571	.75661	10		50	.66697	.89515	1.1171	.74509	10
51	.65408	.86470	1.1565	.75642	9		51	.66718	.89567	1.1165	.74489	9
52	.65430	.86521	1.1558	.75623	8		52	.66740	.89620	1.1158	.74470	8
53	.65452	.86572	1.1551	.75604	7		53	.66762	.89672	1.1152	.74451	7
54	.65474	.86623	1.1544	.75585	6		54	.66783	.89725	1.1145	.74431	6
55	.65496	.86674	1.1538	.75566	5		55	.66805	.89777	1.1139	.74412	5
56	.65518	.86725	1.1531	.75547	4		56	.66827	.89830	1.1132	.74392	4
57	.65540	.86776	1.1524	.75528	3		57	.66848	.89883	1.1126	.74373	3
58	.65562	.86827	1.1517	.75509	2		58	.66870	.89935	1.1119	.74353	2
59	.65584	.86878	1.1510	.75490	1		59	.66891	.89988	1.1113	.74334	1
60	.65606	.86929	1.1504	.75471	0		60	.66913	.90040	1.1106	.74314	0
′	Cos	Ctn	Tan	Sin	′		′	Cos	Ctn	Tan	Sin	′

′	Sin	Tan	Ctn	Cos	′		′	Sin	Tan	Ctn	Cos	′
0	.66913	.90040	1.1106	.74314	60		0	.68200	.93252	1.0724	.73135	60
1	.66935	.90093	1.1100	.74295	59		1	.68221	.93306	1.0717	.73116	59
2	.66956	.90146	1.1093	.74276	58		2	.68242	.93360	1.0711	.73096	58
3	.66978	.90199	1.1087	.74256	57		3	.68264	.93415	1.0705	.73076	57
4	.66999	.90251	1.1080	.74237	56		4	.68285	.93469	1.0699	.73056	56
5	.67021	.90304	1.1074	.74217	55		5	.68306	.93524	1.0692	.73036	55
6	.67043	.90357	1.1067	.74198	54		6	.68327	.93578	1.0686	.73016	54
7	.67064	.90410	1.1061	.74178	53		7	.68349	.93633	1.0680	.72996	53
8	.67086	.90463	1.1054	.74159	52		8	.68370	.93688	1.0674	.72976	52
9	.67107	.90516	1.1048	.74139	51		9	.68391	.93742	1.0668	.72957	51
10	.67129	.90569	1.1041	.74120	50		10	.68412	.93797	1.0661	.72937	50
11	.67151	.90621	1.1035	.74100	49		11	.68434	.93852	1.0655	.72917	49
12	.67172	.90674	1.1028	.74080	48		12	.68455	.93906	1.0649	.72897	48
13	.67194	.90727	1.1022	.74061	47		13	.68476	.93961	1.0643	.72877	47
14	.67215	.90781	1.1016	.74041	46		14	.68497	.94016	1.0637	.72857	46
15	.67237	.90834	1.1009	.74022	45		15	.68518	.94071	1.0630	.72837	45
16	.67258	.90887	1.1003	.74002	44		16	.68539	.94125	1.0624	.72817	44
17	.67280	.90940	1.0996	.73983	43		17	.68561	.94180	1.0618	.72797	43
18	.67301	.90993	1.0990	.73963	42		18	.68582	.94235	1.0612	.72777	42
19	.67323	.91046	1.0983	.73944	41		19	.68603	.94290	1.0606	.72757	41
20	.67344	.91099	1.0977	.73924	40		20	.68624	.94345	1.0599	.72737	40
21	.67366	.91153	1.0971	.73904	39		21	.68645	.94400	1.0593	.72717	39
22	.67387	.91206	1.0964	.73885	38		22	.68666	.94455	1.0587	.72697	38
23	.67409	.91259	1.0958	.73865	37		23	.68688	.94510	1.0581	.72677	37
24	.67430	.91313	1.0951	.73846	36		24	.68709	.94565	1.0575	.72657	36
25	.67452	.91366	1.0945	.73826	35		25	.68730	.94620	1.0569	.72637	35
26	.67473	.91419	1.0939	.73806	34		26	.68751	.94676	1.0562	.72617	34
27	.67495	.91473	1.0932	.73787	33		27	.68772	.94731	1.0556	.72597	33
28	.67516	.91526	1.0926	.73767	32		28	.68793	.94786	1.0550	.72577	32
29	.67538	.91580	1.0919	.73747	31		29	.68814	.94841	1.0544	.72557	31
30	.67559	.91633	1.0913	.73728	30		30	.68835	.94896	1.0538	.72537	30
31	67580	91687	1.0907	.73708	29		31	.68857	.94952	1.0532	.72517	29
32	.67602	91740	1.0900	.73688	28		32	.68878	.95007	1.0526	.72497	28
33	.67623	.91794	1.0894	.73669	27		33	.68899	.95062	1.0519	.72477	27
34	.67645	.91847	1.0888	.73649	26		34	.68920	.95118	1.0513	.72457	26
35	.67666	.91901	1.0881	.73629	25		35	.68941	.95173	1.0507	.72437	25
36	.67688	.91955	1.0875	.73610	24		36	.68962	.95229	1.0501	.72417	24
37	.67709	.92008	1.0869	.73590	23		37	.68983	.95284	1.0495	.72397	23
38	.67730	.92062	1.0862	.73570	22		38	.69004	.95340	1.0489	.72377	22
39	.67752	.92116	1.0856	.73551	21		39	.69025	.95395	1.0483	.72357	21
40	.67773	.92170	1.0850	.73531	20		40	.69046	.95451	1.0477	.72337	20
41	.67795	.92224	1.0843	.73511	19		41	.69067	.95506	1.0470	.72317	19
42	.67816	.92277	1.0837	.73491	18		42	.69088	.95562	1.0464	.72297	18
43	.67837	.92331	1.0831	.73472	17		43	.69109	.95618	1.0458	.72277	17
44	.67859	.92385	1.0824	.73452	16		44	.69130	.95673	1.0452	.72257	16
45	.67880	.92439	1.0818	.73432	15		45	.69151	.95729	1.0446	.72236	15
46	.67901	.92493	1.0812	.73413	14		46	.69172	.95785	1.0440	.72216	14
47	.67923	.92547	1.0805	.73393	13		47	.69193	.95841	1.0434	.72196	13
48	.67944	.92601	1.0799	.73373	12		48	.69214	.95897	1.0428	.72176	12
49	.67965	.92655	1.0793	.73353	11		49	.69235	.95952	1.0422	.72156	11
50	.67987	.92709	1.0786	.73333	10		50	.69256	.96008	1.0416	.72136	10
51	.68008	.92763	1.0780	.73314	9		51	.69277	.96064	1.0410	.72116	9
52	.68029	.92817	1.0774	.73294	8		52	.69298	.96120	1.0404	.72095	8
53	.68051	.92872	1.0768	.73274	7		53	.69319	.96176	1.0398	.72075	7
54	.68072	.92926	1.0761	.73254	6		54	.69340	.96232	1.0392	.72055	6
55	.68093	.92980	1.0755	.73234	5		55	.69361	.96288	1.0385	.72035	5
56	.68115	.93034	1.0749	.73215	4		56	.69382	.96344	1.0379	.72015	4
57	.68136	.93088	1.0742	.73195	3		57	.69403	.96400	1.0373	.71995	3
58	.68157	.93143	1.0736	.73175	2		58	.69424	.96457	1.0367	.71974	2
59	.68179	.93197	1.0730	.73155	1		59	.69445	.96513	1.0361	.71954	1
60	.68200	.93252	1.0724	.73135	0		60	.69466	.96569	1.0355	.71934	0
′	Cos	Ctn	Tan	Sin	′		′	Cos	Ctn	Tan	Sin	′

′	Sin	Tan	Ctn	Cos	′
0	.69466	.96569	1.0355	.71934	60
1	.69487	.96625	1.0349	.71914	59
2	.69508	.96681	1.0343	.71894	58
3	.69529	.96738	1.0337	.71873	57
4	.69549	.96794	1.0331	.71853	56
5	.69570	.96850	1.0325	.71833	55
6	.69591	.96907	1.0319	.71813	54
7	.69612	.96963	1.0313	.71792	53
8	.69633	.97020	1.0307	.71772	52
9	.69654	.97076	1.0301	.71752	51
10	.69675	.97133	1.0295	.71732	50
11	.69696	.97189	1.0289	.71711	49
12	.69717	.97246	1.0283	.71691	48
13	.69737	.97302	1.0277	.71671	47
14	.69758	.97359	1.0271	.71650	46
15	.69779	.97416	1.0265	.71630	45
16	.69800	.97472	1.0259	.71610	44
17	.69821	.97529	1.0253	.71590	43
18	.69842	.97586	1.0247	.71569	42
19	.69862	.97643	1.0241	.71549	41
20	.69883	.97700	1.0235	.71529	40
21	.69904	.97756	1.0230	.71508	39
22	.69925	.97813	1.0224	.71488	38
23	.69946	.97870	1.0218	.71468	37
24	.69966	.97927	1.0212	.71447	36
25	.69987	.97984	1.0206	.71427	35
26	.70008	.98041	1.0200	.71407	34
27	.70029	.98098	1.0194	.71386	33
28	.70049	.98155	1.0188	.71366	32
29	.70070	.98213	1.0182	.71345	31
30	.70091	.98270	1.0176	.71325	30
31	.70112	.98327	1.0170	.71305	29
32	.70132	.98384	1.0164	.71284	28
33	.70153	.98441	1.0158	.71264	27
34	.70174	.98499	1.0152	.71243	26
35	.70195	.98556	1.0147	.71223	25
36	.70215	.98613	1.0141	.71203	24
37	.70236	.98671	1.0135	.71182	23
38	.70257	.98728	1.0129	.71162	22
39	.70277	.98786	1.0123	.71141	21
40	.70298	.98843	1.0117	.71121	20
41	.70319	.98901	1.0111	.71100	19
42	.70339	.98958	1.0105	.71080	18
43	.70360	.99016	1.0099	.71059	17
44	.70381	.99073	1.0094	.71039	16
45	.70401	.99131	1.0088	.71019	15
46	.70422	.99189	1.0082	.70998	14
47	.70443	.99247	1.0076	.70978	13
48	.70463	.99304	1.0070	.70957	12
49	.70484	.99362	1.0064	.70937	11
50	.70505	.99420	1.0058	.70916	10
51	.70525	.99478	1.0052	.70896	9
52	.70546	.99536	1.0047	.70875	8
53	.70567	.99594	1.0041	.70855	7
54	.70587	.99652	1.0035	.70834	6
55	.70608	.99710	1.0029	.70813	5
56	.70628	.99768	1.0023	.70793	4
57	.70649	.99826	1.0017	.70772	3
58	.70670	.99884	1.0012	.70752	2
59	.70690	.99942	1.0006	.70731	1
60	.70711	1.0000	1.0000	.70711	0
′	Cos	Ctn	Tan	Sin	′

COMMON LOGARITHMS
OF NUMBERS
C

N.		0	1	2	3	4	5	6	7	8	9
100	00	000	043	087	130	173	217	260	303	346	389
101		432	475	518	561	604	647	689	732	775	817
102		860	903	945	988	*030	*072	*115	*157	*199	*242
103	01	284	326	368	410	452	494	536	578	620	662
104		703	745	787	828	870	912	953	995	*036	*078
105	02	119	160	202	243	284	325	366	407	449	490
106		531	572	612	653	694	735	776	816	857	898
107		938	979	*019	*060	*100	*141	*181	*222	*262	*302
108	03	342	383	423	463	503	543	583	623	663	703
109		743	782	822	862	902	941	981	*021	*060	*100
110	04	139	179	218	258	297	336	376	415	454	493
111		532	571	610	650	689	727	766	805	844	883
112		922	961	999	*038	*077	*115	*154	*192	*231	*269
113	05	308	346	385	423	461	500	538	576	614	652
114		690	729	767	805	843	881	918	956	994	*032
115	06	070	108	145	183	221	258	296	333	371	408
116		446	483	521	558	595	633	670	707	744	781
117		819	856	893	930	967	*004	*041	*078	*115	*151
118	07	188	225	262	298	335	372	408	445	482	518
119		555	591	628	664	700	737	773	809	846	882
120		918	954	990	*027	*063	*099	*135	*171	*207	*243
121	08	279	314	350	386	422	458	493	529	565	600
122		636	672	707	743	778	814	849	884	920	955
123		991	*026	*061	*096	*132	*167	*202	*237	*272	*307
124	09	342	377	412	447	482	517	552	587	621	656
125		691	726	760	795	830	864	899	934	968	*003
126	10	037	072	106	140	175	209	243	278	312	346
127		380	415	449	483	517	551	585	619	653	687
128		721	755	789	823	857	890	924	958	992	*025
129	11	059	093	126	160	193	227	261	294	327	361
130		394	428	461	494	528	561	594	628	661	694
131		727	760	793	826	860	893	926	959	992	*024
132	12	057	090	123	156	189	222	254	287	320	352
133		385	418	450	483	516	548	581	613	646	678
134		710	743	775	808	840	872	905	937	969	*001
135	13	033	066	098	130	162	194	226	258	290	322
136		354	386	418	450	481	513	545	577	609	640
137		672	704	735	767	799	830	862	893	925	956
138		988	*019	*051	*082	*114	*145	*176	*208	*239	*270
139	14	301	333	364	395	426	457	489	520	551	582
140		613	644	675	706	737	768	799	829	860	891
141		922	953	983	*014	*045	*076	*106	*137	*168	*198
142	15	229	259	290	320	351	381	412	442	473	503
143		534	564	594	625	655	685	715	746	776	806
144		836	866	897	927	957	987	*017	*047	*077	*107
145	16	137	167	197	227	256	286	316	346	376	406
146		435	465	495	524	554	584	613	643	673	702
147		732	761	791	820	850	879	909	938	967	997
148	17	026	056	085	114	143	173	202	231	260	289
149		319	348	377	406	435	464	493	522	551	580
150		609	638	667	696	725	754	782	811	840	869
N.		0	1	2	3	4	5	6	7	8	9

Proportional parts

	44	43	42
1	4.4	4.3	4.2
2	8.8	8.6	8.4
3	13.2	12.9	12.6
4	17.6	17.2	16.8
5	22.0	21.5	21.0
6	26.4	25.8	25.2
7	30.8	30.1	29.4
8	35.2	34.4	33.6
9	39.6	38.7	37.8

	41	40	39
1	4.1	4.0	3.9
2	8.2	8.0	7.8
3	12.3	12.0	11.7
4	16.4	16.0	15.6
5	20.5	20.0	19.5
6	24.6	24.0	23.4
7	28.7	28.0	27.3
8	32.8	32.0	31.2
9	36.9	36.0	35.1

	38	37	36
1	3.8	3.7	3.6
2	7.6	7.4	7.2
3	11.4	11.1	10.8
4	15.2	14.8	14.4
5	19.0	18.5	18.0
6	22.8	22.2	21.6
7	26.6	25.9	25.2
8	30.4	29.6	28.8
9	34.2	33.3	32.4

	35	34	33
1	3.5	3.4	3.3
2	7.0	6.8	6.6
3	10.5	10.2	9.9
4	14.0	13.6	13.2
5	17.5	17.0	16.5
6	21.0	20.4	19.8
7	24.5	23.8	23.1
8	28.0	27.2	26.4
9	31.5	30.6	29.7

	32	31	30
1	3.2	3.1	3.0
2	6.4	6.2	6.0
3	9.6	9.3	9.0
4	12.8	12.4	12.0
5	16.0	15.5	15.0
6	19.2	18.6	18.0
7	22.4	21.7	21.0
8	25.6	24.8	24.0
9	28.8	27.9	27.0

Proportional parts

.00 000 — .17 869

N.		0	1	2	3	4	5	6	7	8	9
150	17	609	638	667	696	725	754	782	811	840	869
151		898	926	955	984	*013	*041	*070	*099	*127	*156
152	18	184	213	241	270	298	327	355	384	412	441
153		469	498	526	554	583	611	639	667	696	724
154		752	780	808	837	865	893	921	949	977	*005
155	19	033	061	089	117	145	173	201	229	257	285
156		312	340	368	396	424	451	479	507	535	562
157		590	618	645	673	700	728	756	783	811	838
158		866	893	921	948	976	*003	*030	*058	*085	*112
159	20	140	167	194	222	249	276	303	330	358	385
160		412	439	466	493	520	548	575	602	629	656
161		683	710	737	763	790	817	844	871	898	925
162		952	978	*005	*032	*059	*085	*112	*139	*165	*192
163	21	219	245	272	299	325	352	378	405	431	458
164		484	511	537	564	590	617	643	669	696	722
165		748	775	801	827	854	880	906	932	958	985
166	22	011	037	063	089	115	141	167	194	220	246
167		272	298	324	350	376	401	427	453	479	505
168		531	557	583	608	634	660	686	712	737	763
169		789	814	840	866	891	917	943	968	994	*019
170	23	045	070	096	121	147	172	198	223	249	274
171		300	325	350	376	401	426	452	477	502	528
172		553	578	603	629	654	679	704	729	754	779
173		805	830	855	880	905	930	955	980	*005	*030
174	24	055	080	105	130	155	180	204	229	254	279
175		304	329	353	378	403	428	452	477	502	527
176		551	576	601	625	650	674	699	724	748	773
177		797	822	846	871	895	920	944	969	993	*018
178	25	042	066	091	115	139	164	188	212	237	261
179		285	310	334	358	382	406	431	455	479	503
180		527	551	575	600	624	648	672	696	720	744
181		768	792	816	840	864	888	912	935	959	983
182	26	007	031	055	079	102	126	150	174	198	221
183		245	269	293	316	340	364	387	411	435	458
184		482	505	529	553	576	600	623	647	670	694
185		717	741	764	788	811	834	858	881	905	928
186		951	975	998	*021	*045	*068	*091	*114	*138	*161
187	27	184	207	231	254	277	300	323	346	370	393
188		416	439	462	485	508	531	554	577	600	623
189		646	669	692	715	738	761	784	807	830	852
190		875	898	921	944	967	989	*012	*035	*058	*081
191	28	103	126	149	171	194	217	240	262	285	307
192		330	353	375	398	421	443	466	488	511	533
193		556	578	601	623	646	668	691	713	735	758
194		780	803	825	847	870	892	914	937	959	981
195	29	003	026	048	070	092	115	137	159	181	203
196		226	248	270	292	314	336	358	380	403	425
197		447	469	491	513	535	557	579	601	623	645
198		667	688	710	732	754	776	798	820	842	863
199		885	907	929	951	973	994	*016	*038	*060	*081
200	30	103	125	146	168	190	211	233	255	276	298
N.		0	1	2	3	4	5	6	7	8	9

Proportional parts

	29	28
1	2.9	2.8
2	5.8	5.6
3	8.7	8.4
4	11.6	11.2
5	14.5	14.0
6	17.4	16.8
7	20.3	19.6
8	23.2	22.4
9	26.1	25.2

	27	26
1	2.7	2.6
2	5.4	5.2
3	8.1	7.8
4	10.8	10.4
5	13.5	13.0
6	16.2	15.6
7	18.9	18.2
8	21.6	20.8
9	24.3	23.4

	25
1	2.5
2	5.0
3	7.5
4	10.0
5	12.5
6	15.0
7	17.5
8	20.0
9	22.5

	24	23
1	2.4	2.3
2	4.8	4.6
3	7.2	6.9
4	9.6	9.2
5	12.0	11.5
6	14.4	13.8
7	16.8	16.1
8	19.2	18.4
9	21.6	20.7

	22	21
1	2.2	2.1
2	4.4	4.2
3	6.6	6.3
4	8.8	8.4
5	11.0	10.5
6	13.2	12.6
7	15.4	14.7
8	17.6	16.8
9	19.8	18.9

Proportional parts

.17 609 — .30 298

N.		0	1	2	3	4	5	6	7	8	9	Proportional parts	
200	30	103	125	146	168	190	211	233	255	276	298		
201		320	341	363	384	406	428	449	471	492	514	22	21
202		535	557	578	600	621	643	664	685	707	728	1 2.2	2.1
203		750	771	792	814	835	856	878	899	920	942	2 4.4	4.2
204		963	984	*006	*027	*048	*069	*091	*112	*133	*154	3 6.6	6.3
												4 8.8	8.4
205	31	175	197	218	239	260	281	302	323	345	366	5 11.0	10.5
206		387	408	429	450	471	492	513	534	555	576	6 13.2	12.6
207		597	618	639	660	681	702	723	744	765	785	7 15.4	14.7
208		806	827	848	869	890	911	931	952	973	994	8 17.6	16.8
209	32	015	035	056	077	098	118	139	160	181	201	9 19.8	18.9
210		222	243	263	284	305	325	346	366	387	408		
211		428	449	469	490	510	531	552	572	593	613	20	
212		634	654	675	695	715	736	756	777	797	818	1 2.0	
213		838	858	879	899	919	940	960	980	*001	*021	2 4.0	
214	33	041	062	082	102	122	143	163	183	203	224	3 6.0	
												4 8.0	
215		244	264	284	304	325	345	365	385	405	425	5 10.0	
216		445	465	486	506	526	546	566	586	606	626	6 12.0	
217		646	666	686	706	726	746	766	786	806	826	7 14.0	
218		846	866	885	905	925	945	965	985	*005	*025	8 16.0	
219	34	044	064	084	104	124	143	163	183	203	223	9 18.0	
220		242	262	282	301	321	341	361	380	400	420		
221		439	459	479	498	518	537	557	577	596	616	19	
222		635	655	674	694	713	733	753	772	792	811	1 1.9	
223		830	850	869	889	908	928	947	967	986	*005	2 3.8	
224	35	025	044	064	083	102	122	141	160	180	199	3 5.7	
												4 7.6	
225		218	238	257	276	295	315	334	353	372	392	5 9.5	
226		411	430	449	468	488	507	526	545	564	583	6 11.4	
227		603	622	641	660	679	698	717	736	755	774	7 13.3	
228		793	813	832	851	870	889	908	927	946	965	8 15.2	
229		984	*003	*021	*040	*059	*078	*097	*116	*135	*154	9 17.1	
230	36	173	192	211	229	248	267	286	305	324	342		
231		361	380	399	418	436	455	474	493	511	530	18	
232		549	568	586	605	624	642	661	680	698	717	1 1.8	
233		736	754	773	791	810	829	847	866	884	903	2 3.6	
234		922	940	959	977	996	*014	*033	*051	*070	*088	3 5.4	
												4 7.2	
235	37	107	125	144	162	181	199	218	236	254	273	5 9.0	
236		291	310	328	346	365	383	401	420	438	457	6 10.8	
237		475	493	511	530	548	566	585	603	621	639	7 12.6	
238		658	676	694	712	731	749	767	785	803	822	8 14.4	
239		840	858	876	894	912	931	949	967	985	*003	9 16.2	
240	38	021	039	057	075	093	112	130	148	166	184		
241		202	220	238	256	274	292	310	328	346	364	17	
242		382	399	417	435	453	471	489	507	525	543	1 1.7	
243		561	578	596	614	632	650	668	686	703	721	2 3.4	
244		739	757	775	792	810	828	846	863	881	899	3 5.1	
												4 6.8	
245		917	934	952	970	987	*005	*023	*041	*058	*076	5 8.5	
246	39	094	111	129	146	164	182	199	217	235	252	6 10.2	
247		270	287	305	322	340	358	375	393	410	428	7 11.9	
248		445	463	480	498	515	533	550	568	585	602	8 13.6	
249		620	637	655	672	690	707	724	742	759	777	9 15.3	
250		794	811	829	846	863	881	898	915	933	950		
N.		0	1	2	3	4	5	6	7	8	9	Proportional parts	

.30 103 — .39 950

N.		0	1	2	3	4	5	6	7	8	9
250	39	794	8̄11	829	846	863	881	898	915	933	950
251		967	985	*002	*019	*037	*054	*071	*088	*106	*123
252	40	140	157	175	192	209	226	243	261	278	295
253		312	329	346	364	381	398	415	432	449	466
254		483	500	518	535	552	569	586	603	620	637
255		654	671	688	705	722	739	756	773	790	807
256		824	841	858	875	892	909	926	943	960	976
257		993	*010	*027	*044	*061	*078	*095	*111	*128	*145
258	41	162	179	196	212	229	246	263	280	296	313
259		330	347	363	380	397	414	430	447	464	481
260		497	514	531	547	564	581	597	614	631	647
261		664	681	697	714	731	747	764	780	797	814
262		830	847	863	880	896	913	929	946	963	979
263		996	*012	*029	*045	*062	*078	*095	*111	*127	*144
264	42	160	177	193	210	226	243	259	275	292	308
265		325	341	357	374	390	406	423	439	455	472
266		488	504	521	537	553	570	586	602	619	635
267		651	667	684	700	716	732	749	765	781	797
268		813	830	846	862	878	894	911	927	943	959
269		975	991	*008	*024	*040	*056	*072	*088	*104	*120
270	43	136	152	169	185	201	217	233	249	265	281
271		297	313	329	345	361	377	393	409	425	441
272		457	473	489	505	521	537	553	569	584	600
273		616	632	648	664	680	696	712	727	743	759
274		775	791	807	823	838	854	870	886	902	917
275		933	949	965	981	996	*012	*028	*044	*059	*075
276	44	091	107	122	138	154	170	185	201	217	232
277		248	264	279	295	311	326	342	358	373	389
278		404	420	436	451	467	483	498	514	529	545
279		560	576	592	607	623	638	654	669	685	700
280		716	731	747	762	778	793	809	824	840	855
281		871	886	902	917	932	948	963	979	994	*010
282	45	025	040	056	071	086	102	117	133	148	163
283		179	194	209	225	240	255	271	286	301	317
284		332	347	362	378	393	408	423	439	454	469
285		484	500	515	530	545	561	576	591	606	621
286		637	652	667	682	697	712	728	743	758	773
287		788	803	818	834	849	864	879	894	909	924
288		939	954	969	984	*000	*015	*030	*045	*060	*075
289	46	090	105	120	135	150	165	180	195	210	225
290		240	255	270	285	300	315	330	345	359	374
291		389	404	419	434	449	464	479	494	509	523
292		538	553	568	583	598	613	627	642	657	672
293		687	702	716	731	746	761	776	790	805	820
294		835	850	864	879	894	909	923	938	953	967
295		982	997	*012	*026	*041	*056	*070	*085	*100	*114
296	47	129	144	159	173	188	202	217	232	246	261
297		276	290	305	319	334	349	363	378	392	407
298		422	436	451	465	480	494	509	524	538	553
299		567	582	596	611	625	640	654	669	683	698
300		712	727	741	756	770	784	799	813	828	842
N.		0	1	2	3	4	5	6	7	8	9

Proportional parts

	18		17		16		15		14
1	1.8	1	1.7	1	1.6	1	1.5	1	1.4
2	3.6	2	3.4	2	3.2	2	3.0	2	2.8
3	5.4	3	5.1	3	4.8	3	4.5	3	4.2
4	7.2	4	6.8	4	6.4	4	6.0	4	5.6
5	9.0	5	8.5	5	8.0	5	7.5	5	7.0
6	10.8	6	10.2	6	9.6	6	9.0	6	8.4
7	12.6	7	11.9	7	11.2	7	10.5	7	9.8
8	14.4	8	13.6	8	12.8	8	12.0	8	11.2
9	16.2	9	15.3	9	14.4	9	13.5	9	12.6

$\log e = 0.43429$

.39 794 — .47 842

N.	0	1	2	3	4	5	6	7	8	9
300	47 712	727	741	756	770	784	799	813	828	842
301	857	871	885	900	914	929	943	958	972	986
302	48 001	015	029	044	058	073	087	101	116	130
303	144	159	173	187	202	216	230	244	259	273
304	287	302	316	330	344	359	373	387	401	416
305	430	444	458	473	487	501	515	530	544	558
306	572	586	601	615	629	643	657	671	686	700
307	714	728	742	756	770	785	799	813	827	841
308	855	869	883	897	911	926	940	954	968	982
309	996	*010	*024	*038	*052	*066	*080	*094	*108	*122
310	49 136	150	164	178	192	206	220	234	248	262
311	276	290	304	318	332	346	360	374	388	402
312	415	429	443	457	471	485	499	513	527	541
313	554	568	582	596	610	624	638	651	665	679
314	693	707	721	734	748	762	776	790	803	817
315	831	845	859	872	886	900	914	927	941	955
316	969	982	996	*010	*024	*037	*051	*065	*079	*092
317	50 106	120	133	147	161	174	188	202	215	229
318	243	256	270	284	297	311	325	338	352	365
319	379	393	406	420	433	447	461	474	488	501
320	515	529	542	556	569	583	596	610	623	637
321	651	664	678	691	705	718	732	745	759	772
322	786	799	813	826	840	853	866	880	893	907
323	920	934	947	961	974	987	*001	*014	*028	*041
324	51 055	068	081	095	108	121	135	148	162	175
325	188	202	215	228	242	255	268	282	295	308
326	322	335	348	362	375	388	402	415	428	441
327	455	468	481	495	508	521	534	548	561	574
328	587	601	614	627	640	654	667	680	693	706
329	720	733	746	759	772	786	799	812	825	838
330	851	865	878	891	904	917	930	943	957	970
331	983	996	*009	*022	*035	*048	*061	*075	*088	*101
332	52 114	127	140	153	166	179	192	205	218	231
333	244	257	270	284	297	310	323	336	349	362
334	375	388	401	414	427	440	453	466	479	492
335	504	517	530	543	556	569	582	595	608	621
336	634	647	660	673	686	699	711	724	737	750
337	763	776	789	802	815	827	840	853	866	879
338	892	905	917	930	943	956	969	982	994	*007
339	53 020	033	046	058	071	084	097	110	122	135
340	148	161	173	186	199	212	224	237	250	263
341	275	288	301	314	326	339	352	364	377	390
342	403	415	428	441	453	466	479	491	504	517
343	529	542	555	567	580	593	605	618	631	643
344	656	668	681	694	706	719	732	744	757	769
345	782	794	807	820	832	845	857	870	882	895
346	908	920	933	945	958	970	983	995	*008	*020
347	54 033	045	058	070	083	095	108	120	133	145
348	158	170	183	195	208	220	233	245	258	270
349	283	295	307	320	332	345	357	370	382	394
350	407	419	432	444	456	469	481	494	506	518
N.	0	1	2	3	4	5	6	7	8	9

Proportional parts

	15
1	1.5
2	3.0
3	4.5
4	6.0
5	7.5
6	9.0
7	10.5
8	12.0
9	13.5

	14
1	1.4
2	2.8
3	4.2
4	5.6
5	7.0
6	8.4
7	9.8
8	11.2
9	12.6

	13
1	1.3
2	2.6
3	3.9
4	5.2
5	6.5
6	7.8
7	9.1
8	10.4
9	11.7

	12
1	1.2
2	2.4
3	3.6
4	4.8
5	6.0
6	7.2
7	8.4
8	9.6
9	10.8

$\log \pi = 0.49715$

.47 712 — .54 518

N.		0	1	2	3	4	5	6	7	8	9
350	54	407	419	432	444	456	469	481	494	506	518
351		531	543	555	568	580	593	605	617	630	642
352		654	667	679	691	704	716	728	741	753	765
353		777	790	802	814	827	839	851	864	876	888
354		900	913	925	937	949	962	974	986	998	*011
355	55	023	035	047	060	072	084	096	108	121	133
356		145	157	169	182	194	206	218	230	242	255
357		267	279	291	303	315	328	340	352	364	376
358		388	400	413	425	437	449	461	473	485	497
359		509	522	534	546	558	570	582	594	606	618
360		630	642	654	666	678	691	703	715	727	739
361		751	763	775	787	799	811	823	835	847	859
362		871	883	895	907	919	931	943	955	967	979
363		991	*003	*015	*027	*038	*050	*062	*074	*086	*098
364	56	110	122	134	146	158	170	182	194	205	217
365		229	241	253	265	277	289	301	312	324	336
366		348	360	372	384	396	407	419	431	443	455
367		467	478	490	502	514	526	538	549	561	573
368		585	597	608	620	632	644	656	667	679	691
369		703	714	726	738	750	761	773	785	797	808
370		820	832	844	855	867	879	891	902	914	926
371		937	949	961	972	984	996	*008	*019	*031	*043
372	57	054	066	078	089	101	113	124	136	148	159
373		171	183	194	206	217	229	241	252	264	276
374		287	299	310	322	334	345	357	368	380	392
375		403	415	426	438	449	461	473	484	496	507
376		519	530	542	553	565	576	588	600	611	623
377		634	646	657	669	680	692	703	715	726	738
378		749	761	772	784	795	807	818	830	841	852
379		864	875	887	898	910	921	933	944	955	967
380		978	990	*001	*013	*024	*035	*047	*058	*070	*081
381	58	092	104	115	127	138	149	161	172	184	195
382		206	218	229	240	252	263	274	286	297	309
383		320	331	343	354	365	377	388	399	410	422
384		433	444	456	467	478	490	501	512	524	535
385		546	557	569	580	591	602	614	625	636	647
386		659	670	681	692	704	715	726	737	749	760
387		771	782	794	805	816	827	838	850	861	872
388		883	894	906	917	928	939	950	961	973	984
389		995	*006	*017	*028	*040	*051	*062	*073	*084	*095
390	59	106	118	129	140	151	162	173	184	195	207
391		218	229	240	251	262	273	284	295	306	318
392		329	340	351	362	373	384	395	406	417	428
393		439	450	461	472	483	494	506	517	528	539
394		550	561	572	583	594	605	616	627	638	649
395		660	671	682	693	704	715	726	737	748	759
396		770	780	791	802	813	824	835	846	857	868
397		879	890	901	912	923	934	945	956	966	977
398		988	999	*010	*021	*032	*043	*054	*065	*076	*086
399	60	097	108	119	130	141	152	163	173	184	195
400		206	217	228	239	249	260	271	282	293	304
N.		0	1	2	3	4	5	6	7	8	9

Proportional parts

	13		12		11		10
1	1.3	1	1.2	1	1.1	1	1.0
2	2.6	2	2.4	2	2.2	2	2.0
3	3.9	3	3.6	3	3.3	3	3.0
4	5.2	4	4.8	4	4.4	4	4.0
5	6.5	5	6.0	5	5.5	5	5.0
6	7.8	6	7.2	6	6.6	6	6.0
7	9.1	7	8.4	7	7.7	7	7.0
8	10.4	8	9.6	8	8.8	8	8.0
9	11.7	9	10.8	9	9.9	9	9.0

.54 407 — .60 304

N.	0	1	2	3	4	5	6	7	8	9
400	60 206	217	228	239	249	260	271	282	293	304
401	314	325	336	347	358	369	379	390	401	412
402	423	433	444	455	466	477	487	498	509	520
403	531	541	552	563	574	584	595	606	617	627
404	638	649	660	670	681	692	703	713	724	735
405	746	756	767	778	788	799	810	821	831	842
406	853	863	874	885	895	906	917	927	938	949
407	959	970	981	991	*002	*013	*023	*034	*045	*055
408	61 066	077	087	098	109	119	130	140	151	162
409	172	183	194	204	215	225	236	247	257	268
410	278	289	300	310	321	331	342	352	363	374
411	384	395	405	416	426	437	448	458	469	479
412	490	500	511	521	532	542	553	563	574	584
413	595	606	616	627	637	648	658	669	679	690
414	700	711	721	731	742	752	763	773	784	794
415	805	815	826	836	847	857	868	878	888	899
416	909	920	930	941	951	962	972	982	993	*003
417	62 014	024	034	045	055	066	076	086	097	107
418	118	128	138	149	159	170	180	190	201	211
419	221	232	242	252	263	273	284	294	304	315
420	325	335	346	356	366	377	387	397	408	418
421	428	439	449	459	469	480	490	500	511	521
422	531	542	552	562	572	583	593	603	613	624
423	634	644	655	665	675	685	696	706	716	726
424	737	747	757	767	778	788	798	808	818	829
425	839	849	859	870	880	890	900	910	921	931
426	941	951	961	972	982	992	*002	*012	*022	*033
427	63 043	053	063	073	083	094	104	114	124	134
428	144	155	165	175	185	195	205	215	225	236
429	246	256	266	276	286	296	306	317	327	337
430	347	357	367	377	387	397	407	417	428	438
431	448	458	468	478	488	498	508	518	528	538
432	548	558	568	579	589	599	609	619	629	639
433	649	659	669	679	689	699	709	719	729	739
434	749	759	769	779	789	799	809	819	829	839
435	849	859	869	879	889	899	909	919	929	939
436	949	959	969	979	988	998	*008	*018	*028	*038
437	64 048	058	068	078	088	098	108	118	128	137
438	147	157	167	177	187	197	207	217	227	237
439	246	256	266	276	286	296	306	316	326	335
440	345	355	365	375	385	395	404	414	424	434
441	444	454	464	473	483	493	503	513	523	532
442	542	552	562	572	582	591	601	611	621	631
443	640	650	660	670	680	689	699	709	719	729
444	738	748	758	768	777	787	797	807	816	826
445	836	846	856	865	875	885	895	904	914	924
446	933	943	953	963	972	982	992	*002	*011	*021
447	65 031	040	050	060	070	079	089	099	108	118
448	128	137	147	157	167	176	186	196	205	215
449	225	234	244	254	263	273	283	292	302	312
450	321	331	341	350	360	369	379	389	398	408
N.	0	1	2	3	4	5	6	7	8	9

Proportional parts

	11		10		9
1	1.1	1	1.0	1	0.9
2	2.2	2	2.0	2	1.8
3	3.3	3	3.0	3	2.7
4	4.4	4	4.0	4	3.6
5	5.5	5	5.0	5	4.5
6	6.6	6	6.0	6	5.4
7	7.7	7	7.0	7	6.3
8	8.8	8	8.0	8	7.2
9	9.9	9	9.0	9	8.1

.60 206 — .65 408

N.		0	1	2	3	4	5	6	7	8	9	Proportional parts	
450	65	321	331	341	350	360	369	379	389	398	408		
451		418	427	437	447	456	466	475	485	495	504		
452		514	523	533	543	552	562	571	581	591	600		
453		610	619	629	639	648	658	667	677	686	696		
454		706	715	725	734	744	753	763	772	782	792		
455		801	811	820	830	839	849	858	868	877	887		
456		896	906	916	925	935	944	954	963	973	982		10
457		992	*001	*011	*020	*030	*039	*049	*058	*068	*077		
458	66	087	096	106	115	124	134	143	153	162	172	1	1.0
459		181	191	200	210	219	229	238	247	257	266	2	2.0
												3	3.0
460		276	285	295	304	314	323	332	342	351	361	4	4.0
461		370	380	389	398	408	417	427	436	445	455	5	5.0
462		464	474	483	492	502	511	521	530	539	549	6	6.0
463		558	567	577	586	596	605	614	624	633	642	7	7.0
464		652	661	671	680	689	699	708	717	727	736	8	8.0
												9	9.0
465		745	755	764	773	783	792	801	811	820	829		
466		839	848	857	867	876	885	894	904	913	922		
467		932	941	950	960	969	978	987	997	*006	*015		
468	67	025	034	043	052	062	071	080	089	099	108		
469		117	127	136	145	154	164	173	182	191	201		
470		210	219	228	237	247	256	265	274	284	293		
471		302	311	321	330	339	348	357	367	376	385		9
472		394	403	413	422	431	440	449	459	468	477	1	0.9
473		486	495	504	514	523	532	541	550	560	569	2	1.8
474		578	587	596	605	614	624	633	642	651	660	3	2.7
												4	3.6
475		669	679	688	697	706	715	724	733	742	752	5	4.5
476		761	770	779	788	797	806	815	825	834	843	6	5.4
477		852	861	870	879	888	897	906	916	925	934	7	6.3
478		943	952	961	970	979	988	997	*006	*015	*024	8	7.2
479	68	034	043	052	061	070	079	088	097	106	115	9	8.1
480		124	133	142	151	160	169	178	187	196	205		
481		215	224	233	242	251	260	269	278	287	296		
482		305	314	323	332	341	350	359	368	377	386		
483		395	404	413	422	431	440	449	458	467	476		
484		485	494	502	511	520	529	538	547	556	565		
485		574	583	592	601	610	619	728	637	646	655		8
486		664	673	681	690	699	708	717	726	735	744		
487		753	762	771	780	789	797	806	815	824	833	1	0.8
488		842	851	860	869	878	886	895	904	913	922	2	1.6
489		931	940	949	958	966	975	984	993	*002	*011	3	2.4
												4	3.2
490	69	020	028	037	046	055	064	073	082	090	099	5	4.0
491		108	117	126	135	144	152	161	170	179	188	6	4.8
492		197	205	214	223	232	241	249	258	267	276	7	5.6
493		285	294	302	311	320	329	338	346	355	364	8	6.4
494		373	381	390	399	408	417	425	434	443	452	9	7.2
495		461	469	478	487	496	504	513	522	531	539		
496		548	557	566	574	583	592	601	609	618	627		
497		636	644	653	662	671	679	688	697	705	714		
498		723	732	740	749	758	767	775	784	793	801		
499		810	819	827	836	845	854	862	871	880	888		
500		897	906	914	923	932	940	949	958	966	975		
N.		0	1	2	3	4	5	6	7	8	9	Proportional parts	

.65 321 — .69 975

N.	0	1	2	3	4	5	6	7	8	9
500	69 897	906	914	923	932	940	949	958	966	975
501	984	992	*001	*010	*018	*027	*036	*044	*053	*062
502	70 070	079	088	096	105	114	122	131	140	148
503	157	165	174	183	191	200	209	217	226	234
504	243	252	260	269	278	286	295	303	312	321
505	329	338	346	355	364	372	381	389	398	406
506	415	424	432	441	449	458	467	475	484	492
507	501	509	518	526	535	544	552	561	569	578
508	586	595	603	612	621	629	638	646	655	663
509	672	680	689	697	706	714	723	731	740	749
510	757	766	774	783	791	800	808	817	825	834
511	842	851	859	868	876	885	893	902	910	919
512	927	935	944	952	961	969	978	986	995	*003
513	71 012	020	029	037	046	054	063	071	079	088
514	096	105	113	122	130	139	147	155	164	172
515	181	189	198	206	214	223	231	240	248	257
516	265	273	282	290	299	307	315	324	332	341
517	349	357	366	374	383	391	399	408	416	425
518	433	441	450	458	466	475	483	492	500	508
519	517	525	533	542	550	559	567	575	584	592
520	600	609	617	625	634	642	650	659	667	675
521	684	692	700	709	717	725	734	742	750	759
522	767	775	784	792	800	809	817	825	834	842
523	850	858	867	875	883	892	900	908	917	925
524	933	941	950	958	966	975	983	991	999	*008
525	72 016	024	032	041	049	057	066	074	082	090
526	099	107	115	123	132	140	148	156	165	173
527	181	189	198	206	214	222	230	239	247	255
528	263	272	280	288	296	304	313	321	329	337
529	346	354	362	370	378	387	395	403	411	419
530	428	436	444	452	460	469	477	485	493	501
531	509	518	526	534	542	550	558	567	575	583
532	591	599	607	616	624	632	640	648	656	665
533	673	681	689	697	705	713	722	730	738	746
534	754	762	770	779	787	795	803	811	819	827
535	835	843	852	860	868	876	884	892	900	908
536	916	925	933	941	949	957	965	973	981	989
537	997	*006	*014	*022	*030	*038	*046	*054	*062	*070
538	73 078	086	094	102	111	119	127	135	143	151
539	159	167	175	183	191	199	207	215	223	231
540	239	247	255	263	272	280	288	296	304	312
541	320	328	336	344	352	360	368	376	384	392
542	400	408	416	424	432	440	448	456	464	472
543	480	488	496	504	512	520	528	536	544	552
544	560	568	576	584	592	600	608	616	624	632
545	640	648	656	664	672	679	687	695	703	711
546	719	727	735	743	751	759	767	775	783	791
547	799	807	815	823	830	838	846	854	862	870
548	878	886	894	902	910	918	926	933	941	949
549	957	965	973	981	989	997	*005	*013	*020	*028
550	74 036	044	052	060	068	076	084	092	099	107
N.	0	1	2	3	4	5	6	7	8	9

Proportional parts

	9		8		7
1	0.9	1	0.8	1	0.7
2	1.8	2	1.6	2	1.4
3	2.7	3	2.4	3	2.1
4	3.6	4	3.2	4	2.8
5	4.5	5	4.0	5	3.5
6	5.4	6	4.8	6	4.2
7	6.3	7	5.6	7	4.9
8	7.2	8	6.4	8	5.6
9	8.1	9	7.2	9	6.3

.69 897 — .74 107

N.	0	1	2	3	4	5	6	7	8	9	Proportional parts
550	74 036	044	052	060	068	076	084	092	099	107	
551	115	123	131	139	147	155	162	170	178	186	
552	194	202	210	218	225	233	241	249	257	265	
553	273	280	288	296	304	312	320	327	335	343	
554	351	359	367	374	382	390	398	406	414	421	
555	429	437	445	453	461	468	476	484	492	500	
556	507	515	523	531	539	547	554	562	570	578	
557	586	593	601	609	617	624	632	640	648	656	
558	663	671	679	687	695	702	710	718	726	733	
559	741	749	757	764	772	780	788	796	803	811	
560	819	827	834	842	850	858	865	873	881	889	
561	896	904	912	920	927	935	943	950	958	966	
562	974	981	989	997	*005	*012	*020	*028	*035	*043	
563	75 051	059	066	074	082	089	097	105	113	120	
564	128	136	143	151	159	166	174	182	189	197	
565	205	213	220	228	236	243	251	259	266	274	
566	282	289	297	305	312	320	328	335	343	351	
567	358	366	374	381	389	397	404	412	420	427	
568	435	442	450	458	465	473	481	488	496	504	
569	511	519	526	534	542	549	557	565	572	580	
570	587	595	603	610	618	626	633	641	648	656	
571	664	671	679	686	694	702	709	717	724	732	
572	740	747	755	762	770	778	785	793	800	808	
573	815	823	831	838	846	853	861	868	876	884	
574	891	899	906	914	921	929	937	944	952	959	
575	967	974	982	989	997	*005	*012	*020	*027	*035	
576	76 042	050	057	065	072	080	087	095	103	110	
577	118	125	133	140	148	155	163	170	178	185	
578	193	200	208	215	223	230	238	245	253	260	
579	268	275	283	290	298	305	313	320	328	335	
580	343	350	358	365	373	380	388	395	403	410	
581	418	425	433	440	448	455	462	470	477	485	
582	492	500	507	515	522	530	537	545	552	559	
583	567	574	582	589	597	604	612	619	626	634	
584	641	649	656	664	671	678	686	693	701	708	
585	716	723	730	738	745	753	760	768	775	782	
586	790	797	805	812	819	827	834	842	849	856	
587	864	871	879	886	893	901	908	916	923	930	
588	938	945	953	960	967	975	982	989	997	*004	
589	77 012	019	026	034	041	048	056	063	070	078	
590	085	093	100	107	115	122	129	137	144	151	
591	159	166	173	181	188	195	203	210	217	225	
592	232	240	247	254	262	269	276	283	291	298	
593	305	313	320	327	335	342	349	357	364	371	
594	379	386	393	401	408	415	422	430	437	444	
595	452	459	466	474	481	488	495	503	510	517	
596	525	532	539	546	554	561	568	576	583	590	
597	597	605	612	619	627	634	641	648	656	663	
598	670	677	685	692	699	706	714	721	728	735	
599	743	750	757	764	772	779	786	793	801	808	
600	815	822	830	837	844	851	859	866	873	880	
N.	0	1	2	3	4	5	6	7	8	9	Proportional parts

Proportional parts:

	8
1	0.8
2	1.6
3	2.4
4	3.2
5	4.0
6	4.8
7	5.6
8	6.4
9	7.2

	7
1	0.7
2	1.4
3	2.1
4	2.8
5	3.5
6	4.2
7	4.9
8	5.6
9	6.3

.74 036 — .77 880

N.		0	1	2	3	4	5	6	7	8	9	Proportional parts
600	77	815	822	830	837	844	851	859	866	873	880	
601		887	895	902	909	916	924	931	938	945	952	
602		960	967	974	981	988	996	*003	*010	*017	*025	
603	78	032	039	046	053	061	068	075	082	089	097	
604		104	111	118	125	132	140	147	154	161	168	
605		176	183	190	197	204	211	219	226	233	240	
606		247	254	262	269	276	283	290	297	305	312	
607		319	326	333	340	347	355	362	369	376	383	
608		390	398	405	412	419	426	433	440	447	455	
609		462	469	476	483	490	497	504	512	519	526	
610		533	540	547	554	561	569	576	583	590	597	
611		604	611	618	625	633	640	647	654	661	668	
612		675	682	689	696	704	711	718	725	732	739	
613		746	753	760	767	774	781	789	796	803	810	
614		817	824	831	838	845	852	859	866	873	880	
615		888	895	902	909	916	923	930	937	944	951	
616		958	965	972	979	986	993	*000	*007	*014	*021	
617	79	029	036	043	050	057	064	071	078	085	092	
618		099	106	113	120	127	134	141	148	155	162	
619		169	176	183	190	197	204	211	218	225	232	
620		239	246	253	260	267	274	281	288	295	302	
621		309	316	323	330	337	344	351	358	365	372	
622		379	386	393	400	407	414	421	428	435	442	
623		449	456	463	470	477	484	491	498	505	511	
624		518	525	532	539	546	553	560	567	574	581	
625		588	595	602	609	616	623	630	637	644	650	
626		657	664	671	678	685	692	699	706	713	720	
627		727	734	741	748	754	761	768	775	782	789	
628		796	803	810	817	824	831	837	844	851	858	
629		865	872	879	886	893	900	906	913	920	927	
630		934	941	948	955	962	969	975	982	989	996	
631	80	003	010	017	024	030	037	044	051	058	065	
632		072	079	085	092	099	106	113	120	127	134	
633		140	147	154	161	168	175	182	188	195	202	
634		209	216	223	229	236	243	250	257	264	271	
635		277	284	291	298	305	312	318	325	332	339	
636		346	353	359	366	373	380	387	393	400	407	
637		414	421	428	434	441	448	455	462	468	475	
638		482	489	496	502	509	516	523	530	536	543	
639		550	557	564	570	577	584	591	598	604	611	
640		618	625	632	638	645	652	659	665	672	679	
641		686	693	699	706	713	720	726	733	740	747	
642		754	760	767	774	781	787	794	801	808	814	
643		821	828	835	841	848	855	862	868	875	882	
644		889	895	902	909	916	922	929	936	943	949	
645		956	963	969	976	983	990	996	*003	*010	*017	
646	81	023	030	037	043	050	057	064	070	077	084	
647		090	097	104	111	117	124	131	137	144	151	
648		158	164	171	178	184	191	198	204	211	218	
649		224	231	238	245	251	258	265	271	278	285	
650		291	298	305	311	318	325	331	338	345	351	
N.		0	1	2	3	4	5	6	7	8	9	Proportional parts

Proportional parts:

	8		7		6
1	0.8	1	0.7	1	0.6
2	1.6	2	1.4	2	1.2
3	2.4	3	2.1	3	1.8
4	3.2	4	2.8	4	2.4
5	4.0	5	3.5	5	3.0
6	4.8	6	4.2	6	3.6
7	5.6	7	4.9	7	4.2
8	6.4	8	5.6	8	4.8
9	7.2	9	6.3	9	5.4

.77 815 — .81 351

N.		0	1	2	3	4	5	6	7	8	9
650	81	291	298	305	311	318	325	331	338	345	351
651		358	365	371	378	385	391	398	405	411	418
652		425	431	438	445	451	458	465	471	478	485
653		491	498	505	511	518	525	531	538	544	551
654		558	564	571	578	584	591	598	604	611	617
655		624	631	637	644	651	657	664	671	677	684
656		690	697	704	710	717	723	730	737	743	750
657		757	763	770	776	783	790	796	803	809	816
658		823	829	836	842	849	856	862	869	875	882
659		889	895	902	908	915	921	928	935	941	948
660		954	961	968	974	981	987	994	*000	*007	*014
661	82	020	027	033	040	046	053	060	066	073	079
662		086	092	099	105	112	119	125	132	138	145
663		151	158	164	171	178	184	191	197	204	210
664		217	223	230	236	243	249	256	263	269	276
665		282	289	295	302	308	315	321	328	334	341
666		347	354	360	367	373	380	387	393	400	406
667		413	419	426	432	439	445	452	458	465	471
668		478	484	491	497	504	510	517	523	530	536
669		543	549	556	562	569	575	582	588	595	601
670		607	614	620	627	633	640	646	653	659	666
571		672	679	685	692	698	705	711	718	724	730
672		737	743	750	756	763	769	776	782	789	795
673		802	808	814	821	827	834	840	847	853	860
674		866	872	879	885	892	898	905	911	918	924
675		930	937	943	950	956	963	969	975	982	988
676		995	*001	*008	*014	*020	*027	*033	*040	*046	*052
677	83	059	065	072	078	085	091	097	104	110	117
678		123	129	136	142	149	155	161	168	174	181
679		187	193	200	206	213	219	225	232	238	245
680		251	257	264	270	276	283	289	296	302	308
681		315	321	327	334	340	347	353	359	366	372
682		378	385	391	398	404	410	417	423	429	436
683		442	448	455	461	467	474	480	487	493	499
684		506	512	518	525	531	537	544	550	556	563
685		569	575	582	588	594	601	607	613	620	626
686		632	639	645	651	658	664	670	677	683	689
687		696	702	708	715	721	727	734	740	746	753
688		759	765	771	778	784	790	797	803	809	816
689		822	828	835	841	847	853	860	866	872	879
690		885	891	897	904	910	916	923	929	935	942
691		948	954	960	967	973	979	985	992	998	*004
692	84	011	017	023	029	036	042	048	055	061	067
693		073	080	086	092	098	105	111	117	123	130
694		136	142	148	155	161	167	173	180	186	192
695		198	205	211	217	223	230	236	242	248	255
696		261	267	273	280	286	292	298	305	311	317
697		323	330	336	342	348	354	361	367	373	379
698		386	392	398	404	410	417	423	429	435	442
699		448	454	460	466	473	479	485	491	497	504
700		510	516	522	528	535	541	547	553	559	566
N.		0	1	2	3	4	5	6	7	8	9

Proportional parts

	7
1	0.7
2	1.4
3	2.1
4	2.8
5	3.5
6	4.2
7	4.9
8	5.6
9	6.3

	6
1	0.6
2	1.2
3	1.8
4	2.4
5	3.0
6	3.6
7	4.2
8	4.8
9	5.4

.81 291 — .84 566

N.		0	1	2	3	4	5	6	7	8	9	Proportional parts
700	84	510	516	522	528	535	541	547	553	559	566	
701		572	578	584	590	597	603	609	615	621	628	
702		634	640	646	652	658	665	671	677	683	689	
703		696	702	708	714	720	726	733	739	745	751	
704		757	763	770	776	782	788	794	800	807	813	
705		819	825	831	837	844	850	856	862	868	874	
706		880	887	893	899	905	911	917	924	930	936	
707		942	948	954	960	967	973	979	985	991	997	
708	85	003	009	016	022	028	034	040	046	052	058	
709		065	071	077	083	089	095	101	107	114	120	
710		126	132	138	144	150	156	163	169	175	181	
711		187	193	199	205	211	217	224	230	236	242	
712		248	254	260	266	272	278	285	291	297	303	
713		309	315	321	327	333	339	345	352	358	364	
714		370	376	382	388	394	400	406	412	418	425	
715		431	437	443	449	455	461	467	473	479	485	
716		491	497	503	509	516	522	528	534	540	546	
717		552	558	564	570	576	582	588	594	600	606	
718		612	618	625	631	637	643	649	655	661	667	
719		673	679	685	691	697	703	709	715	721	727	
720		733	739	745	751	757	763	769	775	781	788	
721		794	800	806	812	818	824	830	836	842	848	
722		854	860	866	872	878	884	890	896	902	908	
723		914	920	926	932	938	944	950	956	962	968	
724		974	980	986	992	998	*004	*010	*016	*022	*028	
725	86	034	040	046	052	058	064	070	076	082	088	
726		094	100	106	112	118	124	130	136	141	147	
727		153	159	165	171	177	183	189	195	201	207	
728		213	219	225	231	237	243	249	255	261	267	
729		273	279	285	291	297	303	308	314	320	326	
730		332	338	344	350	356	362	368	374	380	386	
731		392	398	404	410	415	421	427	433	439	445	
732		451	457	463	469	475	481	487	493	499	504	
733		510	516	522	528	534	540	546	552	558	564	
734		570	576	581	587	593	599	605	611	617	623	
735		629	635	641	646	652	658	664	670	676	682	
736		688	694	700	705	711	717	723	729	735	741	
737		747	753	759	764	770	776	782	788	794	800	
738		806	812	817	823	829	835	841	847	853	859	
739		864	870	876	882	888	894	900	906	911	917	
740		923	929	935	941	947	953	958	964	970	976	
741		982	988	994	999	*005	*011	*017	*023	*029	*035	
742	87	040	046	052	058	064	070	075	081	087	093	
743		099	105	111	116	122	128	134	140	146	151	
744		157	163	169	175	181	186	192	198	204	210	
745		216	221	227	233	239	245	251	256	262	268	
746		274	280	286	291	297	303	309	315	320	326	
747		332	338	344	349	355	361	367	373	379	384	
748		390	396	402	408	413	419	425	431	437	442	
749		448	454	460	466	471	477	483	489	495	500	
750		506	512	518	523	529	535	541	547	552	558	
N.		0	1	2	3	4	5	6	7	8	9	Proportional parts

Proportional parts:

	7
1	0.7
2	1.4
3	2.1
4	2.8
5	3.5
6	4.2
7	4.9
8	5.6
9	6.3

	6
1	0.6
2	1.2
3	1.8
4	2.4
5	3.0
6	3.6
7	4.2
8	4.8
9	5.4

	5
1	0.5
2	1.0
3	1.5
4	2.0
5	2.5
6	3.0
7	3.5
8	4.0
9	4.5

.84 510 — .87 558

N.	0	1	2	3	4	5	6	7	8	9	Proportional parts
750	87 506	512	518	523	529	535	541	547	552	558	
751	564	570	576	581	587	593	599	604	610	616	
752	622	628	633	639	645	651	656	662	668	674	
753	679	685	691	697	703	708	714	720	726	731	
754	737	743	749	754	760	766	772	777	783	·789	
755	795	800	806	812	818	823	829	835	841	846	
756	852	858	864	869	875	881	887	892	898	904	
757	910	915	921	927	933	938	944	950	955	961	
758	967	973	978	984	990	996	*001	*007	*013	*018	
759	88 024	030	036	041	047	053	058	064	070	076	
760	081	087	093	098	104	110	116	121	127	133	
761	138	144	150	156	161	167	173	178	184	190	6
762	195	201	207	213	218	224	230	235	241	247	1 0.6
763	252	258	264	270	275	281	287	292	298	304	2 1.2
764	309	315	321	326	332	338	343	349	355	360	3 1.8
765	366	372	377	383	389	395	400	406	412	417	4 2.4
766	423	429	434	440	446	451	457	463	468	474	5 3.0
767	480	485	491	497	502	508	513	519	525	530	6 3.6
768	536	542	547	553	559	564	570	576	581	587	7 4.2
769	593	598	604	610	615	621	627	632	638	643	8 4.8
770	649	655	660	666	672	677	683	689	694	700	9 5.4
771	705	711	717	722	728	734	739	745	750	756	
772	762	767	773	779	784	790	795	801	807	812	
773	818	824	829	835	840	846	852	857	863	868	
774	874	880	885	891	897	902	908	913	919	925	
775	930	936	941	947	953	958	964	969	975	981	
776	986	992	997	*003	*009	*014	*020	*025	*031	*037	
777	89 042	048	053	059	064	070	076	081	087	092	
778	098	104	109	115	120	126	131	137	143	148	
779	154	159	165	170	176	182	187	193	198	204	
780	209	215	221	226	232	237	243	248	254	260	
781	265	271	276	282	287	293	298	304	310	315	5
782	321	326	332	337	343	348	354	360	365	371	1 0.5
783	376	382	387	393	398	404	409	415	421	426	2 1.0
784	432	437	443	448	454	459	465	470	476	481	3 1.5
785	487	492	498	504	509	515	520	526	531	537	4 2.0
786	542	548	553	559	564	570	575	581	586	592	5 2.5
787	597	603	609	614	620	625	631	636	642	647	6 3.0
788	653	658	664	669	675	680	686	691	697	702	7 3.5
789	708	713	719	724	730	735	741	746	752	757	8 4.0
790	763	768	774	779	785	790	796	801	807	812	9 4.5
791	818	823	829	834	840	845	851	856	862	867	
792	873	878	883	889	894	900	905	911	916	922	
793	927	933	938	944	949	955	960	966	971	977	
794	982	988	993	998	*004	*009	*015	*020	*026	*031	
795	90 037	042	048	053	059	064	069	075	080	086	
796	091	097	102	108	113	119	124	129	135	140	
797	146	151	157	162	168	173	179	184	189	195	
798	200	206	211	217	222	227	233	238	244	249	
799	255	260	266	271	276	282	287	293	298	304	
800	309	314	320	325	331	336	342	347	352	358	
N.	0	1	2	3	4	5	6	7	8	9	Proportional parts

.87 506 — .90 358

N.	0	1	2	3	4	5	6	7	8	9	Proportional parts
800	90 309	314	320	325	331	336	342	347	352	358	
801	363	369	374	380	385	390	396	401	407	412	
802	417	423	428	434	439	445	450	455	461	466	
803	472	477	482	488	493	499	504	509	515	520	
804	526	531	536	542	547	553	558	563	569	574	
805	580	585	590	596	601	607	612	617	623	628	
806	634	639	644	650	655	660	666	671	677	682	
807	687	693	698	703	709	714	720	725	730	736	
808	741	747	752	757	763	768	773	779	784	789	
809	795	800	806	811	816	822	827	832	838	843	
810	849	854	859	865	870	875	881	886	891	897	
811	902	907	913	918	924	929	934	940	945	950	**6**
812	956	961	966	972	977	982	988	993	998	*004	1 0.6
813	91 009	014	020	025	030	036	041	046	052	057	2 1.2
814	062	068	073	078	084	089	094	100	105	110	3 1.8
815	116	121	126	132	137	142	148	153	158	164	4 2.4
816	169	174	180	185	190	196	201	206	212	217	5 3.0
817	222	228	233	238	243	249	254	259	265	270	6 3.6
818	275	281	286	291	297	302	307	312	318	323	7 4.2
819	328	334	339	344	350	355	360	365	371	376	8 4.8
820	381	387	392	397	403	408	413	418	424	429	9 5.4
821	434	440	445	450	455	461	466	471	477	482	
822	487	492	498	503	508	514	519	524	529	535	
823	540	545	551	556	561	566	572	577	582	587	
824	593	598	603	609	614	619	624	630	635	640	
825	645	651	656	661	666	672	677	682	687	693	
826	698	703	709	714	719	724	730	735	740	745	
827	751	756	761	766	772	777	782	787	793	798	
828	803	808	814	819	824	829	834	840	845	850	
829	855	861	866	871	876	882	887	892	897	903	
830	908	913	918	924	929	934	939	944	950	955	
831	960	965	971	976	981	986	991	997	*002	*007	**5**
832	92 012	018	023	028	033	038	044	049	054	059	1 0.5
833	065	070	075	080	085	091	096	101	106	111	2 1.0
834	117	122	127	132	137	143	148	153	158	163	3 1.5
835	169	174	179	184	189	195	200	205	210	215	4 2.0
836	221	226	231	236	241	247	252	257	262	267	5 2.5
837	273	278	283	288	293	298	304	309	314	319	6 3.0
838	324	330	335	340	345	350	355	361	366	371	7 3.5
839	376	381	387	392	397	402	407	412	418	423	8 4.0
840	428	433	438	443	449	454	459	464	469	474	9 4.5
841	480	485	490	495	500	505	511	516	521	526	
842	531	536	542	547	552	557	562	567	572	578	
843	583	588	593	598	603	609	614	619	624	629	
844	634	639	645	650	655	660	665	670	675	681	
845	686	691	696	701	706	711	716	722	727	732	
846	737	742	747	752	758	763	768	773	778	783	
847	788	793	799	804	809	814	819	824	829	834	
848	840	845	850	855	860	865	870	875	881	886	
849	891	896	901	906	911	916	921	927	932	937	
850	942	947	952	957	962	967	973	978	983	988	
N.	0	1	2	3	4	5	6	7	8	9	Proportional parts

.90 309 — .92 988

N.		0	1	2	3	4	5	6	7	8	9
850	92	942	947	952	957	962	967	973	978	983	988
851		993	998	*003	*008	*013	*018	*024	*029	*034	*039
852	93	044	049	054	059	064	069	075	080	085	090
853		095	100	105	110	115	120	125	131	136	141
854		146	151	156	161	166	171	176	181	186	192
855		197	202	207	212	217	222	227	232	237	242
856		247	252	258	263	268	273	278	283	288	293
857		298	303	308	313	318	323	328	334	339	344
858		349	354	359	364	369	374	379	384	389	394
859		399	404	409	414	420	425	430	435	440	445
860		450	455	460	465	470	475	480	485	490	495
861		500	505	510	515	520	526	531	536	541	546
862		551	556	561	566	571	576	581	586	591	596
863		601	606	611	616	621	626	631	636	641	646
864		651	656	661	666	671	676	682	687	692	697
865		702	707	712	717	722	727	732	737	742	747
866		752	757	762	767	772	777	782	787	792	797
867		802	807	812	817	822	827	832	837	842	847
868		852	857	862	867	872	877	882	887	892	897
869		902	907	912	917	922	927	932	937	942	947
870		952	957	962	967	972	977	982	987	992	997
871	94	002	007	012	017	022	027	032	037	042	047
872		052	057	062	067	072	077	082	086	091	096
873		101	106	111	116	121	126	131	136	141	146
874		151	156	161	166	171	176	181	186	191	196
875		201	206	211	216	221	226	231	236	240	245
876		250	255	260	265	270	275	280	285	290	295
877		300	305	310	315	320	325	330	335	340	345
878		349	354	359	364	369	374	379	384	389	394
879		399	404	409	414	419	424	429	433	438	443
880		448	453	458	463	468	473	478	483	488	493
881		498	503	507	512	517	522	527	532	537	542
882		547	552	557	562	567	571	576	581	586	591
883		596	601	606	611	616	621	626	630	635	640
884		645	650	655	660	665	670	675	680	685	689
885		694	699	704	709	714	719	724	729	734	738
886		743	748	753	758	763	768	773	778	783	787
887		792	797	802	807	812	817	822	827	832	836
888		841	846	851	856	861	866	871	876	880	885
889		890	895	900	905	910	915	919	924	929	934
890		939	944	949	954	959	963	968	973	978	983
891		988	993	998	*002	*007	*012	*017	*022	*027	*032
892	95	036	041	046	051	056	061	066	071	075	080
893		085	090	095	100	105	109	114	119	124	129
894		134	139	143	148	153	158	163	168	173	177
895		182	187	192	197	202	207	211	216	221	226
896		231	236	240	245	250	255	260	265	270	274
897		279	284	289	294	299	303	308	313	318	323
898		328	332	337	342	347	352	357	361	366	371
899		376	381	386	390	395	400	405	410	415	419
900		424	429	434	439	444	448	453	458	463	468
N.		0	1	2	3	4	5	6	7	8	9

Proportional parts

	6
1	0.6
2	1.2
3	1.8
4	2.4
5	3.0
6	3.6
7	4.2
8	4.8
9	5.4

	5
1	0.5
2	1.0
3	1.5
4	2.0
5	2.5
6	3.0
7	3.5
8	4.0
9	4.5

	4
1	0.4
2	0.8
3	1.2
4	1.6
5	2.0
6	2.4
7	2.8
8	3.2
9	3.6

.92 942 — .95 468

N.		0	1	2	3	4	5	6	7	8	9
900	95	424	429	434	439	444	448	453	458	463	468
901		472	477	482	487	492	497	501	506	511	516
902		521	525	530	535	540	545	550	554	559	564
903		569	574	578	583	588	593	598	602	607	612
904		617	622	626	631	636	641	646	650	655	660
905		665	670	674	679	684	689	694	698	703	708
906		713	718	722	727	732	737	742	746	751	756
907		761	766	770	775	780	785	789	794	799	804
908		809	813	818	823	828	832	837	842	847	852
909		856	861	866	871	875	880	885	890	895	899
910		904	909	914	918	923	928	933	938	942	947
911		952	957	961	966	971	976	980	985	990	995
912		999	*004	*009	*014	*019	*023	*028	*033	*038	*042
913	96	047	052	057	061	066	071	076	080	085	090
914		095	099	104	109	114	118	123	128	133	137
915		142	147	152	156	161	166	171	175	180	185
916		190	194	199	204	209	213	218	223	227	232
917		237	242	246	251	256	261	265	270	275	280
918		284	289	294	298	303	308	313	317	322	327
919		332	336	341	346	350	355	360	365	369	374
920		379	384	388	393	398	402	407	412	417	421
921		426	431	435	440	445	450	454	459	464	468
922		473	478	483	487	492	497	501	506	511	515
923		520	525	530	534	539	544	548	553	558	562
924		567	572	577	581	586	591	595	600	605	609
925		614	619	624	628	633	638	642	647	652	656
926		661	666	670	675	680	685	689	694	699	703
927		708	713	717	722	727	731	736	741	745	750
928		755	759	764	769	774	778	783	788	792	797
929		802	806	811	816	820	825	830	834	839	844
930		848	853	858	862	867	872	876	881	886	890
931		895	900	904	909	914	918	923	928	932	937
932		942	946	951	956	960	965	970	974	979	984
933		988	993	997	*002	*007	*011	*016	*021	*025	*030
934	97	035	039	044	049	053	058	063	067	072	077
935		081	086	090	095	100	104	109	114	118	123
936		128	132	137	142	146	151	155	160	165	169
937		174	179	183	188	192	197	202	206	211	216
938		220	225	230	234	239	243	248	253	257	262
939		267	271	276	280	285	290	294	299	304	308
940		313	317	322	327	331	336	340	345	350	354
941		359	364	368	373	377	382	387	391	396	400
942		405	410	414	419	424	428	433	437	442	447
943		451	456	460	465	470	474	479	483	488	493
944		497	502	506	511	516	520	525	529	534	539
945		543	548	552	557	562	566	571	575	580	585
946		589	594	598	603	607	612	617	621	626	630
947		635	640	644	649	653	658	663	667	672	676
948		681	685	690	695	699	704	708	713	717	722
949		727	731	736	740	745	749	754	759	763	768
950		772	777	782	786	791	795	800	804	809	813
N.		0	1	2	3	4	5	6	7	8	9

Proportional parts

	5
1	0.5
2	1.0
3	1.5
4	2.0
5	2.5
6	3.0
7	3.5
8	4.0
9	4.5

	4
1	0.4
2	0.8
3	1.2
4	1.6
5	2.0
6	2.4
7	2.8
8	3.2
9	3.6

.95 424 — .97 813

N.		0	1	2	3	4		5	6	7	8	9	Proportional parts
950	97	772	777	782	786	791		795	800	804	809	813	
951		818	823	827	832	836		841	845	850	855	859	
952		864	868	873	877	882		886	891	896	900	905	
953		909	914	918	923	928		932	937	941	946	950	
954		955	959	964	968	973		978	982	987	991	996	
955	98	000	005	009	014	019		023	028	032	037	041	
956		046	050	055	059	064		068	073	078	082	087	
957		091	096	100	105	109		114	118	123	127	132	
958		137	141	146	150	155		159	164	168	173	177	
959		182	186	191	195	200		204	209	214	218	223	
960		227	232	236	241	245		250	254	259	263	268	
961		272	277	281	286	290		295	299	304	308	313	
962		318	322	327	331	336		340	345	349	354	358	
963		363	367	372	376	381		385	390	394	399	403	
964		408	412	417	421	426		430	435	439	444	448	
965		453	457	462	466	471		475	480	484	489	493	
966		498	502	507	511	516		520	525	529	534	538	
967		543	547	552	556	561		565	570	574	579	583	
968		588	592	597	601	605		610	614	619	623	628	
969		632	637	641	646	650		655	659	664	668	673	
970		677	682	686	691	695		700	704	709	713	717	
971		722	726	731	735	740		744	749	753	758	762	
972		767	771	776	780	784		789	793	798	802	807	
973		811	816	820	825	829		834	838	843	847	851	
974		856	860	865	869	874		878	883	887	892	896	
975		900	905	909	914	918		923	927	932	936	941	
976		945	949	954	958	963		967	972	976	981	985	
977		989	994	998	*003	*007		*012	*016	*021	*025	*029	
978	99	034	038	043	047	052		056	061	065	069	074	
979		078	083	087	092	096		100	105	109	114	118	
980		123	127	131	136	140		145	149	154	158	162	
981		167	171	176	180	185		189	193	198	202	207	
982		211	216	220	224	229		233	238	242	247	251	
983		255	260	264	269	273		277	282	286	291	295	
984		300	304	308	313	317		322	326	330	335	339	
985		344	348	352	357	361		366	370	374	379	383	
986		388	392	396	401	405		410	414	419	423	427	
987		432	436	441	445	449		454	458	463	467	471	
988		476	480	484	489	493		498	502	506	511	515	
989		520	524	528	533	537		542	546	550	555	559	
990		564	568	572	577	581		585	590	594	599	603	
991		607	612	616	621	625		629	634	638	642	647	
992		651	656	660	664	669		673	677	682	686	691	
993		695	699	704	708	712		717	721	726	730	734	
994		739	743	747	752	756		760	765	769	774	778	
995		782	787	791	795	800		804	808	813	817	822	
996		826	830	835	839	843		848	852	856	861	865	
997		870	874	878	883	887		891	896	900	904	909	
998		913	917	922	926	930		935	939	944	948	952	
999		957	961	965	970	974		978	983	987	991	996	
1000	00	000	004	009	013	017		022	026	030	035	039	
N.		0	1	2	3	4		5	6	7	8	9	Proportional parts

Proportional parts (right column):

	5
1	0.5
2	1.0
3	1.5
4	2.0
5	2.5
6	3.0
7	3.5
8	4.0
9	4.5

	4
1	0.4
2	0.8
3	1.2
4	1.6
5	2.0
6	2.4
7	2.8
8	3.2
9	3.6

.97 772 — .99 996

N.		0	1	2	3	4	5	6	7	8	9	d.
1000	000	0000	0434	0869	1303	1737	2171	2605	3039	3473	3907	434
1001		4341	4775	5208	5642	6076	6510	6943	7377	7810	8244	434
1002		8677	9111	9544	9977	*0411	*0844	*1277	*1710	*2143	*2576	433
1003	001	3009	3442	3875	4308	4741	5174	5607	6039	6472	6905	433
1004		7337	7770	8202	8635	9067	9499	9932	*0364	*0796	*1228	432
1005	002	1661	2093	2525	2957	3389	3821	4253	4685	5116	5548	432
1006		5980	6411	6843	7275	7706	8138	8569	9001	9432	9863	431
1007	003	0295	0726	1157	1588	2019	2451	2882	3313	3744	4174	431
1008		4605	5036	5467	5898	6328	6759	7190	7620	8051	8481	431
1009		8912	9342	9772	*0203	*0633	*1063	*1493	*1924	*2354	*2784	430
1010	004	3214	3644	4074	4504	4933	5363	5793	6223	6652	7082	430
1011		7512	7941	8371	8800	9229	9659	*0088	*0517	*0947	*1376	429
1012	005	1805	2234	2663	3092	3521	3950	4379	4808	5237	5666	429
1013		6094	6523	6952	7380	7809	8238	8666	9094	9523	9951	429
1014	006	0380	0808	1236	1664	2092	2521	2949	3377	3805	4233	428
1015		4660	5088	5516	5944	6372	6799	7227	7655	8082	8510	428
1016		8937	9365	9792	*0219	*0647	*1074	*1501	*1928	*2355	*2782	427
1017	007	3210	3637	4064	4490	4917	5344	5771	6198	6624	7051	427
1018		7478	7904	8331	8757	9184	9610	*0037	*0463	*0889	*1316	426
1019	008	1742	2168	2594	3020	3446	3872	4298	4724	5150	5576	426
1020		6002	6427	6853	7279	7704	8130	8556	8981	9407	9832	426
1021	009	0257	0683	1108	1533	1959	2384	2809	3234	3659	4084	425
1022		4509	4934	5359	5784	6208	6633	7058	7483	7907	8332	425
1023		8756	9181	9605	*0030	*0454	*0878	*1303	*1727	*2151	*2575	424
1024	010	3000	3424	3848	4272	4696	5120	5544	5967	6391	6815	424
1025		7239	7662	8086	8510	8933	9357	9780	*0204	*0627	*1050	424
1026	011	1474	1897	2320	2743	3166	3590	4013	4436	4859	5282	423
1027		5704	6127	6550	6973	7396	7818	8241	8664	9086	9509	423
1028		9931	*0354	*0776	*1198	*1621	*2043	*2465	*2887	*3310	*3732	422
1029	012	4154	4576	4998	5420	5842	6264	6685	7107	7529	7951	422
1030		8372	8794	9215	9637	*0059	*0480	*0901	*1323	*1744	*2165	422
1031	013	2587	3008	3429	3850	4271	4692	5113	5534	5955	6376	421
1032		6797	7218	7639	8059	8480	8901	9321	9742	*0162	*0583	421
1033	014	1003	1424	1844	2264	2685	3105	3525	3945	4365	4785	420
1034		5205	5625	6045	6465	6885	7305	7725	8144	8564	8984	420
1035		9403	9823	*0243	*0662	*1082	*1501	*1920	*2340	*2759	*3178	420
1036	015	3598	4017	4436	4855	5274	5693	6112	6531	6950	7369	419
1037		7788	8206	8625	9044	9462	9881	*0300	*0718	*1137	*1555	419
1038	016	1974	2392	2810	3229	3647	4065	4483	4901	5319	5737	418
1039		6155	6573	6991	7409	7827	8245	8663	9080	9498	9916	418
1040	017	0333	0751	1168	1586	2003	2421	2838	3256	3673	4090	417
1041		4507	4924	5342	5759	6176	6593	7010	7427	7844	8260	417
1042		8677	9094	9511	9927	*0344	*0761	*1177	*1594	*2010	*2427	417
1043	018	2843	3259	3676	4092	4508	4925	5341	5757	6173	6589	416
1044		7005	7421	7837	8253	8669	9084	9500	9916	*0332	*0747	416
1045	019	1163	1578	1994	2410	2825	3240	3656	4071	4486	4902	415
1046		5317	5732	6147	6562	6977	7392	7807	8222	8637	9052	415
1047		9467	9882	*0296	*0711	*1126^f	*1540	*1955	*2369	*2784	*3198	415
1048	020	3613	4027	4442	4856	5270	5684	6099	6513	6927	7341	414
1049		7755	8169	8583	8997	9411	9824	*0238	*0652	*1066	*1479	414
1050	021	1893	2307	2720	3134	3547	3961	4374	4787	5201	5614	413
N.		0	1	2	3	4	5	6	7	8	9	d.

.000 0000 — .021 5614

N.	0	1	2	3	4	5	6	7	8	9	d.
1050	021 1893	2307	2720	3134	3547	3961	4374	4787	5201	5614	413
1051	6027	6440	6854	7267	7680	8093	8506	8919	9332	9745	413
1052	022 0157	0570	0983	1396	1808	2221	2634	3046	3459	3871	413
1053	4284	4696	5109	5521	5933	6345	6758	7170	7582	7994	412
1054	8406	8818	9230	9642	*0054	*0466	*0878	*1289	*1701	*2113	412
1055	023 2525	2936	3348	3759	4171	4582	4994	5405	5817	6228	411
1056	6639	7050	7462	7873	8284	8695	9106	9517	9928	*0339	411
1057	024 0750	1161	1572	1982	2393	2804	3214	3625	4036	4446	411
1058	4857	5267	5678	6088	6498	6909	7319	7729	8139	8549	410
1059	8960	9370	9780	*0190	*0600	*1010	*1419	*1829	*2239	*2649	410
1060	025 3059	3468	3878	4288	4697	5107	5516	5926	6335	6744	410
1061	7154	7563	7972	8382	8791	9200	9609	*0018	*0427	*0836	409
1062	026 1245	1654	2063	2472	2881	3289	3698	4107	4515	4924	409
1063	5333	5741	6150	6558	6967	7375	7783	8192	8600	9008	408
1064	9416	9824	*0233	*0641	*1049	*1457	*1865	*2273	*2680	*3088	408
1065	027 3496	3904	4312	4719	5127	5535	5942	6350	6757	7165	408
1066	7572	7979	8387	8794	9201	9609	*0016	*0423	*0830	*1237	407
1067	028 1644	2051	2458	2865	3272	3679	4086	4492	4899	5306	407
1068	5713	6119	6526	6932	7339	7745	8152	8558	8964	9371	406
1069	9777	*0183	*0590	*0996	*1402	*1808	*2214	*2620	*3026	*3432	406
1070	029 3838	4244	4649	5055	5461	5867	6272	6678	7084	7489	406
1071	7895	8300	8706	9111	9516	9922	*0327	*0732	*1138	*1543	405
1072	030 1948	2353	2758	3163	3568	3973	4378	4783	5188	5592	405
1073	5997	6402	6807	7211	7616	8020	8425	8830	9234	9638	405
1074	031 0043	0447	0851	1256	1660	2064	2468	2872	3277	3681	404
1075	4085	4489	4893	5296	5700	6104	6508	6912	7315	7719	404
1076	8123	8526	8930	9333	9737	*0140	*0544	*0947	*1350	*1754	403
1077	032 2157	2560	2963	3367	3770	4173	4576	4979	5382	5785	403
1078	6188	6590	6993	7396	7799	8201	8604	9007	9409	9812	403
1079	033 0214	0617	1019	1422	1824	2226	2629	3031	3433	3835	402
1080	4238	4640	5042	5444	5846	6248	6650	7052	7453	7855	402
1081	8257	8659	9060	9462	9864	*0265	*0667	*1068	*1470	*1871	402
1082	034 2273	2674	3075	3477	3878	4279	4680	5081	5482	5884	401
1083	6285	6686	7087	7487	7888	8289	8690	9091	9491	9892	401
1084	035 0293	0693	1094	1495	1895	2296	2696	3096	3497	3897	400
1085	4297	4698	5098	5498	5898	6298	6698	7098	7498	7898	400
1086	8298	8698	9098	9498	9898	*0297	*0697	*1097	*1496	*1896	400
1087	036 2295	2695	3094	3494	3893	4293	4692	5091	5491	5890	399
1088	6289	6688	7087	7486	7885	8284	8683	9082	9481	9880	399
1089	037 0279	0678	1076	1475	1874	2272	2671	3070	3468	3867	399
1090	4265	4663	5062	5460	5858	6257	6655	7053	7451	7849	398
1091	8248	8646	9044	9442	9839	*0237	*0635	*1033	*1431	*1829	398
1092	038 2226	2624	3022	3419	3817	4214	4612	5009	5407	5804	398
1093	6202	6599	6996	7393	7791	8188	8585	8982	9379	9776	397
1094	039 0173	0570	0967	1364	1761	2158	2554	2951	3348	3745	397
1095	4141	4538	4934	5331	5727	6124	6520	6917	7313	7709	397
1096	8106	8502	8898	9294	9690	*0086	*0482	*0878	*1274	*1670	396
1097	040 2066	2462	2858	3254	3650	4045	4441	4837	5232	5628	396
1098	6023	6419	6814	7210	7605	8001	8396	8791	9187	9582	395
1099	9977	*0372	*0767	*1162	*1557	*1952	*2347	*2742	*3137	*3532	395
1100	041 3927	4322	4716	5111	5506	5900	6295	6690	7084	7479	395
N.	0	1	2	3	4	5	6	7	8	9	d.

.021 1893 — .041 7479

N.		0	1	2	3	4	5	6	7	8	9	d.
1100	041	3927	4322	4716	5111	5506	5900	6295	6690	7084	7479	395
1101		7873	8268	8662	9056	9451	9845	*0239	*0633	*1028	*1422	394
1102	042	1816	2210	2604	2998	3392	3786	4180	4574	4968	5361	394
1103		5755	6149	6543	6936	7330	7723	8117	8510	8904	9297	394
1104		9691	*0084	*0477	*0871	*1264	*1657	*2050	*2444	*2837	*3230	393
1105	043	3623	4016	4409	4802	5195	5587	5980	6373	6766	7159	393
1106		7551	7944	8337	8729	9122	9514	9907	*0299	*0692	*1084	393
1107	044	1476	1869	2261	2653	3045	3437	3829	4222	4614	5006	392
1108		5398	5790	6181	6573	6965	7357	7749	8140	8532	8924	392
1109		9315	9707	*0099	*0490	*0882	*1273	*1664	*2056	*2447	*2839	392
1110	045	3230	3621	4012	4403	4795	5186	5577	5968	6359	6750	391
1111		7141	7531	7922	8313	8704	9095	9485	9876	*0267	*0657	391
1112	046	1048	1438	1829	2219	2610	3000	3391	3781	4171	4561	390
1113		4952	5342	5732	6122	6512	6902	7292	7682	8072	8462	390
1114		8852	9242	9632	*0021	*0411	*0801	*1190	*1580	*1970	*2359	390
1115	047	2749	3138	3528	3917	4306	4696	5085	5474	5864	6253	389
1116		6642	7031	7420	7809	8198	8587	8976	9365	9754	*0143	389
1117	048	0532	0921	1309	1698	2087	2475	2864	3253	3641	4030	389
1118		4418	4806	5195	5583	5972	6360	6748	7136	7525	7913	388
1119		8301	8689	9077	9465	9853	*0241	*0629	*1017	*1405	*1792	388
1120	049	2180	2568	2956	3343	3731	4119	4506	4894	5281	5669	388
1121		6056	6444	6831	7218	7606	7993	8380	8767	9154	9541	387
1122		9929	*0316	*0703	*1090	*1477	*1863	*2250	*2637	*3024	*3411	387
1123	050	3798	4184	4571	4958	5344	5731	6117	6504	6890	7277	387
1124		7663	8049	8436	8822	9208	9595	9981	*0367	*0753	*1139	386
1125	051	1525	1911	2297	2683	3069	3455	3841	4227	4612	4998	386
1126		5384	5770	6155	6541	6926	7312	7697	8083	8468	8854	386
1127		9239	9624	*0010	*0395	*0780	*1166	*1551	*1936	*2321	*2706	385
1128	052	3091	3476	3861	4246	4631	5016	5400	5785	6170	6555	385
1129		6939	7324	7709	8093	8478	8862	9247	9631	*0016	*0400	385
1130	053·	0784	1169	1553	1937	2321	2706	3090	3474	3858	4242	384
1131		4626	5010	5394	5778	6162	6546	6929	7313	7697	8081	384
1132		8464	8848	9232	9615	9999	*0382	*0766	*1149	*1532	*1916	384
1133	054	2299	2682	3066	3449	3832	4215	4598	4981	5365	5748	383
1134		6131	6514	6896	7279	7662	8045	8428	8811	9193	9576	383
1135		9959	*0341	*0724	*1106	*1489	*1871	*2254	*2636	*3019	*3401	382
1136	055	3783	4166	4548	4930	5312	5694	6077	6459	6841	7223	382
1137		7605	7987	8369	8750	9132	9514	9896	*0278	*0659	*1041	382
1138	056	1423	1804	2186	2567	2949	3330	3712	4093	4475	4856	381
1139		5237	5619	6000	6381	6762	7143	7524	7905	8287	8668	381
1140		9049	9429	9810	*0191	*0572	*0953	*1334	*1714	*2095	*2476	381
1141	057	2856	3237	3618	3998	4379	4759	5140	5520	5900	6281	381
1142		6661	7041	7422	7802	8182	8562	8942	9322	9702	*0082	380
1143	058	0462	0842	1222	1602	1982	2362	2741	3121	3501	3881	380
1144		4260	4640	5019	5399	5778	6158	6537	6917	7296	7676	380
1145		8055	8434	8813	9193	9572	9951	*0330	*0709	*1088	*1467	379
1146	059	1846	2225	2604	2983	3362	3741	4119	4498	4877	5256	379
1147		5634	6013	6391	6770	7148	7527	7905	8284	8662	9041	379
1148		9419	9797	*0175	*0554	*0932	*1310	*1688	*2066	*2444	*2822	378
1149	060	3200	3578	3956	4334	4712	5090	5468	5845	6223	6601	378
1150		6978	7356	7734	8111	8489	8866	9244	9621	9999	*0376	378
N.		0	1	2	3	4	5	6	7	8	9	d.

.041 3927 — .061 0376

N.	0	1	2	3	4	5	6	7	8	9	d.
1150	060 6978	7356	7734	8111	8489	8866	9244	9621	9999	*0376	378
1151	061 0753	1131	1508	1885	2262	2639	3017	3394	3771	4148	377
1152	4525	4902	5279	5656	6032	6409	6786	7163	7540	7916	377
1153	8293	8670	9046	9423	9799	*0176	*0552	*0929	*1305	*1682	377
1154	062 2058	2434	2811	3187	3563	3939	4316	4692	5068	5444	376
1155	5820	6196	6572	6948	7324	7699	8075	8451	8827	9203	376
1156	9578	9954	*0330	*0705	*1081	*1456	*1832	*2207	*2583	*2958	376
1157	063 3334	3709	4084	4460	4835	5210	5585	5960	6335	6711	375
1158	7086	7461	7836	8211	8585	8960	9335	9710	*0085	*0460	375
1159	064 0834	1209	1584	1958	2333	2708	3082	3457	3831	4205	375
1160	4580	4954	5329	5703	6077	6451	6826	7200	7574	7948	374
1161	8322	8696	9070	9444	9818	*0192	*0566	*0940	*1314	*1688	374
1162	065 2061	2435	2809	3182	3556	3930	4303	4677	5050	5424	374
1163	5797	6171	6544	6917	7291	7664	8037	8410	8784	9157	373
1164	9530	9903	*0276	*0649	*1022	*1395	*1768	*2141	*2514	*2886	373
1165	066 3259	3632	4005	4377	4750	5123	5495	5868	6241	6613	373
1166	6986	7358	7730	8103	8475	8847	9220	9592	9964	*0336	372
1167	067 0709	1081	1453	1825	2197	2569	2941	3313	3685	4057	372
1168	4428	4800	5172	5544	5915	6287	6659	7030	7402	7774	372
1169	8145	8517	8888	9259	9631	*0002	*0374	*0745	*1116	*1487	371
1170	068 1859	2230	2601	2972	3343	3714	4085	4456	4827	5198	371
1171	5569	5940	6311	6681	7052	7423	7794	8164	8535	8906	371
1172	9276	9647	*0017	*0388	*0758	*1129	*1499	*1869	*2240	*2610	370
1173	069 2980	3350	3721	4091	4461	4831	5201	5571	5941	6311	370
1174	6681	7051	7421	7791	8160	8530	8900	9270	9639	*0009	370
1175	070 0379	0748	1118	1487	1857	2226	2596	2965	3335	3704	369
1176	4073	4442	4812	5181	5550	5919	6288	6658	7027	7396	369
1177	7765	8134	8503	8871	9240	9609	9978	*0347	*0715	*1084	369
1178	071 1453	1822	2190	2559	2927	3296	3664	4033	4401	4770	369
1179	5138	5506	5875	6243	6611	6979	7348	7716	8084	8452	368
1180	8820	9188	9556	9924	*0292	*0660	*1028	*1396	*1763	*2131	368
1181	072 2499	2867	3234	3602	3970	4337	4705	5072	5440	5807	368
1182	6175	6542	6910	7277	7644	8011	8379	8746	9113	9480	367
1183	9847	*0215	*0582	*0949	*1316	*1683	*2050	*2416	*2783	*3150	367
1184	073 3517	3884	4251	4617	4984	5351	5717	6084	6450	6817	367
1185	7184	7550	7916	8283	8649	9016	9382	9748	*0114	*0481	366
1186	074 0847	1213	1579	1945	2311	2677	3043	3409	3775	4141	366
1187	4507	4873	5239	5605	5970	6336	6702	7068	7433	7799	366
1188	8164	8530	8895	9261	9626	9992	*0357	*0723	*1088	*1453	365
1189	075 1819	2184	2549	2914	3279	3644	4010	4375	4740	5105	365
1190	5470	5835	6199	6564	6929	7294	7659	8024	8388	8753	365
1191	9118	9482	9847	*0211	*0576	*0940	*1305	*1669	*2034	*2398	364
1192	076 2763	3127	3491	3855	4220	4584	4948	5312	5676	6040	364
1193	6404	6768	7132	7496	7860	8224	8588	8952	9316	9680	364
1194	077 0043	0407	0771	1134	1498	1862	2225	2589	2952	3316	364
1195	3679	4042	4406	4769	5133	5496	5859	6222	6585	6949	363
1196	7312	7675	8038	8401	8764	9127	9490	9853	*0216	*0579	363
1197	078 0942	1304	1667	2030	2393	2755	3118	3480	3843	4206	363
1198	4568	4931	5293	5656	6018	6380	6743	7105	7467	7830	362
1199	8192	8554	8916	9278	9640	*0003	*0365	*0727	*1089	*1451	362
1200	079 1812	2174	2536	2898	3260	3622	3983	4345	4707	5068	362
N.	0	1	2	3	4	5	6	7	8	9	d.

.060 6978 — .079 5068

D COMMON LOGARITHMS OF TRIGONOMETRIC FUNCTIONS

`"`	`'`	L Sin	d	L Tan	c d	L Ctn	L Cos	`'`
0	0						10.00 000	60
60	1	6.46 373	30103	6.46 373	30103	13.53 627	10.00 000	59
120	2	6.76 476	17609	6.76 476	17609	13.23 524	10.00 000	58
180	3	6.94 085	12494	6.94 085	12494	13.05 915	10.00 000	57
240	4	7.06 579	9691	7.06 579	9691	12.93 421	10.00 000	56
300	5	7.16 270	7918	7.16 270	7918	12.83 730	10.00 000	55
360	6	7.24 188	6694	7.24 188	6694	12.75 812	10.00 000	54
420	7	7.30 882	5800	7.30 882	5800	12.69 118	10.00 000	53
480	8	7.36 682	5115	7.36 682	5115	12.63 318	10.00 000	52
540	9	7.41 797	4576	7.41 797	4576	12.58 203	10.00 000	51
600	10	7.46 373	4139	7.46 373	4139	12.53 627	10.00 000	50
660	11	7.50 512	3779	7.50 512	3779	12.49 488	10.00 000	49
720	12	7.54 291	3476	7.54 291	3476	12.45 709	10.00 000	48
780	13	7.57 767	3218	7.57 767	3219	12.42 233	10.00 000	47
840	14	7.60 985	2997	7.60 986	2996	12.39 014	10.00 000	46
900	15	7.63 982	2802	7.63 982	2803	12.36 018	10.00 000	45
960	16	7.66 784	2633	7.66 785	2633	12.33 215	10.00 000	44
1020	17	7.69 417	2483	7.69 418	2482	12.30 582	9.99 999	43
1080	18	7.71 900	2348	7.71 900	2348	12.28 100	9.99 999	42
1140	19	7.74 248	2227	7.74 248	2228	12.25 752	9.99 999	41
1200	20	7.76 475	2119	7.76 476	2119	12.23 524	9.99 999	40
1260	21	7.78 594	2021	7.78 595	2020	12.21 405	9.99 999	39
1320	22	7.80 615	1930	7.80 615	1931	12.19 385	9.99 999	38
1380	23	7.82 545	1848	7.82 546	1848	12.17 454	9.99 999	37
1440	24	7.84 393	1773	7.84 394	1773	12.15 606	9.99 999	36
1500	25	7.86 166	1704	7.86 167	1704	12.13 833	9.99 999	35
1560	26	7.87 870	1639	7.87 871	1639	12.12 129	9.99 999	34
1620	27	7.89 509	1579	7.89 510	1579	12.10 490	9.99 999	33
1680	28	7.91 088	1524	7.91 089	1524	12.08 911	9.99 999	32
1740	29	7.92 612	1472	7.92 613	1473	12.07 387	9.99 998	31
1800	30	7.94 084	1424	7.94 086	1424	12.05 914	9.99 998	30
1860	31	7.95 508	1379	7.95 510	1379	12.04 490	9.99 998	29
1920	32	7.96 887	1336	7.96 889	1336	12.03 111	9.99 998	28
1980	33	7.98 223	1297	7.98 225	1297	12.01 775	9.99 998	27
2040	34	7.99 520	1259	7.99 522	1259	12.00 478	9.99 998	26
2100	35	8.00 779	1223	8.00 781	1223	11.99 219	9.99 998	25
2160	36	8.02 002	1190	8.02 004	1190	11.97 996	9.99 998	24
2220	37	8.03 192	1158	8.03 194	1159	11.96 806	9.99 997	23
2280	38	8.04 350	1128	8.04 353	1128	11.95 647	9.99 997	22
2340	39	8.05 478	1100	8.05 481	1100	11.94 519	9.99 997	21
2400	40	8.06 578	1072	8.06 581	1072	11.93 419	9.99 997	20
2460	41	8.07 650	1046	8.07 653	1047	11.92 347	9.99 997	19
2520	42	8.08 696	1022	8.08 700	1022	11.91 300	9.99 997	18
2580	43	8.09 718	999	8.09 722	998	11.90 278	9.99 997	17
2640	44	8.10 717	976	8.10 720	976	11.89 280	9.99 996	16
2700	45	8.11 693	954	8.11 696	955	11.88 304	9.99 996	15
2760	46	8.12 647	934	8.12 651	934	11.87 349	9.99 996	14
2820	47	8.13 581	914	8.13 585	915	11.86 415	9.99 996	13
2880	48	8.14 495	896	8.14 500	895	11.85 500	9.99 996	12
2940	49	8.15 391	877	8.15 395	878	11.84 605	9.99 996	11
3000	50	8.16 268	860	8.16 273	860	11.83 727	9.99 995	10
3060	51	8.17 128	843	8.17 133	843	11.82 867	9.99 995	9
3120	52	8.17 971	827	8.17 976	828	11.82 024	9.99 995	8
3180	53	8.18 798	812	8.18 804	812	11.81 196	9.99 995	7
3240	54	8.19 610	797	8.19 616	797	11.80 384	9.99 995	6
3300	55	8.20 407	782	8.20 413	782	11.79 587	9.99 994	5
3360	56	8.21 189	769	8.21 195	769	11.78 805	9.99 994	4
3420	57	8.21 958	755	8.21 964	756	11.78 036	9.99 994	3
3480	58	8.22 713	743	8.22 720	742	11.77 280	9.99 994	2
3540	59	8.23 456	730	8.23 462	730	11.76 538	9.99 994	1
3600	60	8.24 186		8.24 192		11.75 808	9.99 993	0
`" ·`	`'`	L Cos	d	L Ctn	c d	L Tan	L Sin	`'`

''	'	L Sin	d	L Tan	c d	L Ctn	L Cos	'
3600	0	8.24 186	717	8.24 192	718	11.75 808	9.99 993	60
3660	1	8.24 903	706	8.24 910	706	11.75 090	9.99 993	59
3720	2	8.25 609	695	8.25 616	696	11.74 384	9.99 993	58
3780	3	8.26 304	684	8.26 312	684	11.73 688	9.99 993	57
3840	4	8.26 988	673	8.26 996	673	11.73 004	9.99 992	56
3900	5	8.27 661	663	8.27 669	663	11.72 331	9.99 992	55
3960	6	8.28 324	653	8.28 332	654	11.71 668	9.99 992	54
4020	7	8.28 997	644	8.28 986	643	11.71 014	9.99 992	53
4080	8	8.29 621	634	8.29 629	634	11.70 371	9.99 992	52
4140	9	8.30 255	624	8.30 263	625	11.69 737	9.99 991	51
4200	10	8.30 879	616	8.30 888	617	11.69 112	9.99 991	50
4260	11	8.31 495	608	8.31 505	607	11.68 495	9.99 991	49
4320	12	8.32 103	599	8.32 112	599	11.67 888	9.99 990	48
4380	13	8.32 702	590	8.32 711	591	11.67 289	9.99 990	47
4440	14	8.33 292	583	8.33 302	584	11.66 698	9.99 990	46
4500	15	8.33 875	575	8.33 886	575	11.66 114	9.99 990	45
4560	16	8.34 450	568	8.34 461	568	11.65 539	9.99 989	44
4620	17	8.35 018	560	8.35 029	561	11.64 971	9.99 989	43
4680	18	8.35 578	553	8.35 590	553	11.64 410	9.99 989	42
4740	19	8.36 131	547	8.36 143	546	11.63 857	9.99 989	41
4800	20	8.36 678	539	8.36 689	540	11.63 311	9.99 988	40
4860	21	8.37 217	533	8.37 229	533	11.62 771	9.99 988	39
4920	22	8.37 750	526	8.37 762	527	11.62 238	9.99 988	38
4980	23	8.38 276	520	8.38 289	520	11.61 711	9.99 987	37
5040	24	8.38 796	514	8.38 809	514	11.61 191	9.99 987	36
5100	25	8.39 310	508	8.39 323	509	11.60 677	9.99 987	35
5160	26	8.39 818	502	8.39 832	502	11.60 168	9.99 986	34
5220	27	8.40 320	496	8.40 334	496	11.59 666	9.99 986	33
5280	28	8.40 816	491	8.40 830	491	11.59 170	9.99 986	32
5340	29	8.41 307	485	8.41 321	486	11.58 679	9.99 985	31
5400	30	8.41 792	480	8.41 807	480	11.58 193	9.99 985	30
5460	31	8.42 272	474	8.42 287	475	11.57 713	9.99 985	29
5520	32	8.42 746	470	8.42 762	470	11.57 238	9.99 984	28
5580	33	8.43 216	464	8.43 232	464	11.56 768	9.99 984	27
5640	34	8.43 680	459	8.43 696	460	11.56 304	9.99 984	26
5700	35	8.44 139	455	8.44 156	455	11.55 844	9.99 983	25
5760	36	8.44 594	450	8.44 611	450	11.55 389	9.99 983	24
5820	37	8.45 044	445	8.45 061	446	11.54 939	9.99 983	23
5880	38	8.45 489	441	8.45 507	441	11.54 493	9.99 982	22
5940	39	8.45 930	436	8.45 948	437	11.54 052	9.99 982	21
6000	40	8.46 366	433	8.46 385	432	11.53 615	9.99 982	20
6060	41	8.46 799	427	8.46 817	428	11.53 183	9.99 981	19
6120	42	8.47 226	424	8.47 245	424	11.52 755	9.99 981	18
6180	43	8.47 650	419	8.47 669	420	11.52 331	9.99 981	17
6240	44	8.48 069	416	8.48 089	416	11.51 911	9.99 980	16
6300	45	8.48 485	411	8.48 505	412	11.51 495	9.99 980	15
6360	46	8.48 896	408	8.48 917	408	11.51 083	9.99 979	14
6420	47	8.49 304	404	8.49 325	404	11.50 675	9.99 979	13
6480	48	8.49 708	400	8.49 729	401	11.50 271	9.99 979	12
6540	49	8.50 108	396	8.50 130	397	11.49 870	9.99 978	11
6600	50	8.50 504	393	8.50 527	393	11.49 473	9.99 978	10
6660	51	8.50 897	390	8.50 920	39)	11.49 080	9.99 977	9
6720	52	8.51 287	386	8.51 310	3>6	11.48 690	9.99 977	8
6780	53	8.51 673	382	8.51 696	333	11.48 304	9.99 977	7
6840	54	8.52 055	379	8.52 079	38)	11.47 921	9.99 976	6
6900	55	8.52 434	376	8.52 459	376	11.47 541	9.99 976	5
6960	56	8.52 810	373	8.52 835	373	11.47 165	9.99 975	4
7020	57	8.53 183	369	8.53 208	370	11.46 792	9.99 975	3
7080	58	8.53 552	367	8.53 578	367	11.46 422	9.99 974	2
7140	59	8.53 919	363	8.53 945	363	11.46 055	9.99 974	1
7200	60	8.54 282		8.54 308		11.45 692	9.99 974	0
''	'	L Cos	d	L Ctn	c d	L Tan	L Sin	'

″	′	L Sin	d	L Tan	c d	L Ctn	L Cos	′
7200	0	8.54 282	360	8.54 308	361	11.45 692	9.99 974	60
7260	1	8.54 642	357	8.54 669	358	11.45 331	9.99 973	59
7320	2	8.54 999	355	8.55 027	355	11.44 973	9.99 973	58
7380	3	8.55 354	351	8.55 382	352	11.44 618	9.99 972	57
7440	4	8.55 705	349	8.55 734	349	11.44 266	9.99 972	56
7500	5	8.56 054	346	8.56 083	346	11.43 917	9.99 971	55
7560	6	8.56 400	343	8.56 429	344	11.43 571	9.99 971	54
7620	7	8.56 743	341	8.56 773	341	11.43 227	9.99 970	53
7680	8	8.57 084	337	8.57 114	338	11.42 886	9.99 970	52
7740	9	8.57 421	336	8.57 452	336	11.42 548	9.99 969	51
7800	10	8.57 757	332	8.57 788	333	11.42 212	9.99 969	50
7860	11	8.58 089	330	8.58 121	330	11.41 879	9.99 968	49
7920	12	8.58 419	328	8.58 451	328	11.41 549	9.99 968	48
7980	13	8.58 747	325	8.58 779	326	11.41 221	9.99 967	47
8040	14	8.59 072	323	8.59 105	323	11.40 895	9.99 967	46
8100	15	8.59 395	320	8.59 428	321	11.40 572	9.99 967	45
8160	16	8.59 715	318	8.59 749	319	11.40 251	9.99 966	44
8220	17	8.60 033	316	8.60 068	316	11.39 932	9.99 966	43
8280	18	8.60 349	313	8.60 384	314	11.39 616	9.99 965	42
8340	19	8.60 662	311	8.60 698	311	11.39 302	9.99 964	41
8400	20	8.60 973	309	8.61 009	310	11.38 991	9.99 964	40
8460	21	8.61 282	307	8.61 319	307	11.38 681	9.99 963	39
8520	22	8.61 589	305	8.61 626	305	11.38 374	9.99 963	38
8580	23	8.61 894	302	8.61 931	303	11.38 069	9.99 962	37
8640	24	8.62 196	301	8.62 234	301	11.37 766	9.99 962	36
8700	25	8.62 497	298	8.62 535	299	11.37 465	9.99 961	35
8760	26	8.62 795	296	8.62 834	297	11.37 166	9.99 961	34
8820	27	8.63 091	294	8.63 131	295	11.36 869	9.99 960	33
8880	28	8.63 385	293	8.63 426	292	11.36 574	9.99 960	32
8940	29	8.63 678	290	8.63 718	291	11.36 282	9.99 959	31
9000	30	8.63 968	288	8.64 009	289	11.35 991	9.99 959	30
9060	31	8.64 256	287	8.64 298	287	11.35 702	9.99 958	29
9120	32	8.64 543	284	8.64 585	285	11.35 415	9.99 958	28
9180	33	8.64 827	283	8.64 870	284	11.35 130	9.99 957	27
9240	34	8.65 110	281	8.65 154	281	11.34 846	9.99 956	26
9300	35	8.65 391	279	8.65 435	280	11.34 565	9.99 956	25
9360	36	8.65 670	277	8.65 715	278	11.34 285	9.99 955	24
9420	37	8.65 947	276	8.65 993	276	11.34 007	9.99 955	23
9480	38	8.66 223	274	8.66 269	274	11.33 731	9.99 954	22
9540	39	8.66 497	272	8.66 543	273	11.33 457	9.99 954	21
9600	40	8.66 769	270	8.66 816	271	11.33 184	9.99 953	20
9660	41	8.67 039	269	8.67 087	269	11.32 913	9.99 952	19
9720	42	8.67 308	267	8.67 356	268	11.32 644	9.99 952	18
9780	43	8.67 575	266	8.67 624	266	11.32 376	9.99 951	17
9840	44	8.67 841	263	8.67 890	264	11.32 110	9.99 951	16
9900	45	8.68 104	263	8.68 154	263	11.31 846	9.99 950	15
9960	46	8.68 367	260	8.68 417	261	11.31 583	9.99 949	14
10020	47	8.68 627	259	8.68 678	260	11.31 322	9.99 949	13
10080	48	8.68 886	258	8.68 938	258	11.31 062	9.99 948	12
10140	49	8.69 144	256	8.69 196	257	11.30 804	9.99 948	11
10200	50	8.69 400	254	8.69 453	255	11.30 547	9.99 947	10
10260	51	8.69 654	253	8.69 708	254	11.30 292	9.99 946	9
10320	52	8.69 907	252	8.69 962	252	11.30 038	9.99 946	8
10380	53	8.70 159	250	8.70 214	251	11.29 786	9.99 945	7
10440	54	8.70 409	249	8.70 465	249	11.29 535	9.99 944	6
10500	55	8.70 658	247	8.70 714	248	11.29 286	9.99 944	5
10560	56	8.70 905	246	8.70 962	246	11.29 038	9.99 943	4
10620	57	8.71 151	244	8.71 208	245	11.28 792	9.99 942	3
10680	58	8.71 395	243	8.71 453	244	11.28 547	9.99 942	2
10740	59	8.71 638	242	8.71 697	243	11.28 303	9.99 941	1
10800	60	8.71 880		8.71 940		11.28 060	9.99 940	0
″	′	L Cos	d	L Ctn	c d	L Tan	L Sin	′

′	L Sin	d	L Tan	c d	L Ctn	L Cos	′	Proportional parts
0	8.71 880	240	8.71 940	241	11.28 060	9.99 940	60	
1	8.72 120	239	8.72 181	239	11.27 819	9.99 940	59	″ 241 239 237 235 234
2	8.72 359	238	8.72 420	239	11.27 580	9.99 939	58	1 4.0 4.0 4.0 3.9 3.9
3	8.72 597	237	8.72 659	237	11.27 341	9.99 938	57	2 8.0 8.0 7.9 7.8 7.8
4	8.72 834	235	8.72 896	236	11.27 104	9.99 938	56	3 12.0 12.0 11.8 11.8 11.7
								4 16.1 15.9 15.8 15.7 15.6
5	8.73 069	234	8.73 132	234	11.26 868	9.99 937	55	5 20.1 19.9 19.8 19.6 19.5
6	8.73 303	232	8.73 366	234	11.26 634	9.99 936	54	6 24.1 23.9 23.7 23.5 23.4
7	8.73 535	232	8.73 600	232	11.26 400	9.99 936	53	7 28.1 27.9 27.6 27.4 27.3
8	8.73 767	230	8.73 832	231	11.26 168	9.99 935	52	8 32.1 31.9 31.6 31.3 31.2
9	8.73 997	229	8.74 063	229	11.25 937	9.99 934	51	9 36.2 35.8 35.6 35.2 35.1
10	8.74 226	228	8.74 292	229	11.25 708	9.99 934	50	″ 232 229 227 225 223
11	8.74 454	226	8.74 521	227	11.25 479	9.99 933	49	1 3.9 3.8 3.8 3.8 3.7
12	8.74 680	226	8.74 748	226	11.25 252	9.99 932	48	2 7.7 7.6 7.6 7.5 7.4
13	8.74 906	224	8.74 974	225	11.25 026	9.99 932	47	3 11.6 11.4 11.4 11.2 11.2
14	8.75 130	223	8.75 199	224	11.24 801	9.99 931	46	4 15.5 15.3 15.1 15.0 14.9
15	8.75 353	222	8.75 423	222	11.24 577	9.99 930	45	5 19.3 19.1 18.9 18.8 18.6
16	8.75 575	220	8.75 645	222	11.24 355	9.99 929	44	6 23.2 22.9 22.7 22.5 22.3
17	8.75 795	220	8.75 867	220	11.24 133	9.99 929	43	7 27.1 26.7 26.5 26.2 26.0
18	8.76 015	219	8.76 087	219	11.23 913	9.99 928	42	8 30.9 30.5 30.3 30.0 29.7
19	8.76 234	217	8.76 306	219	11.23 694	9.99 927	41	9 34.8 34.4 34.0 33.8 33.4
20	8.76 451	216	8.76 525	217	11.23 475	9.99 926	40	″ 222 220 217 215 213
21	8.76 667	216	8.76 742	216	11.23 258	9.99 926	39	1 3.7 3.7 3.6 3.6 3.6
22	8.76 883	214	8.76 958	215	11.23 042	9.99 925	38	2 7.4 7.3 7.2 7.2 7.1
23	8.77 097	213	8.77 173	214	11.22 827	9.99 924	37	3 11.1 11.0 10.8 10.8 10.6
24	8.77 310	212	8.77 387	213	11.22 613	9.99 923	36	4 14.8 14.7 14.5 14.3 14.2
25	8.77 522	211	8.77 600	211	11.22 400	9.99 923	35	5 18.5 18.3 18.1 17.9 17.8
26	8.77 733	210	8.77 811	211	11.22 189	9.99 922	34	6 22.2 22.0 21.7 21.5 21.3
27	8.77 943	209	8.78 022	210	11.21 978	9.99 921	33	7 25.9 25.7 25.3 25.1 24.8
28	8.78 152	208	8.78 232	209	11.21 768	9.99 920	32	8 29.6 29.3 28.9 28.7 28.4
29	8.78 360	208	8.78 441	208	11.21 559	9.99 920	31	9 33.3 33.0 32.6 32.2 32.0
30	8.78 568	206	8.78 649	206	11.21 351	9.99 919	30	″ 211 208 206 203 201
31	8.78 774	205	8.78 855	206	11.21 145	9.99 918	29	1 3.5 3.5 3.4 3.4 3.4
32	8.78 979	204	8.79 061	205	11.20 939	9.99 917	28	2 7.0 6.9 6.9 6.8 6.7
33	8.79 183	203	8.79 266	204	11.20 734	9.99 917	27	3 10.6 10.4 10.3 10.2 10.0
34	8.79 386	202	8.79 470	203	11.20 530	9.99 916	26	4 14.1 13.9 13.7 13.5 13.4
35	8.79 588	201	8.79 673	202	11.20 327	9.99 915	25	5 17.6 17.3 17.2 16.9 16.8
36	8.79 789	201	8.79 875	201	11.20 125	9.99 914	24	6 21.1 20.8 20.6 20.3 20.1
37	8.79 990	199	8.80 076	201	11.19 924	9.99 913	23	7 24.6 24.3 24.0 23.7 23.4
38	8.80 189	199	8.80 277	199	11.19 723	9.99 913	22	8 28.1 27.7 27.5 27.1 26.8
39	8.80 388	197	8.80 476	198	11.19 524	9.99 912	21	9 31.6 31.2 30.9 30.4 30.2
40	8.80 585	197	8.80 674	198	11.19 326	9.99 911	20	″ 199 197 195 193 192
41	8.80 782	196	8.80 872	196	11.19 128	9.99 910	19	1 3.3 3.3 3.2 3.2 3.2
42	8.80 978	195	8.81 068	196	11.18 932	9.99 909	18	2 6.6 6.6 6.5 6.4 6.4
43	8.81 173	194	8.81 264	195	11.18 736	9.99 909	17	3 10.0 9.8 9.8 9.6 9.6
44	8.81 367	133	8.81 459	194	11.18 541	9.99 908	16	4 13.3 13.1 13.0 12.9 12.8
45	8.81 560	192	8.81 653	193	11.18 347	9.99 907	15	5 16.6 16.4 16.2 16.1 16.0
46	8.81 752	192	8.81 846	192	11.18 154	9.99 906	14	6 19.9 19.7 19.5 19.3 19.2
47	8.81 944	190	8.82 038	192	11.17 962	9.99 905	13	7 23.2 23.0 22.8 22.5 22.4
48	8.82 134	190	8.82 230	190	11.17 770	9.99 904	12	8 26.5 26.3 26.0 25.7 25.6
49	8.82 324	189	8.82 420	190	11.17 580	9.99 904	11	9 29.8 29.6 29.2 29.0 28.8
50	8.82 513	188	8.82 610	189	11.17 390	9.99 903	10	″ 189 187 185 183 181
51	8.82 701	187	8.82 799	188	11.17 201	9.99 902	9	1 3.2 3.1 3.1 3.0 3.0
52	8.82 888	187	8.82 987	188	11.17 013	9.99 901	8	2 6.3 6.2 6.2 6.1 6.0
53	8.83 075	186	8.83 175	186	11.16 825	9.99 900	7	3 9.4 9.4 9.2 9.2 9.0
54	8.83 261	185	8.83 361	186	11.16 639	9.99 899	6	4 12.6 12.5 12.3 12.2 12.1
55	8.83 446	184	8.83 547	185	11.16 453	9.99 898	5	5 15.8 15.6 15.4 15.2 15.1
56	8.83 630	183	8.83 732	184	11.16 268	9.99 898	4	6 18.9 18.7 18.5 18.3 18.1
57	8.83 813	183	8.83 916	184	11.16 084	9.99 897	3	7 22.0 21.8 21.6 21.4 21.1
58	8.83 996	181	8.84 100	182	11.15 900	9.99 896	2	8 25.2 24.9 24.7 24.4 24.1
59	8.84 177	181	8.84 282	182	11.15 718	9.99 895	1	9 28.4 28.0 27.8 27.4 27.2
60	8.84 358		8.84 464		11.15 536	9.99 894	0	
′	L Cos	d	L Ctn	c d	L Tan	L Sin	′	Proportional parts

′	L Sin	d	L Tan	c d	L Ctn	L Cos	′
0	8.84 358	181	8.84 464	182	11.15 536	9.99 894	60
1	8.84 539	179	8.84 646	180	11.15 354	9.99 893	59
2	8.84 718	179	8.84 826	180	11.15 174	9.99 892	58
3	8.84 897	178	8.85 006	179	11.14 994	9.99 891	57
4	8.85 075	177	8.85 185	178	11.14 815	9.99 891	56
5	8.85 252	177	8.85 363	177	11.14 637	9.99 890	55
6	8.85 429	176	8.85 540	177	11.14 460	9.99 889	54
7	8.85 605	175	8.85 717	176	11.14 283	9.99 888	53
8	8.85 780	175	8.85 893	176	11.14 107	9.99 887	52
9	8.85 955	173	8.86 069	174	11.13 931	9.99 886	51
10	8.86 128	173	8.86 243	174	11.13 757	9.99 885	50
11	8.86 301	173	8.86 417	174	11.13 583	9.99 884	49
12	8.86 474	171	8.86 591	172	11.13 409	9.99 883	48
13	8.86 645	171	8.86 763	172	11.13 237	9.99 882	47
14	8.86 816	171	8.86 935	172	11.13 065	9.99 881	46
15	8.86 987	169	8.87 106	171	11.12 894	9.99 880	45
16	8.87 156	169	8.87 277	170	11.12 723	9.99 879	44
17	8.87 325	169	8.87 447	169	11.12 553	9.99 879	43
18	8.87 494	167	8.87 616	169	11.12 384	9.99 878	42
19	8.87 661	168	8.87 785	168	11.12 215	9.99 877	41
20	8.87 829	166	8.87 953	167	11.12 047	9.99 876	40
21	8.87 995	166	8.88 120	167	11.11 880	9.99 875	39
22	8.88 161	165	8.88 287	166	11.11 713	9 99 874	38
23	8.88 326	164	8.88 453	165	11.11 547	9.99 873	37
24	8.88 490	164	8.88 618	165	11.11 382	9.99 872	36
25	8.88 654	163	8.88 783	165	11.11 217	9.99 871	35
26	8.88 817	163	8.88 948	163	11.11 052	9.99 870	34
27	8.88 980	162	8.89 111	163	11.10 889	9.99 869	33
28	8.89 142	162	8.89 274	163	11.10 726	9.99 868	32
29	8.89 304	160	8.89 437	161	11.10 563	9.99 867	31
30	8.89 464	161	8.89 598	162	11.10 402	9.99 866	30
31	8.89 625	159	8.89 760	160	11.10 240	9.99 865	29
32	8.89 784	159	8.89 920	160	11.10 080	9.99 864	28
33	8.89 943	159	8.90 080	160	11.09 920	9.99 863	27
34	8.90 102	158	8.90 240	159	11.09 760	9.99 862	26
35	8.90 260	157	8.90 399	158	11.09 601	9.99 861	25
36	8.90 417	157	8.90 557	158	11.09 443	9.99 860	24
37	8.90 574	156	8.90 715	157	11.09 285	9.99 859	23
38	8.90 730	155	8.90 872	157	11.09 128	9.99 858	22
39	8.90 885	155	8.91 029	156	11.08 971	9.99 857	21
40	8.91 040	155	8.91 185	155	11.08 815	9.99 856	20
41	8.91 195	154	8.91 340	155	11.08 660	9.99 855	19
42	8.91 349	153	8.91 495	155	11.08 505	9.99 854	18
43	8.91 502	153	8.91 650	153	11.08 350	9.99 853	17
44	8.91 655	152	8.91 803	154	11.08 197	9.99 852	16
45	8.91 807	152	8.91 957	153	11.08 043	9.99 851	15
46	8.91 959	151	8.92 110	152	11.07 890	9.99 850	14
47	8.92 110	151	8.92 262	152	11.07 738	9.99 848	13
48	8.92 261	150	8.92 414	151	11.07 586	9.99 847	12
49	8.92 411	150	8.92 565	151	11.07 435	9.99 846	11
50	8.92 561	149	8.92 716	150	11.07 284	9.99 845	10
51	8.92 710	149	8.92 866	150	11.07 134	9.99 844	9
52	8.92 859	148	8.93 016	149	11.06 984	9.99 843	8
53	8.93 007	147	8.93 165	148	11.06 835	9.99 842	7
54	8.93 154	147	8.93 313	149	11.06 687	9.99 841	6
55	8.93 301	147	8.93 462	147	11.06 538	9.99 840	5
56	8.93 448	146	8.93 609	147	11.06 391	9.99 839	4
57	8.93 594	146	8.93 756	147	11.06 244	9.99 838	3
58	8.93 740	145	8.93 903	146	11.06 097	9.99 837	2
59	8.93 885	145	8.94 049	146	11.05 951	9.99 836	1
60	8.94 030		8.94 195		11.05 805	9.99 834	0
′	L Cos	d	L Ctn	c d	L Tan	L Sin	′

Proportional parts

′′	182	181	179	178	177
1	3.0	3.0	3.0	3.0	3.0
2	6.1	6.0	6.0	5.9	5.9
3	9.1	9.0	9.0	8.9	8.8
4	12.1	12.1	11.9	11.9	11.8
5	15.2	15.1	14.9	14.8	14.8
6	18.2	18.1	17.9	17.8	17.7
7	21.2	21.1	20.9	20.8	20.6
8	24.3	24.1	23.9	23.7	23.6
9	27.3	27.2	26.8	26.7	26.6

′′	176	175	174	173	172
1	2.9	2.9	2.9	2.9	2.9
2	5.9	5.8	5.8	5.8	5.7
3	8.8	8.8	8.7	8.6	8.6
4	11.7	11.7	11.6	11.5	11.5
5	14.7	14.6	14.5	14.4	14.3
6	17.6	17.5	17.4	17.3	17.2
7	20.5	20.4	20.3	20.2	20.1
8	23.5	23.3	23.2	23.1	22.9
9	26.4	26.2	26.1	26.0	25.8

′′	171	170	169	168	167
1	2.8	2.8	2.8	2.8	2.8
2	5.7	5.7	5.6	5.6	5.6
3	8.6	8.5	8.4	8.4	8.4
4	11.4	11.3	11.3	11.2	11.1
5	14.2	14.2	14.1	14.0	13.9
6	17.1	17.0	16.9	16.8	16.7
7	20.0	19.8	19.7	19.6	19.5
8	22.8	22.7	22.5	22.4	22.3
9	25.6	25.5	25.4	25.2	25.0

′′	166	165	164	163	162
1	2.8	2.8	2.7	2.7	2.7
2	5.5	5.5	5.5	5.4	5.4
3	8.3	8.2	8.2	8.2	8.1
4	11.1	11.0	10.9	10.9	10.8
5	13.8	13.8	13.7	13.6	13.5
6	16.6	16.5	16.4	16.3	16.2
7	19.4	19.2	19.1	19.0	18.9
8	22.1	22.0	21.9	21.7	21.6
9	24.9	24.8	24.6	24.4	24.3

′′	161	160	159	158	157
1	2.7	2.7	2.6	2.6	2.6
2	5.4	5.3	5.3	5.3	5.2
3	8.0	8.0	8.0	7.9	7.8
4	10.7	10.7	10.6	10.5	10.5
5	13.4	13.3	13.2	13.2	13.1
6	16.1	16.0	15.9	15.8	15.7
7	18.8	18.7	18.6	18.4	18.3
8	21.5	21.3	21.2	21.1	20.9
9	24.2	24.0	23.8	23.7	23.6

′′	156	155	154	153	152
1	2.6	2.6	2.6	2.6	2.5
2	5.2	5.2	5.1	5.1	5.1
3	7.8	7.8	7.7	7.6	7.6
4	10.4	10.3	10.3	10.2	10.1
5	13.0	12.9	12.8	12.8	12.7
6	15.6	15.5	15.4	15.3	15.2
7	18.2	18.1	18.0	17.8	17.7
8	20.8	20.7	20.5	20.4	20.3
9	23.4	23.2	23.1	23.0	22.8

′	L Sin	d	L Tan	c d	L Ctn	L Cos	′	Proportional parts				
0	8.94 030	144	8.94 195	145	11.05 805	9.99 834	60	′′	151	149	148	147 146
1	8.94 174	143	8.94 340	145	11.05 660	9.99 833	59	1	2.5	2.5	2.5	2.4 2.4
2	8.94 317	144	8.94 485	145	11.05 515	9.99 832	58	2	5.0	5.0	4.9	4.9 4.9
3	8.94 461	142	8.94 630	143	11.05 370	9.99 831	57	3	7.6	7.4	7.4	7.4 7.3
4	8.94 603	143	8.94 773	144	11.05 227	9.99 830	56	4	10.1	9.9	9.9	9.8 9.7
5	8.94 746	141	8.94 917	143	11.05 083	9.99 829	55	5	12.6	12.4	12.3	12.2 12.2
6	8.94 887	142	8.95 060	142	11.04 940	9.99 828	54	6	15.1	14.9	14.8	14.7 14.6
7	8.95 029	141	8.95 202	142	11.04 798	9.99 827	53	7	17.6	17.4	17.3	17.2 17.0
8	8.95 170	140	8.95 344	142	11.04 656	9.99 825	52	8	20.1	19.9	19.7	19.6 19.5
9	8.95 310	140	8.95 486	141	11.04 514	9.99 824	51	9	22.6	22.4	22.2	22.0 21.9
10	8.95 450	139	8.95 627	140	11.04 373	9.99 823	50	′′	145	144	143	142 141
11	8.95 589	139	8.95 767	141	11.04 233	9.99 822	49	1	2.4	2.4	2.4	2.4 2.4
12	8.95 728	139	8.95 908	139	11.04 092	9.99 821	48	2	4.8	4.8	4.8	4.7 4.7
13	8.95 867	138	8.96 047	140	11.03 953	9.99 820	47	3	7.2	7.2	7.2	7.1 7.0
14	8.96 005	138	8.96 187	138	11.03 813	9.99 819	46	4	9.7	9.6	9.5	9.5 9.4
15	8.96 143	137	8.96 325	139	11.03 675	9.99 817	45	5	12.1	12.0	11.9	11.8 11.8
16	8.96 280	137	8.96 464	138	11.03 536	9.99 816	44	6	14.5	14.4	14.3	14.2 14.1
17	8.96 417	136	8.96 602	137	11.03 398	9.99 815	43	7	16.9	16.8	16.7	16.6 16.4
18	8.96 553	136	8.96 739	138	11.03 261	9.99 814	42	8	19.3	19.2	19.1	18.9 18.8
19	8.96 689	136	8.96 877	136	11.03 123	9.99 813	41	9	21.8	21.6	21.4	21.3 21.2
20	8.96 825	135	8.97 013	137	11.02 987	9.99 812	40	′′	140	139	138	137 136
21	8.96 960	135	8.97 150	135	11.02 850	9.99 810	39	1	2.3	2.3	2.3	2.3 2.3
22	8.97 095	134	8.97 285	136	11.02 715	9.99 809	38	2	4.7	4.6	4.6	4.6 4.5
23	8.97 229	134	8.97 421	135	11.02 579	9.99 808	37	3	7.0	7.0	6.9	6.8 6.8
24	8.97 363	133	8.97 556	135	11.02 444	9.99 807	36	4	9.3	9.3	9.2	9.1 9.1
25	8.97 496	133	8.97 691	134	11.02 309	9.99 806	35	5	11.7	11.6	11.5	11.4 11.3
26	8.97 629	133	8.97 825	134	11.02 175	9.99 804	34	6	14.0	13.9	13.8	13.7 13.6
27	8.97 762	132	8.97 959	133	11.02 041	9.99 803	33	7	16.3	16.2	16.1	16.0 15.9
28	8.97 894	132	8.98 092	133	11.01 908	9.99 802	32	8	18.7	18.5	18.4	18.3 18.1
29	8.98 026	131	8.98 225	133	11.01 775	9.99 801	31	9	21.0	20.8	20.7	20.6 20.4
30	8.98 157	131	8.98 358	132	11.01 642	9.99 800	30	′′	135	134	133	132 131
31	8.98 288	131	8.98 490	132	11.01 510	9.99 798	29	1	2.2	2.2	2.2	2.2 2.2
32	8.98 419	130	8.98 622	131	11.01 378	9.99 797	28	2	4.5	4.5	4.4	4.4 4.4
33	8.98 549	130	8.98 753	131	11.01 247	9.99 796	27	3	6.8	6.7	6.6	6.6 6.6
34	8.98 679	129	8.98 884	131	11.01 116	9.99 795	26	4	9.0	8.9	8.9	8.8 8.7
35	8.98 808	129	8.99 015	130	11.00 985	9.99 793	25	5	11.2	11.2	11.1	11.0 10.9
36	8.98 937	129	8.99 145	130	11.00 855	9.99 792	24	6	13.5	13.4	13.3	13.2 13.1
37	8.99 066	128	8.99 275	130	11.00 725	9.99 791	23	7	15.8	15.6	15.5	15.4 15.3
38	8.99 194	128	8.99 405	129	11.00 595	9.99 790	22	8	18.0	17.9	17.7	17.6 17.5
39	8.99 322	128	8.99 534	128	11.00 466	9.99 788	21	9	20.2	20.1	20.0	19.8 19.6
40	8.99 450	127	8.99 662	129	11.00 338	9.99 787	20	′′	130	129	128	127 126
41	8.99 577	127	8.99 791	128	11.00 209	9.99 786	19	1	2.2	2.2	2.1	2.1 2.1
42	8.99 704	126	8.99 919	127	11.00 081	9.99 785	18	2	4.3	4.3	4.3	4.2 4.2
43	8.99 830	126	9.00 046	128	10.99 954	9.99 783	17	3	6.5	6.4	6.4	6.4 6.3
44	8.99 956	126	9.00 174	127	10.99 826	9.99 782	16	4	8.7	8.6	8.5	8.5 8.4
45	9.00 082	125	9.00 301	126	10.99 699	9.99 781	15	5	10.8	10.8	10.7	10.6 10.5
46	9.00 207	125	9.00 427	126	10.99 573	9.99 780	14	6	13.0	12.9	12.8	12.7 12.6
47	9.00 332	124	9.00 553	126	10.99 447	9.99 778	13	7	15.2	15.0	14.9	14.8 14.7
48	9.00 456	125	9.00 679	126	10.99 321	9.99 777	12	8	17.3	17.2	17.1	16.9 16.8
49	9.00 581	123	9.00 805	125	10.99 195	9.99 776	11	9	19.5	19.4	19.2	19.0 18.9
50	9.00 704	124	9.00 930	125	10.99 070	9.99 775	10	′′	125	124	123	122 121
51	9.00 828	123	9.01 055	124	10.98 945	9.99 773	9	1	2.1	2.1	2.0	2.0 2.0
52	9.00 951	123	9.01 179	124	10.98 821	9.99 772	8	2	4.2	4.1	4.1	4.1 4.0
53	9.01 074	122	9.01 303	124	10.98 697	9.99 771	7	3	6.2	6.2	6.2	6.1 6.0
54	9.01 196	122	9.01 427	123	10.98 573	9.99 769	6	4	8.3	8.3	8.2	8.1 8.1
55	9.01 318	122	9.01 550	123	10.98 450	9.99 768	5	5	10.4	10.3	10.2	10.2 10.1
56	9.01 440	121	9.01 673	123	10.98 327	9.99 767	4	6	12.5	12.4	12.3	12.2 12.1
57	9.01 561	121	9.01 796	122	10.98 204	9.99 765	3	7	14.6	14.5	14.4	14.2 14.1
58	9.01 682	121	9.01 918	122	10.98 082	9.99 764	2	8	16.7	16.5	16.4	16.3 16.1
59	9.01 803	120	9.02 040	122	10.97 960	9.99 763	1	9	18.8	18.6	18.4	18.3 18.2
60	9.01 923		9.02 162		10.97 838	9.99 761	0					
′	L Cos	d	L Ctn	c d	L Tan	L Sin	′	Proportional parts				

′	L Sin	d	L Tan	c d	L Ctn	L Cos	′
0	9.01 923	120	9.02 162	121	10.97 838	9.99 761	60
1	9.02 043	120	9.02 283	121	10.97 717	9.99 760	59
2	9.02 163	120	9.02 404	121	10.97 596	9.99 759	58
3	9.02 283	119	9.02 525	120	10.97 475	9.99 757	57
4	9.02 402	118	9.02 645	121	10.97 355	9.99 756	56
5	9.02 520	119	9.02 766	119	10.97 234	9.99 755	55
6	9.02 639	118	9.02 885	120	10.97 115	9.99 753	54
7	9.02 757	117	9.03 005	119	10.96 995	9.99 752	53
8	9.02 874	118	9.03 124	118	10.96 876	9.99 751	52
9	9.02 992	117	9.03 242	119	10.96 758	9.99 749	51
10	9.03 109	117	9.03 361	118	10.96 639	9.99 748	50
11	9.03 226	116	9.03 479	118	10.96 521	9.99 747	49
12	9.03 342	116	9.03 597	117	10.96 403	9.99 745	48
13	9.03 458	116	9.03 714	118	10.96 286	9.99 744	47
14	9.03 574	116	9.03 832	116	10.96 168	9.99 742	46
15	9.03 690	115	9.03 948	117	10.96 052	9.99 741	45
16	9.03 805	115	9.04 065	116	10.95 935	9.99 740	44
17	9.03 920	114	9.04 181	116	10.95 819	9.99 738	43
18	9.04 034	115	9.04 297	116	10.95 703	9.99 737	42
19	9.04 149	113	9.04 413	115	10.95 587	9.99 736	41
20	9.04 262	114	9.04 528	115	10.95 472	9.99 734	40
21	9.04 376	114	9.04 643	115	10.95 357	9.99 733	39
22	9.04 490	113	9.04 758	115	10.95 242	9.99 731	38
23	9.04 603	112	9.04 873	114	10.95 127	9.99 730	37
24	9.04 715	113	9.04 987	114	10.95 013	9.99 728	36
25	9.04 828	112	9.05 101	113	10.94 899	9.99 727	35
26	9.04 940	112	9.05 214	114	10.94 786	9.99 726	34
27	9.05 052	112	9.05 328	113	10.94 672	9.99 724	33
28	9.05 164	111	9.05 441	112	10.94 559	9.99 723	32
29	9.05 275	111	9.05 553	113	10.94 447	9.99 721	31
30	9.05 386	111	9.05 666	112	10.94 334	9.99 720	30
31	9.05 497	110	9.05 778	112	10.94 222	9.99 718	29
32	9.05 607	110	9.05 890	112	10.94 110	9.99 717	28
33	9.05 717	110	9.06 002	111	10.93 998	9.99 716	27
34	9.05 827	110	9.06 113	111	10.93 887	9.99'714	26
35	9.05 937	109	9.06 224	111	10.93 776	9.99 713	25
36	9.06 046	109	9.06 335	110	10.93 665	9.99 711	24
37	9.06 155	109	9.06 445	111	10.93 555	9.99 710	23
38	9.06 264	108	9.06 556	110	10.93 444	9.99 708	22
39	9.06 372	109	9.06 666	109	10.93 334	9.99 707	21
40	9.06 481	108	9.06 775	110	10.93 225	9.99 705	20
41	9.06 589	107	9.06 885	109	10.93 115	9.99 704	19
42	9.06 696	108	9.06 994	109	10.93 006	9.99 702	18
43	9.06 804	107	9.07 103	108	10.92 897	9.99 701	17
44	9.06 911	107	9.07 211	109	10.92 789	9.99 699	16
45	9.07 018	106	9.07 320	108	10.92 680	9.99 698	15
46	9.07 124	107	9.07 428	108	10.92 572	9.99 696	14
47	9.07 231	106	9.07 536	107	10.92 464	9.99 695	13
48	9.07 337	105	9.07 643	108	10.92 357	9.99 693	12
49	9.07 442	106	9.07 751	107	10.92 249	9.99 692	11
50	9.07 548	105	9.07 858	106	10.92 142	9.99 690	10
51	9.07 653	105	9.07 964	107	10.92 036	9.99 689	9
52	9.07 758	105	9.08 071	106	10.91 929	9.99 687	8
53	9.07 863	105	9.08 177	106	10.91 823	9.99 686	7
54	9.07 968	104	9.08 283	106	10.91 717	9.99 684	6
55	9.08 072	104	9.08 389	106	10.91 611	9.99 683	5
56	9.08 176	104	9.08 495	105	10.91 505	9.99 681	4
57	9.08 280	103	9.08 600	105	10.91 400	9.99 680	3
58	9.08 383	103	9.08 705	105	10.91 295	9.99 678	2
59	9.08 486	103	9.08 810	104	10.91 190	9.99 677	1
60	9.08 589		9.08 914		10.91 086	9.99 675	0
′	L Cos	d	L Ctn	c d	L Tan	L Sin	′

Proportional parts

″	121	120	119	118
1	2.0	2.0	2.0	2.0
2	4.0	4.0	4.0	3.9
3	6.0	6.0	6.0	5.9
4	8.1	8.0	7.9	7.9
5	10.1	10.0	9.9	9.8
6	12.1	12.0	11.9	11.8
7	14.1	14.0	13.9	13.8
8	16.1	16.0	15.9	15.7
9	18.2	18.0	17.8	17.7
10	20.2	20.0	19.8	19.7
20	40.3	40.0	39.7	39.3
30	60.5	60.0	59.5	59.0
40	80.7	80.0	79.3	78.7
50	100.8	100.0	99.2	98.3

″	117	116	115	114
1	2.0	1.9	1.9	1.9
2	3.9	3.9	3.8	3.8
3	5.8	5.8	5.8	5.7
4	7.8	7.7	7.7	7.6
5	9.8	9.7	9.6	9.5
6	11.7	11.6	11.5	11.4
7	13.6	13.5	13.4	13.3
8	15.6	15.5	15.3	15.2
9	17.6	17.4	17.2	17.1
10	19.5	19.3	19.2	19.0
20	39.0	38.7	38.3	38.0
30	58.5	58.0	57.5	57.0
40	78.0	77.3	76.7	76.0
50	97.5	96.7	95.8	95.0

″	113	112	111	110
1	1.9	1.9	1.8	1.8
2	3.8	3.7	3.7	3.7
3	5.6	5.6	5.6	5.5
4	7.5	7.5	7.4	7.3
5	9.4	9.3	9.2	9.2
6	11.3	11.2	11.1	11.0
7	13.2	13.1	13.0	12.8
8	15.1	14.9	14.8	14.7
9	17.0	16.8	16.6	16.5
10	18.8	18.7	18.5	18.3
20	37.7	37.3	37.0	36.7
30	56.5	56.0	55.5	55.0
40	75.3	74.7	74.0	73.3
50	94.2	93.3	92.5	91.7

″	109	108	107	106
1	1.8	1.8	1.8	1.8
2	3.6	3.6	3.6	3.5
3	5.4	5.4	5.4	5.3
4	7.3	7.2	7.1	7.1
5	9.1	9.0	8.9	8.8
6	10.9	10.8	10.7	10.6
7	12.7	12.6	12.5	12.4
8	14.5	14.4	14.3	14.1
9	16.4	16.2	16.0	15.9
10	18.2	18.0	17.8	17.7
20	36.3	36.0	35.7	35.3
30	54.5	54.0	53.5	53.0
40	72.7	72.0	71.3	70.7
50	90.8	90.0	89.2	88.3

Proportional parts

′	L Sin	d	L Tan	c d	L Ctn	L Cos	′	Proportional parts			
0	9.08 589	103	9.08 914	105	10.91 086	9.99 675	60	′′	105	104	103	102
1	9.08 692	103	9.09 019	104	10.90 981	9.99 674	59					
2	9.08 795	102	9.09 123	104	10.90 877	9.99 672	58	1	1.8	1.7	1.7	1.7
3	9.08 897	102	9.09 227	103	10.90 773	9.99 670	57	2	3.5	3.5	3.4	3.4
4	9.08 999	102	9.09 330	104	10.90 670	9.99 669	56	3	5.2	5.2	5.2	5.1
								4	7.0	6.9	6.9	6.8
5	9.09 101	101	9.09 434	103	10.90 566	9.99 667	55					
6	9.09 202	102	9.09 537	103	10.90 463	9.99 666	54	5	8.8	8.7	8.6	8.5
7	9.09 304	101	9.09 640	102	10.90 360	9.99 664	53	6	10.5	10.4	10.3	10.2
8	9.09 405	101	9.09 742	103	10.90 258	9.99 663	52	7	12.2	12.1	12.0	11.9
9	9.09 506	100	9.09 845	102	10.90 155	9.99 661	51	8	14.0	13.9	13.7	13.6
								9	15.8	15.6	15.4	15.3
10	9.09 606	101	9.09 947	102	10.90 053	9.99 659	50					
11	9.09 707	100	9.10 049	101	10.89 951	9.99 658	49	10	17.5	17.3	17.2	17.0
12	9.09 807	100	9.10 150	102	10.89 850	9.99 656	48	20	35.0	34.7	34.3	34.0
13	9.09 907	99	9.10 252	101	10.89 748	9.99 655	47	30	52.5	52.0	51.5	51.0
14	9.10 006	100	9.10 353	101	10.89 647	9.99 653	46	40	70.0	69.3	68.7	68.0
								50	87.5	86.7	85.8	85.0
15	9.10 106	99	9.10 454	101	10.89 546	9.99 651	45					
16	9.10 205	99	9.10 555	101	10.89 445	9.99 650	44	′′	101	100	99	98
17	9.10 304	98	9.10 656	100	10.89 344	9.99 648	43					
18	9.10 402	99	9.10 756	100	10.89 244	9.99 647	42	1	1.7	1.7	1.6	1.6
19	9.10 501	98	9.10 856	100	10.89 144	9.99 645	41	2	3.4	3.3	3.3	3.3
								3	5.0	5.0	5.0	4.9
20	9.10 599	98	9.10 956	100	10.89 044	9.99 643	40	4	6.7	6.7	6.6	6.5
21	9.10 697	98	9.11 056	99	10.88 944	9.99 642	39					
22	9.10 795	98	9.11 155	99	10.88 845	9.99 640	38	5	8.4	8.3	8.2	8.2
23	9.10 893	97	9.11 254	99	10.88 746	9.99 638	37	6	10.1	10.0	9.9	9.8
24	9.10 990	97	9.11 353	99	10.88 647	9.99 637	36	7	11.8	11.7	11.6	11.4
								8	13.5	13.3	13.2	13.1
25	9.11 087	97	9.11 452	99	10.88 548	9.99 635	35	9	15.2	15.0	14.8	14.7
26	9.11 184	97	9.11 551	98	10.88 449	9.99 633	34					
27	9.11 281	96	9.11 649	98	10.88 351	9.99 632	33	10	16.8	16.7	16.5	16.3
28	9.11 377	97	9.11 747	98	10.88 253	9.99 630	32	20	33.7	33.3	33.0	32.7
29	9.11 474	96	9.11 845	98	10.88 155	9.99 629	31	30	50.5	50.0	49.5	49.0
								40	67.3	66.7	66.0	65.3
30	9.11 570	96	9.11 943	97	10.88 057	9.99 627	30	50	84.2	83.3	82.5	81.7
31	9.11 666	95	9.12 040	98	10.87 960	9.99 625	29					
32	9.11 761	96	9.12 138	97	10.87 862	9.99 624	28	′′	97	96	95	94
33	9.11 857	95	9.12 235	97	10.87 765	9.99 622	27					
34	9.11 952	95	9.12 332	96	10.87 668	9.99 620	26	1	1.6	1.6	1.6	1.6
								2	3.2	3.2	3.2	3.1
35	9.12 047	95	9.12 428	97	10.87 572	9.99 618	25	3	4.8	4.8	4.8	4.7
36	9.12 142	94	9.12 525	96	10.87 475	9.99 617	24	4	6.5	6.4	6.3	6.3
37	9.12 236	95	9.12 621	96	10.87 379	9.99 615	23					
38	9.12 331	94	9.12 717	96	10.87 283	9.99 613	22	5	8.1	8.0	7.9	7.8
39	9.12 425	94	9.12 813	96	10.87 187	9.99 612	21	6	9.7	9.6	9.5	9.4
								7	11.3	11.2	11.1	11.0
40	9.12 519	93	9.12 909	95	10.87 091	9.99 610	20	8	12.9	12.8	12.7	12.5
41	9.12 612	94	9.13 004	95	10.86 996	9.99 608	19	9	14.6	14.4	14.2	14.1
42	9.12 706	93	9.13 099	95	10.86 901	9.99 607	18					
43	9.12 799	93	9.13 194	95	10.86 806	9.99 605	17	10	16.2	16.0	15.8	15.7
44	9.12 892	93	9.13 289	95	10.86 711	9.99 603	16	20	32.3	32.0	31.7	31.3
								30	48.5	48.0	47.5	47.0
45	9.12 985	93	9.13 384	94	10.86 616	9.99 601	15	40	64.7	64.0	63.3	62.7
46	9.13 078	93	9.13 478	95	10.86 522	9.99 600	14	50	80.8	80.0	79.2	78.3
47	9.13 171	92	9.13 573	94	10.86 427	9.99 598	13					
48	9.13 263	92	9.13 667	94	10.86 333	9.99 596	12	′′	93	92	91	90
49	9.13 355	92	9.13 761	93	10.86 239	9.99 595	11					
								1	1.6	1.5	1.5	1.5
50	9.13 447	92	9.13 854	94	10.86 146	9.99 593	10	2	3.1	3.1	3.0	3.0
51	9.13 539	91	9.13 948	93	10.86 052	9.99 591	9	3	4.6	4.6	4.6	4.5
52	9.13 630	92	9.14 041	93	10.85 959	9.99 589	8	4	6.2	6.1	6.1	6.0
53	9.13 722	91	9.14 134	93	10.85 866	9.99 588	7					
54	9.13 813	91	9.14 227	93	10.85 773	9.99 586	6	5	7.8	7.7	7.6	7.5
								6	9.3	9.2	9.1	9.0
55	9.13 904	90	9.14 320	92	10.85 680	9.99 584	5	7	10.8	10.7	10.6	10.5
56	9.13 994	91	9.14 412	92	10.85 588	9.99 582	4	8	12.4	12.3	12.1	12.0
57	9.14 085	90	9.14 504	93	10.85 496	9.99 581	3	9	14.0	13.8	13.6	13.5
58	9.14 175	91	9.14 597	91	10.85 403	9.99 579	2					
59	9.14 266	90	9.14 688	92	10.85 312	9.99 577	1	10	15.5	15.3	15.2	15.0
								20	31.0	30.7	,30.3	30.0
60	9.14 356		9.14 780		10.85 220	9.99 575	0	30	46.5	36.0	45.5	45.0
								40	62.0	61.3	60.7	60.0
								50	77.5	76.7	75.8	75.0
′	L Cos	d	L Ctn	c d	L Tan	L Sin	′	Proportional parts			

′	L Sin	d	L Tan	c d	L Ctn	L Cos	′	Proportional parts		
0	9.14 356	89	9.14 780	92	10.85 220	9.99 575	60	′′	92	91	90
1	9.14 455	90	9.14 872	91	10.85 128	9.99 574	59				
2	9.14 535	89	9.14 963	91	10.85 037	9.99 572	58	1	1.5	1.5	1.5
3	9.14 624	90	9.15 054	91	10.84 946	9.99 570	57	2	3.1	3.0	3.0
4	9.14 714	89	9.15 145	91	10.84 855	9.99 568	56	3	4.6	4.6	4.5
								4	6.1	6.1	6.0
5	9.14 803	88	9.15 236	91	10.84 764	9.99 566	55				
6	9.14 891	89	9.15 327	90	10.84 673	9.99 565	54	5	7.7	7.6	7.5
7	9.14 980	89	9.15 417	91	10.84 583	9.99 563	53	6	9.2	9.1	9.0
8	9.15 069	88	9.15 508	90	10.84 492	9.99 561	52	7	10.7	10.6	10.5
9	9.15 157	88	9.15 598	90	10.84 402	9.99 559	51	8	12.3	12.1	12.0
								9	13.8	13.6	13.5
10	9.15 245	88	9.15 688	89	10.84 312	9.99 557	50				
11	9.15 333	88	9.15 777	90	10.84 223	9.99 556	49	10	15.3	15.2	15.0
12	9.15 421	87	9.15 867	89	10.84 133	9.99 554	48	20	30.7	30.3	30.0
13	9.15 508	88	9.15 956	90	10.84 044	9.99 552	47	30	46.0	45.5	45.0
14	9.15 596	87	9.16 046	89	10.83 954	9.99 550	46	40	61.3	60.7	60.0
								50	76.7	75.8	75.0
15	9.15 683	87	9.16 135	89	10.83 865	9.99 548	45				
16	9.15 770	87	9.16 224	88	10.83 776	9.99 546	44	′′	89	88	87
17	9.15 857	87	9.16 312	89	10.83 688	9.99 545	43				
18	9.15 944	86	9.16 401	88	10.83 599	9.99 543	42	1	1.5	1.5	1.4
19	9.16 030	86	9.16 489	88	10.83 511	9.99 541	41	2	3.0	2.9	2.9
								3	4.4	4.4	4.4
20	9.16 116	87	9.16 577	88	10.83 423	9.99 539	40	4	5.9	5.9	5.8
21	9.16 203	86	9.16 665	88	10.83 335	9.99 537	39				
22	9.16 289	85	9.16 753	88	10.83 247	9.99 535	38	5	7.4	7.3	7.2
23	9.16 374	86	9.16 841	87	10.83 159	9.99 533	37	6	8.9	8.8	8.7
24	9.16 460	85	9.16 928	88	10.83 072	9.99 532	36	7	10.4	10.3	10.2
								8	11.9	11.7	11.6
25	9.16 545	86	9.17 016	87	10.82 984	9.99 530	35	9	13.4	13.2	13.0
26	9.16 631	85	9.17 103	87	10.82 897	9.99 528	34				
27	9.16 716	85	9.17 190	87	10.82 810	9.99 526	33	10	14.8	14.7	14.5
28	9.16 801	85	9.17 277	86	10.82 723	9.99 524	32	20	29.7	29.3	29.0
29	9.16 886	84	9.17 363	87	10.82 637	9.99 522	31	30	44.5	44.0	43.5
								40	59.3	58.7	58.0
30	9.16 970	85	9.17 450	86	10.82 550	9.99 520	30	50	74.2	73.3	72.5
31	9.17 055	84	9.17 536	86	10.82 464	9.99 518	29				
32	9.17 139	84	9.17 622	86	10.82 378	9.99 517	28	′′	86	85	84
33	9.17 223	84	9.17 708	86	10.82 292	9.99 515	27				
34	9.17 307	84	9.17 794	86	10.82 206	9.99 513	26	1	1.4	1.4	1.4
								2	2.9	2.8	2.8
35	9.17 391	83	9.17 880	85	10.82 120	9.99 511	25	3	4.3	4.2	4.2
36	9.17 474	84	9.17 965	86	10.82 035	9.99 509	24	4	5.7	5.7	5.6
37	9.17 558	83	9.18 051	85	10.81 949	9.99 507	23				
38	9.17 641	83	9.18 136	85	10.81 864	9.99 505	22	5	7.2	7.1	7.0
39	9.17 724	83	9.18 221	85	10.81 779	9.99 503	21	6	8.6	8.5	8.4
								7	10.0	9.9	9.8
40	9.17 807	83	9.18 306	85	10.81 694	9.99 501	20	8	11.5	11.3	11.2
41	9.17 890	83	9.18 391	84	10.81 609	9.99 499	19	9	12.9	12.8	12.6
42	9.17 973	82	9.18 475	85	10.81 525	9.99 497	18				
43	9.18 055	82	9.18 560	84	10.81 440	9.99 495	17	10	14.3	14.2	14.0
44	9.18 137	83	9.18 644	84	10.81 356	9.99 494	16	20	28.7	28.3	28.0
								30	43.0	42.5	42.0
45	9.18 220	82	9.18 728	84	10.81 272	9.99 492	15	40	57.3	56.7	56.0
46	9.18 302	81	9.18 812	84	10.81 188	9.99 490	14	50	71.7	70.8	70.0
47	9.18 383	82	9.18 896	83	10.81 104	9.99 488	13				
48	9.18 465	82	9.18 979	84	10.81 021	9.99 486	12	′′	83	82	81
49	9.18 547	81	9.19 063	83	10.80 937	9.99 484	11				
								1	1.4	1.4	1.4
50	9.18 628	81	9.19 146	83	10.80 854	9.99 482	10	2	2.8	2.7	2.7
51	9.18 709	81	9.19 229	83	10.80 771	9.99 480	9	3	4.2	4.1	4.0
52	9.18 790	81	9.19 312	83	10.80 688	9.99 478	8	4	5.5	5.5	5.4
53	9.18 871	81	9.19 395	83	10.80 605	9.99 476	7				
54	9.18 952	81	9.19 478	83	10.80 522	9.99 474	6	5	6.9	6.8	6.8
								6	8.3	8.2	8.1
55	9.19 033	80	9.19 561	82	10.80 439	9.99 472	5	7	9.7	9.6	9.4
56	9.19 113	80	9.19 643	82	10.80 357	9.99 470	4	8	11.1	10.9	10.8
57	9.19 193	80	9.19 725	82	10.80 275	9.99 468	3	9	12.4	12.3	12.2
58	9.19 273	80	9.19 807	82	10.80 193	9.99 466	2				
59	9.19 353	80	9.19 889	82	10.80 111	9.99 464	1	10	13.8	13.7	13.5
								20	27.7	27.3	27.0
60	9.19 433		9.19 971		10.80 029	9.99 462	0	30	41.5	41.0	40.5
								40	55.3	54.7	54.0
′	L Cos	d	L Ctn	c d	L Tan	L Sin	′	50	69.2	68.3	67.5
								Proportional parts			

′	L Sin	d	L Tan	c d	L Ctn	L Cos	′	Proportional parts

′	L Sin	d	L Tan	c d	L Ctn	L Cos	′
0	9.19 433	80	9.19 971	82	10.80 029	9.99 462	60
1	9.19 513	79	9.20 053	81	10.79 947	9.99 460	59
2	9.19 592	80	9.20 134	82	10.79 866	9.99 458	58
3	9.19 672	79	9.20 216	81	10.79 784	9.99 456	57
4	9.19 751	79	9.20 297	81	10.79 703	9.99 454	56
5	9.19 830	79	9.20 378	81	10.79 622	9.99 452	55
6	9.19 909	79	9.20 459	81	10.79 541	9.99 450	54
7	9.19 988	79	9.20 540	81	10.79 460	9.99 448	53
8	9.20 067	78	9.20 621	80	10.79 379	9.99 446	52
9	9.20 145	78	9.20 701	81	10.79 299	9.99 444	51
10	9.20 223	79	9.20 782	80	10.79 218	9.99 442	50
11	9.20 302	78	9.20 862	80	10.79 138	9.99 440	49
12	9.20 380	78	9.20 942	80	10.79 058	9.99 438	48
13	9.20 458	77	9.21 022	80	10.78 978	9.99 436	47
14	9.20 535	78	9.21 102	80	10.78 898	9.99 434	46
15	9.20 613	78	9.21 182	79	10.78 818	9.99 432	45
16	9.20 691	77	9.21 261	80	10.78 739	9.99 429	44
17	9.20 768	77	9.21 341	79	10.78 659	9.99 427	43
18	9.20 845	77	9.21 420	79	10.78 580	9.99 425	42
19	9.20 922	77	9.21 499	79	10.78 501	9.99 423	41
20	9.20 999	77	9.21 578	79	10.78 422	9.99 421	40
21	9.21 076	77	9.21 657	79	10.78 343	9.99 419	39
22	9.21 153	76	9.21 736	78	10.78 264	9.99 417	38
23	9.21 229	77	9.21 814	79	10.78 186	9.99 415	37
24	9.21 306	76	9.21 893	78	10.78 107	9.99 413	36
25	9.21 382	76	9.21 971	78	10.78 029	9.99 411	35
26	9.21 458	76	9.22 049	78	10.77 951	9.99 409	34
27	9.21 534	76	9.22 127	78	10.77 873	9.99 407	33
28	9.21 610	75	9.22 205	78	10.77 795	9.99 404	32
29	9.21 685	76	9.22 283	78	10.77 717	9.99 402	31
30	9.21 761	75	9.22 361	77	10.77 639	9.99 400	30
31	9.21 836	76	9.22 438	78	10.77 562	9.99 398	29
32	9.21 912	75	9.22 516	77	10.77 484	9.99 396	28
33	9.21 987	75	9.22 593	77	10.77 407	9.99 394	27
34	9.22 062	75	9.22 670	77	10.77 330	9.99 392	26
35	9.22 137	74	9.22 747	77	10.77 253	9.99 390	25
36	9.22 211	75	9.22 824	77	10.77 176	9.99 388	24
37	9.22 286	75	9.22 901	76	10.77 099	9.99 385	23
38	9.22 361	74	9.22 977	77	10.77 023	9.99 383	22
39	9.22 435	74	9.23 054	76	10.76 946	9.99 381	21
40	9.22 509	74	9.23 130	76	10.76 870	9.99 379	20
41	9.22 583	74	9.23 206	77	10.76 794	9.99 377	19
42	9.22 657	74	9.23 283	76	10.76 717	9.99 375	18
43	9.22 731	74	9.23 359	76	10.76 641	9.99 372	17
44	9.22 805	73	9.23 435	75	10.76 565	9.99 370	16
45	9.22 878	74	9.23 510	76	10.76 490	9.99 368	15
46	9.22 952	73	9.23 586	75	10.76 414	9.99 366	14
47	9.23 025	73	9.23 661	76	10.76 339	9.99 364	13
48	9.23 098	73	9.23 737	75	10.76 263	9.99 362	12
49	9.23 171	73	9.23 812	75	10.76 188	9.99 359	11
50	9.23 244	73	9.23 887	75	10.76 113	9.99 357	10
51	9.23 317	73	9.23 962	75	10.76 038	9.99 355	9
52	9.23 390	72	9.24 037	75	10.75 963	9.99 353	8
53	9.23 462	73	9.24 112	74	10.75 888	9.99 351	7
54	9.23 535	72	9.24 186	75	10.75 814	9.99 348	6
55	9.23 607	72	9.24 261	74	10.75 739	9.99 346	5
56	9.23 679	73	9.24 335	75	10.75 665	9.99 344	4
57	9.23 752	71	9.24 410	74	10.75 590	9.99 342	3
58	9.23 823	72	9.24 484	74	10.75 516	9.99 340	2
59	9.23 895	72	9.24 558	74	10.75 442	9.99 337	1
60	9.23 967		9.24 632		10.75 368	9.99 335	0
′	L Cos	d	L Ctn	c d	L Tan	L Sin	′

Proportional parts

′′	80	79	78	77
1	1.3	1.3	1.3	1.3
2	2.7	2.6	2.6	2.6
3	4.0	4.0	3.9	3.8
4	5.3	5.3	5.2	5.1
5	6.7	6.6	6.5	6.4
6	8.0	7.9	7.8	7.7
7	9.3	9.2	9.1	9.0
8	10.7	10.5	10.4	10.3
9	12.0	11.8	11.7	11.6
10	13.3	13.2	13.0	12.8
20	26.7	26.3	26.0	25.7
30	40.0	39.5	39.0	38.5
40	53.3	52.7	52.0	51.3
50	66.7	65.8	65.0	64.2

′′	76	75	74	73
1	1.3	1.2	1.2	1.2
2	2.5	2.5	2.5	2.4
3	3.8	3.8	3.7	3.6
4	5.1	5.0	4.9	4.9
5	6.3	6.2	6.2	6.1
6	7.6	7.5	7.4	7.3
7	8.9	8.8	8.6	8.5
8	10.1	10.0	9.9	9.7
9	11.4	11.2	11.1	11.0
10	12.7	12.5	12.3	12.2
20	25.3	25.0	24.7	24.3
30	38.0	37.5	37.0	36.5
40	50.7	50.0	49.3	48.7
50	63.3	62.5	61.7	60.8

′′	72	71	3	2
1	1.2	1.2	0.0	0.0
2	2.4	2.4	0.1	0.1
3	3.6	3.6	0.2	0.1
4	4.8	4.7	0.2	0.1
5	6.0	5.9	0.2	0.2
6	7.2	7.1	0.3	0.2
7	8.4	8.3	0.4	0.2
8	9.6	9.5	0.4	0.3
9	10.8	10.6	0.4	0.3
10	12.0	11.8	0.5	0.3
20	24.0	23.7	1.0	0.7
30	36.0	35.5	1.5	1.0
40	48.0	47.3	2.0	1.3
50	60.0	59.2	2.5	1.7

Proportional parts

′	L Sin	d	L Tan	c d	L Ctn	L Cos	d	′	Proportional parts		
0	9.23 967	72	9.24 632	74	10.75 368	9.99 335	2	60			
1	9.24 039	71	9.24 706	73	10.75 294	9.99 333	2	59			
2	9.24 110	71	9.24 779	74	10.75 221	9.99 331	3	58			
3	9.24 181	72	9.24 853	73	10.75 147	9.99 328	2	57			
4	9.24 253	71	9.24 926	74	10.75 074	9.99 326	2	56			
5	9.24 324	71	9.25 000	73	10.75 000	9.99 324	2	55	′′	74	73	72
6	9.24 395	71	9.25 073	73	10.74 927	9.99 322	3	54	1	1 2	1.2	1.2
7	9.24 466	70	9.25 146	73	10.74 854	9.99 319	2	53	2	2.5	2.4	2.4
8	9.24 536	71	9.25 219	73	10.74 781	9.99 317	2	52	3	3.7	3.6	3.6
9	9.24 607	70	9.25 292	73	10.74 708	9.99 315	2	51	4	4.9	4.9	4.8
10	9.24 677	71	9.25 365	72	10.74 635	9.99 313	3	50	5	6.2	6.1	6.0
11	9.24 748	70	9.25 437	73	10.74 563	9.99 310	2	49	6	7.4	7.3	7.2
12	9.24 818	70	9.25 510	72	10.74 490	9.99 308	2	48	7	8.6	8.5	8.4
13	9.24 888	70	9.25 582	73	10.74 418	9.99 306	2	47	8	9.9	9.7	9.6
14	9.24 958	70	9.25 655	72	10.74 345	9.99 304	3	46	9	11.1	11.0	10.8
15	9.25 028	70	9.25 727	72	10.74 273	9.99 301	2	45	10	12.3	12.2	12.0
16	9.25 098	70	9.25 799	72	10.74 201	9.99 299	2	44	20	24.7	24.3	24.0
17	9.25 168	69	9.25 871	72	10.74 129	9.99 297	3	43	30	37.0	36.5	36.0
18	9.25 237	70	9.25 943	72	10.74 057	9.99 294	2	42	40	49.3	48.7	48.0
19	9.25 307	69	9.26 015	71	10.73 985	9.99 292	2	41	50	61.7	60.8	60.0
20	9.25 376	69	9.26 086	72	10.73 914	9.99 290	2	40				
21	9.25 445	69	9.26 158	71	10.73 842	9.99 288	3	39				
22	9.25 514	69	9.26 229	72	10.73 771	9.99 285	2	38				
23	9.25 583	69	9.26 301	71	10.73 699	9.99 283	2	37	′′	71	70	69
24	9.25 652	69	9.26 372	71	10.73 628	9.99 281	3	36	1	1.2	1.2	1.2
25	9.25 721	69	9.26 443	71	10.73 557	9.99 278	2	35	2	2.4	2.3	2.3
26	9.25 790	68	9.26 514	71	10.73 486	9.99 276	2	34	3	3.6	3.5	3.4
27	9.25 858	69	9.26 585	70	10.73 415	9.99 274	3	33	4	4.7	4.7	4.6
28	9.25 927	68	9.26 655	71	10.73 345	9.99 271	2	32				
29	9.25 995	68	9.26 726	71	10.73 274	9.99 269	2	31	5	5.9	5.8	5.8
									6	7.1	7.0	6.9
30	9.26 063	68	9.26 797	70	10.73 203	9.99 267	3	30	7	8.3	8.2	8.0
31	9.26 131	68	9.26 867	70	10.73 133	9.99 264	2	29	8	9.5	9.3	9.2
32	9.26 199	68	9.26 937	71	10.73 063	9.99 262	2	28	9	10.6	10.5	10.4
33	9.26 267	68	9.27 008	70	10.72 992	9.99 260	3	27				
34	9.26 335	68	9.27 078	70	10.72 922	9.99 257	2	26	10	11.8	11.7	11.5
									20	23.7	23.3	23.0
35	9.26 403	67	9.27 148	70	10.72 852	9.99 255	3	25	30	35.5	35.0	34.5
36	9.26 470	68	9.27 218	70	10.72 782	9.99 252	2	24	40	47.3	46.7	46.0
37	9.26 538	67	9.27 288	70	10.72 712	9.99 250	2	23	50	59.2	58.3	57.5
38	9.26 605	67	9.27 357	70	10.72 643	9.99 248	3	22				
39	9.26 672	67	9.27 427	69	10.72 573	9.99 245	2	21				
40	9.26 739	67	9.27 496	70	10.72 504	9.99 243	2	20	′′	68	67	66
41	9.26 806	67	9.27 566	69	10.72 434	9.99 241	3	19	1	1.1	1.1	1.1
42	9.26 873	67	9.27 635	69	10.72 365	9.99 238	2	18	2	2.3	2.2	2.2
43	9.26 940	67	9.27 704	69	10.72 296	9.99 236	3	17	3	3.4	3.4	3.3
44	9.27 007	66	9.27 773	69	10.72 227	9.99 233	2	16	4	4.5	4.5	4.4
45	9.27 073	67	9.27 842	69	10.72 158	9.99 231	2	15	5	5.7	5.6	5.5
46	9.27 140	66	9.27 911	69	10.72 089	9.99 229	3	14	6	6.8	6.7	6.6
47	9.27 206	67	9.27 980	69	10.72 020	9.99 226	2	13	7	7.9	7.8	7.7
48	9.27 273	66	9.28 049	68	10.71 951	9.99 224	3	12	8	9.1	8.9	8.8
49	9.27 339	66	9.28 117	69	10.71 883	9.99 221	2	11	9	10.2	10.0	9.9
50	9.27 405	66	9.28 186	68	10.71 814	9.99 219	2	10	10	11.3	11.2	11.0
51	9.27 471	66	9.28 254	69	10.71 746	9.99 217	3	9	20	22.7	22.3	22.0
52	9.27 537	65	9.28 323	68	10.71 677	9.99 214	2	8	30	34.0	33.5	33.0
53	9.27 602	66	9.28 391	68	10.71 609	9.99 212	3	7	40	45.3	44.7	44.0
54	9.27 668	66	9.28 459	68	10.71 541	9.99 209	2	6	50	56.7	55.8	55.0
55	9.27 734	65	9.28 527	68	10.71 473	9.99 207	3	5				
56	9.27 799	65	9.28 595	67	10.71 405	9.99 204	2	4				
57	9.27 864	66	9.28 662	68	10.71 338	9.99 202	2	3				
58	9.27 930	65	9.28 730	68	10.71 270	9.99 200	3	2				
59	9.27 995	65	9.28 798	67	10.71 202	9.99 197	2	1				
60	9.28 060		9.28 865		10.71 135	9.99 195		0				
′	L Cos	d	L Ctn	c d	L Tan	L Sin	d	′	Proportional parts		

′	L Sin	d	L Tan	c d	L Ctn	L Cos	d	′	Proportional parts
0	9.28 060	65	9.28 865	68	10.71 135	9.99 195	3	60	
1	9.28 125	65	9.28 933	67	10.71 067	9.99 192	2	59	
2	9.28 190	64	9.29 000	67	10.71 000	9.99 190	3	58	
3	9.28 254	65	9.29 067	67	10.70 933	9.99 187	2	57	
4	9.28 319	65	9.29 134	67	10.70 866	9.99 185	3	56	

′	L Sin	d	L Tan	c d	L Ctn	L Cos	d	′		″	65	64	63
5	9.28 384	64	9.29 201	67	10.70 799	9.99 182	2	55					
6	9.28 448	64	9.29 268	67	10.70 732	9.99 180	3	54		1	1.1	1.1	1.0
7	9.28 512	65	9.29 335	67	10.70 665	9.99 177	2	53		2	2.2	2.1	2.1
8	9.28 577	64	9.29 402	66	10.70 598	9.99 175	3	52		3	3.2	3.2	3.2
9	9.28 641	64	9.29 468	67	10.70 532	9.99 172	2	51		4	4.3	4.3	4.2
10	9.28 705	64	9.29 535	66	10.70 465	9.99 170	3	50		5	5.4	5.3	5.2
11	9.28 769	64	9.29 601	67	10.70 399	9.99 167	2	49		6	6.5	6.4	6.3
12	9.28 833	63	9.29 668	66	10.70 332	9.99 165	3	48		7	7.6	7.5	7.4
13	9.28 896	64	9.29 734	66	10.70 266	9.99 162	2	47		8	8.7	8.5	8.4
14	9.28 960	64	9.29 800	66	10.70 200	9.99 160	3	46		9	9.8	9.6	9.4
15	9.29 024	63	9.29 866	66	10.70 134	9.99 157	2	45					
16	9.29 087	63	9.29 932	66	10.70 068	9.99 155	3	44		10	10.8	10.7	10.5
17	9.29 150	64	9.29 998	66	10.70 002	9.99 152	2	43		20	21.7	21.3	21.0
18	9.29 214	63	9.30 064	66	10.69 936	9.99 150	3	42		30	32.5	32.0	31.5
19	9.29 277	63	9.30 130	65	10.69 870	9.99 147	2	41		40	43.3	42.7	42.0
20	9.29 340	63	9.30 195	66	10.69 805	9.99 145	3	40		50	54.2	53.3	52.5
21	9.29 403	63	9.30 261	65	10.69 739	9.99 142	3	39					
22	9.29 466	63	9.30 326	65	10.69 674	9.99 140	3	38					
23	9.29 529	62	9.30 391	66	10.69 609	9.99 137	2	37		″	62	61	60
24	9.29 591	63	9.30 457	65	10.69 543	9.99 135	3	36		1	1.0	1.0	1.0
25	9.29 654	62	9.30 522	65	10.69 478	9.99 132	2	35		2	2.1	2.0	2.0
26	9.29 716	63	9.30 587	65	10.69 413	9.99 130	3	34		3	3.1	3.0	3.0
27	9.29 779	62	9.30 652	65	10.69 348	9.99 127	3	33		4	4.1	4.1	4.0
28	9.29 841	62	9.30 717	65	10.69 283	9.99 124	2	32					
29	9.29 903	63	9.30 782	64	10.69 218	9.99 122	3	31		5	5.2	5.1	5.0
30	9.29 966	62	9.30 846	65	10.69 154	9.99 119	2	30		6	6.2	6.1	6.0
31	9.30 028	62	9.30 911	64	10.69 089	9.99 117	3	29		7	7.2	7.1	7.0
32	9.30 090	61	9.30 975	65	10.69 025	9.99 114	2	28		8	8.3	8.1	8.0
33	9.30 151	62	9.31 040	64	10.68 960	9.99 112	3	27		9	9.3	9.2	9.0
34	9.30 213	62	9.31 104	64	10.68 896	9.99 109	3	26					
35	9.30 275	61	9.31 168	65	10.68 832	9.99 106	2	25		10	10.3	10.2	10.0
36	9.30 336	62	9.31 233	64	10.68 767	9.99 104	3	24		20	20.7	20.3	20.0
37	9.30 398	61	9.31 297	64	10.68 703	9.99 101	2	23		30	31.0	30.5	30.0
38	9.30 459	62	9.31 361	64	10.68 639	9.99 099	3	22		40	41.3	40.7	40.0
39	9.30 521	61	9.31 425	64	10.68 575	9.99 096	3	21		50	51.7	50.8	50.0
40	9.30 582	61	9.31 489	63	10.68 511	9.99 093	2	20		″	59	3	2
41	9.30 643	61	9.31 552	64	10.68 448	9.99 091	3	19		1	1.0	0.0	0.0
42	9.30 704	61	9.31 616	63	10.68 384	9.99 088	2	18		2	2.0	0.1	0.1
43	9.30 765	61	9.31 679	64	10.68 321	9.99 086	3	17		3	3.0	0.2	0.1
44	9.30 826	61	9.31 743	63	10.68 257	9.99 083	3	16		4	3.9	0.2	0.1
45	9.30 887	60	9.31 806	64	10.68 194	9.99 080	2	15		5	4.9	0.2	0.2
46	9.30 947	61	9.31 870	63	10.68 130	9.99 078	3	14		6	5.9	0.3	0.2
47	9.31 008	60	9.31 933	63	10.68 067	9.99 075	3	13		7	6.9	0.4	0.2
48	9.31 068	61	9.31 996	63	10.68 004	9.99 072	2	12		8	7.9	0.4	0.3
49	9.31 129	60	9.32 059	63	10.67 941	9.99 070	3	11		9	8.8	0.4	0.3
50	9.31 189	61	9.32 122	63	10.67 878	9.99 067	3	10		10	9.8	0.5	0.3
51	9.31 250	60	9.32 185	63	10.67 815	9.99 064	2	9		20	19.7	1.0	0.7
52	9.31 310	60	9.32 248	63	10.67 752	9.99 062	3	8		30	29.5	1.5	1.0
53	9.31 370	60	9.32 311	62	10.67 689	9.99 059	3	7		40	39.3	2.0	1.3
54	9.31 430	60	9.32 373	63	10.67 627	9.99 056	2	6		50	49.2	2.5	1.7
55	9.31 490	59	9.32 436	62	10.67 564	9.99 054	3	5					
56	9.31 549	60	9.32 498	63	10.67 502	9.99 051	3	4					
57	9.31 609	60	9.32 561	62	10.67 439	9.99 048	2	3					
58	9.31 669	59	9.32 623	62	10.67 377	9.99 046	3	2					
59	9.31 728	60	9.32 685	62	10.67 315	9.99 043	3	1					
60	9.31 788		9.32 747		10.67 253	9.99 040		0					
′	L Cos	d	L Ctn	c d	L Tan	L Sin	d	′	Proportional parts

′	L Sin	d	L Tan	c d	L Ctn	L Cos	d	′	Proportional parts		
0	9.31 788	59	9.32 747	63	10.67 253	9.99 040	2	60			
1	9.31 847	60	9.32 810	62	10.67 190	9.99 038	3	59			
2	9.31 907	59	9.32 872	61	10.67 128	9.99 035	3	58			
3	9.31 966	59	9.32 933	62	10.67 067	9.99 032	2	57			
4	9.32 025	59	9.32 995	62	10.67 005	9.99 030	3	56			
5	9.32 084	59	9.33 057	62	10.66 943	9.99 027	3	55	″	63	62	61
6	9.32 143	59	9.33 119	61	10.66 881	9.99 024	2	54				
7	9.32 202	59	9.33 180	62	10.66 820	9.99 022	3	53	1	1.0	1.0	1.0
8	9.32 261	58	9.33 242	61	10.66 758	9.99 019	3	52	2	2.1	2.1	2.0
9	9.32 319	59	9.33 303	62	10.66 697	9.99 016	3	51	3	3.2	3.1	3.0
10	9.32 378	59	9.33 365	61	10.66 635	9.99 013	2	50	4	4.2	4.1	4.1
11	9.32 437	58	9.33 426	61	10.66 574	9.99 011	3	49				
12	9.32 495	58	9.33 487	61	10.66 513	9.99 008	3	48	5	5.2	5.2	5.1
13	9.32 553	59	9.33 548	61	10.66 452	9.99 005	3	47	6	6.3	6.2	6.1
14	9.32 612	58	9.33 609	61	10.66 391	9.99 002	2	46	7	7.4	7.2	7.1
15	9.32 670	58	9.33 670	61	10.66 330	9.99 000	3	45	8	8.4	8.3	8.1
16	9.32 728	58	9.33 731	61	10.66 269	9.98 997	3	44	9	9.4	9.3	9.2
17	9.32 786	58	9.33 792	61	10.66 208	9.98 994	3	43				
18	9.32 844	58	9.33 853	60	10.66 147	9.98 991	2	42	10	10.5	10.3	10.2
19	9.32 902	58	9.33 913	61	10.66 087	9.98 989	3	41	20	21.0	20.7	20.3
20	9.32 960	58	9.33 974	60	10.66 026	9.98 986	3	40	30	31.5	31.0	30.5
21	9.33 018	57	9.34 034	61	10.65 966	9.98 983	3	39	40	42.0	41.3	40.7
22	9.33 075	58	9.34 095	60	10.65 905	9.98 980	2	38	50	52.5	51.7	50.8
23	9.33 133	57	9.34 155	60	10.65 845	9.98 978	3	37				
24	9.33 190	58	9.34 215	61	10.65 785	9.98 975	3	36	″	60	59	58
25	9.33 248	57	9.34 276	60	10.65 724	9.98 972	3	35	1	1.0	1.0	1.0
26	9.33 305	57	9.34 336	60	10.65 664	9.98 969	2	34	2	2.0	2.0	1.9
27	9.33 362	58	9.34 396	60	10.65 604	9.98 967	3	33	3	3.0	3.0	2.9
28	9.33 420	57	9.34 456	60	10.65 544	9.98 964	3	32	4	4.0	3.9	3.9
29	9.33 477	57	9.34 516	60	10.65 484	9.98 961	3	31				
30	9.33 534	57	9.34 576	59	10.65 424	9.98 958	3	30	5	5.0	4.9	4.8
31	9.33 591	56	9.34 635	60	10.65 365	9.98 955	2	29	6	6.0	5.9	5.8
32	9.33 647	57	9.34 695	60	10.65 305	9.98 953	3	28	7	7.0	6.9	6.8
33	9.33 704	57	9.34 755	59	10.65 245	9.98 950	3	27	8	8.0	7.9	7.7
34	9.33 761	57	9.34 814	60	10.65 186	9.98 947	3	26	9	9.0	8.8	8.7
35	9.33 818	56	9.34 874	59	10.65 126	9.98 944	3	25	10	10.0	9.8	9.7
36	9.33 874	57	9.34 933	59	10.65 067	9.98 941	3	24	20	20.0	19.7	19.3
37	9.33 931	56	9.34 992	59	10.65 008	9.98 938	2	23	30	30.0	29.5	29.0
38	9.33 987	56	9.35 051	60	10.64 949	9.98 936	3	22	40	40.0	39.3	38.7
39	9.34 043	57	9.35 111	59	10.64 889	9.98 933	3	21	50	50.0	49.2	48.3
40	9.34 100	56	9.35 170	59	10.64 830	9.98 930	3	20	″	57	56	55
41	9.34 156	56	9.35 229	59	10.64 771	9.98 927	3	19	1	1.0	0.9	0.9
42	9.34 212	56	9.35 288	59	10.64 712	9.98 924	3	18	2	1.9	1.9	1.8
43	9.34 268	56	9.35 347	58	10.64 653	9.98 921	2	17	3	2.8	2.8	2.8
44	9.34 324	56	9.35 405	59	10.64 595	9.98 919	3	16	4	3.8	3.7	3.7
45	9.34 380	56	9.35 464	59	10.64 536	9.98 916	3	15	5	4.8	4.7	4.6
46	9.34 436	55	9.35 523	58	10.64 477	9.98 913	3	14	6	5.7	5.6	5.5
47	9.34 491	56	9.35 581	59	10.64 419	9.98 910	3	13	7	6.6	6.5	6.4
48	9.34 547	55	9.35 640	58	10.64 360	9.98 907	3	12	8	7.6	7.5	7.3
49	9.34 602	56	9.35 698	59	10.64 302	9.98 904	3	11	9	8.6	8.4	8.2
50	9.34 658	55	9.35 757	58	10.64 243	9.98 901	3	10	10	9.5	9.3	9.2
51	9.34 713	56	9.35 815	58	10.64 185	9.98 898	2	9	20	19.0	18.7	18.3
52	9.34 769	55	9.35 873	58	10.64 127	9.98 896	3	8	30	28.5	28.0	27.5
53	9.34 824	55	9.35 931	58	10.64 069	9.98 893	3	7	40	38.0	37.3	36.7
54	9.34 879	55	9.35 989	58	10.64 011	9.98 890	3	6	50	47.5	46.7	45.8
55	9.34 934	55	9.36 047	58	10.63 953	9.98 887	3	5				
56	9.34 989	55	9.36 105	58	10.63 895	9.98 884	3	4				
57	9.35 044	55	9.36 163	58	10.63 837	9.98 881	3	3				
58	9.35 099	55	9.36 221	58	10.63 779	9.98 878	3	2				
59	9.35 154	55	9.36 279	57	10.63 721	9.98 875	3	1				
60	9.35 209		9.36 336		10.63 664	9.98 872		0				
′	L Cos	d	L Ctn	c d	L Tan	L Sin	d	′	Proportional parts		

′	L Sin	d	L Tan	c d	L Ctn	L Cos	d	′	Proportional parts		
0	9.35 209	54	9.36 336	58	10.63 664	9.98 872	3	60			
1	9.35 263	55	9.36 394	58	10.63 606	9.98 869	2	59			
2	9.35 318	55	9.36 452	57	10.63 548	9.98 867	3	58			
3	9.35 373	54	9.36 509	57	10.63 491	9.98 864	3	57			
4	9.35 427	54	9.36 566	58	10.63 434	9.98 861	3	56			
5	9.35 481	55	9.36 624	57	10.63 376	9.98 858	3	55	′′	57	56	55
6	9.35 536	54	9.36 681	57	10.63 319	9.98 855	3	54				
7	9.35 590	54	9.36 738	57	10.63 262	9.98 852	3	53	1	1.0	0.9	0.9
8	9.35 644	54	9.36 795	57	10.63 205	9.98 849	3	52	2	1.9	1.9	1.8
9	9.35 698	54	9.36 852	57	10.63 148	9.98 846	3	51	3	2.8	2.8	2.8
10	9.35 752	54	9.36 909	57	10.63 091	9.98 843	3	50	4	3.8	3.7	3.7
11	9.35 806	54	9.36 966	57	10.63 034	9.98 840	3	49				
12	9.35 860	54	9.37 023	57	10.62 977	9.98 837	3	48	5	4.8	4.7	4.6
13	9.35 914	54	9.37 080	57	10.62 920	9.98 834	3	47	6	5.7	5.6	5.5
14	9.35 968	54	9.37 137	56	10.62 863	9.98 831	3	46	7	6.6	6.5	6.4
15	9.36 022	53	9.37 193	57	10.62 807	9.98 828	3	45	8	7.6	7.5	7.3
16	9.36 075	54	9.37 250	56	10.62 750	9.98 825	3	44	9	8.6	8.4	8.2
17	9.36 129	53	9.37 306	57	10.62 694	9.98 822	3	43				
18	9.36 182	54	9.37 363	56	10.62 637	9.98 819	3	42	10	9.5	9.3	9.2
19	9.36 236	53	9.37 419	57	10.62 581	9.98 816	3	41	20	19.0	18.7	18.3
20	9.36 289	53	9.37 476	56	10.62 524	9.98 813	3	40	30	28.5	28.0	27.5
21	9.36 342	53	9.37 532	56	10.62 468	9.98 810	3	39	40	38.0	37.3	36.7
22	9.36 395	54	9.37 588	56	10.62 412	9.98 807	3	38	50	47.5	46.7	45.8
23	9.36 449	53	9.37 644	56	10.62 356	9.98 804	3	37				
24	9.36 502	53	9.37 700	56	10.62 300	9.98 801	3	36	′′	54	53	52
25	9.36 555	53	9.37 756	56	10.62 244	9.98 798	3	35	1	0.9	0.9	0.9
26	9.36 608	52	9.37 812	56	10.62 188	9.98 795	3	34	2	1.8	1.8	1.7
27	9.36 660	53	9.37 868	56	10.62 132	9.98 792	3	33	3	2.7	2.6	2.6
28	9.36 713	53	9.37 924	56	10.62 076	9.98 789	3	32	4	3.6	3.5	3.5
29	9.36 766	53	9.37 980	55	10.62 020	9.98 786	3	31				
30	9.36 819	52	9.38 035	56	10.61 965	9.98 783	3	30	5	4.5	4.4	4.3
31	9.36 871	53	9.38 091	56	10.61 909	9.98 780	3	29	6	5.4	5.3	5.2
32	9.36 924	52	9.38 147	55	10.61 853	9.98 777	3	28	7	6.3	6.2	6.1
33	9.36 976	52	9.38 202	55	10.61 798	9.98 774	3	27	8	7.2	7.1	6.9
34	9.37 028	53	9.38 257	56	10.61 743	9.98 771	3	26	9	8.1	8.0	7.8
35	9.37 081	52	9.38 313	55	10.61 687	9.98 768	3	25	10	9.0	8.8	8.7
36	9.37 133	52	9.38 368	55	10.61 632	9.98 765	3	24	20	18.0	17.7	17.3
37	9.37 185	52	9.38 423	56	10.61 577	9.98 762	3	23	30	27.0	26.5	26.0
38	9.37 237	52	9.38 479	55	10.61 521	9.98 759	3	22	40	36.0	35.3	34.7
39	9.37 289	52	9.38 534	55	10.61 466	9.98 756	3	21	50	45.0	44.2	43.3
40	9.37 341	52	9.38 589	55	10.61 411	9.98 753	3	20				
41	9.37 393	52	9.38 644	55	10.61 356	9.98 750	4	19	′′	51	4	3	2
42	9.37 445	52	9.38 699	55	10.61 301	9.98 746	3	18	1	0.8	0.1	0.0	0.0
43	9.37 497	52	9.38 754	54	10.61 246	9.98 743	3	17	2	1.7	0.1	0.1	0.1
44	9.37 549	51	9.38 808	55	10.61 192	9.98 740	3	16	3	2.6	0.2	0.2	0.1
45	9.37 600	52	9.38 863	55	10.61 137	9.98 737	3	15	4	3.4	0.3	0.2	0.1
46	9.37 652	51	9.38 918	54	10.61 082	9.98 734	3	14					
47	9.37 703	52	9.38 972	55	10.61 028	9.98 731	3	13	5	4.2	0.3	0.2	0.2
48	9.37 755	51	9.39 027	55	10.60 973	9.98 728	3	12	6	5.1	0.4	0.3	0.2
49	9.37 806	52	9.39 082	54	10.60 918	9.98 725	3	11	7	6.0	0.5	0.4	0.2
50	9.37 858	51	9.39 136	54	10.60 864	9.98 722	3	10	8	6.8	0.5	0.4	0.3
51	9.37 909	51	9.39 190	55	10.60 810	9.98 719	4	9	9	7.6	0.6	0.4	0.3
52	9.37 960	51	9.39 245	54	10.60 755	9.98 715	3	8					
53	9.38 011	51	9.39 299	54	10.60 701	9.98 712	3	7	10	8.5	0.7	0.5	0.3
54	9.38 062	51	9.39 353	54	10.60 647	9.98 709	3	6	20	17.0	1.3	1.0	0.7
55	9.38 113	51	9.39 407	54	10.60 593	9.98 706	3	5	30	25.5	2.0	1.5	1.0
56	9.38 164	51	9.39 461	54	10.60 539	9.98 703	3	4	40	34.0	2.7	2.0	1.3
57	9.38 215	51	9.39 515	54	10.60 485	9.98 700	3	3	50	42.5	3.3	2.5	1.7
58	9.38 266	51	9.39 569	54	10.60 431	9.98 697	3	2					
59	9.38 317	51	9.39 623	54	10.60 377	9.98 694	4	1					
60	9.38 368		9.39 677		10.60 323	9.98 690		0					
′	L Cos	d	L Ctn	c d	L Tan	L Sin	d	′	Proportional parts		

′	L Sin	d	L Tan	c d	L Ctn	L Cos	d	′		Proportional parts		
0	9.38 368	50	9.39 677	54	10.60 323	9.98 690	3	60				
1	9.38 418	51	9.39 731	54	10.60 269	9.98 687	3	59				
2	9.38 469	50	9.39 785	53	10.60 215	9.98 684	3	58				
3	9.38 519	51	9.39 838	54	10.60 162	9.98 681	3	57				
4	9.38 570	50	9.39 892	53	10.60 108	9.98 678	3	56				
5	9.38 620	50	9.39 945	54	10.60 055	9.98 675	4	55				
6	9.38 670	51	9.39 999	53	10.60 001	9.98 671	3	54				
7	9.38 721	50	9.40 052	54	10.59 948	9.98 668	3	53				
8	9.38 771	50	9.40 106	53	10.59 894	9.98 665	3	52	′′	54	53	52
9	9.38 821	50	9.40 159	53	10.59 841	9.98 662	3	51	1	0.9	0.9	0.9
									2	1.8	1.8	1.7
10	9.38 871	50	9.40 212	54	10.59 788	9.98 659	3	50	3	2.7	2.6	2.6
11	9.38 921	50	9.40 266	53	10.59 734	9.98 656	4	49	4	3.6	3.5	3.5
12	9.38 971	50	9.40 319	53	10.59 681	9.98 652	3	48				
13	9.39 021	50	9.40 372	53	10.59 628	9.98 649	3	47	5	4.5	4.4	4.3
14	9.39 071	50	9.40 425	53	10.59 575	9.98 646	3	46	6	5.4	5.3	5.2
									7	6.3	6.2	6.1
15	9.39 121	49	9.40 478	53	10.59 522	9.98 643	3	45	8	7.2	7.1	6.9
16	9.39 170	50	9.40 531	53	10.59 469	9.98 640	4	44	9	8.1	8.0	7.8
17	9.39 220	50	9.40 584	52	10.59 416	9.98 636	3	43				
18	9.39 270	49	9.40 636	53	10.59 364	9.98 633	3	42	10	9.0	8.8	8.7
19	9.39 319	50	9.40 689	53	10.59 311	9.98 630	3	41	20	18.0	17.7	17.3
									30	27.0	26.5	26.0
20	9.39 369	49	9.40 742	53	10.59 258	9.98 627	4	40	40	36.0	35.3	34.7
21	9.39 418	49	9.40 795	52	10.59 205	9.98 623	3	39	50	45.0	44.2	43.3
22	9.39 467	50	9.40 847	53	10.59 153	9.98 620	3	38				
23	9.39 517	49	9.40 900	52	10.59 100	9.98 617	3	37				
24	9.39 566	49	9.40 952	53	10.59 048	9.98 614	4	36	′′	51	50	49
									1	0.8	0.8	0.8
25	9.39 615	49	9.41 005	52	10.58 995	9.98 610	3	35	2	1.7	1.7	1.6
26	9.39 664	49	9.41 057	52	10.58 943	9.98 607	3	34	3	2.6	2.5	2.4
27	9.39 713	49	9.41 109	52	10.58 891	9.98 604	3	33	4	3.4	3.3	3.3
28	9.39 762	49	9.41 161	53	10.58 839	9.98 601	4	32				
29	9.39 811	49	9.41 214	52	10.58 786	9.98 597	3	31	5	4.2	4.2	4.1
									6	5.1	5.0	4.9
30	9.39 860	49	9.41 266	52	10.58 734	9.98 594	3	30	7	6.0	5.8	5.7
31	9.39 909	49	9.41 318	52	10.58 682	9.98 591	3	29	8	6.8	6.7	6.5
32	9.39 958	48	9.41 370	52	10.58 630	9.98 588	4	28	9	7.6	7.5	7.4
33	9.40 006	49	9.41 422	52	10.58 578	9.98 584	3	27				
34	9.40 055	48	9.41 474	52	10.58 526	9.98 581	3	26	10	8.5	8.3	8.2
									20	17.0	16.7	16.3
35	9.40 103	49	9.41 526	52	10.58 474	9.98 578	4	25	30	25.5	25.0	24.5
36	9.40 152	48	9.41 578	51	10.58 422	9.98 574	3	24	40	34.0	33.3	32.7
37	9.40 200	49	9.41 629	52	10.58 371	9.98 571	3	23	50	42.5	41.7	40.8
38	9.40 249	48	9.41 681	52	10.58 319	9.98 568	3	22				
39	9.40 297	49	9.41 733	51	10.58 267	9.98 565	4	21	′′	48	47 4	3
									1	0.8	0.8 0.1	0.0
40	9.40 346	48	9.41 784	52	10.58 216	9.98 561	3	20	2	1.6	1.6 0.1	0.1
41	9.40 394	48	9.41 836	51	10.58 164	9.98 558	3	19	3	2.4	2.4 0.2	0.2
42	9.40 442	48	9.41 887	52	10.58 113	9.98 555	4	18	4	3.2	3.1 0.3	0.2
43	9.40 490	48	9.41 939	51	10.58 061	9.98 551	3	17				
44	9.40 538	48	9.41 990	51	10.58 010	9.98 548	3	16	5	4.0	3.9 0.3	0.2
									6	4.8	4.7 0.4	0.3
45	9.40 586	48	9.42 041	52	10.57 959	9.98 545	4	15	7	5.6	5.5 0.5	0.4
46	9.40 634	48	9.42 093	51	10.57 907	9.98 541	3	14	8	6.4	6.3 0.5	0.4
47	9.40 682	48	9.42 144	51	10.57 856	9.98 538	3	13	9	7.2	7.0 0.6	0.4
48	9.40 730	48	9.42 195	51	10.57 805	9.98 535	4	12				
49	9.40 778	47	9.42 246	51	10.57 754	9.98 531	3	11	10	8.0	7.8 0.7	0.5
									20	16.0	15.7 1.3	1.0
50	9.40 825	48	9.42 297	51	10.57 703	9.98 528	3	10	30	24.0	23.5 2.0	1.5
51	9.40 873	48	9.42 348	51	10.57 652	9.98 525	4	9	40	32.0	31.3 2.7	2.0
52	9.40 921	47	9.42 399	51	10.57 601	9.98 521	3	8	50	40.0	39.2 3.3	2.5
53	9.40 968	48	9.42 450	51	10.57 550	9.98 518	3	7				
54	9.41 016	47	9.42 501	51	10.57 499	9.98 515	4	6				
55	9.41 063	48	9.42 552	51	10.57 448	9.98 511	3	5				
56	9.41 111	47	9.42 603	50	10.57 397	9.98 508	3	4				
57	9.41 158	47	9.42 653	51	10.57 347	9.98 505	4	3				
58	9.41 205	47	9.42 704	51	10.57 296	9.98 501	3	2				
59	9.41 252	48	9.42 755	50	10.57 245	9.98 498	4	1				
60	9.41 300		9.42 805		10.57 195	9.98 494		0				
′	L Cos	d	L Ctn	c d	L Tan	L Sin	d	′		Proportional parts		

′	L Sin	d	L Tan	c d	L Ctn	L Cos	d	′	Proportional parts
0	9.41 300	47	9.42 805	51	10.57 195	9.98 494	3	60	
1	9.41 347	47	9.42 856	50	10.57 144	9.98 491	3	59	
2	9.41 394	47	9.42 906	51	10.57 094	9.98 488	4	58	
3	9.41 441	47	9.42 957	50	10.57 043	9.98 484	3	57	
4	9.41 488	47	9.43 007	50	10.56 993	9.98 481	4	56	
5	9.41 535	47	9.43 057	51	10.56 943	9.98 477	3	55	
6	9.41 582	46	9.43 108	50	10.56 892	9.98 474	3	54	
7	9.41 628	47	9.43 158	50	10.56 842	9.98 471	4	53	′′ 51 50 49
8	9.41 675	47	9.43 208	50	10.56 792	9.98 467	3	52	1 0.8 0.8 0.8
9	9.41 722	46	9.43 258	50	10.56 742	9.98 464	4	51	2 1.7 1.7 1.6
									3 2.6 2.5 2.4
10	9.41 768	47	9.43 308	50	10.56 692	9.98 460	3	50	4 3.4 3.3 3.3
11	9.41 815	46	9.43 358	50	10.56 642	9.98 457	4	49	
12	9.41 861	47	9.43 408	50	10.56 592	9.98 453	3	48	5 4.2 4.2 4.1
13	9.41 908	46	9.43 458	50	10.56 542	9.98 450	3	47	6 5.1 5.0 4.9
14	9.41 954	47	9.43 508	50	10.56 492	9.98 447	4	46	7 6.0 5.8 5.7
									8 6.8 6.7 6.5
15	9.42 001	46	9.43 558	49	10.56 442	9.98 443	3	45	9 7.6 7.5 7.4
16	9.42 047	46	9.43 607	50	10.56 393	9.98 440	4	44	
17	9.42 093	47	9.43 657	50	10.56 343	9.98 436	3	43	10 8.5 8.3 8.2
18	9.42 140	46	9.43 707	49	10.56 293	9.98 433	4	42	20 17.0 16.7 16.3
19	9.42 186	46	9.43 756	50	10.56 244	9.98 429	3	41	30 25.5 25.0 24.5
									40 34.0 33.3 32.7
20	9.42 232	46	9.43 806	49	10.56 194	9.98 426	4	40	50 42.5 41.7 40.8
21	9.42 278	46	9.43 855	50	10.56 145	9.98 422	3	39	
22	9.42 324	46	9.43 905	49	10.56 095	9.98 419	4	38	
23	9.42 370	46	9.43 954	50	10.56 046	9.98 415	3	37	′′ 48 47 46
24	9.42 416	45	9.44 004	49	10.55 996	9.98 412	3	36	1 0.8 0.8 0.8
									2 1.6 1.6 1.5
25	9.42 461	46	9.44 053	49	10.55 947	9.98 409	4	35	3 2.4 2.4 2.3
26	9.42 507	46	9.44 102	49	10.55 898	9.98 405	3	34	4 3.2 3.1 3.1
27	9.42 553	46	9.44 151	50	10.55 849	9.98 402	4	33	
28	9.42 599	45	9.44 201	49	10.55 799	9.98 398	3	32	5 4.0 3.9 3.8
29	9.42 644	46	9.44 250	49	10.55 750	9.98 395	4	31	6 4.8 4.7 4.6
									7 5.6 5.5 5.4
30	9.42 690	45	9.44 299	49	10.55 701	9.98 391	3	30	8 6.4 6.3 6.1
31	9.42 735	46	9.44 348	49	10.55 652	9.98 388	4	29	9 7.2 7.0 6.9
32	9.42 781	45	9.44 397	49	10.55 603	9.98 384	3	28	
33	9.42 826	46	9.44 446	49	10.55 554	9.98 381	4	27	10 8.0 7.8 7.7
34	9.42 872	45	9.44 495	49	10.55 505	9.98 377	4	26	20 16.0 15.7 15.3
									30 24.0 23.5 23.0
35	9.42 917	45	9.44 544	48	10.55 456	9.98 373	3	25	40 32.0 31.3 30.7
36	9.42 962	46	9.44 592	49	10.55 408	9.98 370	4	24	50 40.0 39.2 38.3
37	9.43 008	45	9.44 641	49	10.55 359	9.98 366	3	23	
38	9.43 053	45	9.44 690	48	10.55 310	9.98 363	4	22	
39	9.43 098	45	9.44 738	49	10.55 262	9.98 359	3	21	′′ 45 44 4 3
									1 0.8 0.7 0.1 0.0
40	9.43 143	45	9.44 787	49	10.55 213	9.98 356	4	20	2 1.5 1.5 0.1 0.1
41	9.43 188	45	9.44 836	48	10.55 164	9.98 352	3	19	3 2.2 2.2 0.2 0.2
42	9.43 233	45	9.44 884	49	10.55 116	9.98 349	4	18	4 3.0 2.9 0.3 0.2
43	9.43 279	45	9.44 933	48	10.55 067	9.99 345	3	17	
44	9.43 323	44	9.44 981	48	10.55 019	9.98 342	4	16	5 3.8 3.7 0.3 0.2
									6 4.5 4.4 0.4 0.3
45	9.43 367	45	9.45 029	49	10.54 971	9.98 338	4	15	7 5.2 5.1 0.5 0.4
46	9.43 412	45	9.45 078	48	10.54 922	9.98 334	3	14	8 6.0 5.9 0.5 0.4
47	9.43 457	45	9.45 126	48	10.54 874	9.98 331	4	13	9 6.8 6.6 0.6 0.4
48	9.43 502	44	9.45 174	48	10.54 826	9.98 327	3	12	
49	9.43 546	45	9.45 222	49	10.54 778	9.98 324	4	11	10 7.5 7.3 0.7 0.5
									20 15.0 14.7 1.3 1.0
50	9.43 591	44	9.45 271	48	10.54 729	9.98 320	3	10	30 22.5 22.0 2.0 1.5
51	9.43 635	45	9.45 319	48	10.54 681	9.98 317	4	9	40 30.0 29.3 2.7 2.0
52	9.43 680	44	9.45 367	48	10.54 633	9.98 313	4	8	50 37.5 36.7 3.3 2.5
53	9.43 724	45	9.45 415	48	10.54 585	9.98 309	3	7	
54	9.43 769	44	9.45 463	48	10.54 537	9.98 306	4	6	
55	9.43 813	44	9.45 511	48	10.54 489	9.98 302	3	5	
56	9.43 857	44	9.45 559	47	10.54 441	9.98 299	4	4	
57	9.43 901	45	9.45 606	48	10.54 394	9.98 295	4	3	
58	9.43 946	44	9.45 654	48	10.54 346	9.98 291	3	2	
59	9.43 990	44	9.45 702	48	10.54 298	9.98 288	4	1	
60	9.44 034		9.45 750		10.54 250	9.98 284		0	
′	L Cos	d	L Ctn	c d	L Tan	L Sin	d	′	Proportional parts

′	L Sin	d	L Tan	c d	L Ctn	L Cos	d	′	Proportional parts		
0	9.44 034	44	9.45 750	47	10.54 250	9.98 284	3	60			
1	9.44 078	44	9.45 797	48	10.54 203	9.98 281	4	59			
2	9.44 122	44	9.45 845	47	10.54 155	9.98 277	4	58			
3	9.44 166	44	9.45 892	48	10.54 108	9.98 273	3	57			
4	9.44 210	43	9.45 940	47	10.54 060	9.98 270	4	56			
5	9.44 253	44	9.45 987	48	10.54 013	9.98 266	4	55			
6	9.44 297	44	9.46 035	47	10.53 965	9.98 262	3	54			
7	9.44 341	44	9.46 082	48	10.53 918	9.98 259	4	53	′′	48 47 46	
8	9.44 385	43	9.46 130	47	10.53 870	9.98 255	4	52	1	0.8 0.8 0.8	
9	9.44 428	44	9.46 177	47	10.53 823	9.98 251	3	51	2	1.6 1.6 1.5	
10	9.44 472	44	9.46 224	47	10.53 776	9.98 248	4	50	3	2.4 2.4 2.3	
11	9.44 516	43	9.46 271	48	10.53 729	9.98 244	4	49	4	3.2 3.1 3.1	
12	9.44 559	43	9.46 319	47	10.53 681	9.98 240	3	48			
13	9.44 602	44	9.46 366	47	10.53 634	9.98 237	4	47	5	4.0 3.9 3.8	
14	9.44 646	43	9.46 413	47	10.53 587	9.98 233	4	46	6	4.8 4.7 4.6	
15	9.44 689	44	9.46 460	47	10.53 540	9.98 229	3	45	7	5.6 5.5 5.4	
16	9.44 733	43	9.46 507	47	10.53 493	9.98 226	4	44	8	6.4 6.3 6.1	
17	9.44 776	43	9.46 554	47	10.53 446	9.98 222	4	43	9	7.2 7.0 6.9	
18	9.44 819	43	9.46 601	47	10.53 399	9.98 218	3	42			
19	9.44 862	43	9.46 648	46	10.53 352	9.98 215	4	41	10	8.0 7.8 7.7	
20	9.44 905	43	9.46 694	47	10.53 306	9.98 211	4	40	20	16.0 15.7 15.3	
21	9.44 948	44	9.46 741	47	10.53 259	9.98 207	3	39	30	24.0 23.5 23.0	
22	9.44 992	43	9.46 788	47	10.53 212	9.98 204	4	38	40	32.0 31.3 30.7	
23	9.45 035	42	9.46 835	46	10.53 165	9.98 200	4	37	50	40.0 39.2 38.3	
24	9.45 077	43	9.46 881	47	10.53 119	9.98 196	4	36			
25	9.45 120	43	9.46 928	47	10.53 072	9.98 192	3	35	′′	45 44 43	
26	9.45 163	43	9.46 975	46	10.53 025	9.98 189	4	34	1	0.8 0.7 0.7	
27	9.45 206	43	9.47 021	47	10.52 979	9.98 185	4	33	2	1.5 1.5 1.4	
28	9.45 249	43	9.47 068	46	10.52 932	9.98 181	4	32	3	2.2 2.2 2.2	
29	9.45 292	42	9.47 114	46	10.52 886	9.98 177	3	31	4	3.0 2.9 2.9	
30	9.45 334	43	9.47 160	47	10.52 840	9.98 174	4	30	5	3.8 3.7 3.6	
31	9.45 377	42	9.47 207	46	10.52 793	9.98 170	4	29	6	4.5 4.4 4.3	
32	9.45 419	43	9.47 253	46	10.52 747	9.98 166	4	28	7	5.2 5.1 5.0	
33	9.45 462	42	9.47 299	47	10.52 701	9.98 162	3	27	8	6.0 5.9 5.7	
34	9.45 504	43	9.47 346	46	10.52 654	9.98 159	4	26	9	6.8 6.6 6.4	
35	9.45 547	42	9.47 392	46	10.52 608	9.98 155	4	25	10	7.5 7.3 7.2	
36	9.45 589	43	9.47 438	46	10.52 562	9.98 151	4	24	20	15.0 14.7 14.3	
37	9.45 632	42	9.47 484	46	10.52 516	9.98 147	3	23	30	22.5 22.0 21.5	
38	9.45 674	42	9.47 530	46	10.52 470	9.98 144	4	22	40	30.0 29.3 28.7	
39	9.45 716	42	9.47 576	46	10.52 424	9.98 140	4	21	50	37.5 36.7 35.8	
40	9.45 758	43	9.47 622	46	10.52 378	9.98 136	4	20			
41	9.45 801	42	9.47 668	46	10.52 332	9.98 132	3	19	′′	42 41 4 3	
42	9.45 843	42	9.47 714	46	10.52 286	9.98 129	4	18	1	0.7 0.7 0.1 0.0	
43	9.45 885	42	9.47 760	46	10.52 240	9.98 125	4	17	2	1.4 1.4 0.1 0.1	
44	9.45 927	42	9.47 806	46	10.52 194	9.98 121	4	16	3	2.1 2.0 0.2 0.2	
									4	2.8 2.7 0.3 0.2	
45	9.45 969	42	9.47 852	45	10.52 148	9.98 117	4	15	5	3.5 3.4 0.3 0.2	
46	9.46 011	42	9.47 897	46	10.52 103	9.98 113	3	14	6	4.2 4.1 0.4 0.3	
47	9.46 053	42	9.47 943	46	10.52 057	9.98 110	4	13	7	4.9 4.8 0.5 0.4	
48	9.46 095	41	9.47 989	46	10.52 011	9.98 106	4	12	8	5.6 5.5 0.5 0.4	
49	9.46 136	42	9.48 035	45	10.51 965	9.98 102	4	11	9	6.3 6.2 0.6 0.4	
50	9.46 178	42	9.48 080	46	10.51 920	9.98 098	4	10	10	7.0 6.8 0.7 0.5	
51	9.46 220	42	9.48 126	45	10.51 874	9.98 094	4	9	20	14.0 13.7 1.3 1.0	
52	9.46 262	41	9.48 171	46	10.51 829	9.98 090	3	8	30	21.0 20.5 2.0 1.5	
53	9.46 303	42	9.48 217	45	10.51 783	9.98 087	4	7	40	28.0 27.3 2.7 2.0	
54	9.46 345	41	9.48 262	45	10.51 738	9.98 083	4	6	50	35.0 34.2 3.3 2.5	
55	9.46 386	42	9.48 307	46	10.51 693	9.98 079	4	5			
56	9.46 428	41	9.48 353	45	10.51 647	9.98 075	4	4			
57	9.46 469	42	9.48 398	45	10.51 602	9.98 071	4	3			
58	9.46 511	41	9.48 443	46	10.51 557	9.98 067	4	2			
59	9.46 552	42	9.48 489	45	10.51 511	9.98 063	3	1			
60	9 46 594		9.48 534		10.51 466	9.98 060		0			
′	L Cos	d	L Ctn	c d	L Tan	L Sin	d	′	Proportional parts		

′	L Sin	d	L Tan	c d	L Ctn	L Cos	d	′	Proportional parts		
0	9.46 594	41	9.48 534	45	10.51 466	9.98 060	4	60			
1	9.46 635	41	9.48 579	45	10.51 421	9.98 056	4	59			
2	9.46 676	41	9.48 624	45	10.51 376	9.98 052	4	58			
3	9.46 717	41	9.48 669	45	10.51 331	9.98 048	4	57			
4	9.46 758	42	9.48 714	45	10.51 286	9.98 044	4	56			
5	9.46 800	41	9.48 759	45	10.51 241	9.98 040	4	55			
6	9.46 841	41	9.48 804	45	10.51 196	9.98 036	4	54			
7	9.46 882	41	9.48 849	45	10.51 151	9.98 032	3	53	″	45	44	43
8	9.46 923	41	9.48 894	45	10.51 106	9.98 029	4	52	1	0.8	0.7	0.7
9	9.46 964	41	9.48 939	45	10.51 061	9.98 025	4	51	2	1.5	1.5	1.4
10	9.47 005	40	9.48 984	45	10.51 016	9.98 021	4	50	3	2.2	2.2	2.2
11	9.47 045	41	9.49 029	44	10.50 971	9.98 017	4	49	4	3.0	2.9	2.9
12	9.47 086	41	9.49 073	45	10.50 927	9.98 013	4	48				
13	9.47 127	41	9.49 118	45	10.50 882	9.98 009	4	47	5	3.8	3.7	3.6
14	9.47 168	41	9.49 163	44	10.50 837	9.98 005	4	46	6	4.5	4.4	4.3
15	9.47 209	40	9.49 207	45	10.50 793	9.98 001	4	45	7	5.2	5.1	5.0
16	9.47 249	41	9.49 252	44	10.50 748	9.97 997	4	44	8	6.0	5.9	5.7
17	9.47 290	40	9.49 296	45	10.50 704	9.97 993	4	43	9	6.8	6.6	6.4
18	9.47 330	41	9.49 341	44	10.50 659	9.97 989	3	42				
19	9.47 371	40	9.49 385	45	10.50 615	9.97 986	4	41	10	7.5	7.3	7.2
20	9.47 411	41	9.49 430	44	10.50 570	9.97 982	4	40	20	15.0	14.7	14.3
21	9.47 452	40	9.49 474	45	10.50 526	9.97 978	4	39	30	22.5	22.0	21.5
22	9.47 492	41	9.49 519	44	10.50 481	9.97 974	4	38	40	30.0	29.2	28.7
23	9.47 533	40	9.49 563	44	10.50 437	9.97 970	4	37	50	37.5	36.7	35.8
24	9.47 573	40	9.49 607	45	10.50 393	9.97 966	4	36				
25	9.47 613	41	9.49 652	44	10.50 348	9.97 962	4	35	″	42	41	40
26	9.47 654	40	9.49 696	44	10.50 304	9.97 958	4	34	1	0.7	0.7	0.7
27	9.47 694	40	9.49 740	44	10.50 260	9.97 954	4	33	2	1.4	1.4	1.3
28	9.47 734	40	9.49 784	44	10.50 216	9.97 950	4	32	3	2.1	2.0	2.0
29	9.47 774	40	9.49 828	44	10.50 172	9.97 946	4	31	4	2.8	2.7	2.7
30	9.47 814	40	9.49 872	44	10.50 128	9.97 942	4	30	5	3.5	3.4	3.3
31	9.47 854	40	9.49 916	44	10.50 084	9.97 938	4	29	6	4.2	4.1	4.0
32	9.47 894	40	9.49 960	44	10.50 040	9.97 934	4	28	7	4.9	4.8	4.7
33	9.47 934	40	9.50 004	44	10.49 996	9.97 930	4	27	8	5.6	5.5	5.3
34	9.47 974	40	9.50 048	44	10.49 952	9.97 926	4	26	9	6.3	6.2	6.0
35	9.48 014	40	9.50 092	44	10.49 908	9.97 922	4	25	10	7.0	6.8	6.7
36	9.48 054	40	9.50 136	44	10.49 864	9.97 918	4	24	20	14.0	13.7	13.3
37	9.48 094	39	9.50 180	43	10.49 820	9.97 914	4	23	30	21.0	20.5	20.0
38	9.48 133	40	9.50 223	44	10.49 777	9.97 910	4	22	40	28.0	27.3	26.7
39	9.48 173	40	9.50 267	44	10.49 733	9.97 906	4	21	50	35.0	34.2	33.3
40	9.48 213	39	9.50 311	44	10.49 689	9.97 902	4	20	″	39	5 4 3	
41	9.48 252	40	9.50 355	43	10.49 645	9.97 898	4	19	1	0.6	0.1 0.1 0.0	
42	9.48 292	40	9.50 398	44	10.49 602	9.97 894	4	18	2	1.3	0.2 0.1 0.1	
43	9.48 332	39	9.50 442	43	10.49 558	9.97 890	4	17	3	2.0	0.2 0.2 0.2	
44	9.48 371	40	9.50 485	44	10.49 515	9.97 886	4	16	4	2.6	0.3 0.3 0.2	
45	9.48 411	39	9.50 529	43	10.49 471	9.97 882	4	15	5	3.2	0.4 0.3 0.2	
46	9.48 450	40	9.50 572	44	10.49 428	9.97 878	4	14	6	3.9	0.5 0.4 0.3	
47	9.48 490	39	9.50 616	43	10.49 384	9.97 874	4	13	7	4.6	0.6 0.5 0.4	
48	9.48 529	39	9.50 659	44	10.49 341	9.97 870	4	12	8	5.2	0.7 0.5 0.4	
49	9.48 568	39	9.50 703	43	10.49 297	9.97 866	5	11	9	5.8	0.8 0.6 0.4	
50	9.48 607	40	9.50 746	43	10.49 254	9.97 861	4	10	10	6.5	0.8 0.7 0.5	
51	9.48 647	39	9.50 789	44	10.49 211	9.97 857	4	9	20	13.0	1.7 1.3 1.0	
52	9.48 686	39	9.50 833	43	10.49 167	9.97 853	4	8	30	19.5	2.5 2.0 1.5	
53	9.48 725	39	9.50 876	43	10.49 124	9.97 849	4	7	40	26.0	3.3 2.7 2.0	
54	9.48 764	39	9.50 919	43	10.49 081	9.97 845	4	6	20	32.5	4.2 3.3 2.5	
55	9.48 803	39	9.50 962	43	10.49 038	9.97 841	4	5				
56	9.48 842	39	9.51 005	43	10.48 995	9.97 837	4	4				
57	9.48 881	39	9.51 048	44	10.48 952	9.97 833	4	3				
58	9.48 920	39	9.51 092	43	10.48 908	9.97 829	4	2				
59	9.48 959	39	9.51 135	43	10.48 865	9.97 825	4	1				
60	9.48 998		9.51 178		10.48 822	9.97 821		0				
′	L Cos	d	L Ctn	c d	L Tan	L Sin	d	′	Proportional parts		

570 / COMMON LOGARITHMS OF TRIGONOMETRIC FUNCTIONS

'	L Sin	d	L Tan	c d	L Ctn	L Cos	d	'
0	9.48 998	39	9.51 178	43	10.48 822	9.97 821	4	60
1	9.49 037	39	9.51 221	43	10.48 779	9.97 817	5	59
2	9.49 076	39	9.51 264	42	10.48 736	9.97 812	4	58
3	9.49 115	38	9.51 306	43	10.48 694	9.97 808	4	57
4	9.49 153	39	9.51 349	43	10.48 651	9.97 804	4	56
5	9.49 192	39	9.51 392	43	10.48 608	9.97 800	4	55
6	9.49 231	38	9.51 435	43	10.48 565	9.97 796	4	54
7	9.49 269	39	9.51 478	42	10.48 522	9.97 792	4	53
8	9.49 308	39	9.51 520	43	10.48 480	9.97 788	4	52
9	9.49 347	38	9.51 563	43	10.48 437	9.97 784	5	51
10	9.49 385	39	9.51 606	42	10.48 394	9.97 779	4	50
11	9.49 424	38	9.51 648	43	10.48 352	9.97 775	4	49
12	9.49 462	38	9.51 691	43	10.48 309	9.97 771	4	48
13	9.49 500	39	9.51 734	42	10.48 266	9.97 767	4	47
14	9.49 539	38	9.51 776	43	10.48 224	9.97 763	4	46
15	9.49 577	38	9.51 819	42	10.48 181	9.97 759	5	45
16	9.49 615	39	9.51 861	42	10.48 139	9.97 754	4	44
17	9.49 654	38	9.51 903	43	10.48 097	9.97 750	4	43
18	9.49 692	38	9.51 946	42	10.48 054	9.97 746	4	42
19	9.49 730	38	9.51 988	43	10.48 012	9.97 742	4	41
20	9.49 768	38	9.52 031	42	10.47 969	9.97 738	4	40
21	9.49 806	38	9.52 073	42	10.47 927	9.97 734	5	39
22	9.49 844	38	9.52 115	42	10.47 885	9.97 729	4	38
23	9.49 882	38	9.52 157	43	10.47 843	9.97 725	4	37
24	9.49 920	38	9.52 200	42	10.47 800	9.97 721	4	36
25	9.49 958	38	9.52 242	42	10.47 758	9.97 717	4	35
26	9.49 996	38	9.52 284	42	10.47 716	9.97 713	5	34
27	9.50 034	38	9.52 326	42	10.47 674	9.97 708	4	33
28	9.50 072	38	9.52 368	42	10.47 632	9.97 704	4	32
29	9.50 110	38	9.52 410	42	10.47 590	9.97 700	4	31
30	9.50 148	37	9.52 452	42	10.47 548	9.97 696	5	30
31	9.50 185	38	9.52 494	42	10.47 506	9.97 691	4	29
32	9.50 223	38	9.52 536	42	10.47 464	9.97 687	4	28
33	9.50 261	37	9.52 578	42	10.47 422	9.97 683	4	27
34	9.50 298	38	9.52 620	41	10.47 380	9.97 679	5	26
35	9.50 336	38	9.52 661	42	10.47 339	9.97 674	4	25
36	9.50 374	37	9.52 703	42	10.47 297	9.97 670	4	24
37	9.50 411	38	9.52 745	42	10.47 255	9.97 666	4	23
38	9.50 449	37	9.52 787	42	10.47 213	9.97 662	5	22
39	9.50 486	37	9.52 829	41	10.47 171	9.97 657	4	21
40	9.50 523	38	9.52 870	42	10.47 130	9.97 653	4	20
41	9.50 561	37	9.52 912	41	10.47 088	9.97 649	4	19
42	9.50 598	37	9.52 953	42	10.47 047	9.97 645	5	18
43	9.50 635	38	9.52 995	42	10.47 005	9.97 640	4	17
44	9.50 673	37	9.53 037	41	10.46 963	9.97 636	4	16
45	9.50 710	37	9.53 078	42	10.46 922	9.97 632	4	15
46	9.50 747	37	9.53 120	41	10.46 880	9.97 628	5	14
47	9.50 784	37	9.53 161	41	10.46 839	9.97 623	4	13
48	9.50 821	37	9.53 202	41	10.46 798	9.97 619	4	12
49	9.50 858	38	9.53 244	41	10.46 756	9.97 615	5	11
50	9.50 896	37	9.53 285	42	10.46 715	9.97 610	4	10
51	9.50 933	37	9.53 327	41	10.46 673	9.97 606	4	9
52	9.50 970	37	9.53 368	41	10.46 632	9.97 602	5	8
53	9.51 007	36	9.53 409	41	10.46 591	9.97 597	4	7
54	9.51 043	37	9.53 450	41	10.46 550	9.97 593	4	6
55	9.51 080	37	9.53 492	41	10.46 508	9.97 589	5	5
56	9.51 117	37	9.53 533	41	10.46 467	9.97 584	4	4
57	9.51 154	37	9.53 574	41	10.46 426	9.97 580	4	3
58	9.51 191	36	9.53 615	41	10.46 385	9.97 576	5	2
59	9.51 227	37	9.53 656	41	10.46 344	9.97 571	4	1
60	9.51 264		9.53 697		10.46 303	9.97 567		0
'	L Cos	d	L Ctn	c d	L Tan	L Sin	d	'

Proportional parts

''	43	42	41
1	0.7	0.7	0.7
2	1.4	1.4	1.4
3	2.2	2.1	2.0
4	2.9	2.8	2.7
5	3.6	3.5	3.4
6	4.3	4.2	4.1
7	5.0	4.9	4.8
8	5.7	5.6	5.5
9	6.4	6.3	6.2
10	7.2	7.0	6.8
20	14.3	14.0	13.7
30	21.5	21.0	20.5
40	28.7	28.0	27.3
50	35.8	35.0	34.2

''	39	38	37
1	0.6	0.6	0.6
2	1.3	1.3	1.2
3	2.0	1.9	1.8
4	2.6	2.5	2.5
5	3.2	3.2	3.1
6	3.9	3.8	3.7
7	4.6	4.4	4.3
8	5.2	5.1	4.9
9	5.8	5.7	5.6
10	6.5	6.3	6.2
20	13.0	12.7	12.3
30	19.5	19.0	18.5
40	26.0	25.3	24.7
50	32.5	31.7	30.8

''	36	5	4
1	0.6	0.1	0.1
2	1.2	0.2	0.1
3	1.8	0.2	0.2
4	2.4	0.3	0.3
5	3.0	0.4	0.3
6	3.6	0.5	0.4
7	4.2	0.6	0.5
8	4.8	0.7	0.5
9	5.4	0.8	0.6
10	6.0	0.8	0.7
20	12.0	1.7	1.3
30	18.0	2.5	2.0
40	24.0	3.3	2.7
50	30.0	4.2	3.3

Proportional parts

′	L Sin	d	L Tan	c d	L Ctn	L Cos	d	′	Proportional parts		
0	9.51 264	37	9.53 697	41	10.46 303	9.97 567	4	60			
1	9.51 301	37	9.53 738	41	10.46 262	9.97 563	5	59			
2	9.51 338	36	9.53 779	41	10.46 221	9.97 558	4	58			
3	9.51 374	37	9.53 820	41	10.46 180	9.97 554	4	57			
4	9.51 411	36	9.53 861	41	10.46 139	9.97 550	5	56			
5	9.51 447	37	9.53 902	41	10.46 098	9.97 545	4	55	′′	41	40	39
6	9.51 484	36	9.53 943	41	10.46 057	9.97 541	5	54	1	0.7	0.7	0.6
7	9.51 520	37	9.53 984	41	10.46 016	9.97 536	4	53	2	1.4	1.3	1.3
8	9.51 557	36	9.54 025	40	10.45 975	9.97 532	4	52	3	2.0	2.0	2.0
9	9.51 593	36	9.54 065	41	10.45 935	9.97 528	5	51	4	2.7	2.7	2.6
10	9.51 629	37	9.54 106	41	10.45 894	9.97 523	4	50	5	3.4	3.3	3.2
11	9.51 666	36	9.54 147	40	10.45 853	9.97 519	4	49	6	4.1	4.0	3.9
12	9.51 702	36	9.54 187	41	10.45 813	9.97 515	5	48	7	4.8	4.7	4.6
13	9.51 738	36	9.54 228	41	10.45 772	9.97 510	4	47	8	5.5	5.3	5.2
14	9.51 774	37	9.54 269	40	10.45 731	9.97 506	5	46	9	6.2	6.0	5.8
15	9.51 811	36	9.54 309	41	10.45 691	9.97 501	4	45				
16	9.51 847	36	9.54 350	40	10.45 650	9.97 497	5	44	10	6.8	6.7	6.5
17	9.51 883	36	9.54 390	41	10.45 610	9.97 492	4	43	20	13.7	13.3	13.0
18	9.51 919	36	9.54 431	40	10.45 569	9.97 488	4	42	30	20.5	20.0	19.5
19	9.51 955	36	9.54 471	41	10.45 529	9.97 484	5	41	40	27.3	26.7	26.0
20	9.51 991	36	9.54 512	40	10.45 488	9.97 479	4	40	50	34.2	33.3	32.5
21	9.52 027	36	9.54 552	40	10.45 448	9.97 475	5	39				
22	9.52 063	36	9.54 593	40	10.45 407	9.97 470	4	38				
23	9.52 099	36	9.54 633	40	10.45 367	9.97 466	5	37	′′	37	36	35
24	9.52 135	36	9.54 673	41	10.45 327	9.97 461	4	36	1	0.6	0.6	0.6
25	9.52 171	36	9.54 714	40	10.45 286	9.97 457	4	35	2	1.2	1.2	1.2
26	9.52 207	35	9.54 754	40	10.45 246	9.97 453	5	34	3	1.8	1.8	1.8
27	9.52 242	36	9.54 794	41	10.45 206	9.97 448	4	• 33	4	2.5	2.4	2.3
28	9.52 278	36	9.54 835	40	10.45 165	9.97 444	5	32				
29	9.52 314	36	9.54 875	40	10.45 125	9.97 439	4	31	5	3.1	3.0	2.9
									6	3.7	3.6	3.5
30	9.52 350	35	9.54 915	40	10.45 085	9.97 435	5	30	7	4.3	4.2	4.1
31	9.52 385	36	9.54 955	40	10.45 045	9.97 430	4	29	8	4.9	4.8	4.7
32	9.52 421	35	9.54 995	40	10.45 005	9.97 426	5	28	9	5.6	5.4	5.2
33	9.52 456	36	9.55 035	40	10.44 965	9.97 421	4	27				
34	9.52 492	35	9.55 075	40	10.44 925	9.97 417	5	26	10	6.2	6.0	5.8
35	9.52 527	36	9.55 115	40	10.44 885	9.97 412	4	25	20	12.3	12.0	11.7
36	9.52 563	35	9.55 155	40	10.44 845	9.97 408	5	24	30	18.5	18.0	17.5
37	9.52 598	36	9.55 195	40	10.44 805	9.97 403	4	23	40	24.7	24.0	23.3
38	9.52 634	35	9.55 235	40	10.44 765	9.97 399	5	22	50	30.8	30.0	29.2
39	9.52 669	36	9.55 275	40	10.44 725	9.97 394	4	21				
40	9.52 705	35	9.55 315	40	10.44 685	9.97 390	5	20	′′	34	5	4
41	9.52 740	35	9.55 355	40	10.44 645	9.97 385	4	19	1	0.6	0.1	0.1
42	9.52 775	36	9.55 395	39	10.44 605	9.97 381	5	18	2	1.1	0.2	0.1
43	9.52 811	35	9.55 434	40	10.44 566	9.97 376	4	17	3	1.7	0.2	0.2
44	9.52 846	35	9.55 474	40	10.44 526	9.97 372	5	16	4	2.3	0.3	0.3
45	9.52 881	35	9.55 514	40	10.44 486	9.97 367	4	15	5	2.8	0.4	0.3
46	9.52 916	35	9.55 554	39	10.44 446	9.97 363	5	14	6	3.4	0.5	0.4
47	9.52 951	35	9.55 593	40	10.44 407	9.97 358	5	13	7	4.0	0.6	0.5
48	9.52 986	35	9.55 633	40	10.44 367	9.97 353	4	12	8	4.5	0.7	0.5
49	9.53 021	35	9.55 673	39	10.44 327	9.97 349	5	11	9	5.1	0.8	0.6
50	9.53 056	36	9.55 712	40	10.44 288	9.97 344	4	10	10	5.7	0.8	0.7
51	9.53 092	34	9.55 752	39	10.44 248	9.97 340	5	9	20	11.3	1.7	1.3
52	9.53 126	35	9.55 791	40	10.44 209	9.97 335	4	8	30	17.0	2.5	2.0
53	9.53 161	35	9.55 831	39	10.44 169	9.97 331	5	7	40	22.7	3.3	2.7
54	9.53 196	35	9.55 870	40	10.44 130	9.97 326	4	6	50	28.3	4.2	3.3
55	9.53 231	35	9.55 910	39	10.44 090	9.97 322	5	5				
56	9.53 266	35	9.55 949	40	10.44 051	9.97 317	5	4				
57	9.53 301	35	9.55 989	39	10.44 011	9.97 312	4	3				
58	9.53 336	34	9.56 028	39	10.43 972	9.97 308	5	2				
59	9.53 370	35	9.56 067	40	10.43 933	9.97 303	4	1				
60	9.53 405		9.56 107		10.43 893	9.97 299		0				
′	L Cos	d	L Ctn	c d	L Tan	L Sin	d	′	Proportional parts		

′	L Sin	d	L Tan	c d	L Ctn	L Cos	d	′	Proportional parts			
0	9.53 405	35	9.56 107	39	10.43 893	9.97 299	5	60				
1	9.53 440	35	9.56 146	39	10.43 854	9.97 294	5	59				
2	9.53 475	34	9.56 185	39	10.43 815	9.97 289	4	58				
3	9.53 509	35	9.56 224	40	10.43 776	9.97 285	5	57				
4	9.53 544	34	9.56 264	39	10.43 736	9.97 280	4	56				
5	9.53 578	35	9.56 303	39	10.43 697	9.97 276	5	55				
6	9.53 613	34	9.56 342	39	10.43 658	9.97 271	5	54				
7	9.53 647	35	9.56 381	39	10.43 619	9.97 266	4	53	′′	40	39	38
8	9.53 682	34	9.56 420	39	10.43 580	9.97 262	5	52	1	0.7	0.6	0.6
9	9.53 716	35	9.56 459	39	10.43 541	9.97 257	5	51	2	1.3	1.3	1.3
10	9.53 751	34	9.56 498	39	10.43 502	9.97 252	4	50	3	2.0	2.0	1.9
11	9.53 785	34	9.56 537	39	10.43 463	9.97 248	5	49	4	2.7	2.6	2.5
12	9.53 819	35	9.56 576	39	10.43 424	9.97 243	5	48				
13	9.53 854	34	9.56 615	39	10.43 385	9.97 238	4	47	5	3.3	3.2	3.2
14	9.53 888	34	9.56 654	39	10.43 346	9.97 234	5	46	6	4.0	3.9	3.8
15	9.53 922	35	9.56 693	39	10.43 307	9.97 229	5	45	7	4.7	4.6	4.4
16	9.53 957	34	9.56 732	39	10.43 268	9.97 224	4	44	8	5.3	5.2	5.1
17	9.53 991	34	9.56 771	39	10.43 229	9.97 220	5	43	9	6.0	5.8	5.7
18	9.54 025	34	9.56 810	39	10.43 190	9.97 215	5	42				
19	9.54 059	34	9.56 849	38	10.43 151	9.97 210	4	41	10	6.7	6.5	6.3
20	9.54 093	34	9.56 887	39	10.43 113	9.97 206	5	40	20	13.3	13.0	12.7
21	9.54 127	34	9.56 926	39	10.43 074	9.97 201	5	39	30	20.0	19.5	19.0
22	9.54 161	34	9.56 965	39	10.43 035	9.97 196	4	38	40	26.7	26.0	25.3
23	9.54 195	34	9.57 004	38	10.42 996	9.97 192	5	37	50	33.3	32.5	31.7
24	9.54 229	34	9.57 042	39	10.42 958	9.97 187	5	36				
25	9.54 263	34	9.57 081	39	10.42 919	9.97 182	4	35	′′	37	35	34
26	9.54 297	34	9.57 120	38	10.42 880	9.97 178	5	34	1	0.6	0.6	0.6
27	9.54 331	34	9.57 158	39	10.42 842	9.97 173	5	33	2	1.2	1.2	1.1
28	9.54 365	34	9.57 197	38	10.42 803	9.97 168	5	32	3	1.8	1.8	1.7
29	9.54 399	34	9.57 235	39	10.42 765	9.97 163	4	31	4	2.5	2.3	2.3
30	9.54 433	33	9.57 274	38	10.42 726	9.97 159	5	30	5	3.1	2.9	2.8
31	9.54 466	34	9.57 312	39	10.42 688	9.97 154	5	29	6	3.7	3.5	3.4
32	9.54 500	34	9.57 351	38	10.42 649	9.97 149	4	28	7	4.3	4.1	4.0
33	9.54 534	33	9.57 389	39	10.42 611	9.97 145	5	27	8	4.9	4.7	4.5
34	9.54 567	34	9.57 428	38	10.42 572	9.97 140	5	26	9	5.6	5.2	5.1
35	9.54 601	34	9.57 466	38	10.42 534	9.97 135	5	25	10	6.2	5.8	5.7
36	9.54 635	33	9.57 504	39	10.42 496	9.97 130	4	24	20	12.3	11.7	11.3
37	9.54 668	34	9.57 543	38	10.42 457	9.97 126	5	23	30	18.5	17.5	17.0
38	9.54 702	33	9.57 581	38	10.42 419	9.97 121	5	22	40	24.7	23.3	22.7
39	9.54 735	34	9.57 619	39	10.42 381	9.97 116	5	21	50	30.8	29.2	28.3
40	9.54 769	33	9.57 658	38	10.42 342	9.97 111	4	20				
41	9.54 802	34	9.57 696	38	10.42 304	9.97 107	5	19	′′	33	5	4
42	9.54 836	33	9.57 734	38	10.42 266	9.97 102	5	18	1	0.6	0.1	0.1
43	9.54 869	34	9.57 772	38	10.42 228	9.97 097	5	17	2	1.1	0.2	0.1
44	9.54 903	33	9.57 810	39	10.42 190	9.97 092	5	16	3	1.6	0.2	0.2
45	9.54 936	33	9.57 849	38	10.42 151	9.97 087	4	15	4	2.2	0.3	0.3
46	9.54 969	34	9.57 887	38	10.42 113	9.97 083	5	14	5	2.8	0.4	0.3
47	9.55 003	33	9.57 925	38	10.42 075	9.97 078	5	13	6	3.3	0.5	0.4
48	9.55 036	33	9.57 963	38	10.42 037	9.97 073	5	12	7	3.8	0.6	0.5
49	9.55 069	33	9.58 001	38	10.41 999	9.97 068	5	11	8	4.4	0.7	0.5
50	9.55 102	34	9.58 039	38	10.41 961	9.97 063	4	10	9	5.0	0.8	0.6
51	9.55 136	33	9.58 077	38	10.41 923	9.97 059	5	9	10	5.5	0.8	0.7
52	9.55 169	33	9.58 115	38	10.41 885	9.97 054	5	8	20	11.0	1.7	1.3
53	9.55 202	33	9.58 153	38	10.41 847	9.97 049	5	7	30	16.5	2.5	2.0
54	9.55 235	33	9.58 191	38	10.41 809	9.97 044	5	6	40	22.0	3.3	2.7
55	9.55 268	33	9.58 229	38	10.41 771	9.97 039	4	5	50	27.5	4.2	3.3
56	9.55 301	33	9.58 267	37	10.41 733	9.97 035	5	4				
57	9.55 334	33	9.58 304	38	10.41 696	9.97 030	5	3				
58	9.55 367	33	9.58 342	38	10.41 658	9.97 025	5	2				
59	9.55 400	33	9.58 380	38	10.41 620	9.97 020	5	1				
60	9.55 433		9.58 418		10.41 582	9.97 015		0				
′	L Cos	d	L Ctn	c d	L Tan	L Sin	d	′	Proportional parts			

′	L Sin	d	L Tan	c d	L Ctn	L Cos	d	′	Proportional parts		
0	9.55 433	33	9.58 418	37	10.41 582	9.97 015	5	60			
1	9.55 466	33	9.58 455	38	10.41 545	9.97 010	5	59			
2	9.55 499	33	9.58 493	38	10.41 507	9.97 005	4	58			
3	9.55 532	32	9.58 531	38	10.41 469	9.97 001	5	57			
4	9.55 564	33	9.58 569	37	10.41 431	9.96 996	5	56			
5	9.55 597	33	9.58 606	38	10.41 394	9.96 991	5	55			
6	9.55 630	33	9.58 644	37	10.41 356	9.96 986	5	54			
7	9.55 663	32	9.58 681	38	10.41 319	9.96 981	5	53	′′	38	37	36
8	9.55 695	33	9.58 719	38	10.41 281	9.96 976	5	52	1	0.6	0.6	0.6
9	9.55 728	33	9.58 757	37	10.41 243	9.96 971	5	51	2	1.3	1.2	1.2
									3	1.9	1.8	1.8
10	9.55 761	32	9.58 794	38	10.41 206	9.96 966	4	50	4	2.5	2.5	2.4
11	9.55 793	33	9.58 832	37	10.41 168	9.96 962	5	49				
12	9.55 826	32	9.58 869	38	10.41 131	9.96 957	5	48	5	3.2	3.1	3.0
13	9.55 858	33	9.58 907	37	10.41 093	9.96 952	5	47	6	3.8	3.7	3.6
14	9.55 891	32	9.58 944	37	10.41 056	9.96 947	5	46	7	4.4	4.3	4.2
									8	5.1	4.9	4.8
15	9.55 923	33	9.58 981	38	10.41 019	9.96 942	5	45	9	5.7	5.6	5.4
16	9.55 956	32	9.59 019	37	10.40 981	9.96 937	5	44				
17	9.55 988	33	9.59 056	38	10.40 944	9.96 932	5	43	10	6.3	6.2	6.0
18	9.56 021	32	9.59 094	37	10.40 906	9.96 927	5	42	20	12.7	12.3	12.0
19	9.56 053	32	9.59 131	37	10.40 869	9.96 922	5	41	30	19.0	18.5	18.0
									40	25.3	24.7	24.0
20	9.56 085	33	9.59 168	37	10.40 832	9.96 917	5	40	50	31.7	30.8	30.0
21	9.56 118	32	9.59 205	38	10.40 795	9.96 912	5	39				
22	9.56 150	32	9.59 243	37	10.40 757	9.96 907	4	38				
23	9.56 182	33	9.59 280	37	10.40 720	9.96 903	5	37	′′	33	32	31
24	9.56 215	32	9.59 317	37	10.40 683	9.96 898	5	36	1	0.6	0.5	0.5
									2	1.1	1.1	1.0
25	9.56 247	32	9.59 354	37	10.40 646	9.96 893	5	35	3	1.6	1.6	1.6
26	9.56 279	32	9.59 391	38	10.40 609	9.96 888	5	34	4	2.2	2.1	2.1
27	9.56 311	32	9.59 429	37	10.40 571	9.96 883	5	33				
28	9.56 343	32	9.59 466	37	10.40 534	9.96 878	5	32	5	2.8	2.7	2.6
29	9.56 375	33	9.59 503	37	10.40 497	9.96 873	5	31	6	3.3	3.2	3.1
									7	3.8	3.7	3.6
30	9.56 408	32	9.59 540	37	10.40 460	9.96 868	5	30	8	4.4	4.3	4.1
31	9.56 440	32	9.59 577	37	10.40 423	9.96 863	5	29	9	5.0	4.8	4.6
32	9.56 472	32	9.59 614	37	10.40 386	9.96 858	5	28				
33	9.56 504	32	9.59 651	37	10.40 349	9.96 853	5	27	10	5.5	5.3	5.2
34	9.56 536	32	9.59 688	37	10.40 312	9.96 848	5	26	20	11.0	10.7	10.3
									30	16.5	16.0	15.5
35	9.56 568	31	9.59 725	37	10.40 275	9.96 843	5	25	40	22.0	21.3	20.7
36	9.56 599	32	9.59 762	37	10.40 238	9.96 838	5	24	50	27.5	26.7	25.8
37	9.56 631	32	9.59 799	36	10.40 201	9.96 833	5	23				
38	9.56 663	32	9.59 835	37	10.40 165	9.96 828	5	22				
39	9.56 695	32	9.59 872	37	10.40 128	9.96 823	5	21	′′	6	5	4
									1	0.1	0.1	0.1
40	9.56 727	32	9.59 909	37	10.40 091	9.96 818	5	20	2	0.2	0.2	0.1
41	9.56 759	31	9.59 946	37	10.40 054	9.96 813	5	19	3	0.3	0.2	0.2
42	9.56 790	32	9.59 983	36	10.40 017	9.96 808	5	18	4	0.4	0.3	0.3
43	9.56 822	32	9.60 019	37	10.39 981	9.96 803	5	17				
44	9.56 854	32	9.60 056	37	10.39 944	9.96 798	5	16	5	0.5	0.4	0.3
									6	0.6	0.5	0.4
45	9.56 886	31	9.60 093	37	10.39 907	9.96 793	5	15	7	0.7	0.6	0.5
46	9.56 917	32	9.60 130	36	10.39 870	9.96 788	5	14	8	0.8	0.7	0.5
47	9.56 949	31	9.60 166	37	10.39 834	9.96 783	5	13	9	0.9	0.8	0.6
48	9.56 980	32	9.60 203	37	10.39 797	9.96 778	6	12				
49	9.57 012	32	9.60 240	36	10.39 760	9.96 772	5	11	10	1.0	0.8	0.7
									20	2.0	1.7	1.3
50	9.57 044	31	9.60 276	37	10.39 724	9.96 767	5	10	30	3.0	2.5	2.0
51	9.57 075	32	9.60 313	36	10.39 687	9.96 762	5	9	40	4.0	3.3	2.7
52	9.57 107	31	9.60 349	37	10.39 651	9.96 757	5	8	50	5.0	4.2	3.3
53	9.57 138	31	9.60 386	36	10.39 614	9.96 752	5	7				
54	9.57 169	32	9.60 422	37	10.39 578	9.96 747	5	6				
55	9.57 201	31	9.60 459	36	10.39 541	9.96 742	5	5				
56	9.57 232	32	9.60 495	37	10.39 505	9.96 737	5	4				
57	9.57 264	31	9.60 532	36	10.39 468	9.96 732	5	3				
58	9.57 295	31	9.60 568	37	10.39 432	9.96 727	5	2				
59	9.57 326	32	9.60 605	36	10.39 395	9.96 722	5	1				
60	9.57 358		9.60 641		10.39 359	9.96 717		0				
′	L Cos	d	L Ctn	c d	L Tan	L Sin	d	′	Proportional parts		

′	L Sin	d	L Tan	c d	L Ctn	L Cos	d	′	Proportional parts		
0	9.57 358	31	9.60 641	36	10.39 359	9.96 717	6	60			
1	9.57 389	31	9.60 677	37	10.39 323	9.96 711	5	59			
2	9.57 420	31	9.60 714	36	10.39 286	9.96 706	5	58			
3	9.57 451	31	9.60 750	36	10.39 250	9.96 701	5	57			
4	9.57 482	32	9.60 786	37	10.39 214	9.96 696	5	56			
5	9.57 514	31	9.60 823	36	10.39 177	9.96 691	5	55			
6	9.57 545	31	9.60 859	36	10.39 141	9.96 686	5	54			
7	9.57 576	31	9.60 895	36	10.39 105	9.96 681	5	53	′′	37	36	35
8	9.57 607	31	9.60 931	36	10.39 069	9.96 676	6	52	1	0.6	0.6	0.6
9	9.57 638	31	9.60 967	37	10.39 033	9.96 670	5	51	2	1.2	1.2	1.2
10	9.57 669	31	9.61 004	36	10.38 996	9.96 665	5	50	3	1.8	1.8	1.8
11	9.57 700	31	9.61 040	36	10.38 960	9.96 660	5	49	4	2.5	2.4	2.3
12	9.57 731	31	9.61 076	36	10.38 924	9.96 655	5	48			
13	9.57 762	31	9.61 112	36	10.38 888	9.96 650	5	47	5	3.1	3.0	2.9
14	9.57 793	31	9.61 148	36	10.38 852	9.96 645	5	46	6	3.7	3.6	3.5
									7	4.3	4.2	4.1
15	9.57 824	31	9.61 184	36	10.38 816	9.96 640	6	45	8	4.9	4.8	4.7
16	9.57 855	30	9.61 220	36	10.38 780	9.96 634	5	44	9	5.6	5.4	5.2
17	9.57 885	31	9.61 256	36	10.38 744	9.96 629	5	43			
18	9.57 916	31	9.61 292	36	10.38 708	9.96 624	5	42	10	6.2	6.0	5.8
19	9.57 947	31	9.61 328	36	10.38 672	9.96 619	5	41	20	12.3	12.0	11.7
20	9.57 978	30	9.61 364	36	10.38 636	9.96 614	6	40	30	18.5	18.0	17.5
21	9.58 008	31	9.61 400	36	10.38 600	9.96 608	5	39	40	24.7	24.0	23.3
22	9.58 039	31	9.61 436	36	10.38 564	9.96 603	5	38	50	30.8	30.0	29.2
23	9.58 070	31	9.61 472	36	10.38 528	9.96 598	5	37			
24	9.58 101	30	9.61 508	36	10.38 492	9.96 593	5	36	′′	32	31	30
25	9.58 131	31	9.61 544	35	10.38 456	9.96 588	6	35	1	0.5	0.5	0.5
26	9.58 162	30	9.61 579	36	10.38 421	9.96 582	5	34	2	1.1	1.0	1.0
27	9.58 192	31	9.61 615	36	10.38 385	9.96 577	5	33	3	1.6	1.6	1.5
28	9.58 223	30	9.61 651	36	10.38 349	9.96 572	5	32	4	2.1	2.1	2.0
29	9.58 253	31	9.61 687	35	10.38 313	9.96 567	5	31			
									5	2.7	2.6	2.5
30	9.58 284	30	9.61 722	36	10.38 278	9.96 562	6	30	6	3.2	3.1	3.0
31	9.58 314	31	9.61 758	36	10.38 242	9.96 556	5	29	7	3.7	3.6	3.5
32	9.58 345	30	9.61 794	36	10.38 206	9.96 551	5	28	8	4.3	4.1	4.0
33	9.58 375	31	9.61 830	35	10.38 170	9.96 546	5	27	9	4.8	4.6	4.5
34	9.58 406	30	9.61 865	36	10.38 135	9.96 541	6	26			
35	9.58 436	31	9.61 901	35	10.38 099	9.96 535	5	25	10	5.3	5.2	5.0
36	9.58 467	30	9.61 936	36	10.38 064	9.96 530	5	24	20	10.7	10.3	10.0
37	9.58 497	30	9.61 972	36	10.38 028	9.96 525	5	23	30	16.0	15.5	15.0
38	9.58 527	30	9.62 008	36	10.37 992	9.96 520	6	22	40	21.3	20.7	20.0
39	9.58 557	31	9.62 043	36	10.37 957	9.96 514	5	21	50	26.7	25.8	25.0
40	9.58 588	30	9.62 079	35	10.37 921	9.96 509	5	20	′′	29	6	5
41	9.58 618	30	9.62 114	36	10.37 886	9.96 504	6	19	1	0.5	0.1	0.1
42	9.58 648	30	9.62 150	35	10.37 850	9.96 498	5	18	2	1.0	0.2	0.2
43	9.58 678	31	9.62 185	36	10.37 815	9.96 493	5	17	3	1.4	0.3	0.2
44	9.58 709	30	9.62 221	35	10.37 779	9.96 488	5	16	4	1.9	0.4	0.3
45	9.58 739	30	9.62 256	36	10.37 744	9.96 483	6	15	5	2.4	0.5	0.4
46	9.58 769	30	9.62 292	35	10.37 708	9.96 477	5	14	6	2.9	0.6	0.5
47	9.58 799	30	9.62 327	35	10.37 673	9.96 472	5	13	7	3.4	0.7	0.6
48	9.58 829	30	9.62 362	36	10.37 638	9.96 467	6	12	8	3.9	0.8	0.7
49	9.58 859	30	9.62 398	35	10.37 602	9.96 461	5	11	9	4.4	0.9	0.8
50	9.58 889	30	9.62 433	35	10.37 567	9.96 456	5	10	10	4.8	1.0	0.8
51	9.58 919	30	9.62 468	36	10.37 532	9.96 451	6	9	20	9.7	2.0	1.7
52	9.58 949	30	9.62 504	35	10.37 496	9.96 445	5	8	30	14.5	3.0	2.5
53	9.58 979	30	9.62 539	35	10.37 461	9.96 440	5	7	40	19.3	4.0	3.3
54	9.59 009	30	9.62 574	35	10.37 426	9.96 435	6	6	50	24.2	5.0	4.2
55	9.59 039	30	9.62 609	36	10.37 391	9.96 429	5	5			
56	9.59 069	29	9.62 645	35	10.37 355	9.96 424	5	4			
57	9.59 098	30	9.62 680	35	10.37 320	9.96 419	6	3			
58	9.59 128	30	9.62 715	35	10.37 285	9.96 413	5	2			
59	9.59 158	30	9.62 750	35	10.37 250	9.96 408	5	1			
60	9.59 188		9.62 785		10.37 215	9.96 403		0			
′	L Cos	d	L Ctn	c d	L Tan	L Sin	d	′	Proportional parts		

′	L Sin	d	L Tan	c d	L Ctn	L Cos	d	′	Proportional parts
0	9.59 188	30	9.62 785	35	10.37 215	9.96 403	6	60	
1	9.59 218	29	9.62 820	35	10.37 180	9.96 397	5	59	
2	9.59 247	30	9.62 855	35	10.37 145	9.96 392	5	58	
3	9.59 277	30	9.62 890	36	10.37 110	9.96 387	6	57	
4	9.59 307	29	9.62 926	35	10.37 074	9.96 381	5	56	

′	L Sin	d	L Tan	c d	L Ctn	L Cos	d	′
5	9.59 336	30	9.62 961	35	10.37 039	9.96 376	6	55
6	9.59 366	30	9.62 996	35	10.37 004	9.96 370	5	54
7	9.59 396	29	9.63 031	35	10.36 969	9.96 365	5	53
8	9.59 425	30	9.63 066	35	10.36 934	9.96 360	6	52
9	9.59 455	29	9.63 101	34	10.36 899	9.96 354	5	51
10	9.59 484	30	9.63 135	35	10.36 865	9.96 349	6	50
11	9.59 514	29	9.63 170	35	10.36 830	9.96 343	5	49
12	9.59 543	30	9.63 205	35	10.36 795	9.96 338	5	48
13	9.59 573	29	9.63 240	35	10.36 760	9.96 333	6	47
14	9.59 602	30	9.63 275	35	10.36 725	9.96 327	5	46
15	9.59 632	29	9.63 310	35	10.36 690	9.96 322	6	45
16	9.59 661	29	9.63 345	34	10.36 655	9.96 316	5	44
17	9.59 690	30	9.63 379	35	10.36 621	9.96 311	6	43
18	9.59 720	29	9.63 414	35	10.36 586	9.96 305	5	42
19	9.59 749	29	9.63 449	35	10.36 551	9.96 300	6	41
20	9.59 778	30	9.63 484	35	10.36 516	9.96 294	5	40
21	9.59 808	29	9.63 519	34	10.36 481	9.96 289	5	39
22	9.59 837	29	9.63 553	35	10.36 447	9.96 284	6	38
23	9.59 866	29	9.63 588	35	10.36 412	9.96 278	5	37
24	9.59 895	29	9.63 623	34	10.36 377	9.96 273	6	36
25	9.59 924	30	9.63 657	35	10.36 343	9.96 267	5	35
26	9.59 954	29	9.63 692	34	10.36 308	9.96 262	6	34
27	9.59 983	29	9.63 726	35	10.36 274	9.96 256	5	33
28	9.60 012	29	9.63 761	35	10.36 239	9.96 251	6	32
29	9.60 041	29	9.63 796	34	10.36 204	9.96 245	5	31
30	9.60 070	29	9.63 830	35	10.36 170	9.96 240	6	30
31	9.60 099	29	9.63 865	34	10.36 135	9.96 234	5	29
32	9.60 128	29	9.63 899	35	10.36 101	9.96 229	6	28
33	9.60 157	29	9.63 934	34	10.36 066	9.96 223	5	27
34	9.60 186	29	9.63 968	35	10.36 032	9.96 218	6	26
35	9.60 215	29	9.64 003	34	10.35 997	9.96 212	5	25
36	9.60 244	29	9.64 037	35	10.35 963	9.96 207	6	24
37	9.60 273	29	9.64 072	34	10.35 928	9.96 201	5	23
38	9.60 302	29	9.64 106	34	10.35 894	9.96 196	6	22
39	9.60 331	28	9.64 140	35	10.35 860	9.96 190	5	21
40	9.60 359	29	9.64 175	34	10.35 825	9.96 185	6	20
41	9.60 388	29	9.64 209	34	10.35 791	9.96 179	5	19
42	9.60 417	29	9.64 243	35	10.35 757	9.96 174	6	18
43	9.60 446	28	9.64 278	34	10.35 722	9.96 168	6	17
44	9.60 474	29	9.64 312	34	10.35 688	9.96 162	5	16
45	9.60 503	29	9.64 346	35	10.35 654	9.96 157	6	15
46	9.60 532	29	9.64 381	34	10.35 619	9.96 151	5	14
47	9.60 561	28	9.64 415	34	10.35 585	9.96 146	6	13
48	9.60 589	29	9.64 449	34	10.35 551	9.96 140	5	12
49	9.60 618	28	9.64 483	34	10.35 517	9.96 135	6	11
50	9.60 646	29	9.64 517	35	10.35 483	9.96 129	6	10
51	9.60 675	29	9.64 552	34	10.35 448	9.96 123	5	9
52	9.60 704	28	9.64 586	34	10.35 414	9.96 118	6	8
53	9.60 732	29	9.64 620	34	10.35 380	9.96 112	5	7
54	9.60 761	28	9.64 654	34	10.35 346	9.96 107	6	6
55	9.60 789	29	9.64 688	34	10.35 312	9.96 101	6	5
56	9.60 818	28	9.64 722	34	10.35 278	9.96 095	5	4
57	9.60 846	29	9.64 756	34	10.35 244	9.96 090	6	3
58	9.60 875	28	9.64 790	34	10.35 210	9.96 084	5	2
59	9.60 903	28	9.64 824	34	10.35 176	9.96 079	6	1
60	9.60 931		9.64 858		10.35 142	9.96 073		0

′	L Cos	d	L Ctn	c d	L Tan	L Sin	d	′	Proportional parts

Proportional parts

″	36	35	34
1	0.6	0.6	0.6
2	1.2	1.2	1.1
3	1.8	1.8	1.7
4	2.4	2.3	2.3
5	3.0	2.9	2.8
6	3.6	3.5	3.4
7	4.2	4.1	4.0
8	4.8	4.7	4.5
9	5.4	5.2	5.1
10	6.0	5.8	5.7
20	12.0	11.7	11.3
30	18.0	17.5	17.0
40	24.0	23.3	22.7
50	30.0	29.2	28.3

″	30	29	28
1	0.5	0.5	0.5
2	1.0	1.0	0.9
3	1.5	1.4	1.4
4	2.0	1.9	1.9
5	2.5	2.4	2.3
6	3.0	2.9	2.8
7	3.5	3.4	3.3
8	4.0	3.9	3.7
9	4.5	4.4	4.2
10	5.0	4.8	4.7
20	10.0	9.7	9.3
30	15.0	14.5	14.0
40	20.0	19.3	18.7
50	25.0	24.2	23.3

″	6	5
1	0.1	0.1
2	0.2	0.2
3	0.3	0.2
4	0.4	0.3
5	0.5	0.4
6	0.6	0.5
7	0.7	0.6
8	0.8	0.7
9	0.9	0.8
10	1.0	0.8
20	2.0	1.7
30	3.0	2.5
40	4.0	3.3
50	5.0	4.2

′	L Sin	d	L Tan	c d	L Ctn	L Cos	d	′	Proportional parts		
0	9.60 931	29	9.64 858	34	10.35 142	9.96 073	6	60			
1	9.60 960	28	9.64 892	34	10.35 108	9.96 067	5	59			
2	9.60 988	28	9.64 926	34	10.35 074	9.96 062	6	58			
3	9.61 016	29	9.64 960	34	10.35 040	9.96 056	6	57			
4	9.61 045	28	9.64 994	34	10.35 006	9.96 050	5	56			
5	9.61 073	28	9.65 028	34	10.34 972	9.96 045	6	55			
6	9.61 101	28	9.65 062	34	10.34 938	9.96 039	5	54			
7	9.61 129	29	9.65 096	34	10.34 904	9.96 034	6	53	′′	34	33
8	9.61 158	28	9.65 130	34	10.34 870	9.96 028	6	52	1	0.6	0.6
9	9.61 186	28	9.65 164	33	10.34 836	9.96 022	5	51	2	1.1	1.1
10	9.61 214	28	9.65 197	34	10.34 803	9.96 017	6	50	3	1.7	1.6
11	9.61 242	28	9.65 231	34	10.34 769	9.96 011	6	49	4	2.3	2.2
12	9.61 270	28	9.65 265	34	10.34 735	9.96 005	5	48			
13	9.61 298	28	9.65 299	34	10.34 701	9.96 000	6	47	5	2.8	2.8
14	9.61 326	28	9.65 333	33	10.34 667	9.95 994	6	46	6	3.4	3.3
15	9.61 354	28	9.65 366	34	10.34 634	9.95 988	6	45	7	4.0	3.8
16	9.61 382	29	9.65 400	34	10.34 600	9.95 982	5	44	8	4.5	4.4
17	9.61 411	27	9.65 434	33	10.34 566	9.95 977	6	43	9	5.1	5.0
18	9.61 438	28	9.65 467	34	10.34 533	9.95 971	6	42			
19	9.61 466	28	9.65 501	34	10.34 499	9.95 965	5	41	10	5.7	5.5
20	9.61 494	28	9.65 535	33	10.34 465	9.95 960	6	40	20	11.3	11.0
21	9.61 522	28	9.65 568	34	10.34 432	9 95 954	6	39	30	17.0	16.5
22	9.61 550	28	9.65 602	34	10.34 398	9.95 948	6	38	40	22.7	22.0
23	9.61 578	28	9.65 636	33	10.34 364	9.95 942	5	37	50	28.3	27.5
24	9.61 606	28	9.65 669	34	10.34 331	9.95 937	6	36			
25	9.61 634	28	9.65 703	33	10.34 297	9.95 931	6	35	′′	29	28 27
26	9.61 662	27	9.65 736	34	10.34 264	9.95 925	5	34	1	0.5	0.5 0.4
27	9.61 689	28	9.65 770	33	10.34 230	9.95 920	6	33	2	1.0	0.9 0.9
28	9.61 717	28	9.65 803	34	10.34 197	9.95 914	6	32	3	1.4	1.4 1.4
29	9.61 745	28	9.65 837	33	10.34 163	9.95 908	6	31	4	1.9	1.9 1.8
30	9.61 773	27	9.65 870	34	10.34 130	9.95 902	5	30	5	2.4	2.3 2.2
31	9.61 800	28	9.65 904	33	10.34 096	9.95 897	6	29	6	2.9	2.8 2.7
32	9.61 828	28	9.65 937	34	10.34 063	9.95 891	6	28	7	3.4	3.3 3.2
33	9.61 856	27	9.65 971	33	10.34 029	9.95 885	6	27	8	3.9	3.7 3.6
34	9.61 883	28	9.66 004	34	10.33 996	9.95 879	6	26	9	4.4	4.2 4.0
35	9.61 911	28	9.66 038	33	10.33 962	9.95 873	5	25	10	4.8	4.7 4.5
36	9.61 939	27	9.66 071	33	10.33 929	9.95 868	6	24	20	9.7	9.3 9.0
37	9.61 966	28	9.66 104	34	10.33 896	9.95 862	6	23	30	14.5	14.0 13.5
38	9.61 994	27	9.66 138	33	10.33 862	9.95 856	6	22	40	19.3	18.7 18.0
39	9.62 021	28	9.66 171	33	10.33 829	9.95 850	6	21	50	24.2	23.3 22.5
40	9.62 049	27	9.66 204	34	10.33 796	9.95 844	5	20	′′	6	5
41	9.62 076	28	9.66 238	33	10.33 762	9.95 839	6	19	1	0.1	0.1
42	9.62 104	27	9.66 271	33	10.33 729	9.95 833	6	18	2	0.2	0.2
43	9.62 131	28	9.66 304	33	10.33 696	9.95 827	6	17	3	0.3	0.2
44	9.62 159	27	9.66 337	34	10.33 663	9.95 821	6	16	4	0.4	0.3
45	9.62 186	28	9.66 371	33	10.33 629	9.95 815	5	15	5	0.5	0.4
46	9.62 214	27	9.66 404	33	10.33 596	9.95 810	6	14	6	0.6	0.5
47	9.62 241	27	9.66 437	33	10.33 563	9.95 804	6	13	7	0.7	0.6
48	9.62 268	28	9.66 470	33	10.33 530	9 95 798	6	12	8	0.8	0.7
49	9.62 296	27	9.66 503	34	10.33 497	9.95 792	8	11	9	0.9	0.8
50	9.62 323	27	9.66 537	33	10.33 463	9.95 786	6	10	10	1.0	0.8
51	9.62 350	27	9.66 570	33	10.33 430	9.95 780	5	9	20	2.0	1.7
52	9 62 377	28	9.66 603	33	10.33 397	9.95 775	6	8	30	3.0	2.5
53	9.62 405	27	9.66 636	33	10.33 364	9.95 769	6	7	40	4.0	3.3
54	9.62 432	27	9.66 669	33	10.33 331	9.95 763	6	6	50	5.0	4.2
55	9.62 459	27	9.66 702	33	10.33 298	9.95 757	6	5			
56	9.62 486	27	9.66 735	33	10.33 265	9.95 751	6	4			
57	9.62 513	28	9.66 768	33	10.33 232	9.98 745	6	3			
58	9.62 541	27	9.66 801	33	10.33 199	9.95 739	6	2			
59	9.62 568	27	9.66 834	33	10.33 166	9.95 733	5	1			
60	9.62 595		9.66 867		10.33 133	9.95 728		0			
′	L Cos	d	L Ctn	c d	L Tan	L Sin	d	′	Proportional parts		

′	L Sin	d	L Tan	c d	L Ctn	L Cos	d	′	Proportional parts
0	9.62 595	27	9.66 867	33	10.33 133	9.95 728	6	60	
1	9.62 622	27	9.66 900	33	10.33 100	9.95 722	6	59	
2	9.62 649	27	9.66 933	33	10.33 067	9.95 716	6	58	
3	9.62 676	27	9.66 966	33	10.33 034	9.95 710	6	57	
4	9.62 703	27	9.66 999	33	10.33 001	9.95 704	6	56	
5	9.62 730	27	9.67 032	33	10.32 968	9.95 698	5	55	
6	9.62 757	27	9.67 065	33	10.32 935	9.95 692	6	54	″ 33 32
7	9.62 784	27	9.67 098	33	10.32 902	9.95 686	6	53	1 0.6 0.5
8	9.62 811	27	9.67 131	32	10.32 869	9.95 680	6	52	2 1.1 1.1
9	9.62 838	27	9.67 163	33	10.32 837	9.95 674	6	51	3 1.6 1.6
10	9.62 865	27	9.67 196	33	10.32 804	9.95 668	5	50	4 2.2 2.1
11	9.62 892	26	9.67 229	33	10.32 771	9.95 663	6	49	
12	9.62 918	27	9.67 262	33	10.32 738	9.95 657	6	48	5 2.8 2.7
13	9.62 945	27	9.67 295	32	10.32 705	9.95 651	6	47	6 3.3 3.2
14	9.62 972	27	9.67 327	33	10.32 673	9.95 645	6	46	7 3.8 3.7
15	9.62 999	27	9.67 360	33	10.32 640	9.95 639	6	45	8 4.4 4.3
16	9.63 026	26	9.67 393	33	10.32 607	9.95 633	6	44	9 5.0 4.8
17	9.63 052	27	9.67 426	32	10.32 574	9.95 627	6	43	
18	9.63 079	27	9.67 458	33	10.32 542	9.95 621	6	42	10 5.5 5.3
19	9.63 106	27	9.67 491	33	10.32 509	9.95 615	6	41	20 11.0 10.7
20	9.63 133	26	9.67 524	32	10.32 476	9.95 609	6	40	30 16.5 16.0
21	9.63 159	27	9.67 556	33	10.32 444	9.95 603	6	39	40 22.0 21.3
22	9.63 186	27	9.67 589	33	10.32 411	9.95 597	6	38	50 27.5 26.7
23	9.63 213	26	9.67 622	32	10.32 378	9.95 591	6	37	
24	9.63 239	27	9.67 654	33	10.32 346	9.95 585	6	36	″ 27 26
25	9.63 266	26	9.67 687	32	10.32 313	9.95 579	6	35	1 0.4 0.4
26	9.63 292	27	9.67 719	33	10.32 281	9.95 573	6	34	2 0.9 0.9
27	9.63 319	26	9.67 752	33	10.32 248	9.95 567	6	33	3 1.4 1.3
28	9.63 345	27	9.67 785	32	10.32 215	9.95 561	6	32	4 1.8 1.7
29	9.63 372	26	9.67 817	33	10.32 183	9.95 555	6	31	
30	9.63 398	27	9.67 850	32	10.32 150	9.95 549	6	30	5 2.2 2.2
31	9.63 425	26	9.67 882	33	10.32 118	9.95 543	6	29	6 2.7 2.6
32	9.63 451	27	9.67 915	32	10.32 085	9.95 537	6	28	7 3.2 3.0
33	9.63 478	26	9.67 947	33	10.32 053	9.95 531	6	27	8 3.6 3.5
34	9.63 504	27	9.67 980	32	10.32 020	9.95 525	6	26	9 4.0 3.9
35	9.63 531	26	9.68 012	32	10.31 988	9.95 519	6	25	10 4.5 4.3
36	9.63 557	26	9.68 044	33	10.31 956	9.95 513	6	24	20 9.0 8.7
37	9.63 583	27	9.68 077	32	10.31 923	9.95 507	7	23	30 13.5 13.0
38	9.63 610	26	9.68 109	33	10.31 891	9.95 500	6	22	40 18.0 17.3
39	9.63 636	26	9.68 142	32	10.31 858	9.95 494	6	21	50 22.5 21.7
40	9.63 662	27	9.68 174	32	10.31 826	9.95 488	6	20	″ 7 6 5
41	9.63 689	26	9.68 206	33	10.31 794	9.95 482	6	19	1 0.1 0.1 0.1
42	9.63 715	26	9.68 239	32	10.31 761	9.95 476	6	18	2 0.2 0.2 0.2
43	9.63 741	26	9.68 271	32	10.31 729	9.95 470	6	17	3 0.4 0.3 0.2
44	9.63 767	27	9.68 303	33	10.31 697	9.95 464	6	16	4 0.5 0.4 0.3
45	9.63 794	26	9.68 336	32	10.31 664	9.95 458	6	15	5 0.6 0.5 0.4
46	9.63 820	26	9.68 368	32	10.31 632	9.95 452	6	14	6 0.7 0.6 0.5
47	9.63 846	26	9.68 400	32	10.31 600	9.95 446	6	13	7 0.8 0.7 0.6
48	9.63 872	26	9.68 432	33	10.31 568	9.95 440	6	12	8 0.9 0.8 0.7
49	9.63 898	26	9.68 465	32	10.31 535	9.95 434	7	11	9 1.0 0.9 0.8
50	9.63 924	26	9.68 497	32	10.31 503	9.95 427	6	10	10 1.2 1.0 0.8
51	9.63 950	26	9.68 529	32	10.31 471	9.95 421	6	9	20 2.3 2.0 1.7
52	9.63 976	26	9.68 561	32	10.31 439	9.95 415	6	8	30 3.5 3.0 2.5
53	9.64 002	26	9.68 593	33	10.31 407	9.95 409	6	7	40 4.7 4.0 3.3
54	9.64 028	26	9.68 626	32	10.31 374	9.95 403	6	6	50 5.8 5.0 4.2
55	9.64 054	26	9.68 658	32	10.31 342	9.95 397	6	5	
56	9.64 080	26	9.68 690	32	10.31 310	9.95 391	7	4	
57	9.64 106	26	9.68 722	32	10.31 278	9.95 384	6	3	
58	9.64 132	26	9.68 754	32	10.31 246	9.95 378	6	2	
59	9.64 158	26	9.68 786	32	10.31 214	9.95 372	6	1	
60	9.64 184		9.68 818		10.31 182	9.95 366		0	
′	L Cos	d	L Ctn	c d	L Tan	L Sin	d	′	Proportional parts

′	L Sin	d	L Tan	c d	L Ctn	L Cos	d	′
0	9.64 184	26	9.68 818	32	10.31 182	9.95 366	6	60
1	9.64 210	26	9.68 850	32	10.31 150	9 95 360	6	59
2	9.64 236	26	9.68 882	32	10.31 118	9.95 354	6	58
3	9.64 262	26	9.68 914	32	10.31 086	9.95 348	7	57
4	9.64 288	25	9.68 946	32	10.31 054	9.95 341	6	56
5	9.64 313	26	9.68 978	32	10.31 022	9.95 335	6	55
6	9.64 339	26	9.69 010	32	10.30 990	9.95 329	6	54
7	9.64 365	26	9.69 042	32	10.30 958	9.95 323	6	53
8	9.64 391	26	9.69 074	32	10.30 926	9.95 317	7	52
9	9.64 417	25	9.69 106	32	10.30 894	9.95 310	6	51
10	9.64 442	26	9.69 138	32	10.30 862	9.95 304	6	50
11	9.64 468	26	9.69 170	32	10.30 830	9.95 298	6	49
12	9.64 494	25	9.69 202	32	10.30 798	9.95 292	6	48
13	9.64 519	26	9.69 234	32	10.30 766	9.95 286	7	47
14	9.64 545	26	9.69 266	32	10.30 734	9.95 279	6	46
15	9.64 571	25	9.69 298	31	10.30 702	9.95 273	6	45
16	9.64 596	26	9.69 329	32	10.30 671	9.95 267	6	44
17	9.64 622	25	9.69 361	32	10.30 639	9.95 261	7	43
18	9.64 647	26	9.69 393	32	10.30 607	9.95 254	6	42
19	9.64 673	26	9.69 425	32	10.30 575	9.95 248	6	41
20	9.64 698	26	9.69 457	31	10.30 543	9.95 242	6	40
21	9.64 724	25	9.69 488	32	10.30 512	9.95 236	7	39
22	9.64 749	26	9.69 520	32	10.30 480	9.95 229	6	38
23	9.64 775	25	9.69 552	32	10.30 448	9.95 223	6	37
24	9.64 800	26	9.69 584	31	10.30 416	9.95 217	6	36
25	9.64 826	25	9.69 615	32	10.30 385	9.95 211	7	35
26	9.64 851	26	9.69 647	32	10.30 353	9.95 204	6	34
27	9.64 877	25	9.69 679	31	10.30 321	9.95 198	6	33
28	9.64 902	25	9.69 710	32	10.30 290	9.95 192	7	32
29	9.64 927	26	9.69 742	32	10.30 258	9.95 185	6	31
30	9.64 953	25	9.69 774	31	10.30 226	9.95 179	6	30
31	9.64 978	25	9.69 805	32	10.30 195	9.95 173	6	29
32	9.65 003	26	9.69 837	31	10.30 163	9.95 167	7	28
33	9.65 029	25	9.69 868	32	10.30 132	9.95 160	6	27
34	9.65 054	25	9.69 900	32	10.30 100	9.95 154	6	26
35	9.65 079	25	9.69 932	31	10.30 068	9.95 148	7	25
36	9.65 104	26	9.69 963	32	10.30 037	9.95 141	6	24
37	9.65 130	25	9.69 995	31	10.30 005	9.95 135	6	23
38	9.65 155	25	9.70 026	32	10.29 974	9.95 129	7	22
39	9.65 180	25	9.70 058	31	10.29 942	9.95 122	6	21
40	9.65 205	26	9.70 089	32	10.29 911	9.95 116	6	20
41	9.65 230	25	9.70 121	31	10.29 879	9.95 110	7	19
42	9.65 255	26	9.70 152	32	10.29 848	9.95 103	6	18
43	9.65 281	25	9.70 184	31	10.29 816	9.95 097	7	17
44	9.65 306	25	9.70 215	32	10.29 785	9.95 090	6	16
45	9.65 331	25	9.70 247	31	10.29 753	9.95 084	6	15
46	9.65 356	25	9.70 278	31	10.29 722	9.95 078	7	14
47	9.65 381	25	9.70 309	32	10.29 691	9.95 071	6	13
48	9.65 406	25	9.70 341	31	10.29 659	9.95 065	6	12
49	9.65 431	25	9.70 372	32	10.29 628	9.95 059	7	11
50	9.65 456	25	9.70 404	31	10.29 596	9.95 052	6	10
51	9.65 481	25	9.70 435	31	10.29 565	9.95 046	7	9
52	9.65 506	25	9.70 466	32	10.29 534	9.95 039	6	8
53	9.65 531	25	9.70 498	31	10.29 502	9.95 033	6	7
54	9.65 556	24	9.70 529	31	10.29 471	9.95 027	7	6
55	9.65 580	25	9.70 560	32	10.29 440	9.95 020	6	5
56	9.65 605	25	9.70 592	31	10.29 408	9.95 014	7	4
57	9.65 630	25	9.70 623	31	10.29 377	9.95 007	6	3
58	9.65 655	25	9.70 654	31	10.29 346	9.95 001	6	2
59	0.65 680	25	9.70 685	32	10.29 315	9.94 995	7	1
60	9.65 705		9.70 717		10.29 283	9.94 988		0
′	L Cos	d	L Ctn	c d	L Tan	L Sin	d	′

Proportional parts

′′	32	31
1	0.5	0.5
2	1.1	1.0
3	1.6	1.6
4	2.1	2.1
5	2.7	2.6
6	3.2	3.1
7	3.7	3.6
8	4.3	4.1
9	4.8	4.6
10	5.3	5.2
20	10.7	10.3
30	16.0	15.5
40	21.3	20.7
50	26.7	25.8

′′	26	25	24
1	0.4	0.4	0.4
2	0.9	0.8	0.8
3	1.3	1.2	1.2
4	1.7	1.7	1.6
5	2.2	2.1	2.0
6	2.6	2.5	2.4
7	3.0	2.9	2.8
8	3.5	3.3	3.2
9	3.9	3.8	3.6
10	4.3	4.2	4.0
20	8.7	8.3	8.0
30	13.0	12.5	12.0
40	17.3	16.7	16.0
50	21.7	20.8	20.0

′′	7	6
1	0.1	0.1
2	0.2	0.2
3	0.4	0.3
4	0.5	0.4
5	0.6	0.5
6	0.7	0.6
7	0.8	0.7
8	0.9	0.8
9	1.0	0.9
10	1.2	1.0
20	2.3	2.0
30	3.5	3.0
40	4.7	4.0
50	5.8	5.0

′	L Sin	d	L Tan	c d	L Ctn	L Cos	d	′	Proportional parts		
0	9.65 705	24	9.70 717	31	10.29 283	9.94 988	6	60			
1	9.65 729	25	9.70 748	31	10.29 252	9.94 982	7	59			
2	9.65 754	25	9.70 779	31	10.29 221	9.94 975	6	58			
3	9.65 779	25	9.70 810	31	10.29 190	9.94 969	7	57			
4	9.65 804	24	9.70 841	32	10.29 159	9.94 962	6	56			
									′′	32	31	30
5	9.65 828	25	9.70 873	31	10.29 127	9.94 956	7	55			
6	9.65 853	25	9.70 904	31	10.29 095	9.94 949	6	54	1	0.5	0.5	0.5
7	9.65 878	25	9.70 935	31	10.29 065	9.94 943	7	53	2	1.1	1.0	1.0
8	9.65 902	25	9.70 966	31	10.29 034	9.94 936	6	52	3	1.6	1.6	1.5
9	9.65 927	25	9.70 997	31	10.29 003	9.94 930	7	51	4	2.1	2.1	2.0
10	9.65 952	24	9.71 028	31	10.28 972	9.94 923	6	50	5	2.7	2.6	2.5
11	9.65 976	25	9.71 059	31	10.28 941	9.94 917	6	49	6	3.2	3.1	3.0
12	9.66 001	24	9.71 090	31	10.28 910	9.94 911	7	48	7	3.7	3.6	3.5
13	9.66 025	25	9.71 121	32	10.28 879	9.94 904	6	47	8	4.3	4.1	4.0
14	9.66 050	25	9.71 153	31	10.28 847	9.94 898	7	46	9	4.8	4.6	4.5
15	9.66 075	24	9.71 184	31	10.28 816	9.94 891	6	45				
16	9.66 099	25	9.71 215	31	10.28 785	9.94 885	7	44	10	5.3	5.2	5.0
17	9.66 124	24	9.71 246	31	10.28 754	9.94 878	7	43	20	10.7	10.3	10.0
18	9.66 148	25	9.71 277	31	10.28 723	9.94 871	6	42	30	16.0	15.5	15.0
19	9.66 173	24	9.71 308	31	10.28 692	9.94 865	7	41	40	21.3	20.7	20.0
20	9.66 197	24	9.71 339	31	10.28 661	9.94 858	6	40	50	26.7	25.8	25.0
21	9.66 221	25	9.71 370	31	10.28 630	9.94 852	7	39				
22	9.66 246	24	9.71 401	30	10.28 599	9.94 845	6	38				
23	9.66 270	25	9.71 431	31	10.28 569	9.94 839	7	37	′′	25	24	23
24	9.66 295	24	9.71 462	31	10.28 538	9.94 832	6	36	1	0.4	0.4	0.4
25	9.66 319	24	9.71 493	31	10.28 507	9.94 826	7	35	2	0.8	0.8	0.8
26	9.66 343	25	9.71 524	31	10.28 476	9.94 819	6	34	3	1.2	1.2	1.2
27	9.66 368	24	9.71 555	31	10.28 445	9.94 813	7	33	4	1.7	1.6	1.5
28	9.66 392	24	9.71 586	31	10.28 414	9.94 806	7	32				
29	9.66 416	25	9.71 617	31	10.28 383	9.94 799	6	31	5	2.1	2.0	1.9
30	9.66 441	24	9.71 648	31	10.28 352	9.94 793	7	30	6	2.5	2.4	2.3
31	9.66 465	24	9.71 679	30	10.28 321	9.94 786	6	29	7	2.9	2.8	2.7
32	9.66 489	24	9.71 709	31	10.28 291	9.94 780	7	28	8	3.3	3.2	3.1
33	9.66 513	24	9.71 740	31	10.28 260	9.94 773	6	27	9	3.8	3.6	3.4
34	9.66 537	25	9.71 771	31	10.28 229	9.94 767	7	26				
35	9.66 562	24	9.71 802	31	10.28 198	9.94 760	7	25	10	4.2	4.0	3.8
36	9.66 586	24	9.71 833	30	10.28 167	9.94 753	6	24	20	8.3	8.0	7.7
37	9.66 610	24	9.71 863	31	10.28 137	9.94 747	7	23	30	12.5	12.0	11.5
38	9.66 634	24	9.71 894	31	10.28 106	9.94 740	6	22	40	16.7	16.0	15.3
39	9.66 658	24	9.71 925	30	10.28 075	9.94 734	7	21	50	20.8	20.0	19.2
40	9.66 682	24	9.71 955	31	10.28 045	9.94 727	7	20				
41	9.66 706	25	9.71 986	31	10.28 014	9.94 720	6	19	′′		7	6
42	9.66 731	24	9.72 017	31	10.27 983	9.94 714	7	18	1		0.1	0.1
43	9.66 755	24	9.72 048	30	10.27 952	9.94 707	7	17	2		0.2	0.2
44	9.66 779	24	9.72 078	31	10.27 922	9.94 700	6	16	3		0.4	0.3
									4		0.5	0.4
45	9.66 803	24	9.72 109	31	10.27 891	9.94 694	7	15				
46	9.66 827	24	9.72 140	30	10.27 860	9.94 687	7	14	5		0.6	0.5
47	9.66 851	24	9.72 170	31	10.27 830	9.94 680	6	13	6		0.7	0.6
48	9.66 875	24	9.72 201	30	10.27 799	9.94 674	7	12	7		0.8	0.7
49	9.66 899	23	9.72 231	31	10.27 769	9.94 667	7	11	8		0.9	0.8
									9		1.0	0.9
50	9.66 922	24	9.72 262	31	10.27 738	9.94 660	6	10				
51	9.66 946	24	9.72 293	30	10.27 707	9.94 654	7	9	10		1.2	1.0
52	9.66 970	24	9.72 323	31	10.27 677	9.94 647	7	8	20		2.3	2.0
53	9.66 994	24	9.72 354	30	10.27 646	9.94 640	6	7	30		3.5	3.0
54	9.67 018	24	9.72 384	31	10.27 616	9.94 634	7	6	40		4.7	4.0
									50		5.8	5.0
55	9.67 042	24	9.72 415	30	10.27 585	9.94 627	7	5				
56	9.67 066	24	9.72 445	31	10.27 555	9.94 620	6	4				
57	9.67 090	23	9.72 476	30	10.27 524	9.94 614	7	3				
58	9.67 113	24	9.72 506	31	10.27 494	9.94 607	7	2				
59	9.67 137	24	9.72 537	30	10.27 463	9.94 600	7	1				
60	9.67 161		9.72 567		10.27 433	9.94 593		0				
′	L Cos	d	L Ctn	c d	L Tan	L Sin	d	′	Proportional parts		

′	L Sin	d	L Tan	c d	L Ctn	L Cos	d	′	Proportional parts		
0	9.67 161	24	9.72 567	31	10.27 433	9.94 593	6	60			
1	9.67 185	23	9.72 598	30	10.27 402	9.94 587	7	59			
2	9.67 208	24	9.72 628	31	10.27 372	9.94 580	7	58			
3	9.67 232	24	9.72 659	30	10.27 341	9.94 573	6	57			
4	9.67 256	24	9.72 689	31	10.27 311	9.94 567	7	56			
5	9.67 280	23	9.72 720	30	10.27 280	9.94 560	7	55			
6	9.67 303	24	9.72 750	30	10.27 250	9.94 553	7	54			
7	9.67 327	23	9.72 780	31	10.27 220	9.94 546	6	53	′′	31	30	29
8	9.67 350	24	9.72 811	30	10.27 189	9.94 540	7	52	1	0.5	0.5	0.5
9	9.67 374	24	9.72 841	31	10.27 159	9.94 533	7	51	2	1.0	1.0	1.0
10	9.67 398	23	9.72 872	30	10.27 128	9.94 526	7	50	3	1.6	1.5	1.4
11	9.67 421	24	9.72 902	30	10.27 098	9.94 519	6	49	4	2.1	2.0	1.9
12	9.67 445	23	9.72 932	31	10.27 068	9.94 513	7	48				
13	9 67 468	24	9.72 963	30	10.27 037	9.94 506	7	47	5	2.6	2.5	2.4
14	9.67 492	23	9.72 993	30	10.27 007	9.94 499	7	46	6	3.1	3.0	2.9
									7	3.6	3.5	3.4
15	9.67 515	24	9.73 023	31	10.26 977	9.94 492	7	45	8	4.1	4.0	3.9
16	9.67 539	23	9.73 054	30	10.26 946	9.94 485	6	44	9	4.6	4.5	4.4
17	9.67 562	24	9.73 084	30	10.26 916	9.94 479	7	43				
18	9.67 586	23	9.73 114	30	10.26 886	9.94 472	7	42	10	5.2	5.0	4.8
19	9.67 609	24	9.73 144	31	10.26 856	9.94 465	7	41	20	10.3	10.0	9.7
20	9.67 633	23	9.73 175	30	10.26 825	9.94 458	7	40	30	15.5	15.0	14.5
21	9.67 656	24	9.73 205	30	10.26 795	9.94 451	7	39	40	20.7	20.0	19.3
22	9.67 680	23	9.73 235	30	10.26 765	9.94 445	7	38	50	25.8	25.0	24.2
23	9.67 703	23	9.73 265	30	10.26 735	9.94 438	7	37				
24	9.67 726	24	9.73 295	31	10.26 705	9.94 431	7	36	′′	24	23	22
25	9.67 750	23	9.73 326	30	10.26 674	9.94 424	7	35	1	0.4	0.4	0.4
26	9.67 773	23	9.73 356	30	10.26 644	9.94 417	7	34	2	0.8	0.8	0.7
27	9.67 796	24	9.73 386	30	10.26 614	9.94 410	6	33	3	1.2	1.2	1.1
28	9.67 820	23	9.73 416	30	10.26 584	9.94 404	7	32	4	1.6	1.5	1.5
29	9.67 843	23	9.73 446	30	10.26 554	9.94 397	7	31				
30	9.67 866	24	9.73 476	31	10.26 524	9.94 390	7	30	5	2.0	1.9	1.8
31	9.67 890	23	9.73 507	30	10.26 493	9.94 383	7	29	6	2.4	2.3	2.2
32	9.67 913	23	9.73 537	30	10.26 463	9.94 376	7	28	7	2.8	2.7	2.6
33	9.67 936	23	9.73 567	30	10.26 433	9.94 369	7	27	8	3.2	3.1	2.9
34	9.67 959	23	9.73 597	30	10.26 403	9.94 362	7	26	9	3.6	3.4	3.3
35	9.67 982	24	9.73 627	30	10.26 373	9.94 355	6	25	10	4.0	3.8	3.7
36	9.68 006	23	9.73 657	30	10.26 343	9.94 349	7	24	20	8.0	7.7	7.3
37	9.68 029	23	9.73 687	30	10.26 313	9.94 342	7	23	30	12.0	11.5	11.0
38	9.68 052	23	9.73 717	30	10.26 283	9.94 335	7	22	40	16.0	15.3	14.7
39	9.68 075	23	9.73 747	30	10.26 253	9.94 328	7	21	50	20.0	19.2	18.3
40	9.68 098	23	9.73 777	30	10.26 223	9.94 321	7	20				
41	9.68 121	23	9.73 807	30	10.26 193	9.94 314	7	19	′′		7	6
42	9.68 144	23	9.73 837	30	10.26 163	9.94 307	7	18	1		0.1	0.1
43	9.68 167	23	9.73 867	30	10 26 133	9.94 300	7	17	2		0.2	0.2
44	9.68 190	23	9.73 897	30	10 26 103	9.94 293	7	16	3		0.4	0.3
									4		0.5	0.4
45	9.68 213	24	9.73 927	30	10.26 073	9.94 286	7	15				
46	9.68 237	23	9.73 957	30	10.26 043	9.94 279	6	14	5		0.6	0.5
47	9.68 260	23	9.73 987	30	10.26 013	9.94 273	7	13	6		0.7	0.6
48	9.68 283	22	9.74 017	30	10.25 983	9.94 266	7	12	7		0.8	0.7
49	9.68 305	23	9.74 047	30	10.25 953	9.94 259	7	11	8		0.9	0.8
									9		1.0	0.9
50	9.68 328	23	9.74 077	30	10.25 923	9.94 252	7	10				
51	9.68 351	23	9.74 107	30	10.25 893	9.94 245	7	9	10		1.2	1.0
52	9.68 374	23	9.74 137	29	10.25 863	9.94 238	7	8	20		2.3	2.0
53	9.68 397	23	9.74 166	30	10.25 834	9.94 231	7	7	30		3.5	3.0
54	9.68 420	23	9.74 196	30	10.25 804	9.94 224	7	6	40		4.7	4.0
55	9.68 443	23	9.74 226	30	10.25 774	9.94 217	7	5	50		5.8	5.0
56	9.68 466	23	9.74 256	30	10.25 744	9.94 210	7	4				
57	9.68 489	23	9.74 286	30	10.25 714	9.94 203	7	3				
58	9.68 512	22	9.74 316	30	10.25 684	9.94 196	7	2				
59	9.68 534	23	9.74 345	30	10.25 655	9.94 189	7	1				
60	9.68 557		9.74 375		10.25 625	9.94 182		0				
′	L Cos	d	L Ctn	c d	L Tan	L Sin	d	′	Proportional parts		

′	L Sin	d	L Tan	c d	L Ctn	L Cos	d	′	Proportional parts
0	9.68 557	23	9.74 375	30	10.25 625	9.94 182	7	60	
1	9.68 580	23	9.74 405	30	10.25 595	9.94 175	7	59	
2	9.68 603	22	9.74 435	30	10.25 565	9.94 168	7	58	
3	9.68 625	23	9.74 465	29	10.25 535	9.94 161	7	57	
4	9.68 648	23	9.74 494	30	10.25 506	9.94 154	7	56	
5	9.68 671	23	9.74 524	30	10.25 476	9.94 147	7	55	
6	9.68 694	22	9.74 554	29	10.25 446	9.94 140	7	54	
7	9.68 716	23	9.74 583	30	10.25 417	9.94 133	7	53	
8	9.68 739	23	9.74 613	30	10.25 387	9.94 126	7	52	
9	9.68 762	22	9.74 643	30	10.25 357	9.94 119	7	51	
10	9.68 784	23	9.74 673	29	10.25 327	9.94 112	7	50	
11	9.68 807	22	9.74 702	30	10.25 298	9.94 105	7	49	
12	9.68 829	23	9.74 732	30	10.25 268	9.94 098	8	48	
13	9.68 852	23	9.74 762	29	10.25 238	9.94 090	7	47	
14	9.68 875	22	9.74 791	30	10.25 209	9.94 083	7	46	
15	9.68 897	23	9.74 821	30	10.25 179	9.94 076	7	45	
16	9.68 920	22	9.74 851	29	10.25 149	9.94 069	7	44	
17	9.68 942	23	9.74 880	30	10.25 120	9.94 062	7	43	
18	9.68 965	22	9.74 910	29	10.25 090	9.94 055	7	42	
19	9.68 987	23	9.74 939	30	10.25 061	9.94 048	7	41	
20	9.69 010	22	9.74 969	29	10.25 031	9.94 041	7	40	
21	9.69 032	23	9.74 998	30	10.25 002	9.94 034	7	39	
22	9.69 055	22	9.75 028	30	10.24 972	9.94 027	7	38	
23	9.69 077	23	9.75 058	29	10.24 942	9.94 020	8	37	
24	9.69 100	22	9.75 087	30	10.24 913	9.94 012	7	36	
25	9.69 122	22	9.75 117	29	10.24 883	9.94 005	7	35	
26	9.69 144	23	9.75 146	30	10.24 854	9.93 998	7	34	
27	9.69 167	22	9.75 176	29	10.24 824	9.93 991	7	33	
28	9.69 189	23	9.75 205	30	10.24 795	9.93 984	7	32	
29	9.69 212	22	9.75 235	29	10.24 765	9.93 977	7	31	
30	9.69 234	22	9.75 264	30	10.24 736	9.93 970	7	30	
31	9.69 256	23	9.75 294	29	10.24 706	9.93 963	8	29	
32	9.69 279	22	9.75 323	30	10.24 677	9.93 955	7	28	
33	9.69 301	22	9.75 353	29	10.24 647	9.93 948	7	27	
34	9.69 323	22	9.75 382	29	10.24 618	9.93 941	7	26	
35	9.69 345	23	9.75 411	30	10.24 589	9.93 934	7	25	
36	9.69 368	22	9.75 441	29	10.24 559	9.93 927	7	24	
37	9.69 390	22	9.75 470	30	10.24 530	9.93 920	8	23	
38	9.69 412	22	9.75 500	29	10.24 500	9.93 912	7	22	
39	9.69 434	22	9.75 529	29	10.24 471	9.93 905	7	21	
40	9.69 456	23	9.75 558	30	10.24 442	9.93 898	7	20	
41	9.69 479	22	9.75 588	29	10.24 412	9.93 891	7	19	
42	9.69 501	22	9.75 617	30	10.24 383	9.93 884	8	18	
43	9.69 523	22	9.75 647	29	10.24 353	9.93 876	7	17	
44	9.69 545	22	9.75 676	29	10.24 324	9.93 869	7	16	
45	9.69 567	22	9.75 705	30	10.24 295	9.93 862	7	15	
46	9.69 589	22	9.75 735	29	10.24 265	9.93 855	8	14	
47	9.69 611	22	9.75 764	29	10.24 236	9.93 847	7	13	
48	9.69 633	22	9.75 793	29	10.24 207	9.93 840	7	12	
49	9.69 655	22	9.75 822	30	10.24 178	9.93 833	7	11	
50	9.69 677	22	9.75 852	29	10.24 148	9.93 826	7	10	
51	9.69 699	22	9.75 881	29	10.24 119	9.93 819	8	9	
52	9.69 721	22	9.75 910	29	10.24 090	9.93 811	7	8	
53	9.69 743	22	9.75 939	30	10.24 061	9.93 804	7	7	
54	9.69 765	22	9.75 969	29	10.24 031	9.93 797	8	6	
55	9.69 787	22	9.75 998	29	10.24 002	9.93 789	7	5	
56	9.69 809	22	9.76 027	29	10.23 973	9.93 782	7	4	
57	9.69 831	22	9.76 056	30	10.23 944	9.93 775	7	3	
58	9.69 853	22	9.76 086	29	10.23 914	9.93 768	8	2	
59	9.69 875	22	9.76 115	29	10.23 885	9.93 760	7	1	
60	9.69 897		9.76 144		10.23 856	9.93 753		0	
′	L Cos	d	L Ctn	c d	L Tan	L Sin	d	′	Proportional parts

Proportional parts:

′′	30	29	23
1	0.5	0.5	0.4
2	1.0	1.0	0.8
3	1.5	1.4	1.2
4	2.0	1.9	1.5
5	2.5	2.4	1.9
6	3.0	2.9	2.3
7	3.5	3.4	2.7
8	4.0	3.9	3.1
9	4.5	4.4	3.4
10	5.0	4.8	3.8
20	10.0	9.7	7.7
30	15.0	14.5	11.5
40	20.0	19.3	15.3
50	25.0	24.2	19.2

′′	22	8	7
1	0.4	0.1	0.1
2	0.7	0.3	0.2
3	1.1	0.4	0.4
4	1.5	0.5	0.5
5	1.8	0.7	0.6
6	2.2	0.8	0.7
7	2.6	0.9	0.8
8	2.9	1.1	0.9
9	3.3	1.2	1.0
10	3.7	1.3	1.2
20	7.3	2.7	2.3
30	11.0	4.0	3.5
40	14.7	5.3	4.7
50	18.3	6.7	5.8

′	L Sin	d	L Tan	c d	L Ctn	L Cos	d	′	Proportional parts
0	9.69 897	22	9.76 144	29	10.23 856	9.93 753	7	60	
1	9.69 919	22	9.76 173	29	10.23 827	9.93 746	8	59	
2	9.69 941	22	9.76 202	29	10.23 798	9.93 738	7	58	
3	9.69 963	21	9.76 231	30	10.23 769	9.93 731	7	57	
4	9.69 984	22	9.76 261	29	10.23 739	9.93 724	7	56	
5	9.70 006	22	9.76 290	29	10.23 710	9.93 717	8	55	
6	9.70 028	22	9.76 319	29	10.23 681	9.93 709	7	54	
7	9.70 050	22	9.76 348	29	10.23 652	9.93 702	7	53	″ 30 29 28
8	9.70 072	21	9.76 377	29	10.23 623	9.93 695	8	52	1 0.5 0.5 0.5
9	9.70 093	22	9.76 406	29	10.23 594	9.93 687	7	51	2 1.0 1.0 0.9
									3 1.5 1.4 1.4
10	9.70 115	22	9.76 435	29	10.23 565	9.93 680	7	50	4 2.0 1.9 1.9
11	9.70 137	22	9.76 464	29	10.23 536	9.93 673	8	49	
12	9.70 159	21	9.76 493	29	10.23 507	9.93 665	7	48	5 2.5 2.4 2.3
13	9.70 180	22	9.76 522	29	10.23 478	9.93 758	8	47	6 3.0 2.9 2.8
14	9.70 202	22	9.76 551	29	10.23 449	9.93 650	7	46	7 3.5 3.4 3.3
									8 4.0 3.9 3.7
15	9.70 224	21	9.76 580	29	10.23 420	9.93 643	7	45	9 4.5 4.4 4.2
16	9.70 245	22	9.76 609	30	10.23 391	9.93 636	8	44	
17	9.70 267	21	9.76 639	29	10.23 361	9.93 628	7	43	10 5.0 4.8 4.7
18	9.70 288	22	9.76 668	29	10.23 332	9.93 621	7	42	20 10.0 9.7 9.3
19	9.70 310	22	9.76 697	28	10.23 303	9.93 614	8	41	30 15.0 14.5 14.0
									40 20.0 19.3 18.7
20	9.70 332	21	9.76 725	29	10.23 275	9.93 606	7	40	50 25.0 24.2 23.3
21	9.70 353	22	9.76 754	29	10.23 246	9.93 599	8	39	
22	9.70 375	21	9.76 783	29	10.23 217	9.93 591	7	38	
23	9.70 396	22	9.76 812	29	10.23 188	9.93 584	7	37	″ 22 21
24	9.70 418	21	9.76 841	29	10.23 159	9.93 577	8	36	1 0.4 0.4
									2 0.7 0.7
25	9.70 439	22	9.76 870	29	10.23 130	9.93 569	7	35	3 1.1 1.0
26	9.70 461	21	9.76 899	29	10.23 101	9.93 562	8	34	4 1.5 1.4
27	9.70 482	22	9.76 928	29	10.23 072	9.93 554	7	33	
28	9.70 504	21	9.76 957	29	10.23 043	9.93 547	8	32	5 1.8 1.8
29	9.70 525	22	9.76 986	29	10.23 014	9.93 539	7	31	6 2.2 2.1
									7 2.6 2.4
30	9.70 547	21	9.77 015	29	10.22 985	9.93 532	7	30	8 2.9 2.8
31	9.70 568	22	9.77 044	29	10.22 956	9.93 525	8	29	9 3.3 3.2
32	9.70 590	21	9.77 073	28	10.22 927	9.93 517	7	28	
33	9.70 611	22	9.77 101	29	10.22 899	9.93 510	8	27	10 3.7 3.5
34	9.70 633	21	9.77 130	29	10.22 870	9.93 502	7	26	20 7.3 7.0
									30 11.0 10.5
35	9.70 654	21	9.77 159	29	10.22 841	9.93 495	8	25	40 14.7 14.0
36	9.70 675	22	9.77 188	29	10.22 812	9.93 487	7	24	50 18.3 17.5
37	9.70 697	21	9.77 217	29	10.22 783	9.93 480	8	23	
38	9.70 718	21	9.77 246	28	10.22 754	9.93 472	7	22	
39	9.70 739	22	9.77 274	29	10.22 726	9.93 465	8	21	″ 8 7
									1 0.1 0.1
40	9.70 761	21	9.77 303	29	10.22 697	9.93 457	7	20	2 0.3 0.2
41	9.70 782	21	9.77 332	29	10.22 668	9.93 450	8	19	3 0.4 0.4
42	9.70 803	21	9.77 361	29	10.22 639	9.93 442	7	18	4 0.5 0.5
43	9.70 824	22	9.77 390	28	10.22 610	9.93 435	8	17	
44	9.70 846	21	9.77 418	29	10.22 582	9.93 427	7	16	5 0.7 0.6
									6 0.8 0.7
45	9.70 867	21	9.77 447	29	10.22 553	9.93 420	8	15	7 0.9 0.8
46	9.70 888	21	9.77 476	29	10.22 524	9.93 412	7	14	8 1.1 0.9
47	9.70 909	22	9.77 505	28	10.22 495	9.93 405	8	13	9 1.2 1.0
48	9.70 931	21	9.77 533	29	10.22 467	9.93 397	7	12	
49	9.70 952	21	9.77 562	29	10.22 438	9.93 390	8	11	10 1.3 1.2
									20 2.7 2.3
50	9.70 973	21	9.77 591	28	10.22 409	9.93 382	7	10	30 4.0 3.5
51	9.70 994	21	9.77 619	29	10.22 381	9.93 375	8	9	40 5.3 4.7
52	9.71 015	21	9.77 648	29	10.22 352	9.93 367	7	8	50 6.7 5.8
53	9.71 036	22	9.77 677	29	10.22 323	9.93 360	8	7	
54	9.71 058	21	9.77 706	28	10.22 294	9.93 352	8	6	
55	9.71 079	21	9.77 734	29	10.22 266	9.93 344	7	5	
56	9.71 100	21	9.77 763	28	10.22 237	9.93 337	8	4	
57	9.71 121	21	9.77 791	29	10.22 209	9.93 329	7	3	
58	9.71 142	21	9.77 820	29	10.22 180	9.93 322	8	2	
59	9.71 163	21	9.77 849	28	10.22 151	9.93 314	7	1	
60	9.71 184		9.77 877		10.22 123	9.93 307		0	
′	L Cos	d	L Ctn	c d	L Tan	L Sin	d	′	Proportional parts

′	L Sin	d	L Tan	c d	L Ctn	L Cos	d	′	Proportional parts
0	9.71 184	21	9.77 877	29	10.22 123	9.93 307	8	60	
1	9.71 205	21	9.77 906	29	10.22 094	9.93 299	8	59	
2	9.71 226	21	9.77 935	28	10.22 065	9.93 291	7	58	
3	9.71 247	21	9.77 963	29	10.22 037	9.93 284	8	57	
4	9.71 268	21	9.77 992	28	10.22 008	9.93 276	7	56	

									″		29	28

′	L Sin	d	L Tan	c d	L Ctn	L Cos	d	′
5	9.71 289	21	9.78 020	29	10.21 980	9.93 269	8	55
6	9.71 310	21	9.78 049	28	10.21 951	9.93 261	8	54
7	9.71 331	21	9.78 077	29	10.21 923	9.93 253	7	53
8	9.71 352	21	9.78 106	29	10.21 894	9.93 246	8	52
9	9.71 373	20	9.78 135	28	10.21 865	9.93 238	8	51
10	9.71 393	21	9.78 163	29	10.21 837	9.93 230	7	50
11	9.71 414	21	9.78 192	28	10.21 808	9.93 223	8	49
12	9.71 435	21	9.78 220	29	10.21 780	9.93 215	8	48
13	9.71 456	21	9.78 249	28	10.21 751	9.93 207	7	47
14	9.71 477	21	9.78 277	29	10.21 723	9.93 200	8	46
15	9.71 498	21	9.78 306	28	10.21 694	9.93 192	8	45
16	9.71 519	20	9.78 334	29	10.21 666	9.93 184	7	44
17	9.71 539	21	9.78 363	28	10.21 637	9.93 177	8	43
18	9.71 560	21	9.78 391	28	10.21 609	9.93 169	8	42
19	9.71 581	21	9.78 419	29	10.21 581	9.93 161	7	41
20	9.71 602	20	9.78 448	28	10.21 552	9.93 154	8	40
21	9.71 622	21	9.78 476	29	10.21 524	9.93 146	8	39
22	9.71 643	21	9.78 505	28	10.21 495	9.93 138	7	38
23	9.71 664	21	9.78 533	29	10.21 467	9.93 131	8	37
24	9.71 685	20	9.78 562	28	10.21 438	9.93 123	8	36
25	9.71 705	21	9.78 590	28	10.21 410	9.93 115	7	35
26	9.71 726	21	9.78 618	29	10.21 382	9.93 108	8	34
27	9.71 747	20	9.78 647	28	10.21 353	9.93 100	8	33
28	9.71 767	21	9.78 675	29	10.21 325	9.93 092	8	32
29	9.71 788	21	9.78 704	28	10.21 296	9.93 084	7	31
30	9.71 809	20	9.78 732	28	10.21 268	9.93 077	8	30
31	9.71 829	21	9.78 760	29	10.21 240	9.93 069	8	29
32	9.71 850	20	9.78 789	28	10.21 211	9.93 061	8	28
33	9.71 870	21	9.78 817	28	10.21 183	9.93 053	7	27
34	9.71 891	20	9.78 845	29	10.21 155	9.93 046	8	26
35	9.71 911	21	9.78 874	28	10.21 126	9.93 038	8	25
36	9.71 932	20	9.78 902	28	10.21 098	9.93 030	8	24
37	9.71 952	21	9.78 930	29	10.21 070	9.93 022	8	23
38	9.71 973	21	9.78 959	28	10.21 041	9.93 014	7	22
39	9.71 994	20	9.78 987	28	10.21 013	9.93 007	8	21
40	9.72 014	20	9.79 015	28	10.20 985	9.92 999	8	20
41	9.72 034	21	9.79 043	29	10.20 957	9.92 991	8	19
42	9.72 055	20	9.79 072	28	10.20 928	9.92 983	7	18
43	9.72 075	21	9.79 100	28	10.20 900	9.92 976	8	17
44	9.72 096	20	9.79 128	28	10.20 872	9.92 968	8	16
45	9.72 116	21	9.79 156	29	10.20 844	9.92 960	8	15
46	9.72 137	20	9.79 185	28	10.20 815	9.92 952	8	14
47	9.72 157	20	9.79 213	28	10.20 787	9.92 944	8	13
48	9.72 177	21	9.79 241	28	10.20 759	9.92 936	7	12
49	9.72 198	20	9.79 269	28	10.20 731	9.92 929	8	11
50	9.72 218	20	9.79 297	29	10.20 703	9.92 921	8	10
51	9.72 238	21	9.79 326	28	10.20 674	9.92 913	8	9
52	9.72 259	20	9.79 354	28	10.20 646	9.92 905	8	8
53	9.72 279	20	9.79 382	28	10.20 618	9.92 897	8	7
54	9.72 299	21	9.79 410	28	10.20 590	9.92 889	8	6
55	9.72 320	20	9.79 438	28	10.20 562	9.92 881	7	5
56	9.72 340	20	9.79 466	29	10.20 534	9.92 874	8	4
57	9.72 360	21	9.79 495	28	10.20 505	9.92 866	8	3
58	9.72 381	20	9.79 523	28	10.20 477	9.92 858	8	2
59	9.72 401	20	9.79 551	28	10.20 449	9.92 850	8	1
60	9.72 421		9.79 579		10.20 421	9.92 842		0
′	L Cos	d	L Ctn	c d	L Tan	L Sin	d	′

Proportional parts:

″	29	28
1	0.5	0.5
2	1.0	0.9
3	1.4	1.4
4	1.9	1.9
5	2.4	2.3
6	2.9	2.8
7	3.4	3.3
8	3.9	3.7
9	4.4	4.2
10	4.8	4.7
20	9.7	9.3
30	14.5	14.0
40	19.3	18.7
50	24.2	23.3

″	21	20
1	0.4	0.3
2	0.7	0.7
3	1.0	1.0
4	1.4	1.3
5	1.8	1.7
6	2.1	2.0
7	2.4	2.3
8	2.8	2.7
9	3.2	3.0
10	3.5	3.3
20	7.0	6.7
30	10.5	10.0
40	14.0	13.3
50	17.5	16.7

″	8	7
1	0.1	0.1
2	0.3	0.2
3	0.4	0.4
4	0.5	0.5
5	0.7	0.6
6	0.8	0.7
7	0.9	0.8
8	1.1	0.9
9	1.2	1.0
10	1.3	1.2
20	2.7	2.3
30	4.0	3.5
40	5.3	4.7
50	6.7	5.8

Proportional parts

′	L Sin	d	L Tan	c d	L Ctn	L Cos	d	′
0	9.72 421	20	9.79 579	28	10.20 421	9.92 842	8	60
1	9.72 441	20	9.79 607	28	10.20 393	9.92 834	8	59
2	9.72 461	21	9.79 635	28	10.20 365	9.92 826	8	58
3	9.72 482	20	9.79 663	28	10.20 337	9.92 818	8	57
4	9.72 502	20	9.79 691	28	10.20 309	9.92 810	7	56
5	9.72 522	20	9.79 719	28	10.20 281	9.92 803	8	55
6	9.72 542	20	9.79 747	29	10.20 253	9.92 795	8	54
7	9.72 562	20	9.79 776	28	10.20 224	9.92 787	8	53
8	9.72 582	20	9.79 804	28	10.20 196	9.92 779	8	52
9	9.72 602	20	9.79 832	28	10.20 168	9.92 771	8	51
10	9.72 622	21	9.79 860	28	10.20 140	9.92 763	8	50
11	9.72 643	20	9.79 888	28	10.20 112	9.92 755	8	49
12	9.72 663	20	9.79 916	28	10.20 084	9.92 747	8	48
13	9.72 683	20	9.79 944	28	10.20 056	9.92 739	8	47
14	9.72 703	20	9.79 972	28	10.20 028	9.92 731	8	46
15	9.72 723	20	9.80 000	28	10.20 000	9.92 723	8	45
16	9.72 743	20	9.80 028	28	10.19 972	9.92 715	8	44
17	9.72 763	20	9.80 056	28	10.19 944	9.92 707	8	43
18	9.72 783	20	9.80 084	28	10.19 916	9.92 699	8	42
19	9.72 803	20	9.80 112	28	10.19 888	9.92 691	8	41
20	9.72 823	20	9.80 140	28	10.19 860	9.92 683	8	40
21	9.72 843	20	9.80 168	27	10.19 832	9.92 675	8	39
22	9.72 863	20	9.80 195	28	10.19 805	9.92 667	8	38
23	9.72 883	19	9.80 223	28	10.19 777	9.92 659	8	37
24	9.72 902	20	9.80 251	28	10.19 749	9.92 651	8	36
25	9.72 922	20	9.80 279	28	10.19 721	9.92 643	8	35
26	9.72 942	20	9.80 307	28	10.19 693	9.92 635	8	34
27	9.72 962	20	9.80 335	28	10.19 665	9.92 627	8	33
28	9.72 982	20	9.80 363	28	10.19 637	9.92 619	8	32
29	9.73 002	20	9.80 391	28	10.19 609	9.92 611	8	31
30	9.73 022	19	9.80 419	28	10.19 581	9.92 603	8	30
31	9.73 041	20	9.80 447	27	10.19 553	9.92 595	8	29
32	9.73 061	20	9.80 474	28	10.19 526	9.92 587	8	28
33	9.73 081	20	9.80 502	28	10.19 498	9.92 579	8	27
34	9.73 101	20	9.80 530	28	10.19 470	9.92 571	8	26
35	9.73 121	19	9.80 558	28	10.19 442	9.92 563	8	25
36	9.73 140	20	9.80 586	28	10.19 414	9.92 555	9	24
37	9.73 160	20	9.80 614	28	10.19 386	9.92 546	8	23
38	9.73 180	20	9.80 642	27	10.19 358	9.92 538	8	22
39	9.73 200	19	9.80 669	28	10.19 331	9.92 530	8	21
40	9.73 219	20	9.80 697	28	10.19 303	9.92 522	8	20
41	9.73 239	20	9.80 725	28	10.19 275	9.92 514	8	19
42	9.73 259	19	9.80 753	28	10.19 247	9.92 506	8	18
43	9.73 278	20	9.80 781	27	10.19 219	9.92 498	8	17
44	9.73 298	20	9.80 808	28	10.19 192	9.92 490	8	16
45	9.73 318	19	9.80 836	28	10.19 164	9.92 482	9	15
46	9.73 337	20	9.80 864	28	10.19 136	9.92 473	8	14
47	9.73 357	20	9.80 892	27	10.19 108	9.92 465	8	13
48	9.73 377	19	9.80 919	28	10.19 081	9.92 457	8	12
49	9.73 396	20	9.80 947	28	10.19 053	9.92 449	8	11
50	9.73 416	19	9.80 975	28	10.19 025	9.92 441	8	10
51	9.73 435	20	9.81 003	27	10.18 997	9.92 433	8	9
52	9.73 455	19	9.81 030	28	10.18 970	9.92 425	9	8
53	9.73 474	20	9.81 058	28	10.18 942	9.92 416	8	7
54	9.73 494	19	9.81 086	28	10.18 914	9.92 408	8	6
55	9.73 513	20	9.81 113	28	10.18 887	9.92 400	8	5
56	9.73 533	19	9.81 141	28	10.18 859	9.92 392	8	4
57	9.73 552	19	9.81 169	27	10.18 831	9.92 384	8	3
58	9.73 572	19	9.81 196	28	10.18 804	9.92 376	9	2
59	9.73 591	20	9.81 224	28	10.18 776	9.92 367	8	1
60	9.73 611		9.81 252		10.18 748	9.92 359		0
′	L Cos	d	L Ctn	c d	L Tan	L Sin	d	′

Proportional parts

″	29	28	27
1	0.5	0.5	0.4
2	1.0	0.9	0.9
3	1.4	1.4	1.4
4	1.9	1.9	1.8
5	2.4	2.3	2.2
6	2.9	2.8	2.7
7	3.4	3.3	3.2
8	3.9	3.7	3.6
9	4.4	4.2	4.0
10	4.8	4.7	4.5
20	9.7	9.3	9.0
30	14.5	14.0	13.5
40	19.3	18.7	18.0
50	24.2	23.3	22.5

″	21	20	19
1	0.4	0.3	0.3
2	0.7	0.7	0.6
3	1.0	1.0	1.0
4	1.4	1.3	1.3
5	1.8	1.7	1.6
6	2.1	2.0	1.9
7	2.4	2.3	2.2
8	2.8	2.7	2.5
9	3.2	3.0	2.8
10	3.5	3.3	3.2
20	7.0	6.7	6.3
30	10.5	10.0	9.5
40	14.0	13.3	12.7
50	17.5	16.7	15.8

″	9	8	7
1	0.2	0.1	0.1
2	0.3	0.3	0.2
3	0.4	0.4	0.4
4	0.6	0.5	0.5
5	0.8	0.7	0.6
6	0.9	0.8	0.7
7	1.0	0.9	0.8
8	1.2	1.1	0.9
9	1.4	1.2	1.0
10	1.5	1.3	1.2
20	3.0	2.7	2.3
30	4.5	4.0	3.5
40	6.0	5.3	4.7
50	7.5	6.7	5.8

Proportional parts

′	L Sin	d	L Tan	c d	L Ctn	L Cos	d	′	Proportional parts		
0	9.73 611	19	9.81 252	27	10.18 748	9.92 359	8	60			
1	9.73 630	20	9.81 279	28	10.18 721	9.92 351	8	59			
2	9.73 650	19	9.81 307	28	10.18 693	9.92 343	8	58			
3	9.73 669	20	9.81 335	27	10.18 665	9.92 335	9	57			
4	9.73 689	19	9.81 362	28	10.18 638	9.92 326	8	56			
5	9.73 708	19	9.81 390	28	10.18 610	9.92 318	8	55			
6	9.73 727	20	9.81 418	27	10.18 582	9.92 310	8	54	′′	28	27
7	9.73 747	19	9.81 445	28	10.18 555	9.92 302	9	53	1	0.5	0.4
8	9.73 766	19	9.81 473	27	10.18 527	9.92 293	8	52	2	0.9	0.9
9	9.73 785	20	9.81 500	28	10.18 500	9.92 285	8	51	3	1.4	1.4
10	9.73 805	19	9.81 528	28	10.18 472	9.92 277	8	50	4	1.9	1.8
11	9.73 824	19	9.81 556	27	10.18 444	9.92 269	9	49			
12	9.73 843	20	9.81 583	28	10.18 417	9.92 260	8	48	5	2.3	2.2
13	9.73 863	19	9.81 611	27	10.18 389	9.92 252	8	47	6	2.8.	2.7
14	9.73 882	19	9.81 638	28	10.18 362	9.92 244	9	46	7	3.3	3.2
									8	3.7	3.6
15	9.73 901	20	9.81 666	27	10.18 334	9.92 235	8	45	9	4.2	4.0
16	9.73 921	19	9.81 693	28	10.18 307	9.92 227	8	44			
17	9.73 940	19	9.81 721	27	10.18 279	9.92 219	8	43	10	4.7	4.5
18	9.73 959	19	9.81 748	28	10.18 252	9.92 211	9	42	20	9.3	9.0
19	9.73 978	19	9.81 776	27	10.18 224	9.92 202	8	41	30	14.0	13.5
									40	18.7	18.0
20	9.73 997	20	9.81 803	28	10.18 197	9.92 194	8	40	50	23.3	22.5
21	9.74 017	19	9.81 831	27	10.18 169	9.92 186	9	39			
22	9.74 036	19	9.81 858	28	10.18 142	9.92 177	8	38			
23	9.74 055	19	9.81 886	27	10.18 114	9.92 169	8	37	′′	20 19	18
24	9.74 074	19	9.81 913	28	10.18 087	9.92 161	9	36	1	0.3 0.3	0.3
									2	0.7 0.6	0.6
25	9.74 093	20	9.81 941	27	10.18 059	9.92 152	8	35	3	1.0 1.0	0.9
26	9.74 113	19	9.81 968	28	10.18 032	9.92 144	8	34	4	1.3 1.3	1.2
27	9.74 132	19	9.81 996	27	10.18 004	9.92 136	9	33			
28	9.74 151	19	9.82 023	28	10.17 977	9.92 127	8	32	5	1.7 1.6	1.5
29	9.74 170	19	9.82 051	27	10.17 949	9.92 119	8	31	6	2.0 1.9	1.8
									7	2.3 2.2	2.1
30	9.74 189	19	9.82 078	28	10.17 922	9.92 111	9	30	8	2.7 2.5	2.4
31	9.74 208	19	9.82 106	27	10.17 894	9.92 102	8	29	9	3.0 2.8	2.7
32	9.74 227	19	9.82 133	28	10.17 867	9.92 094	8	28			
33	9.74 246	19	9.82 161	27	10.17 839	9.92 086	9	27	10	3.3 3.2	3.0
34	9.74 265	19	9.82 188	27	10.17 812	9.92 077	8	26	20	6.7 6.3	6.0
									30	10.0 9.5	9.0
35	9.74 284	19	9.82 215	28	10.17 785	9.92 069	9	25	40	13.3 12.7	12.0
36	9.74 303	19	9.82 243	27	10.17 757	9.92 060	8	24	50	16.7 15.8	15.0
37	9.74 322	19	9.82 270	28	10.17 730	9.92 052	8	23			
38	9.74 341	19	9.82 298	27	10.17 702	9.92 044	9	22			
39	9.74 360	19	9.82 325	27	10.17 675	9.92 035	8	21	′′	9	8
40	9.74 379	19	9.82 352	28	10.17 648	9.92 027	9	20	1	0.2	0.1
41	9.74 398	19	9.82 380	27	10.17 620	9.92 018	8	19	2	0.3	0.3
42	9.74 417	19	9.82 407	28	10.17 593	9.92 010	8	18	3	0.4	0.4
43	9.74 436	19	9.82 435	27	10.17 565	9.92 002	9	17	4	0.6	0.5
44	9.74 455	19	9.82 462	27	10.17 538	9.91 993	8	16			
									5	0.8	0.7
45	9.74 474	19	9.82 489	28	10.17 511	9.91 985	9	15	6	0.9	0.8
46	9.74 493	19	9.82 517	27	10.17 483	9.91 976	8	14	7	1.0	0.9
47	9.74 512	19	9.82 544	27	10.17 456	9.91 968	9	13	8	1.2	1.1
48	9.74 531	18	9.82 571	28	10.17 429	9.91 959	8	12	9	1.4	1.2
49	9.74 549	19	9.82 599	27	10.17 401	9.91 951	9	11			
									10	1.5	1.3
50	9.74 568	19	9.82 626	27	10.17 374	9.91 942	8	10	20	3.0	2.7
51	9.74 587	19	9.82 653	28	10.17 347	9.91 934	9	9	30	4.5	4.0
52	9.74 606	19	9.82 681	27	10.17 319	9.91 925	8	8	40	6.0	5.3
53	9.74 625	19	9.82 708	27	10.17 292	9.91 917	9	7	50	7.5	6.7
54	9.74 644	18	9.82 735	27	10.17 265	9.91 908	8	6			
55	9.74 662	19	9.82 762	28	10.17 238	9.91 900	9	5			
56	9.74 681	19	9.82 790	27	10.17 210	9.91 891	8	4			
57	9.74 700	19	9.82 817	27	10.17 183	9.91 883	9	3			
58	9.74 719	18	9.82 844	27	10.17 156	9.91 874	8	2			
59	9.74 737	19	9.82 871	28	10.17 129	9.91 866	9	1			
60	9.74 756		9.82 899		10.17 101	9.91 857		0			
′	L Cos	d	L Ctn	c d	L Tan	L Sin	d	′	Proportional parts		

′	L Sin	d	L Tan	c d	L Ctn	L Cos	d	′	Proportional parts		
0	9.74 756	19	9.82 899	27	10.17 101	9.91 857	8	60			
1	9.74 775	19	9.82 926	27	10.17 074	9.91 849	9	59			
2	9.74 794	18	9.82 953	27	10.17 047	9.91 840	8	58			
3	9.74 812	19	9.82 980	28	10.17 020	9.91 832	9	57			
4	9.74 831	19	9.83 008	27	10.16 992	9.91 823	8	56			
5	9.74 850	18	9.83 035	27	10.16 965	9.91 815	9	55	″	28	27	26
6	9.74 868	19	9.83 062	27	10.16 938	9.91 806	8	54				
7	9.74 887	19	9.83 089	28	10.16 911	9.91 798	9	53	1	0.5	0.4	0.4
8	9.74 906	18	9.83 117	27	10.16 883	9.91 789	8	52	2	0.9	0.9	0.9
9	9.74 924	19	9.83 144	27	10.16 856	9.91 781	9	51	3	1.4	1.4	1.3
10	9.74 943	18	9.83 171	27	10.16 829	9.91 772	9	50	4	1.9	1.8	1.7
11	9.74 961	19	9.83 198	27	10.16 802	9.91 763	8	49				
12	9.74 980	19	9.83 225	27	10.16 775	9.91 755	9	48	5	2.3	2.2	2.2
13	9.74 999	18	9.83 252	28	10.16 748	9.91 746	8	47	6	2.8	2.7	2.6
14	9.75 017	19	9.83 280	27	10.16 720	9.91 738	9	46	7	3.3	3.2	3.0
15	9.75 036	18	9.83 307	27	10.16 693	9.91 729	9	45	8	3.7	3.6	3.5
16	9.75 054	19	9.83 334	27	10.16 666	9.91 720	8	44	9	4.2	4.0	3.9
17	9.75 073	18	9.83 361	27	10.16 639	9.91 712	9	43				
18	9.75 091	19	9.83 388	27	10.16 612	9.91 703	8	42	10	4.7	4.5	4.3
19	9.75 110	18	9.83 415	27	10.16 585	9.91 695	9	41	20	9.3	9.0	8.7
20	9.75 128	19	9.83 442	28	10.16 558	9.91 686	9	40	30	14.0	13.5	13.0
21	9.75 147	18	9.83 470	27	10.16 530	9.91 677	8	39	40	18.7	18.0	17.3
22	9.75 165	19	9.83 497	27	10.16 503	9.91 669	9	38	50	23.3	22.5	21.7
23	9.75 184	18	9.83 524	27	10.16 476	9.91 660	9	37				
24	9.75 202	19	9.83 551	27	10.16 449	9.91 651	8	36	″		19	18
25	9.75 221	18	9.83 578	27	10.16 422	9.91 643	9	35	1		0.3	0.3
26	9.75 239	19	9.83 605	27	10.16 395	9.91 634	9	34	2		0.6	0.6
27	9.75 258	18	9.83 632	27	10.16 368	9.91 625	8	33	3		1.0	0.9
28	9.75 276	18	9.83 659	27	10.16 341	9.91 617	9	32	4		1.3	1.2
29	9.75 294	19	9.83 686	27	10.16 314	9.91 608	9	31				
30	9.75 313	18	9.83 713	27	10.16 287	9.91 599	8	30	5		1.6	1.5
31	9.75 331	19	9.83 740	28	10.16 260	9.91 591	9	29	6		1.9	1.8
32	9.75 350	18	9.83 768	27	10.16 232	9.91 582	9	28	7		2.2	2.1
33	9.75 368	18	9.83 795	27	10.16 205	9.91 573	8	27	8		2.5	2.4
34	9.75 386	19	9.83 822	27	10.16 178	9.91 565	9	26	9		2.8	2.7
35	9.75 405	18	9.83 849	27	10.16 151	9.91 556	9	25	10		3.2	3.0
36	9.75 423	18	9.83 876	27	10.16 124	9.91 547	9	24	20		6.3	6.0
37	9.75 441	18	9.83 903	27	10.16 097	9.91 538	8	23	30		9.5	9.0
38	9.75 459	19	9.83 930	27	10.16 070	9.91 530	9	22	40		12.7	12.0
39	9.75 478	18	9.83 957	27	10.16 043	9.91 521	9	21	50		15.8	15.0
40	9.75 496	18	9.83 984	27	10.16 016	9.91 512	8	20				
41	9.75 514	19	9.84 011	27	10.15 989	9.91 504	9	19	″		9	8
42	9.75 533	18	9.84 038	27	10.15 962	9.91 495	9	18	1		0.2	0.1
43	9.75 551	18	9.84 065	27	10.15 935	9.91 486	9	17	2		0.3	0.3
44	9.75 569	18	9.84 092	27	10.15 908	9.91 477	8	16	3		0.4	0.4
45	9.75 587	18	9.84 119	27	10.15 881	9.91 469	9	15	4		0.6	0.5
46	9.75 605	19	9.84 146	27	10.15 854	9.91 460	9	14				
47	9.75 624	18	9.84 173	27	10.15 827	9.91 451	9	13	5		0.8	0.7
48	9.75 642	18	9.84 200	27	10.15 800	9.91 442	9	12	6		0.9	0.8
49	9.75 660	18	9.84 227	27	10.15 773	9.91 433	8	11	7		1.0	0.9
50	9.75 678	18	9.84 254	26	10.15 746	9.91 425	9	10	8		1.2	1.1
51	9.75 696	18	9.84 280	27	10.15 720	9.91 416	9	9	9		1.4	1.2
52	9.75 714	19	9.84 307	27	10.15 693	9.91 407	9	8				
53	9.75 733	18	9.84 334	27	10.15 666	9.91 398	9	7	10		1.5	1.3
54	9.75 751	18	9.84 361	27	10.15 639	9.91 389	8	6	20		3.0	2.7
55	9.75 769	18	9.84 388	27	10.15 612	9.91 381	9	5	30		4.5	4.0
56	9 75 787	18	9.84 415	27	10.15 585	9.91 372	9	4	40		6.0	5.3
57	9.75 805	18	9.84 442	27	10.15 558	9.91 363	9	3	50		7.5	6.7
58	9.75 823	18	9.84 469	27	10.15 531	9.91 354	9	2				
59	9.75 841	18	9.84 496	27	10.15 504	9.91 345	9	1				
60	9.75 859		9.84 523		10.15 477	9.91 336		0				
′	L Cos	d	L Ctn	c d	L Tan	L Sin	d	′	Proportional parts		

′	L Sin	d	L Tan	cd	L Ctn	L Cos	d	′	Proportional parts			
0	9.75 859	18	9.84 523	27	10.15 477	9.91 336	8	60				
1	9.75 877	18	9.84 550	26	10.15 450	9.91 328	9	59				
2	9.75 895	18	9.84 576	27	10.15 424	9.91 319	9	58				
3	9.75 913	18	9.84 603	27	10.15 397	9.91 310	9	57				
4	9.75 931	18	9.84 630	27	10.15 370	9.91 301	9	56				
5	9.75 949	18	9.84 657	27	10.15 343	9.91 292	9	55				
6	9.75 967	18	9.84 684	27	10.15 316	9.91 283	9	54				
7	9.75 985	18	9.84 711	27	10.15 289	9.91 274	8	53	′′	27	26	18
8	9.76 003	18	9.84 738	26	10.15 262	9.91 266	9	52	1	0.4	0.4	0.3
9	9.76 021	18	9.84 764	27	10.15 236	9.91 257	9	51	2	0.9	0.9	0.6
10	9.76 039	18	9.84 791	27	10.15 209	9.91 248	9	50	3	1.4	1.3	0.9
11	9.76 057	18	9.84 818	27	10.15 182	9.91 239	9	49	4	1.8	1.7	1.2
12	9.76 075	18	9.84 845	27	10.15 155	9.91 230	9	48				
13	9.76 093	18	9.84 872	27	10.15 128	9.91 221	9	47	5	2.2	2.2	1.5
14	9.76 111	18	9.84 899	26	10.15 101	9.91 212	9	46	6	2.7	2.6	1.8
15	9.76 129	17	9.84 925	27	10.15 075	9.91 203	9	45	7	3.2	3.0	2.1
16	9.76 146	18	9.84 952	27	10.15 048	9.91 194	9	44	8	3.6	3.5	2.4
17	9.76 164	18	9.84 979	27	10.15 021	9.91 185	9	43	9	4.0	3.9	2.7
18	9.76 182	18	9.85 006	27	10.14 994	9.91 176	9	42				
19	9.76 200	18	9.85 033	26	10.14 967	9.91 167	9	41	10	4.5	4.3	3.0
20	9.76 218	18	9.85 059	27	10.14 941	9.91 158	9	40	20	9.0	8.7	6.0
21	9.76 236	17	9.85 086	27	10.14 914	9.91 149	8	39	30	13.5	13.0	9.0
22	9.76 253	18	9.85 113	27	10.14 887	9.91 141	9	38	40	18.0	17.3	12.0
23	9.76 271	18	9.85 140	26	10.14 860	9.91 132	9	37	50	22.5	21.7	15.0
24	9.76 289	18	9.85 166	27	10.14 834	9.91 123	9	36				
25	9.76 307	17	9.85 193	27	10.14 807	9.91 114	9	35	′′	17	10	
26	9.76 324	18	9.85 220	27	10.14 780	9.91 105	9	34	1	0.3	0.2	
27	9.76 342	18	9.85 247	26	10.14 753	9.91 096	9	33	2	0.6	0.3	
28	9.76 360	18	9.85 273	27	10.14 727	9.91 087	9	32	3	0.8	0.5	
29	9.76 378	17	9.85 300	27	10.14 700	9.91 078	9	31	4	1.1	0.7	
30	9.76 395	18	9.85 327	27	10.14 673	9.91 069	9	30	5	1.4	0.8	
31	9.76 413	18	9.85 354	26	10.14 646	9.91 060	9	29	6	1.7	1.0	
32	9.76 431	17	9.85 380	27	10.14 620	9.91 051	9	28	7	2.0	1.2	
33	9.76 448	18	9.85 407	27	10.14 593	9.91 042	9	27	8	2.3	1.3	
34	9.76 466	18	9.85 434	26	10.14 566	9.91 033	10	26	9	2.6	1.5	
35	9.76 484	17	9.85 460	27	10.14 540	9.91 023	9	25				
36	9.76 501	18	9.85 487	27	10.14 513	9.91 014	9	24	10	2.8	1.7	
37	9.76 519	18	9.85 514	26	10.14 486	9.91 005	9	23	20	5.7	3.3	
38	9.76 537	17	9.85 540	27	10.14 460	9.90 996	9	22	30	8.5	5.0	
39	9.76 554	18	9.85 567	27	10.14 433	9.90 987	9	21	40	11.3	6.7	
40	9.76 572	18	9.85 594	26	10.14 406	9.90 978	9	20	50	14.2	8.3	
41	9.76 590	17	9.85 620	27	10.14 380	9.90 969	9	19				
42	9.76 607	18	9.85 647	27	10.14 353	9.90 960	9	18	′′	9	8	
43	9.76 625	17	9.85 674	26	10.14 326	9.90 951	9	17	1	0.2	0.1	
44	9.76 642	18	9.85 700	27	10.14 300	9.90 942	9	16	2	0.3	0.3	
45	9.76 660	17	9.85 727	27	10.14 273	9.90 933	9	15	3	0.4	0.4	
46	9.76 677	18	9.85 754	26	10.14 246	9.90 924	9	14	4	0.6	0.5	
47	9.76 695	17	9.85 780	27	10.14 220	9.90 915	9	13				
48	9.76 712	18	9.85 807	27	10.14 193	9.90 906	10	12	5	0.8	0.7	
49	9.76 730	17	9.85 834	26	10.14 166	9.90 896	9	11	6	0.9	0.8	
50	9.76 747	18	9.85 860	27	10.14 140	9.90 887	9	10	7	1.0	0.9	
51	9.76 765	17	9.85 887	26	10.14 113	9.90 878	9	9	8	1.2	1.1	
52	9.76 782	18	9.85 913	27	10.14 087	9.90 869	9	8	9	1.4	1.2	
53	9.76 800	17	9.85 940	27	10.14 060	9.90 860	9	7				
54	9.76 817	18	9.85 967	26	10.14 033	9.90 851	9	6	10	1.5	1.3	
55	9.76 835	17	9.85 993	27	10.14 007	9.90 842	10	5	20	3.0	2.7	
56	9.76 852	18	9.86 020	26	10.13 980	9.90 832	9	4	30	4.5	4.0	
57	9.76 870	17	9.86 046	27	10.13 954	9.90 823	9	3	40	6.0	5.3	
58	9.76 887	17	9.86 073	27	10.13 927	9.90 814	9	2	50	7.5	6.7	
59	9.76 904	18	9.86 100	26	10.13 900	9.90 805	9	1				
60	9.76 922	—	9.86 126		10.13 874	9.90 796	—	0				
′	L Cos	d	L Ctn	c d	L Tan	L Sin	d	′	Proportional parts			

′	L Sin	d	L Tan	c d	L Ctn	L Cos	d	′
0	9.76 922	17	9.86 126	27	10.13 874	9.90 796	9	60
1	9.76 939	18	9.86 153	26	10.13 847	9.90 787	10	59
2	9.76 957	17	9.86 179	27	10.13 821	9.90 777	9	58
3	9.76 974	17	9.86 206	26	10.13 794	9.90 768	9	57
4	9.76 991	18	9.86 232	27	10.13 768	9.90 759	9	56
5	9.77 009	17	9.86 259	26	10.13 741	9.90 750	9	55
6	9.77 026	17	9.86 285	27	10.13 715	9.90 741	10	54
7	9.77 043	18	9.86 312	26	10.13 688	9.90 731	9	53
8	9.77 061	17	9.86 338	27	10.13 662	9.90 722	9	52
9	9.77 078	17	9.86 365	27	10.13 635	9.90 713	9	51
10	9.77 095	17	9.86 392	26	10.13 608	9.90 704	10	50
11	9.77 112	18	9.86 418	27	10.13 582	9.90 694	9	49
12	9.77 130	17	9.86 445	26	10.13 555	9.90 685	9	48
13	9.77 147	17	9.86 471	27	10.13 529	9.90 676	9	47
14	9.77 164	17	9.86 498	26	10.13 502	9.90 667	10	46
15	9.77 181	18	9.86 524	27	10.13 476	9.90 657	9	45
16	9.77 199	17	9.86 551	26	10.13 449	9.90 648	9	44
17	9.77 216	17	9.86 577	26	10.13 423	9.90 639	9	43
18	9.77 233	17	9.86 603	27	10.13 397	9.90 630	10	42
19	9.77 250	18	9.86 630	26	10.13 370	9.90 620	9	41
20	9.77 268	17	9.86 656	27	10.13 344	9.90 611	9	40
21	9.77 285	17	9.86 683	26	10.13 317	9.90 602	10	39
22	9.77 302	17	9.86 709	27	10.13 291	9.90 592	9	38
23	9.77 319	17	9.86 736	26	10.13 264	9.90 583	9	37
24	9.77 336	17	9.86 762	27	10.13 238	9.90 574	9	36
25	9.77 353	17	9.86 789	26	10.13 211	9.90 565	10	35
26	9.77 370	17	9.86 815	27	10.13 185	9.90 555	9	34
27	9.77 387	18	9.86 842	26	10.13 158	9.90 546	9	33
28	9.77 405	17	9.86 868	26	10.13 132	9.90 537	10	32
29	9.77 422	17	9.86 894	27	10.13 106	9.90 527	9	31
30	9.77 439	17	9.86 921	26	10.13 079	9.90 518	9	30
31	9.77 456	17	9.86 947	27	10.13 053	9.90 509	10	29
32	9.77 473	17	9.86 974	26	10.13 026	9.90 499	10	28
33	9.77 490	17	9.87 000	27	10.13 000	9.90 490	10	27
34	9.77 507	17	9.87 027	26	10.12 973	9.90 480	9	26
35	9.77 524	17	9.87 053	26	10.12 947	9.90 471	9	25
36	9.77 541	17	9.87 079	27	10.12 921	9.90 462	10	24
37	9.77 558	17	9.87 106	26	10.12 894	9.90 452	9	23
38	9.77 575	17	9.87 132	26	10.12 868	9.90 443	9	22
39	9.77 592	17	9.87 158	27	10.12 842	9.90 434	10	21
40	9.77 609	17	9.87 185	26	10.12 815	9.90 424	9	20
41	9.77 626	17	9.87 211	27	10.12 789	9.90 415	10	19
42	9.77 643	17	9.87 238	26	10.12 762	9.90 405	9	18
43	9.77 660	17	9.87 264	26	10.12 736	9.90 396	10	17
44	9.77 677	17	9.87 290	27	10.12 710	9.90 386	9	16
45	9.77 694	17	9.87 317	26	10.12 683	9.90 377	9	15
46	9.77 711	17	9.87 343	26	10.12 657	9.90 368	10	14
47	9.77 728	16	9.87 369	27	10 12 631	9.90 358	9	13
48	9.77 744	17	9.87 396	26	10.12 604	9.90 349	10	12
49	9.77 761	17	9.87 422	26	10.12 578	9.90 339	9	11
50	9.77 778	17	9.87 448	27	10.12 552	9.90 330	10	10
51	9.77 795	17	9.87 475	26	10.12 525	9.90 320	9	9
52	9.77 812	17	9.87 501	26	10.12 499	9.90 311	10	8
53	9.77 829	17	9.87 527	27	10.12 473	9.90 301	9	7
54	9.77 846	16	9.87 554	26	10.12 446	9.90 292	10	6
55	9.77 862	17	9.87 580	26	10.12 420	9.90 282	9	5
56	9.77 879	17	9.87 606	27	10.12 394	9.90 273	10	4
57	9.77 896	17	9.87 633	26	10.12 367	9.90 263	9	3
58	9.77 913	17	9.87 659	26	10.12 341	9.90 254	10	2
59	9.77 930	16	9.87 685	26	10.12 315	9.90 244	9	1
60	9.77 946		9.87 711		10.12 289	9.90 235		0
′	L Cos	d	L Ctn	c d	L Tan	L Sin	d	′

Proportional parts

′′	27	26
1	0.4	0.4
2	0.9	0.9
3	1.4	1.3
4	1.8	1.7
5	2.2	2.2
6	2.7	2.6
7	3.2	3.0
8	3.6	3.5
9	4.0	3.9
10	4.5	4.3
20	9.0	8.7
30	13.5	13.0
40	18.0	17.3
50	22.5	21.7

′′	18	17	16
1	0.3	0.3	0.3
2	0.6	0.6	0.5
3	0.9	0.8	0.8
4	1.2	1.1	1.1
5	1.5	1.4	1.3
6	1.8	1.7	1.6
7	2.1	2.0	1.9
8	2.4	2.3	2.1
9	2.7	2.6	2.4
10	3.0	2.8	2.7
20	6.0	5.7	5.3
30	9.0	8.5	8.0
40	12.0	11.3	10.7
50	15.0	14.2	13.3

′′	10	9
1	0.2	0.2
2	0.3	0.3
3	0.5	0.4
4	0.7	0.6
5	0.8	0.8
6	1.0	0.9
7	1.2	1.0
8	1.3	1.2
9	1.5	1.4
10	1.7	1.5
20	3.3	3.0
30	5.0	4.5
40	6.7	6.0
50	8.3	7.5

′	L Sin	d	L Tan	c d	L Ctn	L Cos	d	′	Proportional parts		
0	9.77 946	17	9.87 711	27	10.12 289	9.90 235	10	60			
1	9.77 963	17	9.87 738	26	10.12 262	9.90 225	9	59			
2	9.77 980	17	9.87 764	26	10.12 236	9.90 216	10	58			
3	9.77 997	16	9.87 790	27	10.12 210	9.90 206	9	57			
4	9.78 013	17	9.87 817	26	10.12 183	9.90 197	10	56			
5	9.78 030	17	9.87 843	26	10.12 157	9.90 187	9	55			
6	9.78 047	16	9.87 869	26	10.12 131	9.90 178	10	54			
7	9.78 063	17	9.87 895	27	10.12 105	9.90 168	9	53	′′	27	26
8	9.78 080	17	9.87 922	26	10.12 078	9.90 159	10	52	1	0.4	0.4
9	9.78 097	16	9.87 948	26	10.12 052	9.90 149	10	51	2	0.9	0.9
10	9.78 113	17	9.87 974	26	10.12 026	9.90 139	9	50	3	1.4	1.3
11	9.78 130	17	9.88 000	27	10.12 000	9.90 130	10	49	4	1.8	1.7
12	9.78 147	16	9.88 027	26	10.11 973	9.90 120	9	48			
13	9.78 163	17	9.88 053	26	10.11 947	9.90 111	10	47	5	2.2	2.2
14	9.78 180	17	9.88 079	26	10.11 921	9.90 101	10	46	6	2.7	2.6
									7	3.2	3.0
15	9.78 197	16	9.88 105	26	10.11 895	9.90 091	9	45	8	3.6	3.5
16	9.78 213	17	9.88 131	27	10.11 869	9.90 082	10	44	9	4.0	3.9
17	9.78 230	16	9.88 158	26	10.11 842	9.90 072	9	43			
18	9.78 246	17	9.88 184	26	10.11 816	9.90 063	10	42	10	4.5	4.3
19	9.78 263	17	9.88 210	26	10.11 790	9.90 053	10	41	20	9.0	8.7
									30	13.5	13.0
20	9.78 280	16	9.88 236	26	10.11 764	9.90 043	9	40	40	18.0	17.3
21	9.78 296	17	9.88 262	27	10.11 738	9.90 034	10	39	50	22.5	21.7
22	9.78 313	16	9.88 289	26	10.11 711	9.90 024	10	38			
23	9.78 329	17	9.88 315	26	10.11 685	9.90 014	9	37			
24	9.78 346	16	9.88 341	26	10.11 659	9.90 005	10	36	′′	17	16
25	9.78 362	17	9.88 367	26	10.11 633	9.89 995	10	35	1	0.3	0.3
26	9.78 379	16	9.88 393	27	10.11 607	9.89 985	9	34	2	0.6	0.5
27	9.78 395	17	9.88 420	26	10.11 580	9.89 976	10	33	3	0.8	0.8
28	9.78 412	16	9.88 446	26	10.11 554	9.89 966	10	32	4	1.1	1.1
29	9.78 428	17	9.88 472	26	10.11 528	9.89 956	9	31	5	1.4	1.3
									6	1.7	1 6
30	9.78 445	16	9.88 498	26	10.11 502	9.89 947	10	30	7	2.0	1.9
31	9.78 461	17	9.88 524	26	10.11 476	9.89 937	10	29	8	2.3	2.1
32	9.78 478	16	9.88 550	27	10.11 450	9.89 927	9	28	9	2.6	2.4
33	9.78 494	16	9.88 577	26	10.11 423	9.89 918	10	27			
34	9.78 510	17	9.88 603	26	10.11 397	9.89 908	10	26	10	2.8	2.7
									20	5.7	5.3
35	9.78 527	16	9.88 629	26	10.11 371	9.89 898	10	25	30	8.5	8.0
36	9.78 543	17	9.88 655	26	10.11 345	9.89 888	9	24	40	11.3	10.7
37	9.78 560	16	9.88 681	26	10.11 319	9.89 879	10	23	50	14.2	13.3
38	9.78 576	16	9.88 707	26	10.11 293	9.89 869	10	22			
39	9.78 592	17	9.88 733	26	10.11 267	9.89 859	10	21			
									′′	10	9
40	9.78 609	16	9.88 759	27	10.11 241	9.89 849	9	20	1	0.2	0.2
41	9.78 625	17	9.88 786	26	10.11 214	9.89 840	10	19	2	0.3	0.3
42	9.78 642	16	9.88 812	26	10.11 188	9.89 830	10	18	3	0.5	0.4
43	9.78 658	16	9.88 838	26	10.11 162	9.89 820	10	17	4	0.7	0.6
44	9.78 674	17	9.88 864	26	10.11 136	9.89 810	9	16			
									5	0.8	0.8
45	9.78 691	16	9.88 890	26	10.11 110	9.89 801	10	15	6	1.0	0.9
46	9.78 707	16	9.88 916	26	10.11 084	9.89 791	10	14	7	1.2	1.0
47	9.78 723	16	9.88 942	26	10.11 058	9.89 781	10	13	8	1.3	1.2
48	9.78 739	17	9.88 968	26	10.11 032	9.89 771	10	12	9	1.5	1.4
49	9.78 756	16	9.88 994	26	10.11 006	9.89 761	9	11			
									10	1.7	1.5
50	9.78 772	16	9.89 020	26	10.10 980	9.89 752	10	10	20	3.3	3.0
51	9.78 788	17	9.89 046	27	10.10 954	9.89 742	10	9	30	5.0	4.5
52	9.78 805	16	9.89 073	26	10.10 927	9.89 732	10	8	40	6.7	6.0
53	9.78 821	16	9.89 099	26	10.10 901	9.89 722	10	7	50	8.3	7.5
54	9.78 837	16	9.89 125	26	10.10 875	9.89 712	10	6			
55	9.78 853	16	9.89 151	26	10.10 849	9.89 702	9	5			
56	9.78 869	17	9.89 177	26	10.10 823	9.89 693	10	4			
57	9.78 886	16	9.89 203	26	10.10 797	9.89 683	10	3			
58	9.78 902	16	9.89 229	26	10.10 771	9.89 673	10	2			
59	9.78 918	16	9.89 255	26	10.10 745	9.89 663	10	1			
60	9.78 934		9.89 281		10.10 719	9.89 653		0			
′	L Cos	d	L Ctn	c d	L Tan	L Sin	d	′	Proportional parts		

′	L Sin	d	L Tan	c d	L Ctn	L Cos	d	′
0	9.78 934	16	9.89 281	26	10.10 719	9.89 653	10	60
1	9.78 950	17	9.89 307	26	10.10 693	9.89 643	10	59
2	9.78 967	16	9.89 333	26	10.10 667	9.89 633	9	58
3	9.78 983	16	9.89 359	26	10.10 641	9.89 624	10	57
4	9.78 999	16	9.89 385	26	10.10 615	9.89 614	10	56
5	9.79 015	16	9.89 411	26	10.10 589	9.89 604	10	55
6	9.79 031	16	9.89 437	26	10.10 563	9.89 594	10	54
7	9.79 047	16	9.89 463	26	10.10 537	9.89 584	10	53
8	9.79 063	16	9.89 489	26	10.10 511	9.89 574	10	52
9	9.79 079	16	9.89 515	26	10.10 485	9.89 564	10	51
10	9.79 095	16	9.89 541	26	10.10 459	9.89 554	10	50
11	9.79 111	17	9.89 567	26	10.10 433	9.89 544	10	49
12	9.79 128	16	9.89 593	26	10.10 407	9.89 534	10	48
13	9.79 144	16	9.89 619	26	10.10 381	9.89 524	10	47
14	9.79 160	16	9.89 645	26	10.10 355	9.89 514	10	46
15	9.79 176	16	9.89 671	26	10.10 329	9.89 504	9	45
16	9.79 192	16	9.89 697	26	10.10 303	9.89 495	10	44
17	9.79 208	16	9.89 723	26	10.10 277	9.89 485	10	43
18	9.79 224	16	9.89 749	26	10.10 251	9.89 475	10	42
19	9.79 240	16	9.89 775	26	10.10 225	9.89 465	10	41
20	9.79 256	16	9.89 801	26	10.10 199	9.89 455	10	40
21	9.79 272	16	9.89 827	26	10.10 173	9.89 445	10	39
22	9.79 288	16	9.89 853	26	10.10 147	9.89 435	10	38
23	9.79 304	15	9.89 879	26	10.10 121	9.89 425	10	37
24	9.79 319	16	9.89 905	26	10.10 095	9.89 415	10	36
25	9.79 335	16	9.89 931	26	10.10 069	9.89 405	10	35
26	9.79 351	16	9.89 957	28	10.10 043	9.89 395	10	34
27	9.79 367	16	9.89 983	26	10.10 017	9.89 385	10	33
28	9.79 383	16	9.90 009	26	10.09 991	9.89 375	11	32
29	9.79 399	16	9.90 035	26	10.09 965	9.89 364	10	31
30	9.79 415	16	9.90 061	25	10.09 939	9.89 354	10	30
31	9.79 431	16	9.90 086	26	10.09 914	9.89 344	10	29
32	9.79 447	16	9.90 112	26	10.09 888	9.89 334	10	28
33	9.79 463	15	9.90 138	26	10.09 862	9.89 324	10	27
34	9.79 478	16	9.90 164	26	10.09 836	9.89 314	10	26
35	9.79 494	16	9.90 190	26	10.09 810	9.89 304	10	25
36	9.79 510	16	9.90 216	26	10.09 784	9.89 294	10	24
37	9.79 526	16	9.90 242	26	10.09 758	9.89 284	10	23
38	9.79 542	16	9.90 268	26	10.09 732	9.89 274	10	22
39	9.79 558	15	9.90 294	26	10.09 706	9.89 264	10	21
40	9.79 573	16	9.90 320	26	10.09 680	9.89 254	10	20
41	9.79 589	16	9.90 346	25	10.09 654	9.89 244	11	19
42	9.79 605	16	9.90 371	26	10.09 629	9.89 233	10	18
43	9.79 621	15	9.90 397	26	10.09 603	9.89 223	10	17
44	9.79 636	16	9.90 423	26	10.09 577	9.89 213	10	16
45	9.79 652	16	9.90 449	26	10.09 551	9.89 203	10	15
46	9.79 668	16	9.90 475	26	10.09 525	9.89 193	10	14
47	9.79 684	15	9.90 501	26	10.09 499	9.89 183	10	13
48	9.79 699	16	9.90 527	26	10.09 473	9.89 173	11	12
49	9.79 715	16	9.90 553	25	10.09 447	9.89 162	10	11
50	9.79 731	15	9.90 578	26	10.09 422	9.89 152	10	10
51	9.79 746	16	9.90 604	26	10.09 396	9.89 142	10	9
52	9.79 762	16	9.90 630	26	10.09 370	9.89 132	10	8
53	9.79 778	15	9.90 656	26	10.09 344	9.89 122	10	7
54	9.79 793	16	9.90 682	26	10.09 318	9.89 112	11	6
55	9.79 809	16	9.90 708	26	10.09 292	9.89 101	10	5
56	9.79 825	15	9.90 734	25	10.09 266	9.89 091	10	4
57	9.79 840	16	9.90 759	26	10.09 241	9.69 081	10	3
58	9.79 856	16	9.90 785	26	10.09 215	9.89 071	11	2
59	9.79 872	15	9.90 811	26	10.09 189	9.89 060	10	1
60	9.79 887		9.90 837		10.09 163	9.89 050		0
′	L Cos	d	L Ctn	c d	L Tan	L Sin	d	′

Proportional parts

″	26	25
1	0.4	0.4
2	0.9	0.8
3	1.3	1.2
4	1.7	1.7
5	2.2	2.1
6	2.6	2.5
7	3.0	2.9
8	3.5	3.3
9	3.9	3.8
10	4.3	4.2
20	8.7	8.3
30	13.0	12.5
40	17.3	16.7
50	21.7	20.8

″	17	16	15
1	0.3	0.3	0.2
2	0.6	0.5	0.5
3	0.8	0.8	0.8
4	1.1	1.1	1.0
5	1.4	1.3	1.2
6	1.7	1.6	1.5
7	2.0	1.9	1.8
8	2.3	2.1	2.0
9	2.6	2.4	2.2
10	2.8	2.7	2.5
20	5.7	5.3	5.0
30	8.5	8.0	7.5
40	11.3	10.7	10.0
50	14.2	13.3	12.5

″	11	10	9
1	0.2	0.2	0.2
2	0.4	0.3	0.3
3	0.6	0.5	0.4
4	0.7	0.7	0.6
5	0.9	0.8	0.8
6	1.1	1.0	0.9
7	1.3	1.2	1.0
8	1.5	1.3	1.2
9	1.6	1.5	1.4
10	1.8	1.7	1.5
20	3.7	3.3	3.0
30	5.5	5.0	4.5
40	7.3	6.7	6.0
50	9.2	8.3	7.5

′	L Sin	d	L Tan	c d	L Ctn	L Cos	d	′	Proportional parts		
0	9.79 887	16	9.90 837	26	10.09 163	9.89 050	10	60			
1	9.79 903	15	9.90 863	26	10.09 137	9.89 040	10	59			
2	9.79 918	16	9.90 889	25	10.09 111	9.89 030	10	58			
3	9.79 934	16	9.90 914	26	10.09 086	9.89 020	11	57			
4	9.79 950	15	9.90 940	26	10.09 060	9.89 009	10	56			
5	9.79 965	16	9.90 966	26	10.09 034	9.88 999	10	55			
6	9.79 981	15	9.90 992	26	10.09 008	9.88 989	11	54			
7	9.79 996	16	9.91 018	26	10.08 982	9.88 978	10	53	′′	26	25
8	9.80 012	15	9.91 043	26	10.08 957	9.88 968	10	52	1	0.4	0.4
9	9.80 027	16	9.91 069	26	10.08 931	9.88 958	10	51	2	0.9	0.8
10	9.80 043	15	9.91 095	26	10.08 905	9.88 948	11	50	3	1.3	1.2
11	9.80 058	16	9.91 121	26	10.08 879	9.88 937	10	49	4	1.7	1.7
12	9.80 074	15	9.91 147	25	10.08 853	9.88 927	10	48			
13	9.80 089	16	9.91 172	26	10.08 828	9.88 917	11	47	5	2.2	2.1
14	9.80 105	15	9.91 198	26	10.08 802	9.88 906	10	46	6	2.6	2.5
									7	3.0	2.9
15	9.80 120	16	9.91 224	26	10.08 776	9.88 896	10	45	8	3.5	3.3
16	9.80 136	15	9.91 250	26	10.08 750	9.88 886	11	44	9	3.9	3.8
17	9.80 151	15	9.91 276	25	10.08 724	9.88 875	10	43			
18	9.80 166	16	9.91 301	26	10.08 699	9.88 865	10	42	10	4.3	4.2
19	9.80 182	15	9.91 327	26	10.08 673	9.88 855	11	41	20	8.7	8.3
									30	13.0	12.5
20	9.80 197	16	9.91 353	26	10.08 647	9.88 844	10	40	40	17.3	16.7
21	9.80 213	15	9.91 379	25	10.08 621	9.88 834	10	39	50	21.7	20.8
22	9.80 228	16	9.91 404	26	10.08 596	9.88 824	11	38			
23	9.80 244	15	9.91 430	26	10.08 570	9.88 813	10	37			
24	9.80 259	15	9.91 456	26	10.08 544	9.88 803	10	36	′′	16	15
25	9.80 274	16	9.91 482	25	10.08 518	9.88 793	11	35	1	0.3	0.2
26	9.80 290	15	9.91 507	26	10.08 493	9.88 782	10	34	2	0.5	0.5
27	9.80 305	15	9.91 533	26	10.08 467	9.88 772	11	33	3	0.8	0.8
28	9.80 320	16	9.91 559	26	10.08 441	9.88 761	10	32	4	1.1	1.0
29	9.80 336	15	9.91 585	25	10.08 415	9.88 751	10	31			
									5	1.3	1.2
30	9.80 351	15	9.91 610	26	10.08 390	9.88 741	11	30	6	1.6	1.5
31	9.80 366	16	9.91 636	26	10.08 364	9.88 730	10	29	7	1.9	1.8
32	9.80 382	15	9.91 662	26	10.08 338	9.88 720	11	28	8	2.1	2.0
33	9.80 397	15	9.91 688	25	10.08 312	9.88 709	10	27	9	2.4	2.2
34	9.80 412	16	9.91 713	26	10.08 287	9.88 699	11	26			
									10	2.7	2.5
35	9.80 428	15	9.91 739	26	10.08 261	9.88 688	10	25	20	5.3	5.0
36	9.80 443	15	9.91 765	26	10.08 235	9.88 678	10	24	30	8.0	7.5
37	9.80 458	15	9.91 791	25	10.08 209	9.88 668	11	23	40	10.7	10.0
38	9.80 473	16	9.91 816	26	10.08 184	9.88 657	10	22	50	13.3	12.5
39	9.80 489	15	9.91 842	26	10.08 158	9.88 647	11	21			
40	9.80 504	15	9.91 868	25	10.08 132	9.88 636	10	20	′′	11	10
41	9.80 519	15	9.91 893	26	10.08 107	9.88 626	11	19	1	0.2	0.2
42	9.80 534	16	9.91 919	26	10.08 081	9.88 615	10	18	2	0.4	0.3
43	9.80 550	15	9.91 945	26	10.08 055	9.88 605	11	17	3	0.6	0.5
44	9.80 565	15	9.91 971	25	10.08 029	9.88 594	10	16	4	0.7	0.7
									5	0.9	0.8
45	9.80 580	15	9.91 996	26	10.08 004	9.88 584	11	15	6	1.1	1.0
46	9.80 595	15	9.92 022	26	10.07 978	9.88 573	10	14	7	1.3	1.2
47	9.80 610	15	9.92 048	25	10.07 952	9.88 563	11	13	8	1.5	1.3
48	9.80 625	16	9.92 073	26	10.07 927	9.88 552	10	12	9	1.6	1.5
49	9.80 641	15	9.92 099	26	10.07 901	9.88 542	11	11			
									10	1.8	1.7
50	9.80 656	15	9.92 125	25	10.07 875	9.88 531	10	10	20	3.7	3.3
51	9.80 671	15	9.92 150	26	10.07 850	9.88 521	11	9	30	5.5	5.0
52	9.80 686	15	9.92 176	26	10.07 824	9.88 510	11	8	40	7.3	6.7
53	9.80 701	15	9.92 202	25	10.07 798	9.88 499	10	7	50	9.2	8.3
54	9.80 716	15	9.92 227	26	10.07 773	9.88 489	11	6			
55	9.80 731	15	9.92 253	26	10.07 747	9.88 478	10	5			
56	9.80 746	16	9.92 279	25	10.07 721	9.88 468	11	4			
57	9.80 762	15	9.92 304	26	10.07 696	9.88 457	10	3			
58	9.80 777	15	9.92 330	26	10.07 670	9.88 447	11	2			
59	9.80 792	15	9.92 356	25	10.07 644	9.88 436	11	1			
60	9.80 807		9.92 381		10.07 619	9.88 425		0			
′	L Cos	d	L Ctn	c d	L Tan	L Sin	d	′	Proportional parts		

′	L Sin	d	L Tan	c d	L Ctn	L Cos	d	′	Proportional parts
0	9.80 807	15	9.92 381	26	10.07 619	9.88 425	10	60	
1	9.80 822	15	9.92 407	26	10.07 593	9.88 415	11	59	
2	9.80 837	15	9.92 433	25	10.07 567	9.88 404	10	58	
3	9.80 852	15	9.92 458	26	10.07 542	9.88 394	11	57	
4	9.80 867	15	9.92 484	26	10.07 516	9.88 383	11	56	
5	9.80 882	15	9.92 510	25	10.07 490	9.88 372	10	55	
6	9.80 897	15	9.92 535	26	10.07 465	9.88 362	11	54	
7	9.80 912	15	9.92 561	26	10.07 439	9.88 351	11	53	′′ 26 25
8	9.80 927	15	9.92 587	25	10.07 413	9.88 340	10	52	1 0.4 0.4
9	9.80 942	15	9.92 612	26	10.07 388	9.88 330	11	51	2 0.9 0.8
10	9.80 957	15	9.92 638	25	10.07 362	9.88 319	11	50	3 1.3 1.2
11	9.80 972	15	9.92 663	26	10.07 337	9.88 308	10	49	4 1.7 1.7
12	9.80 987	15	9.92 689	26	10.07 311	9.88 298	11	48	
13	9.81 002	15	9.92 715	25	10.07 285	9.88 287	11	47	5 2.2 2.1
14	9.81 017	15	9.92 740	26	10.07 260	9.88 276	10	46	6 2.6 2.5
15	9.81 032	15	9.92 766	26	10.07 234	9.88 266	11	45	7 3.0 2.9
16	9.81 047	14	9.92 792	25	10.07 208	9.88 255	11	44	8 3.5 3.3
17	9.81 061	15	9.92 817	26	10.07 183	9.88 244	10	43	9 3.9 3.8
18	9.81 076	15	9.92 843	25	10.07 157	9.88 234	11	42	
19	9.81 091	15	9.92 868	26	10.07 132	9.88 223	11	41	10 4.3 4.2
20	9.81 106	15	9.92 894	26	10.07 106	9.88 212	11	40	20 8.7 8.3
21	9.81 121	15	9.92 920	25	10.07 080	9.88 201	10	39	30 13.0 12.5
22	9.81 136	15	9.92 945	26	10.07 055	9.88 191	11	38	40 17.3 16.7
23	9.81 151	15	9.92 971	25	10.07 029	9.88 180	11	37	50 21.7 20.8
24	9.81 166	14	9.92 996	26	10.07 004	9.88 169	11	36	
25	9.81 180	15	9.93 022	26	10.06 978	9.88 158	10	35	′′ 15 14
26	9.81 195	15	9.93 048	25	10.06 952	9.88 148	11	34	1 0.2 0.2
27	9.81 210	15	9.93 073	26	10.06 927	9.88 137	11	33	2 0.5 0.5
28	9.81 225	15	9.93 099	25	10.06 901	9.88 126	11	32	3 0.8 0.7
29	9.81 240	14	9.93 124	26	10.06 876	9.88 115	10	31	4 1.0 0.9
30	9.81 254	15	9.93 150	25	10.06 850	9.88 105	11	30	5 1.2 1.2
31	9.81 269	15	9.93 175	26	10.06 825	9.88 094	11	29	6 1.5 1.4
32	9.81 284	15	9.93 201	26	10.06 799	9.88 083	11	28	7 1.8 1.6
33	9.81 299	15	9.93 227	25	10.06 773	9.88 072	11	27	8 2.0 1.9
34	9.81 314	14	9.93 252	26	10.06 748	9.88 061	10	26	9 2.2 2.1
35	9.81 328	15	9.93 278	25	10.06 722	9.88 051	11	25	
36	9.81 343	15	9.93 303	26	10.06 697	9.88 040	11	24	10 2.5 2.3
37	9.81 358	14	9.93 329	25	10.06 671	9.88 029	11	23	20 5.0 4.7
38	9.81 372	15	9.93 354	26	10.06 646	9.88 018	11	22	30 7.5 7.0
39	9.81 387	15	9.93 380	26	10.06 620	9.88 007	11	21	40 10.0 9.3
40	9.81 402	15	9.93 406	25	10.06 594	9.87 996	11	20	50 12.5 11.7
41	9.81 417	14	9.93 431	26	10.06 569	9.87 985	10	19	
42	9.81 431	15	9.93 457	25	10.06 543	9.87 975	11	18	′′ 11 10
43	9.81 446	15	9.93 482	26	10.06 518	9.87 964	11	17	1 0.2 0.2
44	9.81 461	14	9.93 508	25	10.06 492	9.87 953	11	16	2 0.4 0.3
45	9.81 475	15	9.93 533	26	10.06 467	9.87 942	11	15	3 0.6 0.5
46	9.81 490	15	9.93 559	25	10.06 441	9.87 931	11	14	4 0.7 0.7
47	9.81 505	14	9.93 584	26	10.06 416	9.87 920	11	13	
48	9.81 519	15	9.93 610	26	10.06 390	9.87 909	11	12	5 0.9 0.8
49	9.81 534	15	9.93 636	25	10.06 364	9.87 898	11	11	6 1.1 1.0
50	9.81 549	14	9.93 661	26	10.06 339	9.87 887	10	10	7 1.3 1.2
51	9.81 563	15	9.93 687	25	10.06 313	9.87 877	11	9	8 1.5 1.3
52	9.81 578	14	9.93 712	26	10.06 288	9.87 866	11	8	9 1.6 1.5
53	9.81 592	15	9.93 738	25	10.06 262	9.87 855	11	7	
54	9.81 607	15	9.93 763	26	10.06 237	9.87 844	11	6	10 1.8 1.7
55	9.81 622	14	9.93 789	25	10.06 211	9.87 833	11	5	20 3.7 3.3
56	9.81 636	15	9.93 814	26	10.06 186	9.87 822	11	4	30 6.5 5.0
57	9.81 651	14	9.93 840	25	10.06 160	9.87 811	11	3	40 7.3 6.7
58	9.81 665	15	9.93 865	26	10.06 135	9.87 800	11	2	50 9.2 8.3
59	9.81 680	14	9.93 891	25	10.06 109	9.87 789	11	1	
60	9.81 694		9.93 916		10.06 084	9.87 778		0	
′	L Cos	d	L Ctn	c d	L Tan	L Sin	d	′	Proportional parts

′	L Sin	d	L Tan	c d	L Ctn	L Cos	d	′	Proportional parts		
0	9.81 694	15	9.93 916	26	10.06 084	9.87 778	11	60			
1	9.81 709	14	9.93 942	25	10.06 058	9.87 767	11	59			
2	9.81 723	15	9.93 967	26	10.06 033	9.87 756	11	58			
3	9.81 738	14	9.93 993	25	10.06 007	9.87 745	11	57			
4	9.81 752	15	9.94 018	26	10.05 982	9.87 734	11	56			
5	9.81 767	14	9.94 044	26	10.05 956	9.87 723	11	55			
6	9.81 781	15	9.94 069	26	10.05 931	9.87 712	11	54			
7	9.81 796	14	9.94 095	25	10.05 905	9.87 701	11	53	′′	26	25
8	9.81 810	15	9.94 120	26	10.05 880	9.87 690	11	52	1	0.4	0.4
9	9.81 825	14	9.94 146	25	10.05 854	9.87 679	11	51	2	0.9	0.8
10	9.81 839	15	9.94 171	26	10.05 829	9.87 668	11	50	3	1.3	1.2
11	9.81 854	14	9.94 197	25	10.05 803	9.87 657	11	49	4	1.7	1.7
12	9.81 868	14	9.94 222	26	10.05 778	9.87 646	11	48			
13	9.81 882	15	9.94 248	25	10.05 752	9.87 635	11	47	5	2.2	2.1
14	9.81 897	14	9.94 273	26	10.05 727	9.87 624	11	46	6	2.6	2.5
15	9.81 911	15	9.94 299	25	10.05 701	9.87 613	12	45	7	3.0	2.9
16	9.81 926	14	9.94 324	26	10.05 676	9.87 601	11	44	8	3.5	3.3
17	9.81 940	15	9.94 350	25	10.05 650	9.87 590	11	43	9	3.9	3.8
18	9.81 955	14	9.94 375	26	10.05 625	9.87 579	11	42			
19	9.81 969	14	9.94 401	25	10.05 599	9.87 568	11	41	10	4.3	4.2
20	9.81 983	15	9.94 426	26	10.05 574	9.87 557	11	40	20	8.7	8.3
21	9.81 998	14	9.94 452	25	10.05 548	9.87 546	11	39	30	13.0	12.5
22	9.82 012	14	9.94 477	26	10.05 523	9.87 535	11	38	40	17.3	16.7
23	9.82 026	15	9.94 503	25	10.05 497	9.87 524	11	37	50	21.7	20.8
24	9.82 041	14	9.94 528	26	10.05 472	9.87 513	12	36			
25	9.82 055	14	9.94 554	25	10.05 446	9.87 501	11	35	′′	15	14
26	9.82 069	15	9.94 579	25	10.05 421	9.87 490	11	34	1	0.2	0.2
27	9.82 084	14	9.94 604	26	10.05 396	9.87 479	11	33	2	0.5	0.5
28	9.82 098	14	9.94 630	25	10.05 370	9.87 468	11	32	3	0.8	0.7
29	9.82 112	14	9.94 655	26	10.05 345	9.87 457	11	31	4	1.0	0.9
30	9.82 126	15	9.94 681	25	10.05 319	9.87 446	12	30	5	1.2	1.2
31	9.82 141	14	9.94 706	26	10.05 294	9.87 434	11	29	6	1.5	1.4
32	9.82 155	14	9.94 732	25	10.05 268	9.87 423	11	28	7	1.8	1.6
33	9.82 169	15	9.94 757	26	10.05 243	9.87 412	11	27	8	2.0	1.9
34	9.82 184	14	9.94 783	25	10.05 217	9.87 401	11	26	9	2.2	2.1
35	9.82 198	14	9.94 808	26	10.05 192	9.87 390	12	25	10	2.5	2.3
36	9.82 212	14	9.94 834	25	10.05 166	9.87 378	11	24	20	5.0	4.7
37	9.82 226	14	9.94 859	25	10.05 141	9.87 367	11	23	30	7.5	7.0
38	9.82 240	15	9.94 884	26	10.05 116	9.87 356	11	22	40	10.0	9.3
39	9.82 255	14	9.94 910	25	10.05 090	9.87 345	11	21	50	12.5	11.7
40	9.82 269	14	9.94 935	26	10.05 065	9.87 334	12	20			
41	9.82 283	14	9.94 961	25	10.05 039	9.87 322	11	19	′′	12	11
42	9.82 297	14	9.94 986	26	10.05 014	9.87 311	11	18	1	0.2	0.2
43	9.82 311	15	9.95 012	25	10.04 988	9.87 300	12	17	2	0.4	0.4
44	9.82 326	14	9.95 037	25	10.04 963	9.87 288	11	16	3	0.6	0.6
45	9.82 340	14	9.95 062	26	10.04 938	9.87 277	11	15	4	0.8	0.7
46	9.82 354	14	9.95 088	25	10.04 912	9.87 266	11	14	5	1.0	0.9
47	9.82 368	14	9.95 113	26	10.04 887	9.87 255	12	13	6	1.2	1.1
48	9.82 382	14	9.95 139	25	10.04 861	9.87 243	11	12	7	1.4	1.3
49	9.82 396	14	9.95 164	26	10.04 836	9.87 232	11	11	8	1.6	1.5
50	9.82 410	14	9.95 190	25	10.04 810	9.87 221	12	10	9	1.8	1.6
51	9.82 424	15	9.95 215	25	10.04 785	9.87 209	11	9	10	2.0	1.8
52	9.82 439	14	9.95 240	26	10.04 760	9.87 198	11	8	20	4.0	3.7
53	9.82 453	14	9.95 266	25	10.04 734	9.87 187	12	7	30	6.0	5.5
54	9.82 467	14	9.95 291	26	10.04 709	9.87 175	11	6	40	8.0	7.3
55	9.82 481	14	9.95 317	25	10.04 683	9.87 164	11	5	50	10.0	9.2
56	9.82 495	14	9.95 342	26	10.04 658	9.87 153	12	4			
57	9.82 509	14	9.95 368	25	10.04 632	9.87 141	11	3			
58	9.82 523	14	9.95 393	26	10.04 607	9.87 130	11	2			
59	9.82 537	14	9.95 418	26	10.04 582	9.87 119	12	1			
60	9.82 551		9.95 444		10.04 556	9.87 107		0			
′	L Cos	d	L Ctn	c d	L Tan	L Sin	d	′	Proportional parts		

′	L Sin	d	L Tan	c d	L Ctn	L Cos	d	′	Proportional parts		
0	9.82 551	14	9.95 444	25	10.04 556	9.87 107	11	60			
1	9.82 565	14	9.95 469	26	10.04 531	9.87 096	11	59			
2	9.82 579	14	9.95 495	25	10.04 505	9.87 085	12	58			
3	9.82 593	14	9.95 520	25	10.04 480	9.87 073	11	57			
4	9.82 607	14	9.95 545	26	10.04 455	9.87 062	12	56			
5	9.82 621	14	9.95 571	25	10.04 429	9.87 050	11	55			
6	9.82 635	14	9.95 596	26	10.04 404	9.87 039	11	54			
7	9.82 649	14	9.95 622	25	10.04 378	9.87 028	12	53	′′	26	25
8	9.82 663	14	9.95 647	25	10.04 353	9.87 016	11	52	1	0.4	0.4
9	9.82 677	14	9.95 672	26	10.04 328	9.87 005	12	51	2	0.9	0.8
									3	1.3	1.2
10	9.82 691	14	9.95 698	25	10.04 302	9.86 993	11	50	4	1.7	1.7
11	9.82 705	14	9.95 723	25	10.04 277	9.86 982	12	49			
12	9.82 719	14	9.95 748	26	10.04 252	9.86 970	11	48	5	2.2	2.1
13	9.82 733	14	9.95 774	25	10.04 226	9.86 959	12	47	6	2.6	2.5
14	9.82 747	14	9.95 799	26	10.04 201	9.86 947	11	46	7	3.0	2.9
									8	3.5	3.3
15	9.82 761	14	9.95 825	25	10.04 175	9.86 936	12	45	9	3.9	3.8
16	9.82 775	13	9.95 850	25	10.04 150	9.86 924	11	44			
17	9.82 788	14	9.95 875	26	10.04 125	9.86 913	11	43	10	4.3	4.2
18	9.82 802	14	9.95 901	25	10.04 099	9.86 902	12	42	20	8.7	8.3
19	9.82 816	14	9.95 926	26	10.04 074	9.86 890	11	41	30	13.0	12.5
									40	17.3	16.7
20	9.82 830	14	9.95 952	25	10.04 048	9.86 879	12	40	50	21.7	20.8
21	9.82 844	14	9.95 977	25	10.04 023	9.86 867	12	39			
22	9.82 858	14	9.96 002	26	10.03 998	9.86 855	11	38			
23	9.82 872	13	9.96 028	25	10.03 972	9.86 844	12	37	′′	14	13
24	9.82 885	14	9.96 053	25	10.03 947	9.86 832	11	36	1	0.2	0.2
									2	0.5	0.4
25	9.82 899	14	9.96 078	26	10.03 922	9.86 821	12	35	3	0.7	0.6
26	9.82 913	14	9.96 104	25	10.03 896	9.86 809	11	34	4	0.9	0.9
27	9.82 927	14	9.96 129	26	10.03 871	9.86 798	12	33			
28	9.82 941	14	9.96 155	25	10.03 845	9.86 786	11	32	5	1.2	1.1
29	9.82 955	13	9.96 180	25	10.03 820	9.86 775	12	31	6	1.4	1.3
									7	1.6	1.5
30	9.82 968	14	9.96 205	26	10.03 795	9.86 763	11	30	8	1.9	1.7
31	9.82 982	14	9.96 231	25	10.03 769	9.86 752	12	29	9	2.1	2.0
32	9.82 996	14	9.96 256	25	10.03 744	9.86 740	12	28			
33	9.83 010	13	9.96 281	26	10.03 719	9.86 728	11	27	10	2.3	2.2
34	9.83 023	14	9.96 307	25	10.03 693	9.86 717	12	26	20	4.7	4.3
									30	7.0	6.5
35	9.83 037	14	9.96 332	25	10.03 668	9.86 705	11	25	40	9.3	8.7
36	9.83 051	14	9.96 357	26	10.03 643	9.86 694	12	24	50	11.7	10.8
37	9.83 065	13	9.96 383	25	10.03 617	9.86 682	12	23			
38	9.83 078	14	9.96 408	25	10.03 592	9.86 670	11	22			
39	9.83 092	14	9.96 433	26	10.03 567	9.86 659	12	21	′′	12	11
									1	0.2	0.2
40	9.83 106	14	9.96 459	25	10.03 541	9.86 647	12	20	2	0.4	0.4
41	9.83 120	13	9.96 484	26	10.03 516	9.86 635	11	19	3	0.6	0.6
42	9.83 133	14	9.96 510	25	10.03 490	9.86 624	12	18	4	0.8	0.7
43	9.83 147	14	9.96 535	25	10.03 465	9.86 612	12	17			
44	9.83 161	13	9.96 560	26	10.03 440	9.86 600	11	16	5	1.0	0.9
									6	1.2	1.1
45	9.83 174	14	9.96 586	25	10.03 414	9.86 589	12	15	7	1.4	1.3
46	9.83 188	14	9.96 611	25	10.03 389	9.86 577	12	14	8	1.6	1.5
47	9.83 202	13	9.96 636	26	10.03 364	9.86 565	11	13	9	1.8	1.6
48	9.83 215	14	9.96 662	25	10.03 338	9.86 554	12	12			
49	9.83 229	13	9.96 687	25	10.03 313	9.86 542	12	11	10	2.0	1.8
									20	4.0	3.7
50	9.83 242	14	9.96 712	26	10.03 288	9.86 530	12	10	30	6.0	5.5
51	9.83 256	14	9.96 738	25	10.03 262	9.86 518	11	9	40	8.0	7.3
52	9.83 270	13	9.96 763	25	10.03 237	9.86 507	12	8	50	10.0	9.2
53	9.83 283	14	9.96 788	26	10.03 212	9.86 495	12	7			
54	9.83 297	13	9.96 814	25	10.03 186	9.86 483	11	6			
55	9.83 310	14	9.96 839	25	10.03 161	9.86 472	12	5			
56	9.83 324	14	9.96 864	26	10.03 136	9.86 460	12	4			
57	9.83 338	13	9.96 890	25	10.03 110	9.86 448	12	3			
58	9.83 351	14	9.96 915	25	10.03 085	9.86 436	11	2			
59	9.83 365	13	9.96 940	26	10.03 060	9.86 425	12	1			
60	9.83 378		9.96 966		10.03 034	9.86 413		0			
′	L Cos	d	L Ctn	c d	L Tan	L Sin	d	′	Proportional parts		

′	L Sin	d	L Tan	c d	L Ctn	L Cos	d	′	Proportional parts
0	9.83 378	14	9.96 966	25	10.03 034	9.86 413	12	60	
1	9.83 392	13	9.96 991	25	10.03 009	9.86 401	12	59	
2	9.83 405	14	9.97 016	26	10.02 984	9.86 389	12	58	
3	9.83 419	13	9.97 042	25	10.02 958	9.86 377	11	57	
4	9.83 432	14	9.97 067	25	10.02 933	9.86 366	12	56	
5	9.83 446	13	9.97 092	26	10.02 908	9.86 354	12	55	
6	9.83 459	14	9.97 118	25	10.02 882	9.86 342	12	54	
7	9.83 473	13	9.97 143	25	10.02 857	9.86 330	12	53	′′ 26 25
8	9.83 486	14	9.97 168	25	10.02 832	9.86 318	12	52	1 0.4 0.4
9	9.83 500	13	9.97 193	26	10.02 807	9.86 306	11	51	2 0.9 0.8
10	9.83 513	14	9.97 219	25	10.02 781	9.86 295	12	50	3 1.3 1.2
11	9.83 527	13	9.97 244	25	10.02 756	9.86 283	12	49	4 1.7 1.7
12	9.83 540	14	9.97 269	26	10.02 731	9.86 271	12	48	
13	9.83 554	13	9.97 295	25	10.02 705	9.86 259	12	47	5 2.2 2.1
14	9.83 567	14	9.97 320	25	10.02 680	9.86 247	12	46	6 2.6 2.5
15	9.83 581	13	9.97 345	26	10.02 655	9.86 235	12	45	7 3.0 2.9
16	9.83 594	14	9.97 371	25	10.02 629	9.86 223	12	44	8 3.5 3.3
17	9.83 608	13	9.97 396	25	10.02 604	9.86 211	11	43	9 3.9 3.8
18	9.83 621	13	9.97 421	26	10.02 579	9.86 200	12	42	
19	9.83 634	14	9.97 447	25	10.02 553	9.86 188	12	41	10 4.3 4.2
20	9.83 648	13	9.97 472	25	10.02 528	9.86 176	12	40	20 8.7 8.3
21	9.83 661	13	9.97 497	26	10.02 503	9.86 164	12	39	30 13.0 12.5
22	9.83 674	14	9.97 523	25	10.02 477	9.86 152	12	38	40 17.3 16.7
23	9.83 688	13	9.97 548	25	10.02 452	9.86 140	12	37	50 21.7 20.8
24	9.83 701	14	9.97 573	25	10.02 427	9.86 128	12	36	
25	9.83 715	13	9.97 598	26	10.02 402	9.86 116	12	35	′′ 14 13
26	9.83 728	13	9.97 624	25	10.02 376	9.86 104	12	34	1 0.2 0.2
27	9.83 741	14	9.97 649	25	10.02 351	9.86 092	12	33	2 0.5 0.4
28	9.83 755	13	9.97 674	26	10.02 326	9.86 080	12	32	3 0.7 0.6
29	9.83 768	13	9.97 700	25	10.02 300	9.86 068	12	31	4 0.9 0.9
30	9.83 781	14	9.97 725	25	10.02 275	9.86 056	12	30	
31	9.83 795	13	9.97 750	26	10.02 250	9.86 044	12	29	5 1.2 1.1
32	9.83 808	13	9.97 776	25	10.02 224	9.86 032	12	28	6 1.4 1.3
33	9.83 821	13	9.97 801	25	10.02 199	9.86 020	12	27	7 1.6 1.5
34	9.83 834	14	9.97 826	26	10.02 174	9.86 008	12	26	8 1.9 1.7
35	9.83 848	13	9.97 851	26	10.02 149	9.85 996	12	25	9 2.1 2.0
36	9.83 861	13	9.97 877	25	10.02 123	9.85 984	12	24	
37	9.83 874	14	9.97 902	25	10.02 098	9.85 972	12	23	10 2.3 2.2
38	9.83 887	14	9.97 927	25	10.02 073	9.85 960	12	22	20 4.7 4.3
39	9.83 901	13	9.97 953	25	10.02 047	9.85 948	12	21	30 7.0 6.5
40	9.83 914	13	9.97 978	25	10.02 022	9.85 936	12	20	40 9.3 8.7
41	9.83 927	13	9.98 003	26	10.01 997	9.85 924	12	19	50 11.7 10.8
42	9.83 940	14	9.98 029	25	10.01 971	9.85 912	12	18	
43	9.83 954	13	9.98 054	25	10.01 946	9.85 900	12	17	′′ 12 11
44	9.83 967	13	9.98 079	25	10.01 921	9.85 888	12	16	1 0.2 0.2
45	9.83 980	13	9.98 104	26	10.01 896	9.85 876	12	15	2 0.4 0.4
46	9.83 993	13	9.98 130	25	10.01 870	9.85 864	13	14	3 0.6 0.6
47	9.84 006	14	9.98 155	25	10.01 845	9.85 851	12	13	4 0.8 0.7
48	9.84 020	13	9.98 180	26	10.01 820	9.85 839	12	12	
49	9.84 033	13	9.98 206	25	10.01 794	9.85 827	12	11	5 1.0 0.9
50	9.84 046	13	9.98 231	25	10.01 769	9.85 815	12	10	6 1.2 1.1
51	9.84 059	13	9.98 256	25	10.01 744	9.85 803	12	9	7 1.4 1.3
52	9.84 072	13	9.98 281	26	10.01 719	9.85 791	12	8	8 1.6 1.5
53	9.84 085	13	9.98 307	25	10.01 693	9.85 779	13	7	9 1.8 1.6
54	9.84 098	14	9.98 332	25	10.01 668	9.85 766	12	6	
55	9.84 112	13	9.98 357	26	10.01 643	9.85 754	12	5	10 2.0 1.8
56	9.84 125	13	9.98 383	25	10.01 617	9.85 742	12	4	20 4.0 3.7
57	9.84 138	13	9.98 408	25	10.01 592	9.85 730	12	3	30 6.0 5.5
58	9.84 151	13	9.98 433	25	10.01 567	9.85 718	12	2	40 8.0 7.3
59	9.84 164	13	9.98 458	26	10.01 542	9.85 706	13	1	50 10.0 9.2
60	9.84 177		9.98 484		10.01 516	9.85 693		0	
′	L Cos	d	L Ctn	c d	L Tan	L Sin	d	′	Proportional parts

′	L Sin	d	L Tan	c d	L Ctn	L Cos	d	′
0	9.84 177	13	9.98 484	25	10.01 516	9.85 693	12	60
1	9.84 190	13	9.98 509	25	10.01 491	9.85 681	12	59
2	9.84 203	13	9.98 534	26	10.01 466	9.85 669	12	58
3	9.84 216	13	9.98 560	25	10.01 440	9.85 657	12	57
4	9.84 229	13	9.98 585	25	10.01 415	9.85 645	13	56
5	9.84 242	13	9.98 610	25	10.01 390	9.85 632	12	55
6	9.84 255	14	9.98 635	26	10.01 365	9.85 620	12	54
7	9.84 269	13	9.98 661	25	10.01 399	9.85 608	12	53
8	9.84 282	13	9.98 686	25	10.01 314	9.85 596	12	52
9	9.84 295	13	9.98 711	26	10.01 289	9.85 583	12	51
10	9.84 308	13	9.98 737	25	10.01 263	9.85 571	12	50
11	9.84 321	13	9.98 762	25	10.01 238	9.85 559	12	49
12	9.84 334	13	9.98 787	25	10.01 213	9.85 547	13	48
13	9.84 347	13	9.98 812	26	10.01 188	9.85 534	12	47
14	9.84 360	13	9.98 838	25	10.01 162	9.85 522	12	46
15	9.84 373	12	9.98 863	25	10.01 137	9.85 510	13	45
16	9.84 385	13	9.98 888	25	10.01 112	9.85 497	12	44
17	9.84 398	13	9.98 913	26	10.01 087	9.85 485	12	43
18	9.84 411	13	9.98 939	25	10.01 061	9.85 473	13	42
19	9.84 424	13	9.98 964	25	10.01 036	9.85 460	12	41
20	9.84 437	13	9.98 989	26	10.01 011	9.85 448	12	40
21	9.84 450	13	9.99 015	25	10.00 985	9.85 436	13	39
22	9.84 463	13	9.99 040	25	10.00 960	9.85 423	12	38
23	9.84 476	13	9.99 065	25	10.00 935	9.85 411	12	37
24	9.84 489	13	9.99 090	26	10.00 910	9.85 399	13	36
25	9.84 502	13	9.99 116	25	10.00 884	9.85 386	12	35
26	9.84 515	13	9.99 141	25	10.00 859	9.85 374	13	34
27	9.84 528	12	9.99 166	25	10.00 834	9.85 361	12	33
28	9.84 540	13	9.99 191	26	10.00 809	9.85 349	12	32
29	9.84 553	13	9.99 217	25	10.00 783	9.85 337	13	31
30	9.84 566	13	9.99 242	25	10.00 758	9.85 324	12	30
31	9.84 579	13	9.99 267	26	10.00 733	9.85 312	13	29
32	9.84 592	13	9.99 293	25	10.00 707	9.85 299	12	28
33	9.84 605	13	9.99 318	25	10.00 682	9.85 287	13	27
34	9.84 618	12	9.99 343	25	10.00 657	9.85 274	12	26
35	9.84 630	13	9.99 368	26	10.00 632	9.85 262	12	25
36	9.84 643	13	9.99 394	25	10.00 606	9.85 250	13	24
37	9.84 656	13	9.99 419	25	10.00 581	9.85 237	12	23
38	9.84 669	13	9.99 444	25	10.00 556	9.85 225	13	22
39	9.84 682	12	9.99 469	26	10.00 531	9.85 212	12	21
40	9.84 694	13	9.99 495	25	10.00 505	9.85 200	13	20
41	9.84 707	13	9.99 520	25	10.00 480	9.85 187	12	19
42	9.84 720	13	9.99 545	25	10.00 455	9.85 175	13	18
43	9.84 733	12	9.99 570	26	10.00 430	9.85 162	12	17
44	9.84 745	13	9.99 596	25	10.00 404	9.85 150	13	16
45	9.84 758	13	9.99 621	25	10.00 379	9.85 137	12	15
46	9.84 771	13	9.99 646	25	10.00 354	9.85 125	13	14
47	9.84 784	12	9.99 672	25	10.00 328	9.85 112	12	13
48	9.84 796	13	9.99 697	25	10.00 303	9.85 100	13	12
49	9.84 809	13	9.99 722	26	10.00 278	9.85 087	13	11
50	9.84 822	13	9.99 747	26	10.00 253	9.85 074	12	10
51	9.84 835	12	9.99 773	25	10.00 227	9.85 062	13	9
52	9.84 847	13	9.99 798	25	10.00 202	9.85 049	12	8
53	9.84 860	13	9.99 823	25	10.00 177	9.85 037	13	7
54	9.84 873	12	9.99 848	26	10.00 152	9.85 024	12	6
55	9.84 885	13	9.99 874	25	10.00 126	9.85 012	13	5
56	9.84 898	13	9.99 899	25	10.00 101	9.84 999	13	4
57	9.84 911	12	9.99 924	25	10.00 076	9.84 986	12	3
58	9.84 923	13	9.99 949	26	10.00 051	9.84 974	13	2
59	9.84 936	13	9.99 975	25	10.00 025	9.84 961	12	1
60	9.84 949		10.00 000		10.00 000	9.84 949		0
′	L Cos	d	L Ctn	c d	L Tan	L Sin	d	′

Proportional parts

″	26	25
1	0.4	0.4
2	0.9	0.8
3	1.3	1.2
4	1.7	1.7
5	2.2	2.1
6	2.6	2.5
7	3.0	2.9
8	3.5	3.3
9	3.9	3.8
10	4.3	4.2
20	8.7	8.3
30	13.0	12.5
40	17.3	16.7
50	21.7	20.8

″	14	13	12
1	0.2	0.2	0.2
2	0.5	0.4	0.4
3	0.7	0.6	0.6
4	0.9	0.9	0.8
5	1.2	1.1	1.0
6	1.4	1.3	1.2
7	1.6	1.5	1.4
8	1.9	1.7	1.6
9	2.1	2.0	1.8
10	2.3	2.2	2.0
20	4.7	4.3	4.0
30	7.0	6.5	6.0
40	9.3	8.7	8.0
50	11.7	10.8	10.0

INDEX